6/68   125,
              659

QP
801
V5
D9.5

THE CHEMISTRY OF NATURAL PRODUCTS

K. W. BENTLEY, *Editor*

Volume I
THE ALKALOIDS
By K. W. Bentley

Volume II
MONO- AND SESQUITERPENOIDS
By P. de Mayo

Volume III
THE HIGHER TERPENOIDS
By P. de Mayo

Volume IV
THE NATURAL PIGMENTS
By K. W. Bentley

Volume V
THE CARBOHYDRATES
By S. F. Dyke

Volume VI
THE CHEMISTRY OF THE VITAMINS
By S. F. Dyke

Volume VII
THE ALKALOIDS Part II
By K. W. Bentley

Additional volumes in preparation

THE CHEMISTRY OF NATURAL PRODUCTS

A series of texts on the constitution of natural products

K. W. BENTLEY, *Editor*

VOLUME VI

THE CHEMISTRY OF
THE VITAMINS

S. F. DYKE

The College of Science and Technology
Bristol, England

1965
INTERSCIENCE PUBLISHERS
a division of John Wiley & Sons Ltd.
LONDON – NEW YORK – SYDNEY

Library of Congress Catalog Card Number 65–16694
ALL RIGHTS RESERVED
Copyright © 1965 by John Wiley & Sons Ltd.

Text set in Monophoto Ehrhardt 11 on 12 point.
Printed by offset litho in Great Britain by
William Clowes and Sons Ltd, London and Beccles

Preface

This volume in the series on the chemistry of natural products is devoted to a study of the fifteen or so compounds which are well established and recognized as vitamins. The treatment throughout emphasizes the chemistry of these compounds—the elucidation of structure, and synthesis—although possible modes of biosynthesis of individual compounds are indicated briefly where appropriate. The biological function of the vitamins is mentioned in outline only, to try to indicate just why these compounds are vital to the living organism. Since the completion of the manuscript two important works on vitamins have appeared, namely *The Biosynthesis of Vitamins and Related Compounds* by T. W. Goodwin, published by Academic Press, London, 1963, and *Vitamins and Coenzymes* by A. F. Wagner and K. Folkers, Interscience, New York, 1964.

The author wishes to acknowledge his debt to *The Chemistry and Physiology of the Vitamins* by H. R. Rosenberg, Interscience, New York, 1945, and to *The Vitamins: Chemistry, Physiology and Pathology*, Volumes I to III, edited by W. H. Sebrill and R. S. Harris and published by Academic Press, New York, 1954, which proved to be valuable guides to leading references.

It is a pleasure to thank Dr. R. V. Brunt for helpful discussions concerning some parts of this book and Mr. M. Sainsbury of this department for reading and checking the proofs.

S. F. DYKE

Department of Chemistry
Bristol College of Science and Technology
April, 1964

D. HIDEN RAMSEY LIBRARY
ASHEVILLE-BILTMORE COLLEGE
ASHEVILLE, NORTH CAROLINA

To Ena

Contents

1 Introduction   1

2 Vitamin B_1 (Thiamine)   4

3 Vitamin B_2 (Riboflavin)   31

4 Pteroylglutamic Acid (Folic Acid)   52

5 The Vitamins B_6 75

6 Nicotinamide and Nicotinic Acid (The PP Factor)   97

7 Vitamin B_{12} (Cyanocobalamin)   107

8 Pantothenic Acid (Vitamin B_3)   150

9 Biotin (Vitamin H)   161

10 Lipoic Acid (6-Thiotic Acid)   182

11 Vitamin C (L-Ascorbic Acid)   191

12 The Vitamins A   208

13 The Vitamins E (Tocopherols)   256

14 The Vitamins D   271

15 The Vitamins K   318

16 Essential Fatty Acids (Vitamins F)   336

17 Myoinositol (or Mesoinositol)   347

Index   355

CHAPTER 1

Introduction

VITAMINS are organic compounds which, in addition to fats, carbo-hydrates, proteins, minerals and water, are necessary for the normal health and development of the animal organism (and also for some bacteria and microorganisms); they cannot be synthesized by the organism requiring them. Relatively small amounts of vitamins are necessary to perform specific and vital functions, such as energy transfer and regulation of metabolism in general. At the present time much progress is being made in elucidating the biochemical functions of these compounds.

In general, fresh, natural foods contain all the vitamins needed in adequate amount, but for man and domesticated animals who depend largely upon processed foods, a deficiency of vitamins can, and does, arise. Deficiency of a particular vitamin usually results in a specific disease—the deficiency disease—which may lead ultimately to the death of the organism.

The vitamin requirements of animals vary with the age and with the species; for example, dogs do not require an external source of vitamin C, but man does.

Detailed accounts of the history of the discovery and development of the concept of vitamins have been published[3,5,7,9] and will not be discussed here. The term 'vitamine' was introduced in 1912 by Funk who believed that four compounds existed which are required in the diet in very small amounts to prevent beriberi, scurvy, pellagra and rickets. He thought that each of these substances contained nitrogen, and were thus vital amines. It is now known that many more such vital compounds exist and that some of them are devoid of nitrogen, but the modified term 'vitamin' is retained for their classification.

Before any of the vitamins had been isolated in a pure condition, they were classified[6] as 'fat-soluble A', which cured night-blindness, and 'water-soluble B', which was said to cure beriberi. The antiscurvy factor which was detected later then became known as vitamin C, and as vitamins have been discovered subsequently they have been named by using the letters of the alphabet consecutively. Unfortunately, 'vitamin

1

B' proved to be a complex mixture from which at least eight pure compounds have been isolated. They were differentiated by subscript numerals, vitamins B_1, B_2, etc. Other vitamins have also proved to be mixtures (A, D, E and K) and these also were given subscript numerals. The nomenclature of the vitamins used in this book is based upon the recent recommendations of the International Union of Pure and Applied Chemistry[4], which are summarized in Table 1.1.

Table 1.1. Nomenclature of vitamins[4].

Customary designation	Name adopted
Vitamin A_1	Retinol
Vitamin A_2	3-Dehydroretinol
Vitamin B_1	Thiamine
Vitamin B_2	Riboflavin
Vitamin B_6 (group)	Pyridoxine
Vitamin B_{12} (collectively)	Cobalamin
(pure substance)	Cyanocobalamin
Vitamin B_{12b}	Aquocobalamin
Vitamin B_{12c}	Nitritocobalamin
Vitamin C	Ascorbic acid
Vitamin D_2	Ergocalciferol
Vitamin D_3	Cholecalciferol
Other D vitamins derived from 7-dehydrosteroids	To be named analogously as above
Vitamin E	α, β-, γ-, etc., Tocopherols
Vitamin K_1	Phylloquinone
Vitamin K_2	Farnoquinone
p-Aminobenzoic acid	p-Aminobenzoic acid
Biotin (Vitamin H)	Biotin
Choline	Choline
Folic acid (Vitamin B_c)	Pteroylmonoglutamic acid
Lipoic acid 6-Thiotic acid	Lipoic acid
Mesoinositol	Mesoinositol (or Myoinositol)
Pantothenic acid (Vitamin B_3)	Pantothenic acid
Vitamin P	
Vitamin PP	Nicotinamide

The compounds described in this book are, in the main, those universally recognized as being vitamins for animals, bacteria or microorganisms. Other, more doubtful, compounds have been excluded; these have been reviewed elsewhere[8,10]. Each vitamin is described in a separate chapter, and the order of presentation is an arbitrary one, except that the more important members of the vitamin B complex are described first since these compounds have been conclusively proved to be constituents of several coenzymes, and hence biologically related to each other.

It is unlikely that all the vitamins have been discovered and much effort is being devoted to nutritional research at the present time. The dietary requirements of many of the lower animals have not been investigated in any detail. The discovery of vitamin $B_T{}^2$ as an essential growth factor for *Tenebrio molitor* and its identification[1] as carnitine (the betaine of γ-amino-β-hydroxybutyric acid, which also occurs in higher animals although its function is not known) illustrates that much remains to be done. A knowledge of such factors may aid in the design of antimetabolites directed against specific organisms.

BIBLIOGRAPHY

1. Carter, H. E., P. K. Bhattacharyya, K. R. Weidman and G. Fraenkel, *Arch. Biochem. Biophys.*, 35, 241 (1952).
2. Fraenkel, G. and M. Blewitt, *Biochem. J.*, 41, 469 (1947).
3. Harris, L. J., *Vitamins in Theory and Practice*, Cambridge University Press, 1955.
4. International Union of Pure and Applied Chemistry Commission on the Nomenclature of Biological Chemistry, *J. Am. Chem. Soc.*, 82, 5575 (1960).
5. Needham, J., *Hopkins and Biochemistry*, Heffer, Cambridge, 1949.
6. Osborne, T. B. and L. B. Mendel, *J. Biol. Chem.*, 20, 379 (1915).
7. Rosenberg, H. R., *Chemistry and Physiology of the Vitamins*, Interscience, New York, 1945.
8. Sebrell, W. H. and R. S. Harris, *The Vitamins: Chemistry, Physiology and Pathology*, Vols I–III, Academic Press, New York, 1954.
9. *Vitamins. A Survey of Recent Knowledge*, Medical Research Council Report, 1932.
10. Wohl, M. G. and R. S. Goodhart, *Modern Nutrition in Health and Disease: Dietotherapy*, Lea and Febiger, Philadelphia, 1955.

CHAPTER 2

Vitamin B$_1$ (Thiamine)

INTRODUCTION – Thiazoles – Pyrimidines – THIAMINE – Occurrence – Deficiency disease – Daily requirement – Properties – Structure – Synthesis – Thiochrome – The action of alkali on thiamine – Biosynthesis of thiamine – Biological function of thiamine – Thiamine analogues and antagonists – BIBLIOGRAPHY

INTRODUCTION

THIAMINE possesses the structure 1 and thus contains a pyrimidine and a thiazole nucleus.

Thiazoles[32a]

The conventional method of numbering the thiazole ring system is shown in 2; substituted thiazoles (5) are usually prepared by the reaction between α-halocarbonyl compounds (3) and thioamides (4). By using thiourea in place of 4, 2-aminothiazoles (6) are produced.

The aromatic character of thiazoles is indicated by the general stability of the nucleus, and by substitution rather than addition reactions. Thiazoles resemble pyridines in their properties; nucleophilic substitution occurs more readily than electrophilic substitution. Thiazolium salts (7), which can be prepared by the action of alkyl halides on thiazoles, are decomposed by alkaline plumbite solutions, probably via 8 and 9.

Pyrimidines[29a,33]

The ring system and numbering of pyrimidine is shown in 10, but pyrimidine is more properly regarded as a resonance hybrid of the two uncharged structures 10 and 11 and the charged canonical forms 12 to 17. Pyrimidines possess some aromatic character, and from the above structures it is deduced that whereas electrophilic substitution is difficult and occurs almost exclusively at position 5, the molecule is susceptible to nucleophilic attack, particularly at positions 2, 4 or 6. Substituents at position 5 possess similar properties to the corresponding 3-substituted

4

products, whereas substituents at positions 2 and 4 are analogous to
the 2-(α-substituted amino)methyl pyrimidine moiety of aneurin sulfonic
structure at position 2. A most useful pyrimidine for silver reduction
and its analogous. The vitamin itself has been
little studied owing to the inaccessibility for it. Recently, been obtained. The development of pyrimidine-4,6-dicarboxylic acid.

The most versatile method of synthesizing pyrimidine derivatives
involves the condensation between intermediate and (18) and the
corresponding amino-enamine. The latter is usually provided in urea, thiourea, amidines, guanidine and their derivatives,
whereas (19) is derived from synthetic acetals as β-ketones and their derivatives.

$$\text{(1)}$$

$$\text{(2)}$$

$$\text{(3)} + \text{(4)} \longrightarrow \text{(5)}$$

$$\text{(6)} \quad \text{(7)} \xrightarrow[\text{H}^+]{\text{OH}^-} \text{(8)} \quad \text{(9)}$$

$$\text{(10)} \quad \text{(12)} \quad \text{(13)} \quad \text{(14)}$$

$$\text{(11)} \quad \text{(15)} \quad \text{(16)} \quad \text{(17)}$$

pyridines, whereas substituents at positions 2, 4 and 6 are analogous to the 2- or 4-substituted pyridines. In particular, hydroxyl or amino substituents at positions 2, 4 or 6 in the pyrimidine ring allow tautomerism and are analogous to the pyridine derivatives. Pyrimidine itself has been little studied owing to its inaccessibility, but it has recently been obtained[26] by the decarboxylation of pyrimidine-4,6-dicarboxylic acid.

The most versatile method[33] of synthesizing pyrimidine derivatives involves the condensation between a three-carbon unit (19) and the corresponding nitrogen-containing unit (18). The latter is usually provided by urea, thiourea, amidines, guanidines and their derivatives, whereas 19 is derived from malonic ester, cyanoacetic ester, ethyl acetoacetate or β-diketones and their derivatives.

THIAMINE

Occurrence

Vitamin B_1 occurs in all living cells as its pyrophosphate ester, cocarboxylase, and is also present in the husks of rice and wheat. The most common foods containing appreciable quantities of thiamine include eggs, meat, beans, peas, wholemeal bread and yeast. The vitamin was first isolated[28,29] from rice pericarp.

Deficiency disease

Polyneuritis (disfunctioning of the nervous system) or beriberi is the disease associated with thiamine deficiency in man, and is still prevalent in the Far East where the diet consists almost entirely of 'polished' rice, i.e. rice from which the pericarp has been removed.

Daily requirement

Man requires preformed thiamine (the average daily requirement being 1–3 mg) in his diet, as do animals, some bacteria and some fungi. Some bacteria can synthesize thiamine if provided with the pyrimidine or the thiazole part of the molecule, whereas plants are capable of totally synthesizing the vitamin.

Properties

Thiamine is usually isolated in the form of its chloride hydrochloride and as such is soluble in water. The free base has been obtained as an amorphous solid by treatment of its aqueous salt solutions with silver oxide. The ultraviolet spectrum of thiamine (Figure 2.1) exhibits maxima at 235 mμ and 267 mμ in both the solution, and a single maximum at 245 mμ in acid solution. The thiamine is soluble in strongly acid solution, but at pH 5 (a zwitterion sulphate solution) the molecule is cleaved [structure (45) below]. Mild cleaving agents convert thiamine into the pyrimidine sulfonate yields to give the derivative

(18)   (19)

[...]

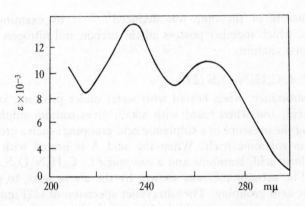

Figure 2.1. The ultraviolet spectrum of thiamine **(45)** (in water). [Reproduced, by permission, from H. R. Rosenberg, *The Chemistry and Physiology of the Vitamins*, Interscience, New York, 1945, p. 103.]

at 235 mμ and 267 mμ in alkaline solution, and a single maximum at 245–247 mμ in acid solution. The vitamin is stable in strongly acid solution, but at pH 5–6 (e.g. in sodium sulphite solution) the molecule is cleaved into two fragments (see below). Mild oxidizing agents convert thiamine into thiochrome and mild reduction yields a dihydro derivative.

Structure

This was established (1934–1937) by Williams and his coworkers, who also announced the first synthesis of the vitamin. The investigation of the structure is one of the first examples where ultraviolet spectra were used extensively[38,69].

Thiamine chloride hydrochloride has the molecular formula $C_{12}H_{18}Cl_2N_4OS$. The molecule is cleaved quantitatively by sodium sulphite into an *acid A* and a *base B* according to the equation

$$C_{12}H_{18}Cl_2N_4OS \longrightarrow C_6H_9N_3O_3S + C_6H_9NOS$$
$$\text{Thiamine} \qquad\qquad \text{Acid A} \qquad \text{Base B}$$

The structure of thiamine was deduced[59,60,62] by examining these products, which together possess all the carbon and nitrogen atoms of the original vitamin.

The acid A, $C_6H_9N_3O_3S$ (29)

This substance, when heated with water under pressure, yields sulphuric acid, and when fused with alkali, gives sodium sulphite, thus indicating the presence of a sulphonic acid grouping; such a group is not present in thiamine itself. When the acid A is heated with aqueous hydrochloric acid, ammonia and a *compound C*, $C_6H_8N_2O_4S$, are produced. The substance C was shown, by the above tests, to possess a sulphonic acid grouping. The ultraviolet spectrum of C (Figure 2.2) is very similar to the spectra of 6-hydroxypyrimidines, and the formation of C from A is a typical reaction of a 6-aminopyrimidine. The ultraviolet spectrum of A (Figure 2.3) is also characteristic of a 6-aminopyrimidine. Hence the acid A can be expressed by the part-structure 20. Reduction of A with sodium in liquid ammonia[15,63] yields a compound, which was shown by synthesis[65] to be 4-amino-2,5-dimethylpyrimidine (21). Formylpropionic ester (23) was condensed with acetamidine (22) to give the hydroxypyrimidine 24, which, on treatment with phosphorus oxychloride followed by alcoholic ammonia, yielded 21. This was shown to

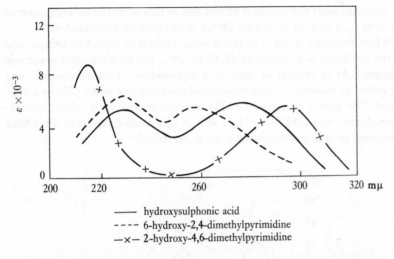

Figure 2.2. The ultraviolet spectrum of compound C (31). [Reproduced, by permission, from R. A. Morton, *Application of Absorption Spectra to the Study of Vitamins, Hormones and Co-Enzymes*, 2nd ed., Hilger, London, 1942, p. 147.]

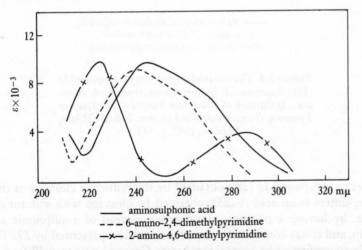

Figure 2.3. The ultraviolet spectrum of the acid A (29). [Reproduced, by permission, from R. A. Morton, *Application of Absorption Spectra to the Study of Vitamins, Hormones and Co-Enzymes*, 2nd ed., Hilger, London, 1942, p. 147.]

be identical with the product of sodium in liquid ammonia reduction of the acid A. The part-structure **20** for A can now be expanded to **25**.

When thiamine itself is reduced with sodium in liquid ammonia, one of the products is a *compound D*, $C_6H_{10}N_4$, whose ultraviolet spectrum (Figure 2.4) is typical of that of a pyrimidine. This compound was identified as 4-amino-5-aminomethyl-2-methylpyrimidine (**28**) by a synthesis[20] in which acetamidine (**22**) was condensed with ethoxymethylenemalononitrile (**26**) to yield **27** which was hydrogenated to **28**. Other variations of this synthesis have been described[25].

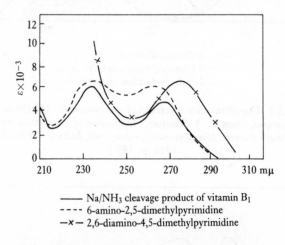

———— Na/NH_3 cleavage product of vitamin B_1
- - - - 6-amino-2,5-dimethylpyrimidine
—×— 2,6-diamino-4,5-dimethylpyrimidine

Figure 2.4. The ultraviolet spectrum of compound D (**28**). [Reproduced, by permission, from R. A. Morton, *Application of Absorption Spectra to the Study of Vitamins, Hormones and Co-Enzymes*, 2nd ed., Hilger, London, 1942, p. 148.]

Hence compound D (**28**), obtained by the reductive cleavage of thiamine, differs from acid A (**25**), obtained by cleavage with sodium sulphite, by having a primary amino group instead of a sulphonic acid group, and it was concluded[63] that the acid A is represented by **29**. This has been confirmed by several syntheses; Grewe[21] prepared **29** from **28** by treatment with hydrogen bromide, to yield **30**, followed by reaction with sodium sulphite. With **29** secured as the structure of A, it follows that compound C is **31**, and this, too, has been confirmed by syntheses[15].

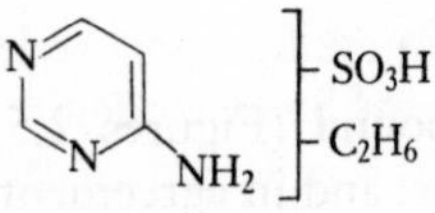

(20)

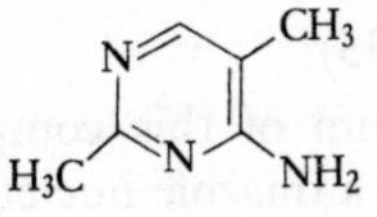

(21)

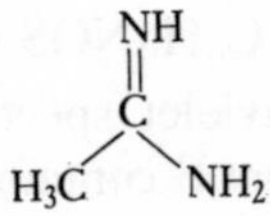

(22)

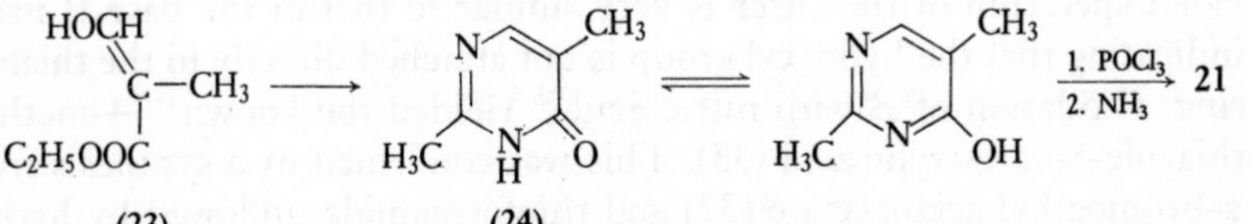

(23) (24)

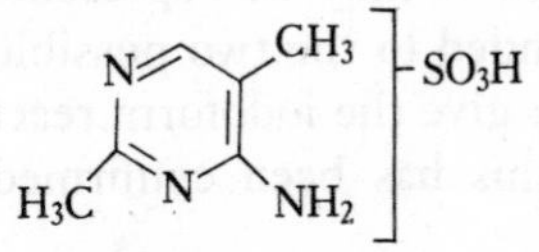

(25)

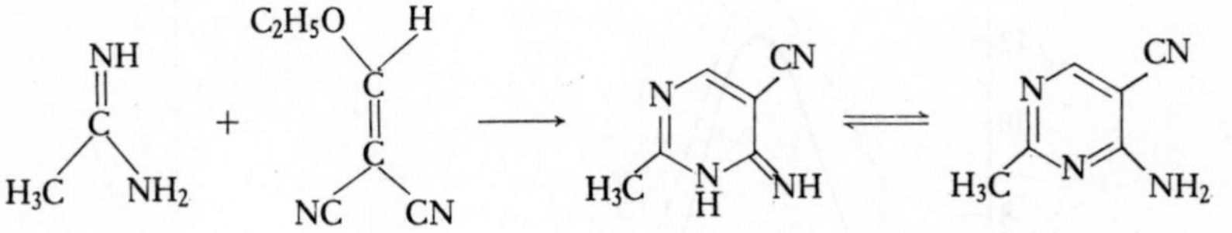

(22) (26) (27)

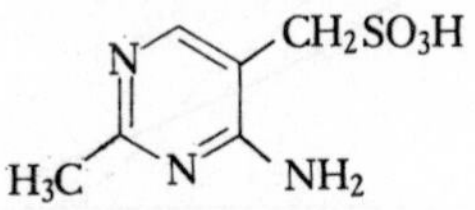

(29)

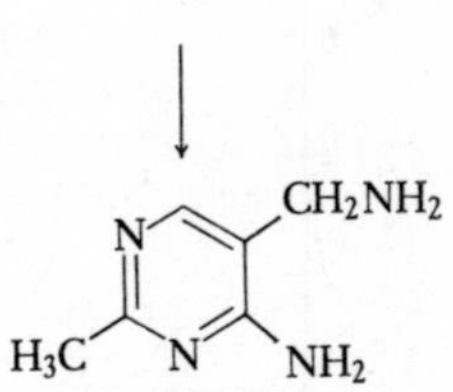

(28)

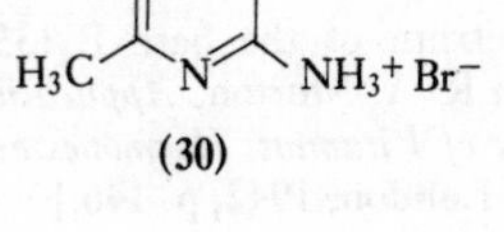

(30)

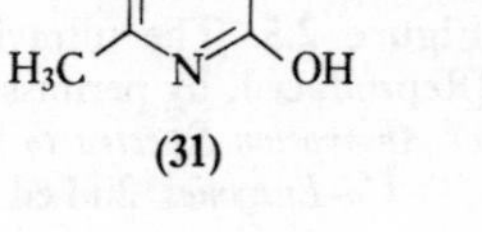

(31)

The base B, C_6H_9NOS (35)

The ultraviolet spectrum of this compound (Figures 2.5 and 2.6) suggested that B contains a thiazole nucleus, and in agreement with this the sulphur atom is lost when B is treated with alkaline plumbite solution. The oxygen atom was shown to be present as an alcoholic hydroxyl group since B forms a *p*-nitrobenzoate and also a chloride. The ultraviolet spectrum of the latter is very similar to that of the base B itself, indicating that the hydroxyl group is not attached directly to the thiazole ring. Oxidation of B with nitric acid[13] yielded the known[70] 4-methylthiazole-5-carboxylic acid (33). This was confirmed by a synthesis from α-bromoethyl acetoacetate (32) and thioformamide, followed by hydrolysis. Thus the base B may be represented by the part-structure 34, which can be expanded to the two possible structures 35 and 36. Since the base B does not give the iodoform reaction and is not resolvable, 35 must be correct; this has been confirmed by a synthesis[14] in which

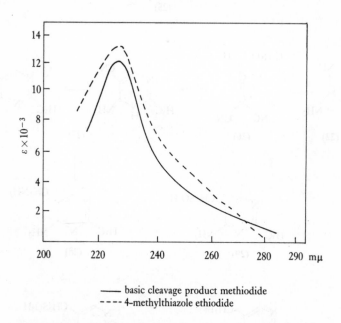

—— basic cleavage product methiodide
- - - - 4-methylthiazole ethiodide

Figure 2.5. The ultraviolet spectrum of the base B (35). [Reproduced, by permission, from R. A. Morton, *Application of Absorption Spectra to the Study of Vitamins, Hormones and Co-Enzymes*, 2nd ed., Hilger, London, 1942, p. 146.]

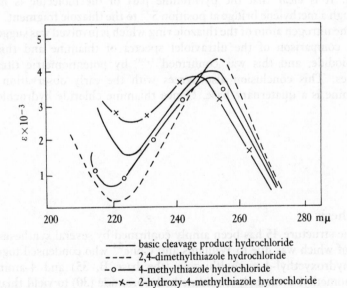

Figure 2.6. The ultraviolet spectrum of the base B (35).
[Reproduced, by permission, from R. A. Morton, *Application of Absorption Spectra to the Study of Vitamins, Hormones and Co-Enzymes*, 2nd ed., Hilger, London, 1942, p. 146.]

thioformamide was condensed with 3-chloro-5-ethoxy-2-pentanone (37), followed by hydrolysis of the product 38. The required intermediate 37 was prepared from ethyl acetoacetate (39) and β-bromodiethyl ether as shown in 39 → 40 → 37.

Several variations of the synthesis of the base B have been described[1,4,12,21,47,48,51,57]; in one[12], thioformamide was condensed with 44, the latter being prepared as shown in 39 → 41 → 44. This method was simplified when it was found[57] that the chlorolactone 43 condensed with thioformamide to yield the base B directly.

The full structure of thiamine

It has been established above that cleavage of thiamine with sodium sulphite yielded the acid A (29) and the base B (35), the sulphonic acid grouping in A being introduced during the cleavage. Since these two fragments contain all of the carbon and nitrogen atoms of the original vitamin, all that remains is to establish the mode of linkage between them. It is clear that the pyrimidine part of the molecule is linked through a methylene bridge at position 5[35] to the thiazole fragment. That it is the nitrogen atom of the thiazole ring which is involved was suggested by a comparison of the ultraviolet spectra of thiamine and thiazole methiodide, and this was confirmed[61,66] by potentiometric titration studies. This conclusion also agrees with the early observation that thiamine is a quaternary base. Hence thiamine chloride hydrochloride is 45.

Synthesis

The structure 45 has been amply confirmed by several syntheses, the first of which was due to Williams and Cline[64] who condensed together 5-β-hydroxyethyl-4-methylthiazole (the base B, 35) and 4-amino-5-bromomethyl-2-methylpyrimidine hydrobromide (30) to yield thiamine bromide hydrobromide, which was converted[16] into 45 by treatment with silver chloride. This synthesis has been employed in the large-scale production of the vitamin. The pyrimidine 30 has been prepared by several methods, one of which was outlined earlier in the description of the synthesis of the acid A, but it was synthesized by Williams from

$$
\underset{(37)}{\overset{\displaystyle \begin{array}{c} NH \\ \| \\ CH \\ | \\ SH \end{array}}{}} \;+\; \underset{(38)}{\left[\begin{array}{c} CH_3 \\ N \diagup \diagdown \\ S \diagdown \diagup CH_2CH_2OC_2H_5 \end{array} \right]} \longrightarrow 35
$$

$$
\underset{(39)}{\begin{array}{c} CH_3 \\ | \\ CO \\ | \\ CH_2 \\ | \\ COOC_2H_5 \end{array}} \xrightarrow[\text{2. BrCH}_2CH_2OC_2H_5]{\text{1. NaOC}_2H_5} \underset{(40)}{\begin{array}{c} CH_3 \\ | \\ CO \\ | \\ CH \\ \diagup \quad \diagdown \\ C_2H_5OOC \quad CH_2CH_2OC_2H_5 \end{array}} \xrightarrow[\text{2. Ketonic hydrolysis}]{\text{1. SO}_2Cl_2} 37
$$

$$
C_{12}H_{18}N_4OSCl_2 \xrightarrow{Na_2SO_3} \underset{(29)}{\begin{array}{c} CH_2SO_3H \\ N \diagup \diagdown \\ H_3C \diagdown N \diagup NH_2 \end{array}} \;+\; \underset{(35)}{\begin{array}{c} CH_3 \\ N \diagup \diagdown \\ S \diagdown \diagup CH_2CH_2OH \end{array}}
$$

$$
\underset{(39)}{\begin{array}{c} CH_3 \\ | \\ CO \\ | \\ CH_2 \\ | \\ COOC_2H_5 \end{array}} \xrightarrow{\overset{O}{CH_2-CH_2}} \underset{(41)}{\left[\begin{array}{c} CH_3 \\ | \\ CO \\ | \\ CHCH_2CH_2OH \\ | \\ COOC_2H_5 \end{array} \right]} \longrightarrow \underset{(42)}{\begin{array}{c} CH_3CO \\ O \end{array}}
$$

$$
\downarrow SO_2Cl_2
$$

$$
35 \xleftarrow{HN=CH-SH} \underset{(44)}{\begin{array}{c} CH_3 \\ | \\ CO \\ | \\ CHCl \\ | \\ CH_2CH_2OH \end{array}} \xleftarrow[(-CO_2)]{HCl} \underset{(43)}{\begin{array}{c} COCH_3 \\ Cl \\ O \end{array}}
$$

$$
\underset{(45)}{\begin{array}{c} \overset{\bar{C}l}{} \\ N \diagup \diagdown \qquad CH_3 \\ \| \qquad \qquad CH_2 \overset{+}{N} \diagup \diagdown \\ H_3C \diagdown N \diagup NH_3^+Cl^- \qquad S \diagdown \diagup CH_2CH_2OH \end{array}}
$$

β-ethoxyethylpropionate (46). This was condensed with ethyl formate in the presence of sodium to yield 47, which reacted with acetamidine to give the pyrimidine 48. Treatment of the latter with phosphorus oxychloride, followed by alcoholic ammonia gave 49, and this yielded the required 30 upon hydrolysis with hydrobromic acid. Other methods for the preparation of 30 have also been described[20,1,3].

A different method was employed by Todd[49] who converted the pyrimidine 28 (compound D) into 4-amino-2-methyl-5-thioformamido-methylpyrimidine (50) and condensed this with 3-chloro-5-hydroxy-2-pentanone (51) to yield thiamine (45) directly.

Andersag and Westphal[2] described a synthesis from the thiazole 52 which was condensed with acetamidine to give 53, and this was converted by standard reactions into thiamine (45).

Yet another method of approach[53] involved the treatment of 54 with alkali, carbon disulphide and the chloroketone 55. The intermediate thiathiamine was converted into 45 by treatment with hydrogen peroxide (see page 18 for formulae).

Thiochrome[56]

Thiochrome is produced when thiamine is oxidized with potassium permanganate or manganese dioxide in neutral solution, or with alkaline potassium ferricyanide or hydrogen peroxide. It has also been isolated from yeast[31], but it is probably an artefact of the isolation process. The structure 56 proposed for thiochrome has been confirmed by a synthesis[46] in which the pyrimidine 60 was condensed with the aminothiazole 61. The pyrimidine 60 was prepared by the condensation of acetamidine with formylsuccinic ester to yield 57, from which 58 was obtained by Curtius degradation. Treatment of 58 with nitrous acid gave 59 which was converted into 60 by phosphorus pentachloride. The thiazole fragment (61) was obtained by the condensation of thiourea with 3-chloro-5-hydroxy-2-pentanone (44).

Thiochrome gives a blue fluorescence which can be measured photometrically, thus giving an accurate method for the determination of thiamine itself.

The action of alkali on thiamine

This has been studied quite extensively in the past and again more recently[34]. On titrating thiamine (45) with alkali, a pseudobase 62 is formed which is then converted into the colourless thiol 63; the latter forms a disulphide on oxidation. When thiamine is added to a solution of

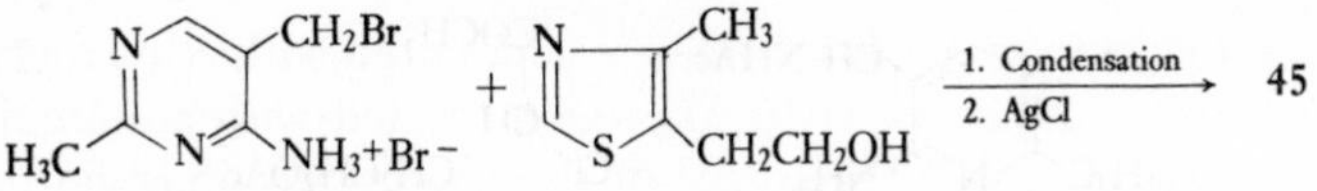

(30)   (35)

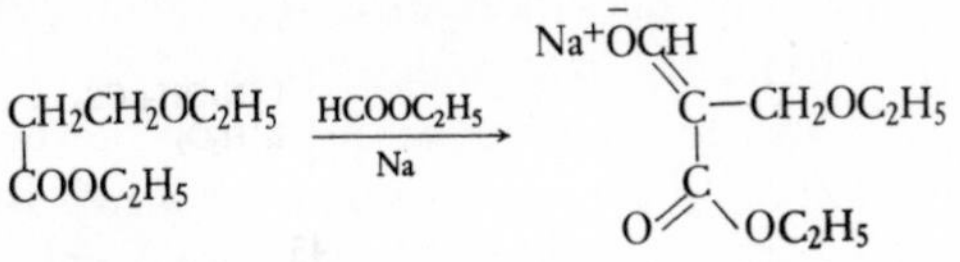

1. Condensation
2. AgCl
→ 45

(46)   (47)

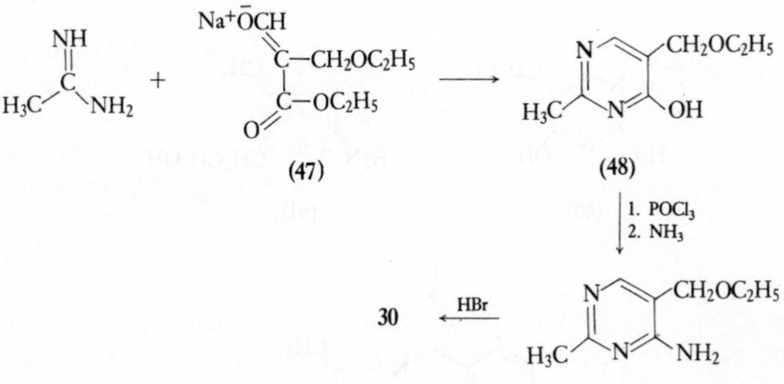

HCOOC$_2$H$_5$
Na

(47)   (48)

1. POCl$_3$
2. NH$_3$

30     $\xleftarrow{\text{HBr}}$

(49)

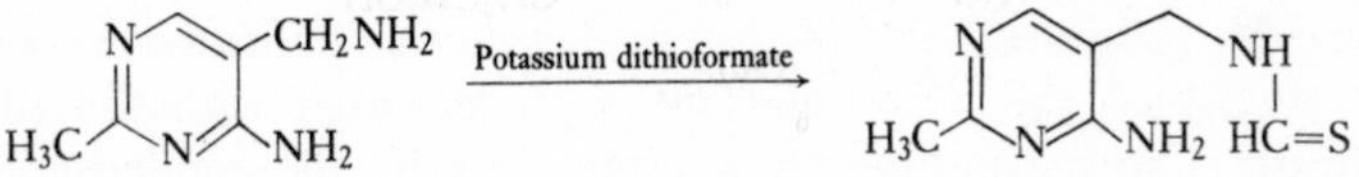

(28)   Potassium dithioformate   (50)

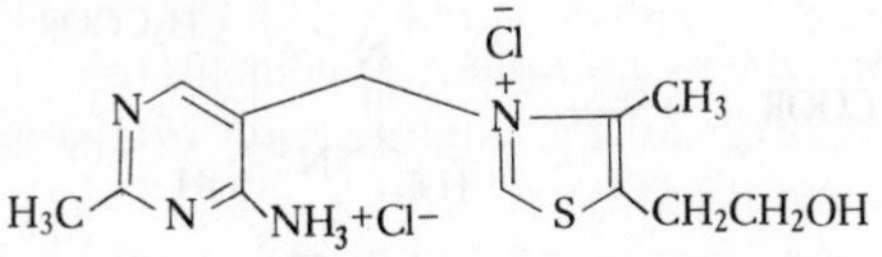

(45) 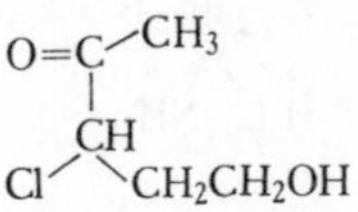   (51)

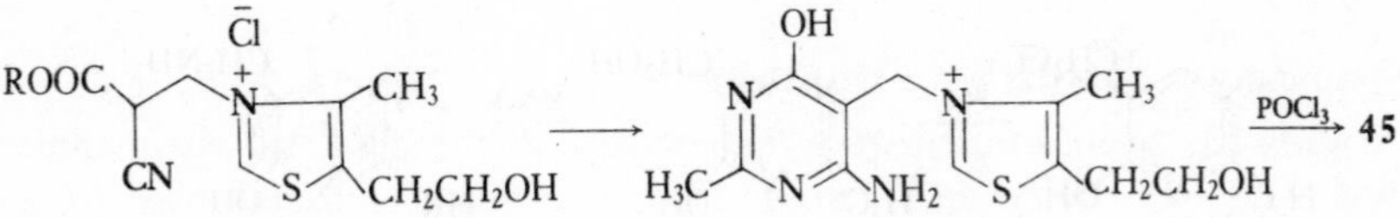

(52)   (53) $\xrightarrow{\text{POCl}_3}$ 45

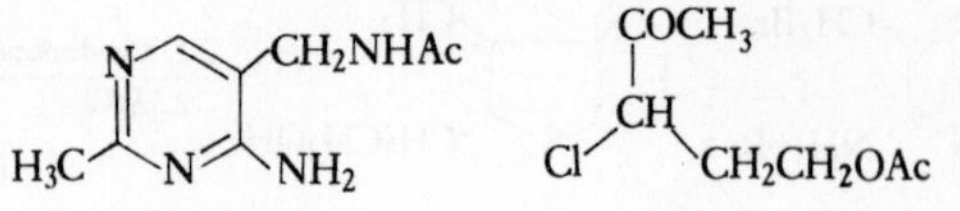

(54)

(55)

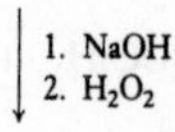

1. NaOH + CS₂
2. H₂O₂

45

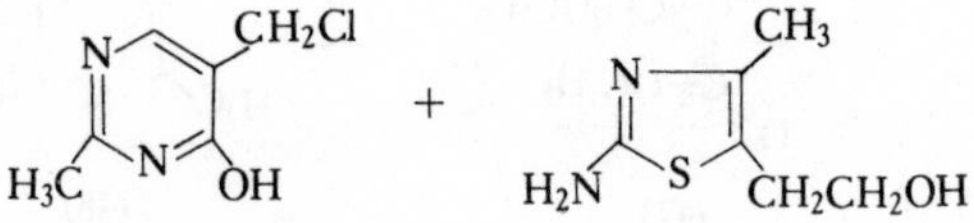

(60)   +   (61)

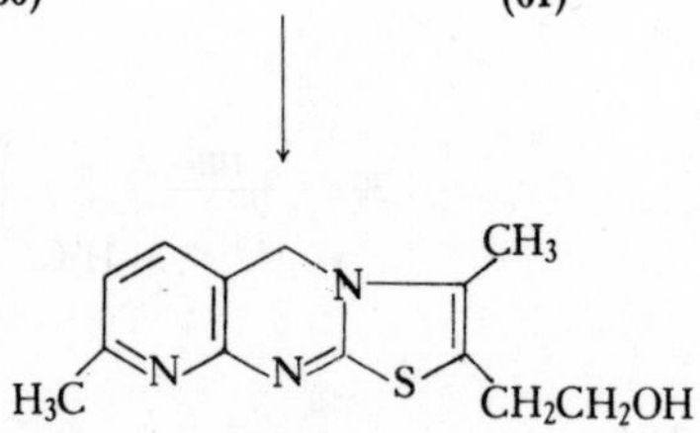

(56)

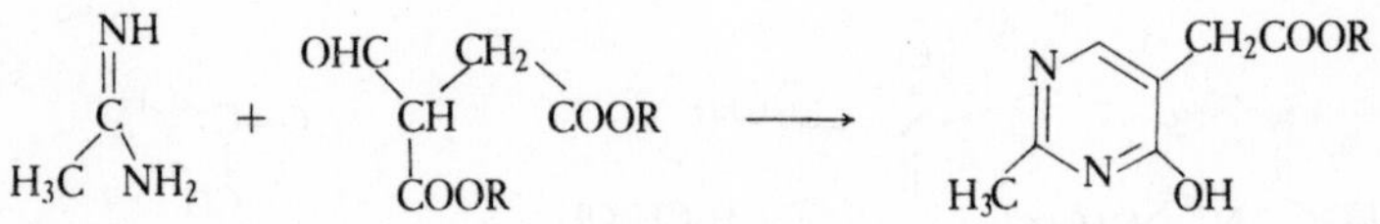

(57)

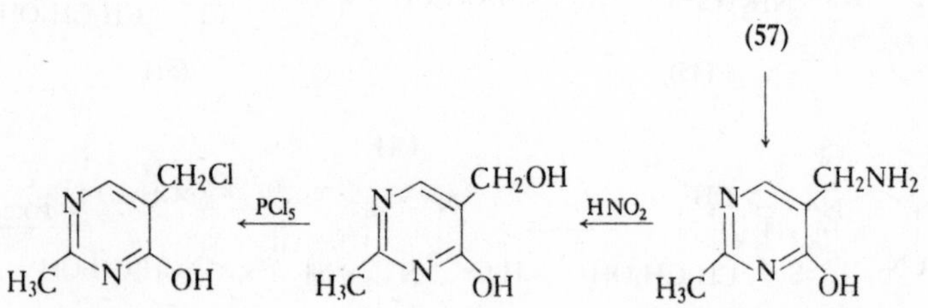

(60)   PCl₅   (59)   HNO₂   (58)

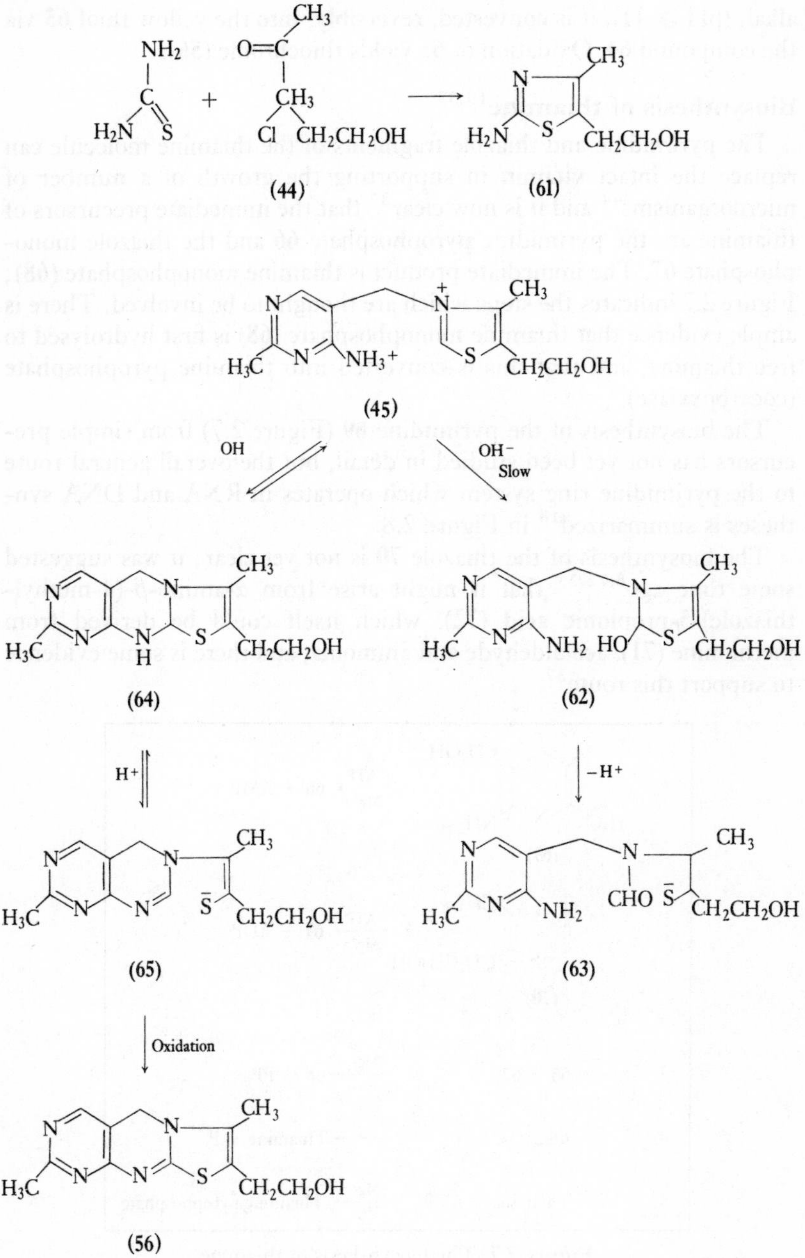

(44)
(61)
(45)
OH
OH⁻
Slow
(64)
(62)
H⁺
−H⁺
(65)
(63)
Oxidation
(56)

alkali (pH $\geqslant$ 11), it is converted, reversibly, into the yellow thiol **65** via the compound **64**. Oxidation of **65** yields thiochrome (**56**).

Biosynthesis of thiamine[19,37]

The pyrimidine and thiazole fragments of the thiamine molecule can replace the intact vitamin in supporting the growth of a number of microorganisms[44] and it is now clear[37] that the immediate precursors of thiamine are the pyrimidine pyrophosphate **66** and the thiazole mono-phosphate **67**. The immediate product is thiamine monophosphate (**68**); Figure 2.7 indicates the steps which are thought to be involved. There is ample evidence that thiamine monophosphate (**68**) is first hydrolysed to free thiamine, and that this is converted into thiamine pyrophosphate (cocarboxylase).

The biosynthesis of the pyrimidine **69** (Figure 2.7) from simple pre-cursors has not yet been studied in detail, but the overall general route to the pyrimidine ring system which operates in RNA and DNA syn-theses is summarized[18] in Figure 2.8.

The biosynthesis of the thiazole **70** is not yet clear; it was suggested some time ago[8,22,23] that it might arise from α-amino-β-(4-methyl-thiazole)-5-propionic acid (**72**), which itself could be derived from methionine (**71**), acetaldehyde and ammonia, and there is some evidence to support this route[37].

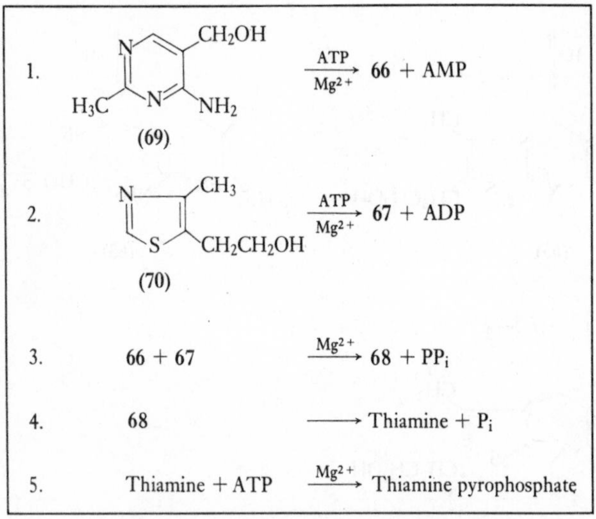

Figure 2.7. The biosynthesis of thiamine.

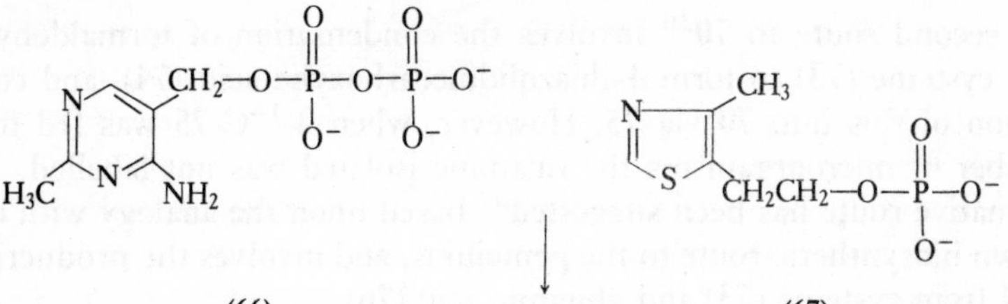

(66)

(67)

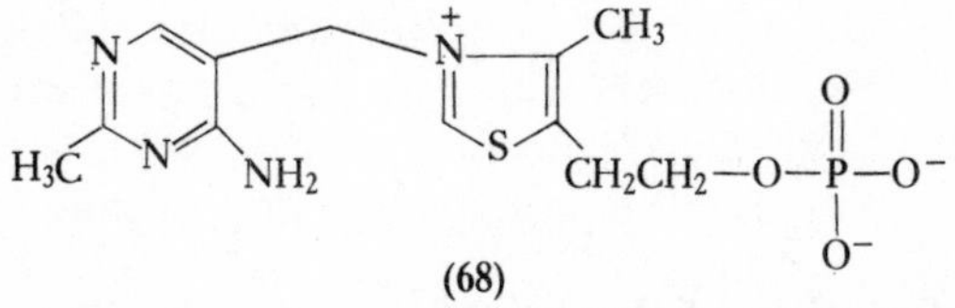

(68)

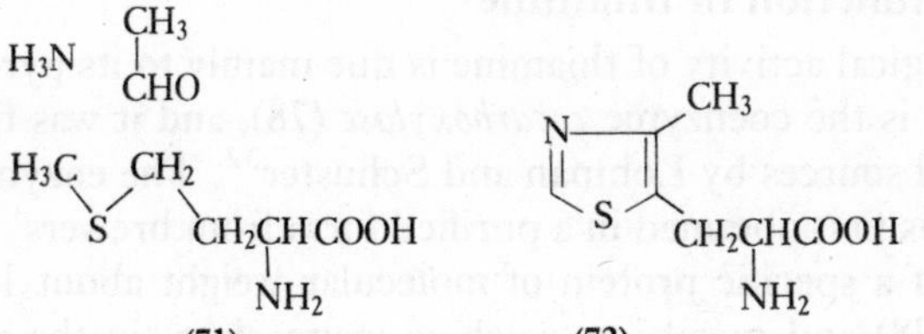

(71)

(72)

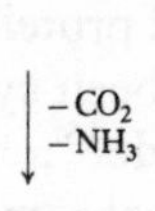

$-CO_2$
$-NH_3$

70

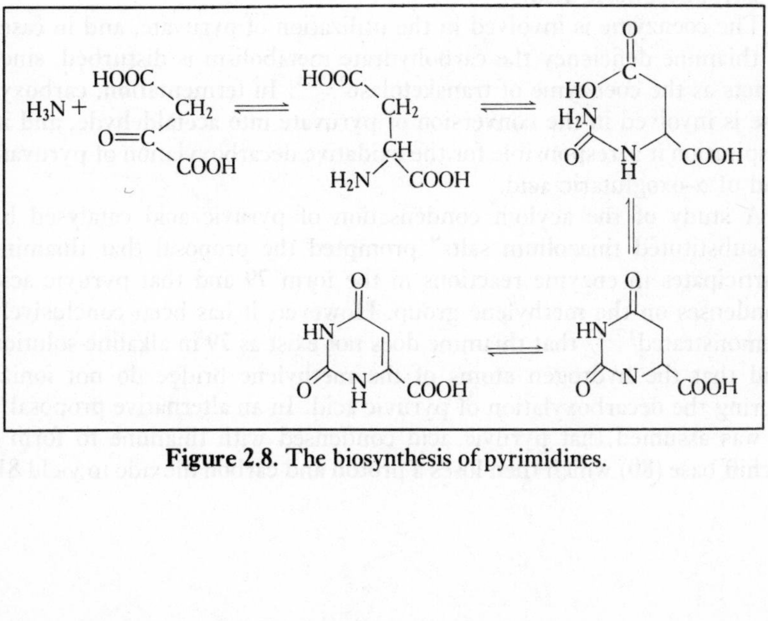

Figure 2.8. The biosynthesis of pyrimidines.

A second route to **70**[36] involves the condensation of formaldehyde with cysteine (**73**) to form 4-thiazolidinecarboxylic acid (**74**), and conversion of this into **70** via **75**. However, when 2-[14]C-**75** was fed to a number of microorganisms the thiamine isolated was not labelled. An alternative route has been suggested[37] based upon the analogy with the known biosynthetic route to the penicillins, and involves the production of **77** from cysteine (**73**) and glutamic acid (**76**).

Biological function of thiamine[67]

The biological activity of thiamine is due mainly to its pyrophosphate ester, which is the coenzyme *cocarboxylase* (**78**), and it was first isolated from natural sources by Lohman and Schuster[32]. The enzyme carboxylase itself was first obtained in a purified form from brewers' yeast[32] and it consists of a specific protein of molecular weight about 150,000, the coenzyme (**78**) and metal ions such as magnesium, in the ratio of one molecular equivalent of protein to one of **78** to five atoms of magnesium. The coenzyme **78** has been synthesized in low yield from thiamine and phosphorus oxychloride[45]; better yields were obtained[55,56] when thiamine bromide hydrobromide was treated with silver pyrophosphate in pyrophosphoric acid.

The coenzyme is involved in the utilization of pyruvate, and in cases of thiamine deficiency the carbohydrate metabolism is disturbed, since it acts as the coenzyme of transketolase[11,24]. In fermentation, carboxylase is involved in the conversion of pyruvate into acetaldehyde, and in respiration it is responsible for the oxidative decarboxylation of pyruvate and of α-oxoglutaric acid.

A study of the acyloin condensation of pyruvic acid catalysed by N-substituted thiazolium salts[9] prompted the proposal that thiamine participates in enzyme reactions in the form **79** and that pyruvic acid condenses on the methylene group. However, it has been conclusively demonstrated[17,27] that thiamine does not exist as **79** in alkaline solution and that the hydrogen atoms of the methylene bridge do not ionize during the decarboxylation of pyruvic acid. In an alternative proposal[58] it was assumed that pyruvic acid condensed with thiamine to form a Schiff base (**80**) which then loses a proton and carbon dioxide to yield **81**.

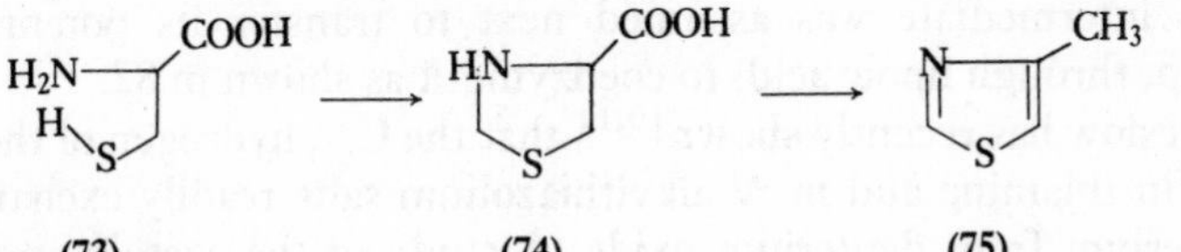

(73) ⟶ (74) ⟶ (75)

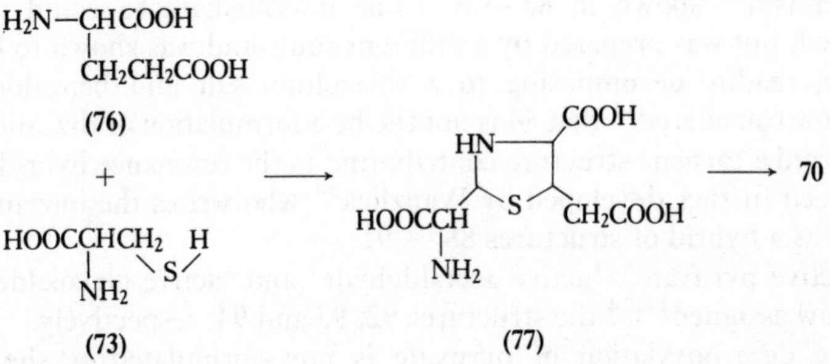

H₂N—CHCOOH
        |
    CH₂CH₂COOH

(76)

+

HOOCCHCH₂   H
        | \
       NH₂   S

(73)

⟶

(77) ⟶ 70

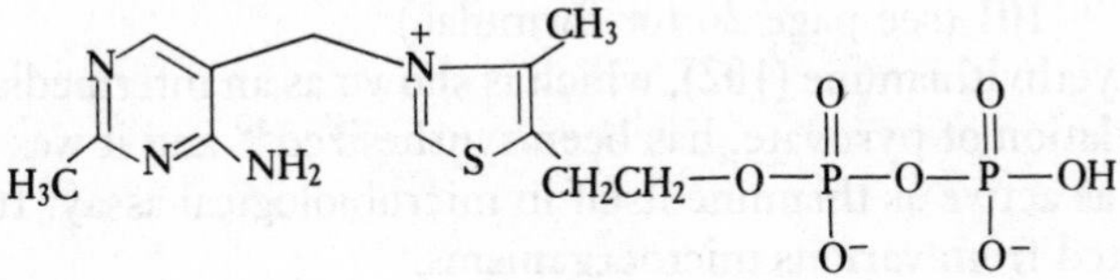

(78)

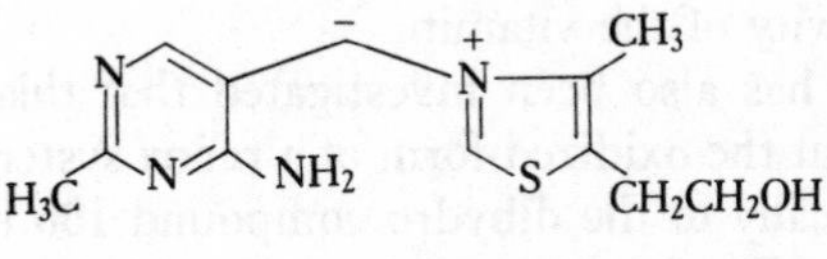

(79)

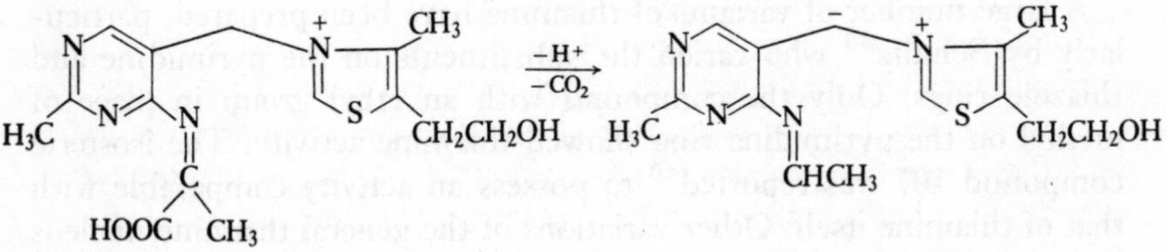

(80) ⟶ (81)

This intermediate was assumed next to transfer its potential acetyl group, through lipoic acid, to coenzyme A as shown in 82.

Breslow has recently shown[10,11] that the $C_{(2)}$ hydrogen of the thiazole ring in thiamine and in N-alkylthiazolium salts readily exchanges with deuterium from deuterium oxide. A study of the acetoin and benzoin condensations, using N-alkylthiazolium salts as catalysts, led to the mechanism[11] shown in 83 → 87. The intermediate 85 could not be isolated, but was prepared by a different route and was shown to be unstable, readily decomposing to a thiazolium salt and benzaldehyde. Breslow considered[11] that 84 is not the best formulation of the anion and preferred a carbene structure contributing to the resonance hybrid. This has been further developed by Wanzlick[54] who writes the intermediate anion as a hybrid of structures 88 → 91.

'Active pyruvate', 'active acetaldehyde' and 'active glycolaldehyde' are now assigned[11,24] the structures 92, 93 and 94, respectively.

The decarboxylation of pyruvate is now formulated as shown in 95 → 98 → 102, and the acyloin condensation as shown in 95 → 98 → 99 → 100 + 101 (see page 26 for formulae).

Hydroxyethylthiamine (102), which is shown as an intermediate in the decarboxylation of pyruvate, has been synthesized[30] and it was found to be almost as active as thiamine itself in microbiological assay. It has also been isolated from various microorganisms.

Thiamine itself is the reduced form of a reversible redox system[73] 103 → 104 → 105, and this system is involved in dehydrogenation reactions brought about by cocarboxylase. The disulphide 105 possesses the full biological activity of the vitamin.

The possibility has also been investigated that thiamine represents not the reduced but the oxidized form of a redox system. Thiamine can be reduced chemically to the dihydro compound 106 but this does not possess any vitamin B_1 activity.

Thiamine analogues and antagonists[72]

A large number of variants of thiamine have been prepared, particularly by Schultz[39] who varied the substituents on the pyrimidine and thiazole rings. Only the compound with an ethyl group in place of methyl on the pyrimidine ring showed thiamine activity. The isosteric compound 107 was reported[40] to possess an activity comparable with that of thiamine itself. Other variations of the general thiamine nucleus include 108, $R^1 = NH_2$, $R^2 = CH_3$, $R^3 = CH_3$, $R^4 = H$, and 108, $R^1 = OH$, $R^2 = CH_3$, $R^3 = CH_3$, $R^4 = CH_2CH_2OH$, which were

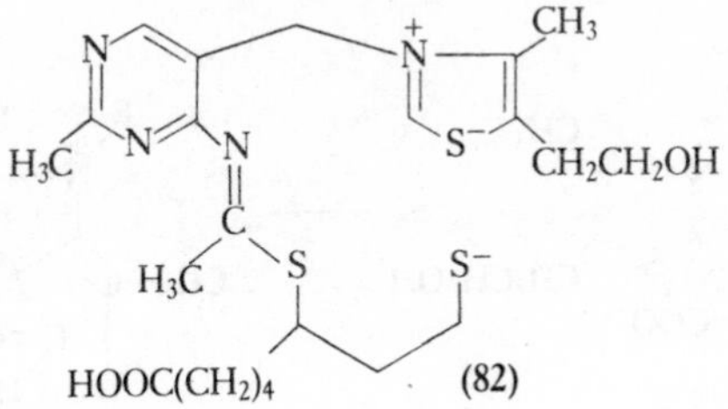

$$H_3C \quad \text{(82)}$$

CH$_3$

CH$_2$CH$_2$OH

HOOC(CH$_2$)$_4$ (82)

R Base R C$_6$H$_5$CHO R

H (83) (84) OH C$_6$H$_5$—C (85) H

OH C$_6$H$_5$ C$_6$H$_5$CHO R OH

C$_6$H$_5$—C—C—S C$_6$H$_5$—C

H OH (87) (86)

C$_6$H$_5$CHOHCOC$_6$H$_5$ + 84

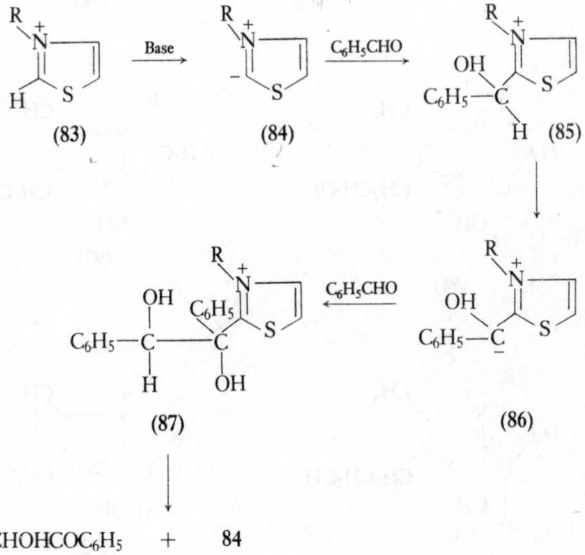

(88) (89) (90) (91)

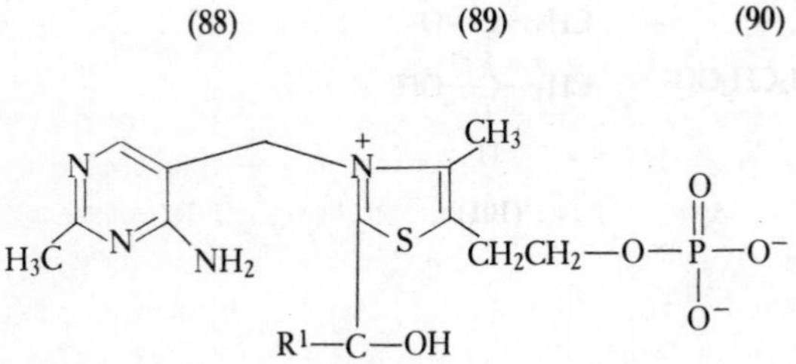

H$_3$C N NH$_2$ CH$_3$

CH$_2$CH$_2$—O—P—O$^-$

R^1—C—OH

CH$_2$R^2

(92, R^1 = COO$^-$, R^2 = H;
93, R^1 = H, R^2 = H;
94, R^1 = H, R^2 = OH)

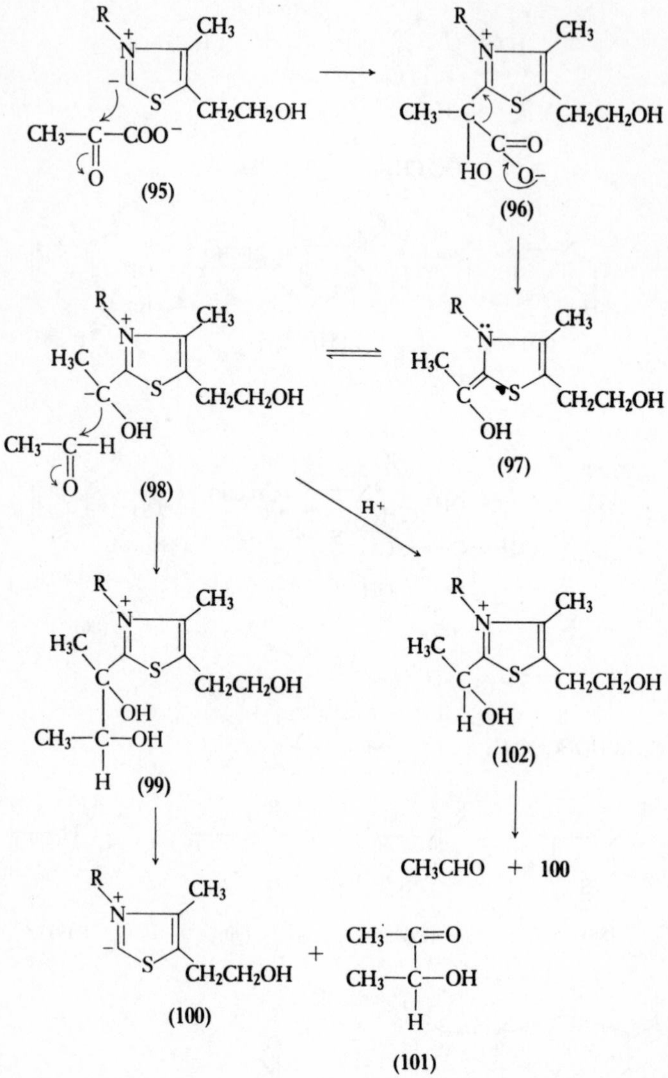
(95)
(96)
(97)
(98)
H+
(99)
(102)
CH3CHO + 100
(100)
(101)

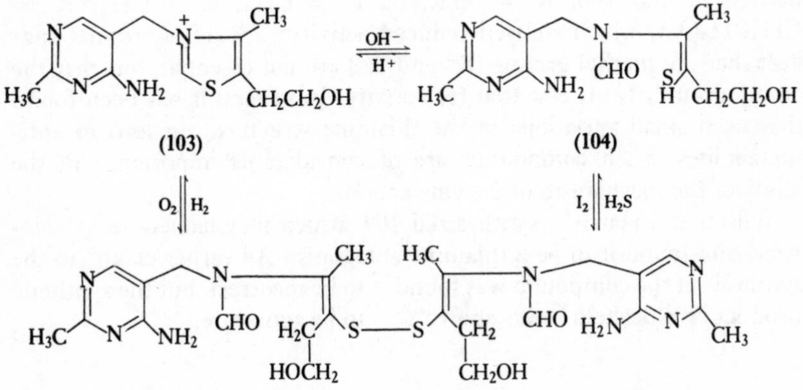

(103) (104) (105)

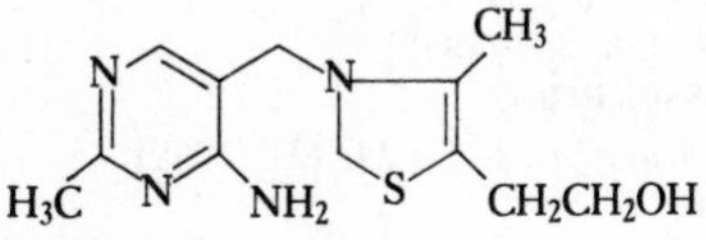

(106)

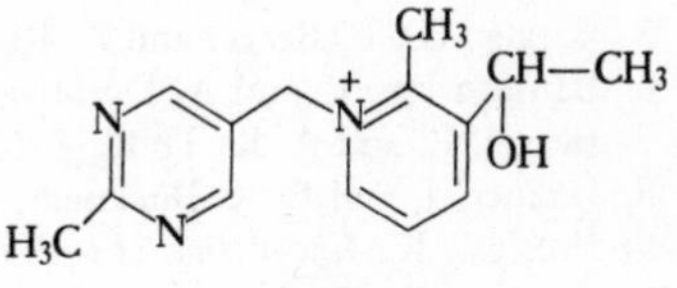

(107)

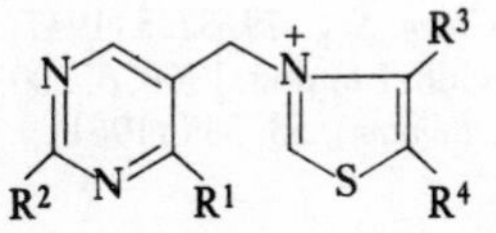

(108)

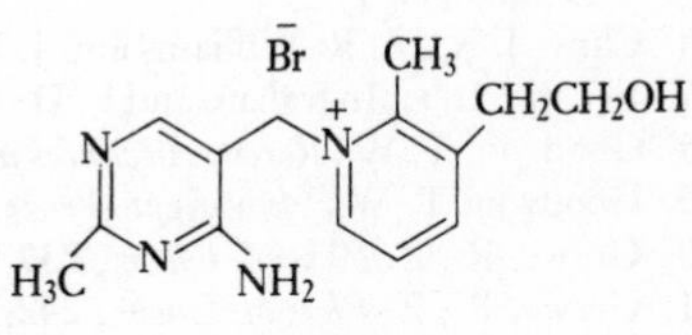

(109)

inactive[50], and **108**, $R^1 = NHCH_3$, $R^2 = CH_3$, $R^3 = CH_3$, $R^4 = CH_2CH_2OH$, which showed reduced activity[39,43]. These results suggest that the methyl groups (R^2 and R^3) are not essential, but that the amino group (R^1) is essential for activity. In general it has been found that even small variations in the thiamine structure can lead to antimetabolites. Such compounds are of considerable importance in the study of the mechanism of enzyme action.

Wilson and Harris[68] synthesized **109**, which they named *neopyrthiamine*, and found it to be a thiamine antagonist. An earlier claim[6] to the synthesis of the compound was found[52] to be incorrect, but the synthetic product of Elderfield[52] was shown[68,71] to be a mixture.

BIBLIOGRAPHY

1. Andersag, H. and K. Westphal, *Ber.*, **70**, 2035 (1937).
2. Andersag, H. and K. Westphal, *Fr. Pat.*, 816,432.
3. Andersag, H. and K. Westphal, *Ger. Pat.*, 671,787.
4. Barger, G., F. Bergel and A. R. Todd, *Ber.*, **68**, 2257 (1935).
5. Barger, G., F. Bergel and A. R. Todd, *Nature*, **136**, 259 (1935).
6. Baumgarten, P. and A. Dornow, *Ber.*, **73**, 44, 156, 353 (1940).
7. Bergel, F. and A. R. Todd, *J. Chem. Soc.*, 1559 (1936).
8. Bonner, J. and E. R. Buckman, *Proc. Natl. Acad. Sci. U.S.*, **24**, 431 (1939).
9. Breslow, R., *Chem. Ind.* (*London*), R.28 (1956).
10. Breslow, R., *J. Am. Chem. Soc.*, **79**, 1762 (1957).
11. Breslow, R., *J. Am. Chem. Soc.*, **80**, 3719 (1958).
12. Buckman, E. R., *J. Am. Chem. Soc.*, **58**, 1803 (1936).
13. Buckman, E. R., R. R. Williams and J. C. Keresztesy, *J. Am. Chem. Soc.*, **57**, 1849 (1935).
14. Clarke, H. T. and S. Gurin, *J. Am. Chem. Soc.*, **57**, 1876 (1935).
15. Cline, J. K., R. R. Williams, A. E. Ruehle and R. E. Waterman, *J. Am. Chem. Soc.*, **59**, 530 (1937).
16. Cline, J. K., R. R. Williams and J. Finkelstein, *J. Am. Chem. Soc.*, **59**, 1052 (1937).
17. Fry, K., L. L. Ingraham and F. H. Westheimer, *J. Am. Chem. Soc.*, **79**, 5225 (1957).
18. Goodwin, T. W., *Recent Advances in Biochemistry*, Churchill, London, 1960, p. 200.
19. Goodwin, T. W., *Ann. Rept. Progr. Chem.* (*Chem. Soc., London*), **58**, 389 (1961).
20. Grewe, R., *Z. Physiol. Chem.*, **237**, 98 (1935).
21. Grewe, R., *Z. Physiol. Chem.*, **242**, 89 (1936).
22. Harington, C. R. and R. C. G. Moggridge, *J. Chem. Soc.*, 443 (1939).
23. Harington, C. R. and R. C. G. Moggridge, *Biochem. J.*, **34**, 685 (1940).
24. Holzer, H., *Angew. Chem.*, **73**, 721 (1961).
25. Hromatka, O., *Ger. Pat.*, 667,990; *Ger. Pat.*, 670,635.
26. Hunt, R. R., J. F. W. McOmie and E. R. Sayer, *J. Chem. Soc.*, 525 (1959).
27. Ingraham, L. L. and F. H. Westheimer, *Chem. Ind.* (*London*), 846 (1956).

28. Jansen, B. C. P. and W. F. Donath, *Chem. Weekblad*, **23**, 201 (1926).
29. Jansen, B. C. P. and W. F. Donath, *Proc. Koninkl. Ned. Akad. Wetenschap.*, **29**, 1390 (1926).
29a. Kenner, G. W. and A. R. Todd in *Heterocyclic Compounds*, Vol. VI (Ed. by R. C. Elderfield), Wiley, New York, 1957.
30. Krampitz, L. O., G. Gruull, C. S. Miller, J. B. Bicking, H. R. Skeggs and J. M. Sprague, *J. Am. Chem. Soc.*, **80**, 5893 (1958).
31. Kuhn, R., T. Wagner-Jauregg, F. W. von Klareren and H. Vetter, *Z. Physiol. Chem.*, **234**, 196 (1935).
32. Lohmann, K. and P. Schuster, *Biochem. Z.*, **294**, 188 (1937).
32a. Louden, J. D. in *Chemistry of Carbon Compounds*, Vol. IV^A (Ed. by E. H. Rodd), Elsevier, Amsterdam, 1957, p. 385.
33. Lythgoe, B., *Quart. Rev. (London)*, **3**, 181 (1949).
34. Maier, G. D. and D. E. Metzler, *J. Am. Chem. Soc.*, **79**, 4386 (1957).
35. Makino, K. and T. Iniai, *Z. Physiol. Chem.*, **239**, 1 (1936).
36. Nakayamo, H., *Vitamins (Kyōto)*, **11**, 169 (1956); *Chem. Abstracts*, **51**, 18091 (1957).
37. Plaut, G. W. E., *Ann. Rev. Biochem.*, **30**, 409 (1961).
38. Ruehle, A. E., *J. Am. Chem. Soc.*, **57**, 1887 (1935).
39. Schultz, F., *Z. Physiol. Chem.*, **265**, 113 (1940).
40. Schmelkes, F. C. and R. R. Joiner, *J. Am. Chem. Soc.*, **61**, 2562 (1939).
41. Stern, K. G. and J. W. Hofer, *Enzymologia*, **3**, 82 (1937).
42. Stokstad, E. L. R., *Ann. Rev. Biochem.*, **31**, 451 (1962).
43. Sykes, P., *J. Chem. Soc.*, 3057 (1954).
44. Tatum, E. L. and T. T. Bell, *Am. J. Botany*, **33**, 15 (1946).
45. Tauber, H., *J. Am. Chem. Soc.*, **60**, 730 (1938).
46. Todd, A. R., F. Bergel, H. L. Fraenkel-Conrat and A. Jacobs, *J. Chem. Soc.*, 1601 (1936).
47. Todd, A. R., F. Bergel and A. Jacobs, *J. Chem. Soc.*, 1555 (1936).
48. Todd, A. R., F. Bergel and Karimullah, *Ber.*, **69**, 217 (1936).
49. Todd, A. R. and F. Bergel, *J. Chem. Soc.*, 364 (1937).
50. Todd, A. R. and F. Bergel, *J. Chem. Soc.*, 1504 (1937).
51. Todd, A. R., F. Bergel, Karimullah and R. Keller, *J. Chem. Soc.*, 361 (1937).
52. Tracy, A. H. and R. C. Elderfield, *J. Org. Chem.*, **6**, 54 (1941).
53. Tursin, V. M., L. G. Chebotarua, L. N. Belousoia and N. D. Kolotilova, *Zh. Prikl. Khim.*, **34**, 229 (1961).
54. Wanzlick, H. W., *Angew. Chem., Intern. Ed. English*, **1**, 75 (1962).
55. Weil-Malberber, H., *J. Soc. Chem. Ind.*, **58**, 1021 (1939).
56. Weil-Malberber, H., *Biochem. J.*, **34**, 980 (1940).
57. Wenz, A., *Ger. Pat.*, 664,789.
58. Wiesner, K. and Z. Valenta, *Experientia*, **12**, 190 (1956).
59. Williams, R. R., *J. Am. Chem. Soc.*, **57**, 229 (1935).
60. Williams, R. R., E. R. Buckman and A. E. Ruehle, *J. Am. Chem. Soc.*, **57**, 109 (1935).
61. Williams, R. R. and A. E. Ruehle, *J. Am. Chem. Soc.*, **57**, 1856 (1935).
62. Williams, R. R., R. E. Waterman, J. C. Keresztesy and E. R. Buckman, *J. Am. Chem. Soc.*, **57**, 536 (1935).
63. Williams, R. R., *J. Am. Chem. Soc.*, **58**, 1063 (1936).
64. Williams, R. R. and J. K. Cline, *J. Am. Chem. Soc.*, **58**, 1504 (1936).

65. Williams, R. R., A. E. Ruehle and J. Finkelstein, *J. Am. Chem. Soc.*, **59**, 526 (1937).
66. Williams, R. R. and T. O. Spies, *Vitamin B₁ and its Uses in Medicine*, Macmillan, New York, 1938, p. 163.
67. Williams, R. J., R. E. Eakin, E. Beerstecker and W. Shive, *The Biochemistry of the B Vitamins* (Am. Chem. Soc. Monograph No. 110), Reinhold, New York, 1950.
68. Wilson, A. N. and S. A. Harris, *J. Am. Chem. Soc.*, **71**, 2231 (1949).
69. Wintersteiner, O., R. R. Williams and A. E. Ruehle, *J. Am. Chem. Soc.*, **57**, 517 (1935).
70. Wöhmann, M., *Ann.*, **259**, 299 (1890).
71. Woolley, D. W., *J. Am. Chem. Soc.*, **72**, 5763 (1950).
72. Woolley, D. W., *A Study of Antimetabolites*, Wiley, New York, 1952.
73. Zima, O. and R. R. Williams, *Ber.*, **73**, 941 (1940).

CHAPTER 3

Vitamin B₂ (Riboflavin)

INTRODUCTION – RIBOFLAVIN – Occurrence – Deficiency disease –
Daily requirement – Structure – Lumiflavin – Lumichrome – Synthesis – Biosynthesis – Biological function of riboflavin – Analogues of
riboflavin – BIBLIOGRAPHY

INTRODUCTION

RIBOFLAVIN (1) is sensitive to light and can be photolysed to yield
lumiflavin (2) or lumichrome (3). The latter is a derivative of alloxazine
(4), whereas riboflavin and lumiflavin are derivatives of isoalloxazine (5).
Alloxazine (4) is tautomeric with 2,4-dihydroxybenzopteridine (6) and
with the (hypothetical) isoalloxazine (5). A substituent in position 9
fixes the ring system in the isoalloxazine form. The ultraviolet spectra of
alloxazines are quite different from those of isoalloxazines[62]. Alloxazines
are weakly acidic, whereas isoalloxazines are feebly amphoteric. Alloxazines, which may be methylated directly at the pyrimidine nitrogen
atoms, are cleaved by alkali to yield a hydroxyquinoxalinecarboxylic
acid (7). Alkaline hydrolysis of isoalloxazines, on the other hand, affords
urea and a ketodihydroquinoxalinecarboxylic acid (8).

Alloxazines (and isoalloxazines) are usually prepared[26] by the condensation of suitably substituted o-phenylenediamines with alloxan (9).

RIBOFLAVIN

Occurrence

Riboflavin, which is a water-soluble, yellow, crystalline, heat-stable
solid is widely distributed in both the plant and animal kingdoms. It
occurs either as the free vitamin, as the phosphate, or bound to specific
proteins to form enzymes. The best sources of the vitamin are yeast,
liver, wheat germ, egg yolk, milk, fish and green vegetables. It was first
isolated in a pure state from whey[29].

2*

Deficiency disease

In man, a deficiency in riboflavin results in chellosis (cracking of the lips and corners of the mouth), and in cases of severe deficiency, in corneal opacity. Riboflavin is a growth factor in most of the animal kingdom.

Daily requirement

Some animals do not require an external supply of vitamin B_2; some species of intestinal bacteria, for example, are capable of synthesizing it. The average healthy adult human requires 2–3 mg per day.

Structure

Work on the elucidation of structure of riboflavin (which was carried out independently by Kuhn and by Karrer) was hampered by the instability of the substance to light. However, the structure was finally deduced by an investigation of some of the photolysis products.

Riboflavin has a molecular formula of $C_{17}H_{20}N_4O_6$. Acetylation yields[30,31] a tetra-O-acetate, whereas oxidation with lead tetraacetate yields[30,31] formaldehyde. Riboflavin forms a diacetone derivative, thus indicating the presence[37] of two α-glycol systems; one of these must be $HOCH_2$—$CHOH$— to account for the production of formaldehyde upon oxidation. There is no observable reaction when riboflavin is treated with nitrous acid, so primary amino groups are absent. Riboflavin gives a positive murexide test and is hydrolysed by alkali to form urea[31]. The

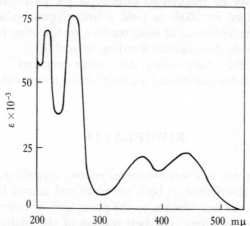

Figure 3.1. The ultraviolet spectrum of riboflavin (in water). [Reproduced, by permission, from H. R. Rosenberg, *The Chemistry and Physiology of the Vitamins*, Interscience, New York, 1945, p. 157.]

(1)

(2)

(3)

(4) ⇌ (5)

(6)

(7)

(8)

(9)

vitamin is easily reduced (for example, by catalytic hydrogenation, sodium dithionite, zinc in acetic acid or titanous chloride) to give a colourless dihydro compound which is readily reoxidized to riboflavin on exposure to air. The ultraviolet spectrum is shown in Figure 3.1.

Irradiation of an alkaline solution of riboflavin yields[30,70] a new compound *lumiflavin* (lumilactoflavin), whereas similar treatment of an acid or neutral solution[16] gives *lumichrome*. The structure of the vitamin was deduced largely as a result of the study of these two photolysis products.

Lumiflavin

The photolysis reaction which yields lumiflavin may be represented by the equation

$$C_{17}H_{20}N_4O_6 \xrightarrow{hv} C_{13}H_{12}N_4O_2 + C_4H_8O_4$$

The product has an ultraviolet spectrum very similar to that of riboflavin, thus indicating that a chromophoric group has not been lost in the reaction. Lumiflavin does not react with lead tetraacetate and it cannot be acetylated, so that the C_4 fragment is a tetrahydroxybutyl side-chain. Furthermore, since it was shown[35] that lumiflavin possesses a methylimino group, which is not present in riboflavin, this side-chain must be attached in riboflavin at the position occupied by the methylimino group in lumiflavin.

Alkaline hydrolysis of lumiflavin yields urea and a monocarboxylic acid A. Since two molecules of water are involved in the reaction

$$C_{13}H_{12}N_4O_2 + 2\,H_2O \longrightarrow C_{12}H_{12}N_2O_3 + CH_4N_2O$$
$$A$$

it was concluded[34] that the urea arises from a ring system.

The acid A is *easily* decarboxylated on heating[31,34] to yield a substance B, $C_{11}H_{12}N_2O$. This suggests that the compound A is a β-keto acid and the hydrolysis of lumiflavin may be written as $10 \rightarrow 11$.

Compound B possesses the properties of a lactam, and on heating with sodium hydroxide it yields a substance which was identified[35] as 4,5-dimethyl-2-methylaminoaniline (12).

The lactam B must therefore be 13, the acid A is 14 and lumiflavin itself is the isoalloxazine 15.

The structure 15 for lumiflavin was confirmed by a synthesis[32,33] based upon that used by Kuhling[26,27,28] in his syntheses of alloxazines; 4,5-dimethyl-2-methylaminoaniline (12) was condensed with alloxan (9). The *o*-phenylenediamine was prepared by Kuhn as shown in $16 \rightarrow 20 \rightarrow 12$.

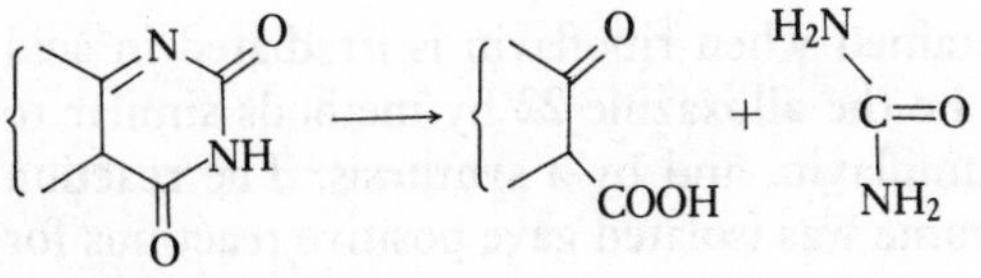

(10)　　　　　　(11) 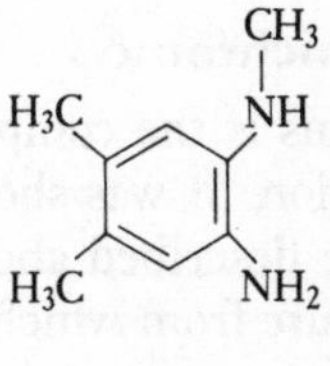　　　　　　(12)

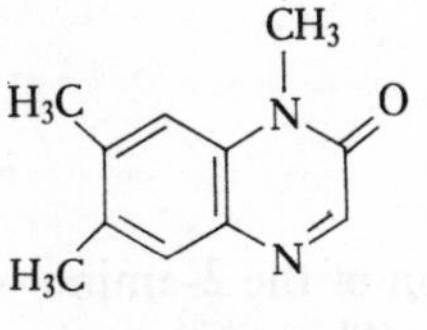

(13) 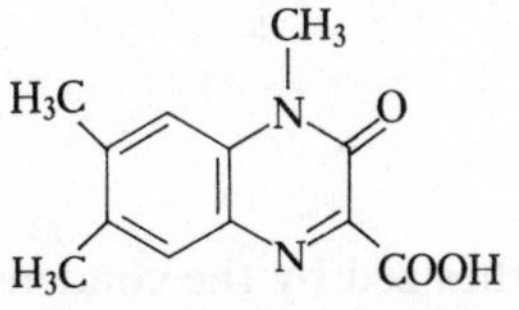　　　　　　(14) 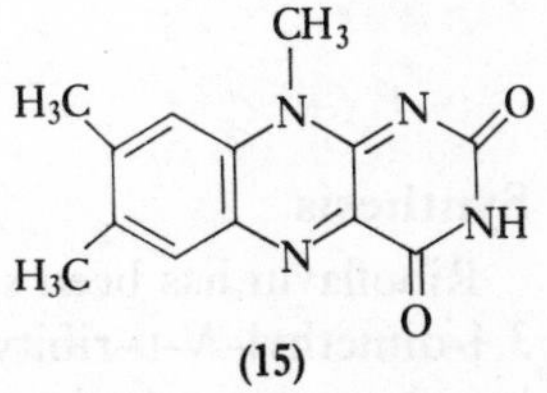　　　　　　(15)

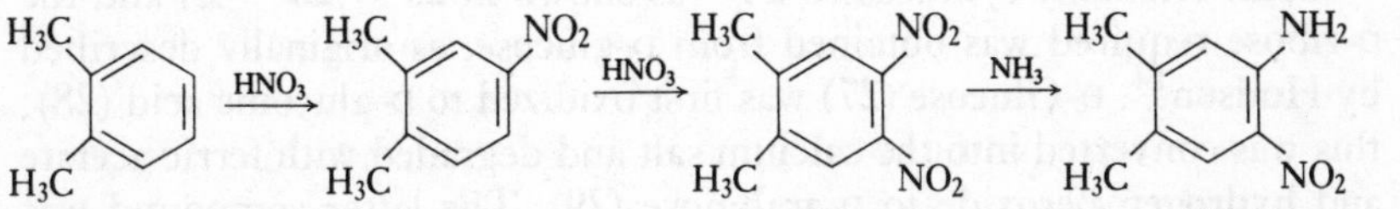

(16)　　　(17)　　　(18)　　　(19)

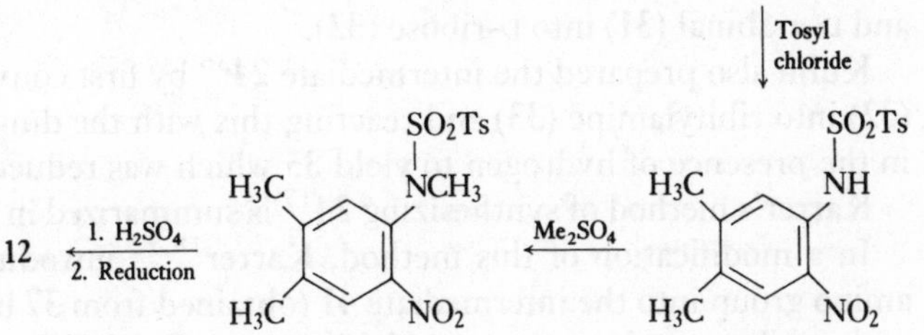

Tosyl chloride

12　$\xleftarrow{\begin{array}{c}1.\ H_2SO_4 \\ 2.\ \text{Reduction}\end{array}}$

(21)　　　　　　(20)

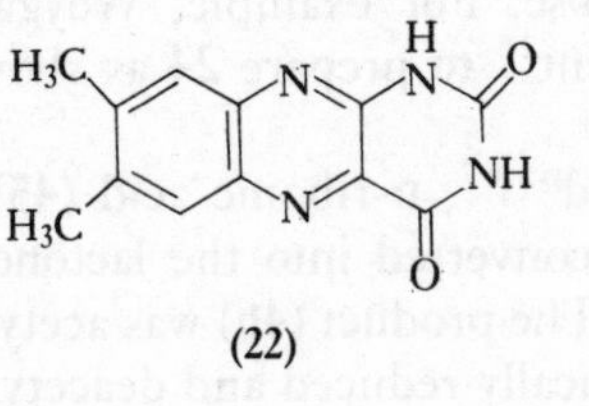

(22)

Lumichrome

This is the compound obtained when riboflavin is irradiated in acid solution. It was shown[16] to be the alloxazine **22** by methods similar to those described above for lumiflavin, and by a synthesis. The reaction mixture from which lumichrome was isolated gave positive reactions for a pentose sugar.

Thus, riboflavin itself is represented by **23**; the actual nature of the side-chain at position 9 (D-ribityl) was proved by synthesis[20].

Synthesis

Riboflavin has been synthesized by the condensation of the 2-amino-3,4-dimethyl-N-D-ribitylaniline (**24**) with alloxan (**9**). The main problem, however, was the synthesis of **24**; this has now been prepared in a number of ways.

Kuhn originally synthesized **24**[38] as shown in **25** → **26** → **24** and the D-ribose required was obtained from D-glucose, as originally described by Hudson[14]. D-Glucose (**27**) was first oxidized to D-gluconic acid (**28**); this was converted into the calcium salt and degraded with ferric acetate and hydrogen peroxide to D-arabinose (**29**). The latter compound was then converted via 2,3,5-tri-O-acetyl-α-D-arabofuranosidyl bromide (**30**) and D-arabinal (**31**) into D-ribose (**32**).

Kuhn also prepared the intermediate **24**[36] by first converting D-ribose (**32**) into ribitylamine (**33**) and reacting this with the dinitro-o-xylene **34** in the presence of hydrogen to yield **35** which was reduced to **24**.

Karrer's method of synthesizing **24**[17] is summarized in **36** → **40** → **24**.

In a modification of this method, Karrer[18,22] introduced the second amino group into the intermediate **41** (obtained from **37** by condensation with D-ribose in the presence of hydrogen and nickel) by diazo coupling, followed by reduction.

Other methods for the preparation of **24** have been developed which do not require D-ribose. For example, Weygand[71] made use of the Amadori rearrangement[15] to prepare **24** as shown in **37** → **42** → **43** → **41** → **24**.

In Tishler's method[65,67], D-ribonic acid (**45**), obtained from D-arabonic acid (**44**), was converted into the lactone and reacted with 3,4-dimethylaniline (**37**). The product (**46**) was acetylated, converted into its iminochloride, catalytically reduced and deacetylated to yield the amine

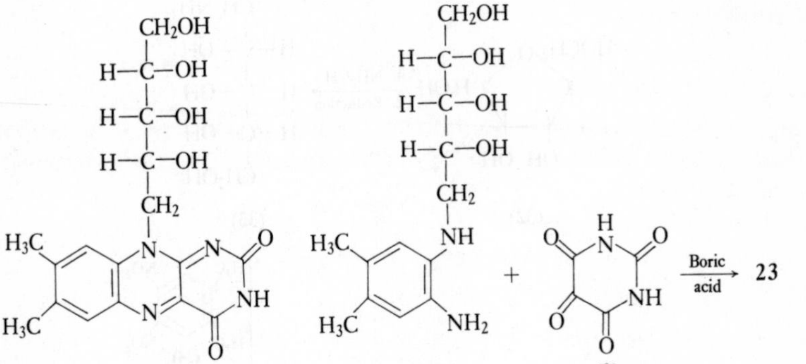

(23) (24) (9) $\xrightarrow[\text{acid}]{\text{Boric}}$ 23

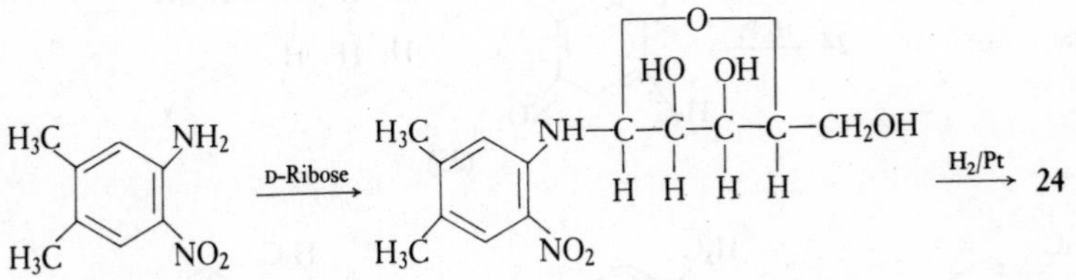

(25) $\xrightarrow{\text{D-Ribose}}$ (26) $\xrightarrow{\text{H}_2/\text{Pt}}$ 24

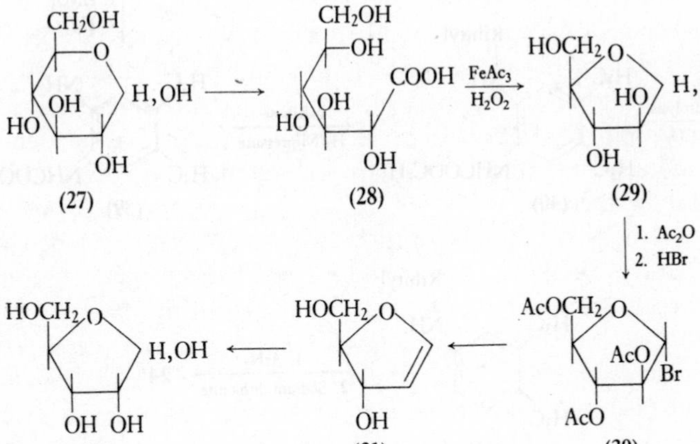

(27) (28) $\xrightarrow[\text{H}_2\text{O}_2]{\text{FeAc}_3}$ (29)

1. Ac$_2$O
2. HBr

(32) (31) (30)

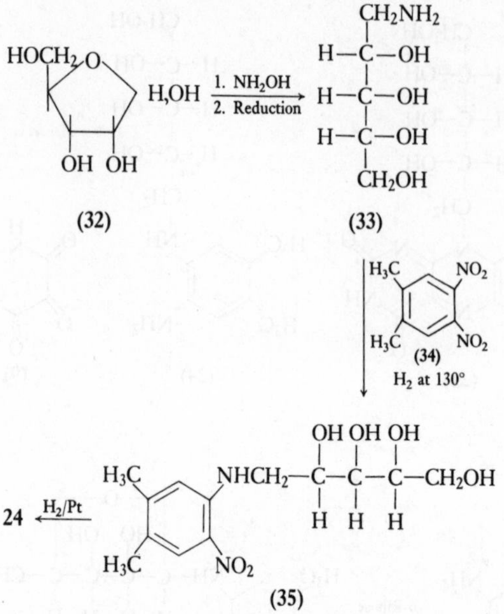

HOCH2
H,OH
OH OH
1. NH2OH
2. Reduction
CH2NH2
H—C—OH
H—C—OH
H—C—OH
CH2OH
(32)
(33)
H3C
NO2
H3C
NO2
(34)
H2 at 130°
H3C
NHCH2—C—C—C—CH2OH
OH OH OH
H H H
H3C
NO2
24
H2/Pt
(35)

H3C
H3C
NO2
(36)
H2/Pt
H3C
H3C
NH2
(37)
ClCOOC2H5
H3C
H3C
NHCOOC2H5
(38)
1. HNO3
2. H2/Pt
H3C
NH2
H3C
NHCOOC2H5
(39)
D-Ribose
H2/Ni/pressure
Ribityl
H3C
NH
H3C
NHCOOC2H5
(40)
24
1. Hydrolysis
2. − CO2

Ribityl
H3C
NH
H3C
(41)
1. ArN2+
2. Sodium dithionite
24

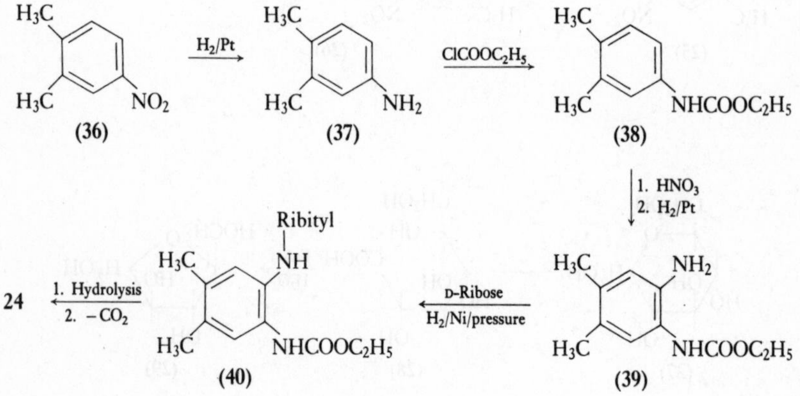

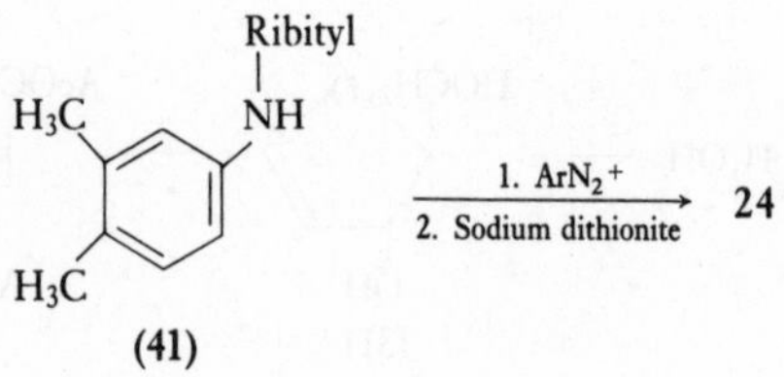

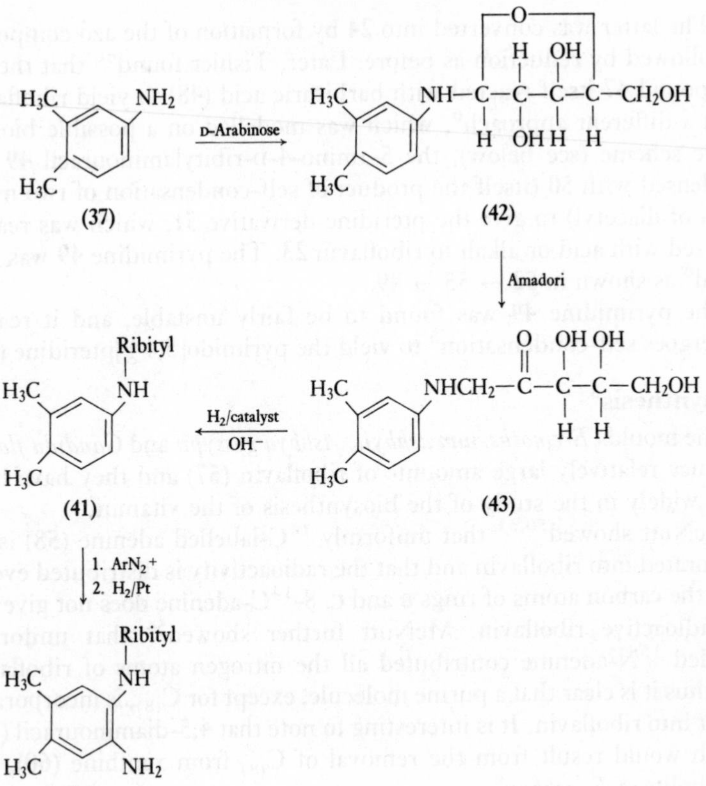
D-Arabinose
Amadori
H_2/catalyst
OH^-
1. ArN_2^+
2. H_2/Pt
Ribityl

(37) (42) (43) (41) (24)

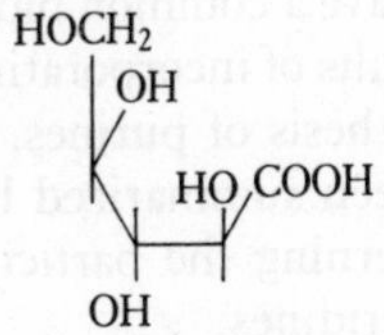

(44)

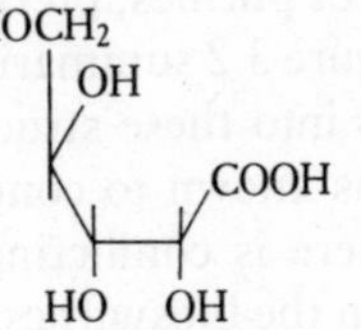

(45)

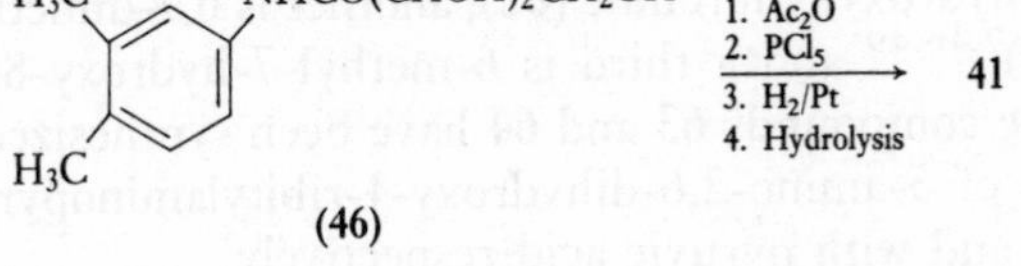
1. Ac_2O
2. PCl_5
3. H_2/Pt
4. Hydrolysis
41

(46)

41. The latter was converted into **24** by formation of the azo compound **47** followed by reduction as before. Later, Tishler found[66] that the azo compound **47** itself reacted with barbituric acid (**48**) to yield riboflavin.

In a different approach[6], which was modelled on a possible biosynthetic scheme (see below), the 5-amino-4-D-ribitylaminouracil **49** was condensed with **50** (itself the product of self-condensation of two molecules of diacetyl) to give the pteridine derivative **51**, which was readily cyclized with acid or alkali to riboflavin **23**. The pyrimidine **49** was prepared[6] as shown in **52 → 55 → 49**.

The pyrimidine **49** was found to be fairly unstable, and it readily undergoes self-condensation[5] to yield the pyrimido[5,4-g]pteridine (**56**).

Biosynthesis[57]

The moulds *Eremothecium ashbyii*, *Ashbya gossypii* and *Candida flaveri* produce relatively large amounts of riboflavin (**57**) and they have been used widely in the study of the biosynthesis of the vitamin.

McNutt showed[50,51] that uniformly ^{14}C-labelled adenine (**58**) is incorporated into riboflavin and that the radioactivity is distributed evenly over the carbon atoms of rings B and C. 8-^{14}C-adenine does not give rise to radioactive riboflavin. McNutt further showed[54] that uniformly labelled ^{15}N-adenine contributed all the nitrogen atoms of riboflavin, and thus it is clear that a purine molecule, except for $C_{(8)}$, is incorporated intact into riboflavin. It is interesting to note that 4,5-diaminouracil (**59**), which would result from the removal of $C_{(8)}$ from xanthine (**60**), is a metabolite of *E. ashbyii*[9].

Evidence is accumulating[57] to indicate that certain portions of the structures of purines, pteridines and flavins have a common biosynthetic origin. Figure 3.2 summarizes some of the results of incorporating simple precursors into these structures. The biosynthesis of purines, in which folic acid is known to contribute $C_{(8)}$, has been summarized by Goodwin[10]. There is conflicting evidence[57] concerning the participation of folic acid in the biosynthesis of flavins and pteridines.

Masuda has found[47] that *E. ashbyii* produces, apart from riboflavin, considerable quantities of riboflavin–adenine dinucleotide (FAD) (**61**) and some other compounds, some of which have been characterized. One is[68] L-3-hydroxykynurenine (**62**), another is 6,7-dimethyl-8-ribityllumazine (**63**)[7,46,49] and a third is 6-methyl-7-hydroxy-8-ribityllumazine (**64**). The compounds **63** and **64** have been synthesized[43,45] by the condensation of 5-amino-2,6-dihydroxy-4-ribitylaminopyrimidine (**49**) with diacetyl and with pyruvic acid respectively.

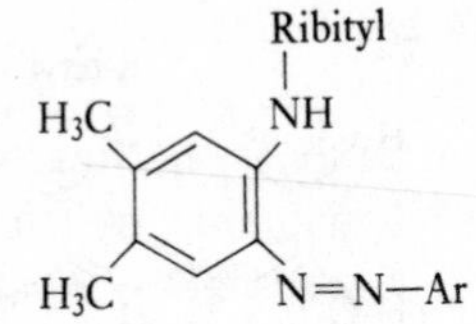

Ribityl
|
NH
H$_3$C

H$_3$C
N=N—Ar

(47)

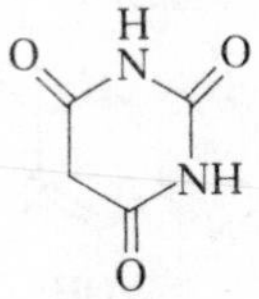

(48)

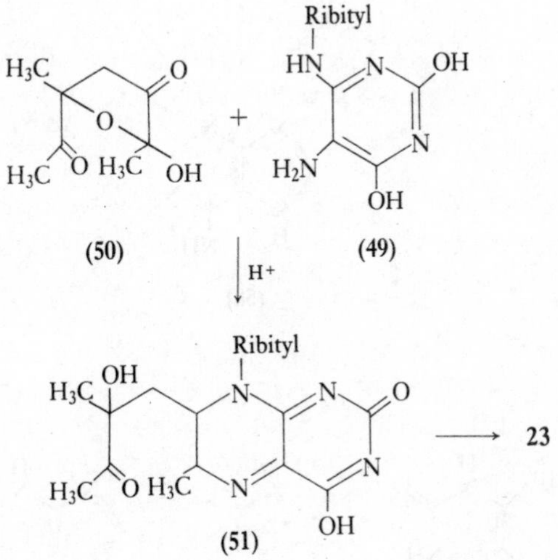

H$_3$C
O
O H$_3$C OH
H$_3$C O

(50)

+

Ribityl
|
HN   N   OH

H$_2$N   N
OH

(49)

$\downarrow$ H$^+$

Ribityl
|
H$_3$C OH
N   N   O
H$_3$C O H$_3$C   N
N
OH

(51)

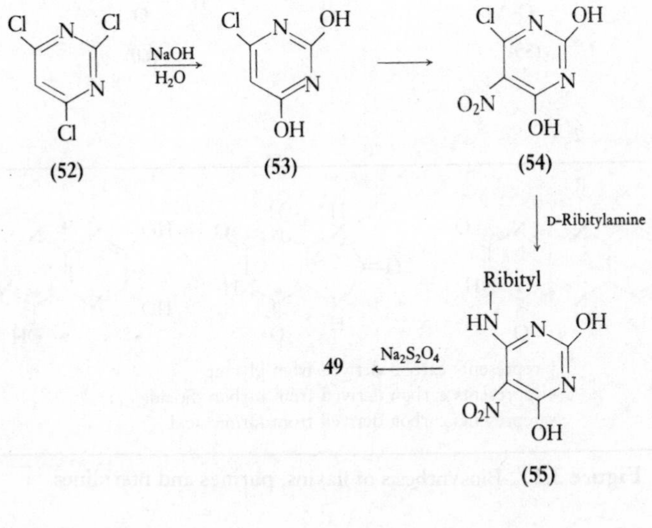

$\longrightarrow$ **23**

Cl   Cl
N

N
Cl

(52)

$\xrightarrow{\text{NaOH} \atop \text{H}_2\text{O}}$

Cl   N   OH

N
OH

(53)

$\longrightarrow$

Cl   N   OH

O$_2$N   N
OH

(54)

$\downarrow$ D-Ribitylamine

Ribityl
|
HN   N   OH

O$_2$N   N
OH

(55)

49 $\xleftarrow{\text{Na}_2\text{S}_2\text{O}_4}$

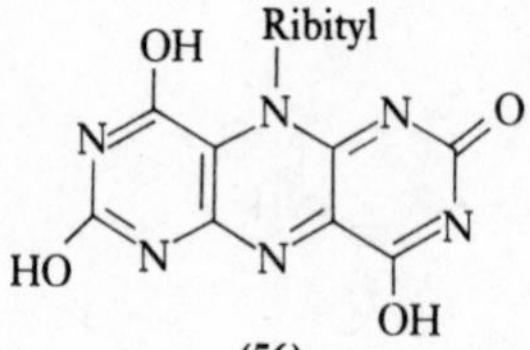

(56)

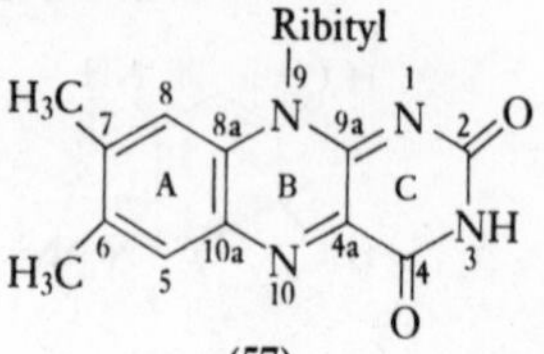

(57)

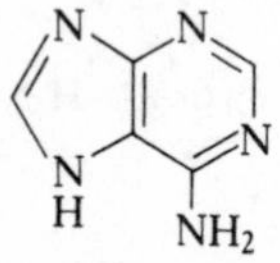

(58)

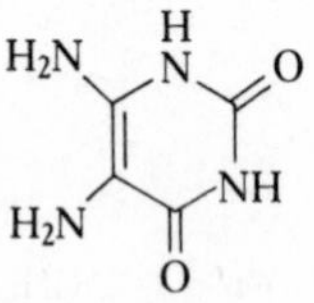

(59)

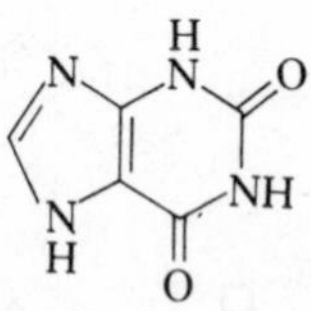

(60)

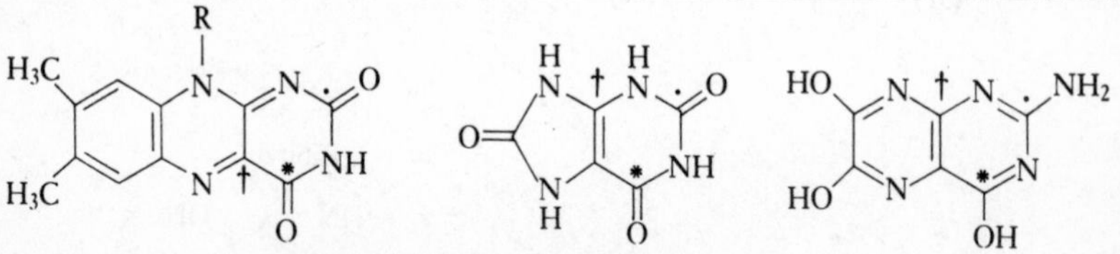

† represents carbon derived from glycine
* represents carbon derived from carbon dioxide
· represents carbon derived from formic acid

Figure 3.2[57]. Biosynthesis of flavins, purines and pteridines.

(61)

(62)

(63)

(64)

The lumazine 63 can be converted *in vivo* into 64, and this transformation is considered[60] to proceed via the intermediate 65. Uniformly ^{14}C-labelled adenine and guanine are incorporated[52,53,55] into the pyrimidine part of 63 and 64 in *E. ashbyii* and in *A. gossypii* but the biochemical origin of the extra carbon atoms of these two lumazines is still uncertain; it has been suggested[58] that $C_{(8)}$ and $C_{(9)}$ of the pyrazine ring of pterins arise from glucose, which is converted via ribose into a purine nucleotide. The latter loses $C_{(8)}$, whilst $C_{(1)}$ and $C_{(2)}$ of the ribose unit at $N_{(9)}$ provide $C_{(8)}$ and $C_{(9)}$ of the pteridine ring, and $C_{(3)}$, $C_{(4)}$ and $C_{(5)}$ provide the side-chain.

The lumazine 63 is an efficient precursor of riboflavin in cell-free extracts of *A. gossypii*[44], *E. ashbyii*[25] and *C. flaveri*[11] and a chemical synthesis of riboflavin has been reported[48] by the condensation of 63 with diacetyl. It is known[57] that 63 is not a biological degradation product of riboflavin and thus it must be a precursor of the vitamin.

Many suggestions have been made[57] concerning the origin of the four extra carbon atoms required in the biological conversion of 63 into riboflavin, but it has recently been shown[56] by the use of radioactive 63, labelled as shown in 66, that *all* of the carbon atoms of the *o*-xylene moiety of riboflavin are derived from the lumazine 63. The radioactive riboflavin obtained was degraded and thus shown to be labelled as indicated in 67. The required radioactive compound 66 had been synthesized previously by Goodwin[8]. The conversion of 63 into riboflavin has also been carried out in the absence of enzymes[61]; merely heating a solution of 63 under reflux in a phosphate buffer gave a 55% yield of riboflavin, based upon two molecules of 63 for one of product. The substance resulting from the removal of a four carbon unit from the second molecule of 63 has not been detected in biological systems, but in the chemical synthesis[61] it was isolated as the pyrimidopteridine 56, characterized earlier[5] as the self-condensation product of 49.

The mechanism suggested[61] for the conversion of 63 into riboflavin involves nucleophilic attack at position 7 in the lumazine 63 to give 68, followed by ring opening to 69, which then undergoes an aldol-type condensation to 70, as already suggested by Birch[2], and finally cyclization of 70 to riboflavin with the loss of a diaminopyrimidine residue.

Biological function of riboflavin

Riboflavin is a component of two important coenzymes, riboflavin mononucleotide 71 and riboflavin–adenine dinucleotide (FAD) (61).

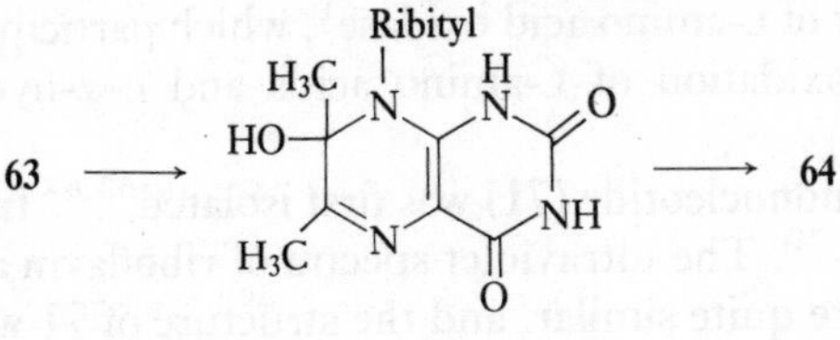

63 $\longrightarrow$ 64

(65)

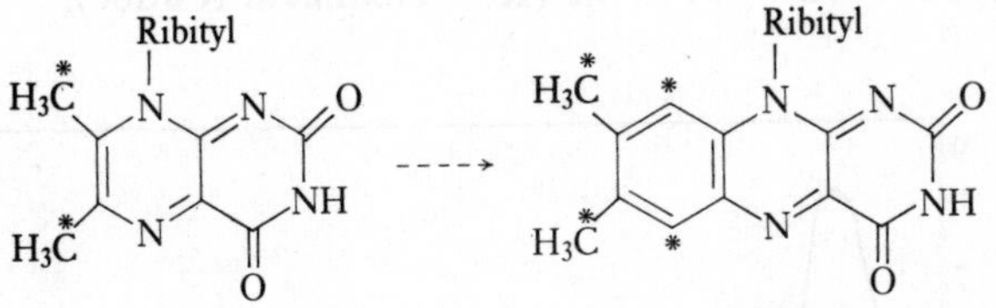

(66) - - - → (67)

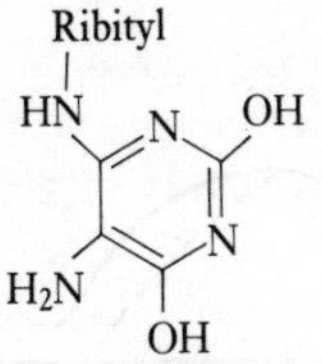

(49) 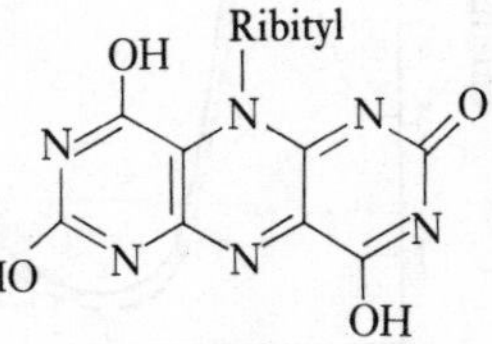   (56)

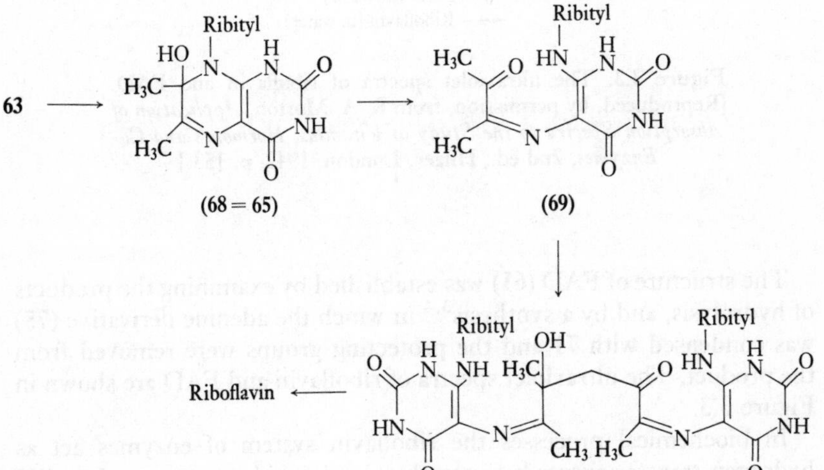

63 $\longrightarrow$

(68 = 65)   (69)

Riboflavin $\longleftarrow$

(70)

Riboflavin is part of L-amino acid oxidase[1], which participates in systems controlling the oxidation of L-amino acids and L-α-hydroxy acids to α-keto acids.

Riboflavin mononucleotide (71) was first isolated[63,64] from Warburg's yellow enzyme[69,70]. The ultraviolet spectra of riboflavin and Warburg's yellow enzyme are quite similar, and the structure of 71 was deduced by periodate oxidation experiments[24] and a synthesis[39,40] which is summarized in 23 → 72 → 74 → 71 (R = riboflavin residue).

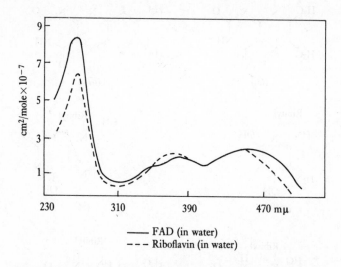

—— FAD (in water)
- - - Riboflavin (in water)

Figure 3.3. The ultraviolet spectra of riboflavin and FAD. [Reproduced, by permission, from R. A. Morton, *Application of Absorption Spectra to the Study of Vitamins, Hormones and Co-Enzymes*, 2nd ed., Hilger, London, 1942, p. 153.]

The structure of FAD (61) was established by examining the products of hydrolysis, and by a synthesis[3,4] in which the adenine derivative (75) was condensed with 71 and the protecting groups were removed from the product. The ultraviolet spectra of riboflavin and FAD are shown in Figure 3.3.

In biochemical processes the riboflavin system of enzymes act as hydrogen-transfer agents between the nicotinamide coenzymes I and II and the iron–porphyrin type cytochromes, in which the intermediates

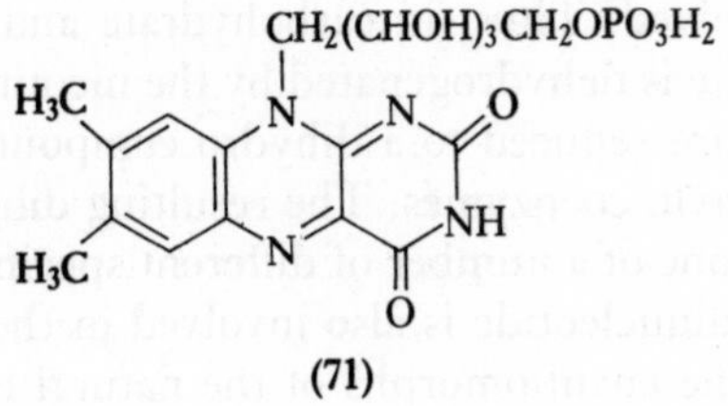
CH2(CHOH)3CH2OPO3H2
H3C
N
N
O
NH
H3C
N
O

(71)

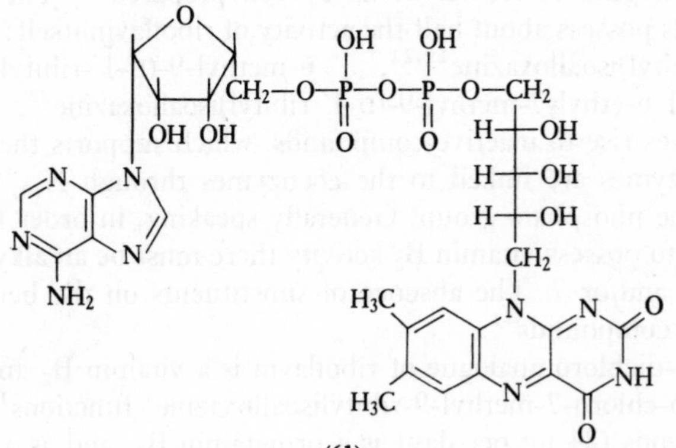
O
OH
OH
CH2—O—P—O—P—O—CH2
OH OH
O
O
H—OH
H—OH
H—OH
CH2
N
N
N
N
NH2
H3C
N
N
O
NH
H3C
N
O

(61)

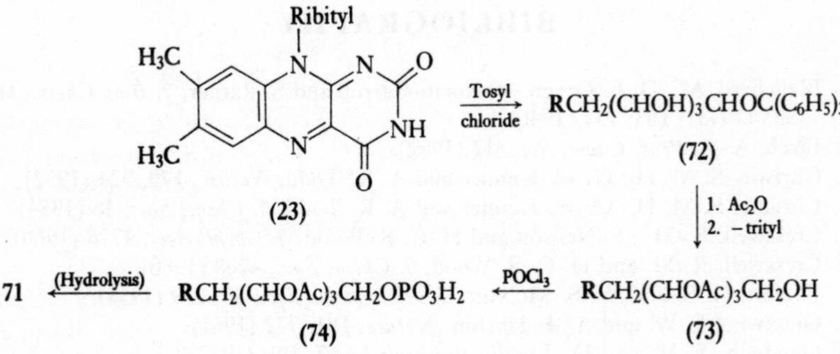
Ribityl
H3C
N
N
O
NH
H3C
N
O
(23)
Tosyl
chloride
RCH2(CHOH)3CHOC(C6H5)3
(72)
1. Ac2O
2. – trityl
71
(Hydrolysis)
RCH2(CHOAc)3CH2OPO3H2
(74)
POCl3
RCH2(CHOAc)3CH2OH
(73)

76 and **77** are involved. Thus, in carbohydrate and amino acid metabolism, the substrate is dehydrogenated by the nicotinamide coenzymes, which themselves are reduced to a dihydro compound; they are reoxidized by the riboflavin coenzymes. The resulting dihydroriboflavins are then reoxidized in one of a number of different specific reactions.

Flavin–adenine dinucleotide is also involved in the conversion of the D-α-amino acids (the enantiomorphs of the natural L-amino acids) into keto acids **78 → 80**.

Analogues of riboflavin

Structure specificity is not so high in riboflavin as it is in thiamine, and several analogues of riboflavin have been prepared[59]. The following compounds possess about half the activity of riboflavin itself: 7-methyl-9-(D-1′-ribityl)isoalloxazine[19,21], 6-methyl-9-(D-1′-ribityl)isoalloxazine[19] and 6-ethyl-7-methyl-9-(D-1′-ribityl)isoalloxazine[23]. Alkylation of $N_{(3)}$ gives rise to inactive compounds, which supports the view that the apoenzymes are linked to the coenzymes through $N_{(3)}$ as well as through the phosphate group. Generally speaking, in order for an isoalloxazine to possess vitamin B_2 activity there must be an alkyl group at position 6 and/or 7. The absence of substituents on the benzene ring gives toxic compounds[41].

The 6,7-dichloro analogue of riboflavin is a vitamin B_2 antagonist[42] whereas 6-chloro-7-methyl-9-ribitylisoalloxazine functions[12] at low concentrations (24 µg per day) as a provitamin B_2, and as a reversible antagonist at high concentrations (500 µg per day).

It is interesting to note that the L-lyxoflavin (which has been synthesized, and which possesses vitamin B_2 activity) has been isolated[13] from human mycocardium.

BIBLIOGRAPHY

1. Blanchard, M., D. E. Green, V. Nociti-Carroll and S. Ratner, *J. Biol. Chem.*, **161**, 583 (1945); **163**, 137 (1946).
2. Birch, A. J., *Proc. Chem. Soc.*, 11 (1962).
3. Christie, S. M. H., G. W. Kenner and A. R. Todd, *Nature*, **170**, 924 (1952).
4. Christie, S. M. H., G. W. Kenner and A. R. Todd, *J. Chem. Soc.*, 46 (1954).
5. Cresswell, R. M., T. Neilson and H. C. S. Wood, *J. Chem. Soc.*, 4776 (1960).
6. Cresswell, R. M. and H. C. S. Wood, *J. Chem. Soc.*, 4768 (1960).
7. Forrest, H. S. and W. S. McNutt, *J. Am. Chem. Soc.*, **80**, 739 (1958).
8. Goodwin, T. W. and A. A. Horton, *Nature*, **191**, 772 (1961).
9. Goodwin, T. W. and D. Treble, *Biochem. J.*, **67**, 10P (1957).

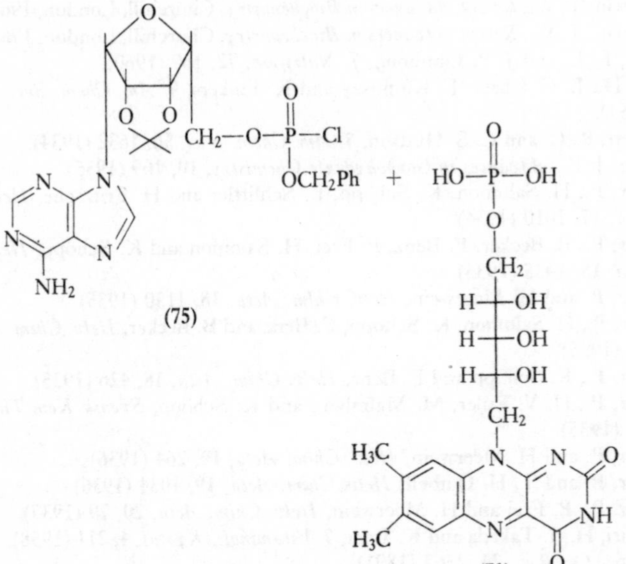

(75)   +   (71)

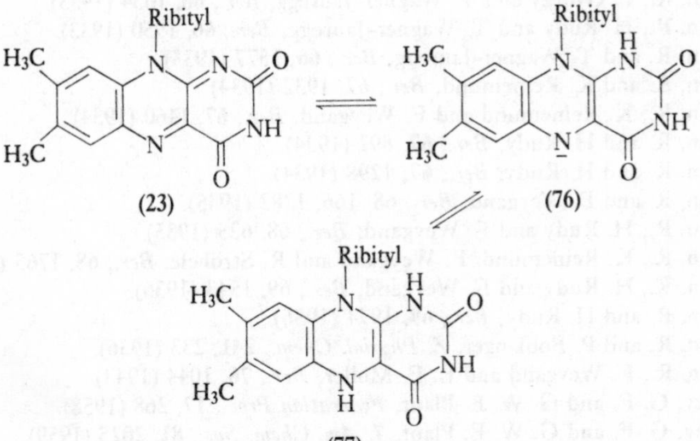

(23)   ⇌   (76)

(77)

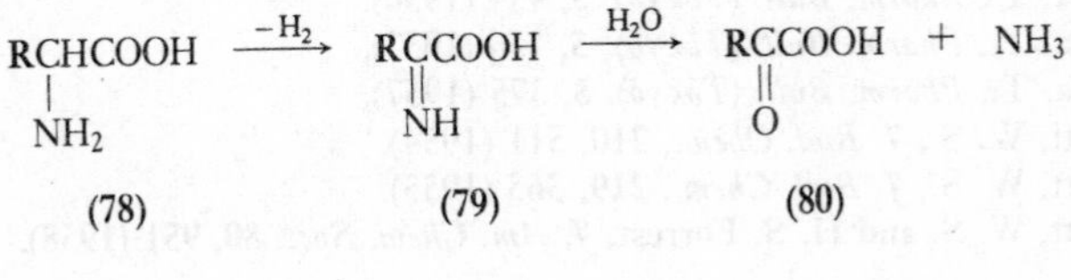

$$RCHCOOH \xrightarrow{-H_2} RCCOOH \xrightarrow{H_2O} RCCOOH + NH_3$$
$$\underset{NH_2}{\mid} \qquad \underset{NH}{\parallel} \qquad \underset{O}{\parallel}$$

(78)   (79)   (80)

10. Goodwin, T. W., *Recent Advances in Biochemistry*, Churchill, London, 1960, p. 190.
11. Goodwin, T. W., *Recent Advances in Biochemistry*, Churchill, London, 1960, p. 218.
12. Haley, E. E. and J. P. Lamboog, *J. Nutrition*, 72, 169 (1960).
13. Heyl, D., E. C. Chase, F. Koniuszy and K. Folkers, *J. Am. Chem. Soc.*, 73, 3826 (1951).
14. Hockett, R. C. and C. S. Hudson, *J. Am. Chem. Soc.*, 56, 1632 (1934).
15. Hodge, J. E., *Advances in Carbohydrate Chemistry*, 10, 169 (1955).
16. Karrer, P., H. Salomon, K. Schöpp, E. Schlittler and H. Fritzsche, *Helv. Chim. Acta*, 17, 1010 (1934).
17. Karrer, P., B. Becker, F. Benz, P. Frei, H. Salomon and K. Schöpp, *Helv. Chim. Acta*, 18, 1435 (1935).
18. Karrer, P. and H. Meerwein, *Helv. Chim. Acta*, 18, 1130 (1935).
19. Karrer, P., H. Salomon, K. Schöpp, F. Benz and B. Becker, *Helv. Chim. Acta*, 18, 908 (1935).
20. Karrer, P., K. Schöpp and F. Benz, *Helv. Chim. Acta*, 18, 426 (1935).
21. Karrer, P., H. V. Euler, M. Malmberg and K. Schöpp, *Svensk Kem Tidskr.*, 47, 153 (1935).
22. Karrer, P. and H. Meerwein, *Helv. Chim. Acta*, 19, 264 (1936).
23. Karrer, P. and T. H. Quibell, *Helv. Chim. Acta*, 19, 1034 (1936).
24. Karrer, P., P. Frei and H. Meerwein, *Helv. Chim. Acta*, 20, 79 (1937).
25. Katagiri, H., I. Takeda and K. Imai, *J. Vitaminol. (Kyōto)*, 4, 211 (1958).
26. Kuhling, O., *Ber.*, 24, 2363 (1891).
27. Kuhling, O., *Ber.*, 27, 2116 (1894).
28. Kuhling, O., *Ber.*, 28, 1968 (1895).
29. Kuhn, R., P. György and T. Wagner-Jauregg, *Ber.*, 66, 1034 (1933).
30. Kuhn, R., H. Rudy and T. Wagner-Jauregg, *Ber.*, 66, 1950 (1933).
31. Kuhn, R. and T. Wagner-Jauregg, *Ber.*, 66, 1577 (1933).
32. Kuhn, R. and K. Reinemund, *Ber.*, 67, 1932 (1934).
33. Kuhn, R., K. Reinemund and F. Weygand, *Ber.*, 67, 1460 (1934).
34. Kuhn, R. and H. Rudy, *Ber.*, 67, 892 (1934).
35. Kuhn, R. and H. Rudy, *Ber.*, 67, 1298 (1934).
36. Kuhn, R. and F. Weygand, *Ber.*, 68, 166, 1282 (1935).
37. Kuhn, R., H. Rudy and F. Weygand, *Ber.*, 68, 625 (1935).
38. Kuhn, R., K. Reinemund, F. Weygand and R. Ströhele, *Ber.*, 68, 1765 (1935).
39. Kuhn, R., H. Rudy and F. Weygand, *Ber.*, 69, 1543 (1936).
40. Kuhn, R. and H. Rudy, *Ber.*, 69, 1974 (1936).
41. Kuhn, R. and P. Boulanger, *Z. Physiol. Chem.*, 241, 233 (1936).
42. Kuhn, R., F. Weygand and E. F. Moller, *Ber.*, 76, 1044 (1943).
43. Maley, G. F. and G. W. E. Plaut, *Federation Proc.*, 17, 268 (1958).
44. Maley, G. F. and G. W. E. Plaut, *J. Am. Chem. Soc.*, 81, 2025 (1959).
45. Maley, G. F. and G. W. E. Plaut, *J. Biol. Chem.*, 234, 641 (1959).
46. Masuda, T., *Pharm. Bull. (Tōkyō)*, 4, 375 (1956).
47. Masuda, T., *Pharm. Bull. (Tōkyō)*, 3, 434 (1956).
48. Masuda, T., *Pharm. Bull. (Tōkyō)*, 5, 136 (1957).
49. Masuda, T., *Pharm. Bull. (Tōkyō)*, 5, 375 (1957).
50. McNutt, W. S., *J. Biol. Chem.*, 210, 511 (1954).
51. McNutt, W. S., *J. Biol. Chem.*, 219, 365 (1955).
52. McNutt, W. S. and H. S. Forrest, *J. Am. Chem. Soc.*, 80, 951 (1958).

53. McNutt, W. S., *J. Am. Chem. Soc.*, **82**, 217 (1960).
54. McNutt, W. S., *Federation Proc.*, **19**, 157 (1960).
55. Plaut, G. W. E. and G. F. Maley, *Arch. Biochem. Biophys.*, **80**, 219 (1959).
56. Plaut, G. W. E., *J. Biol. Chem.*, **235**, PC41 (1960).
57. Plaut, G. W. E., *Ann. Rev. Biochem.*, **30**, 409 (1961).
58. Pinder, A. R., *Ann. Rept. Progr. Chem.* (*Chem. Soc., London*), **58**, 280 (1961).
59. Robinson, F. A., *The Vitamin B Complex*, Chapman and Hall, London, 1951, p. 206.
60. Rowan, T., H. C. S. Wood and P. Hemmerick, *Proc. Chem. Soc.*, 260 (1961).
61. Rowan, T. and H. C. S. Wood, *Proc. Chem. Soc.*, 21 (1963).
62. Stern, K. G. and E. R. Holiday, *Ber.*, **67**, 1442 (1934).
63. Theorell, H., *Biochem. Z.*, **275**, 37, 344 (1934).
64. Theorell, H., *Biochem. Z.*, **278**, 263 (1935).
65. Tishler, M., N. L. Wendler, K. Ladenburg and J. W. Wellman, *J. Am. Chem. Soc.*, **66**, 1328 (1944).
66. Tishler, M., J. W. Wellman and K. Ladenburg, *J. Am. Chem. Soc.*, **67**, 2165 (1945).
67. Tishler, M., N. L. Wendler, K. Ladenburg and J. W. Wellman, *U.S. Pat.*, 2420210.
68. Tsukihara, K., *J. Vitaminol.* (*Kyōto*), **6**, 68 (1960).
69. Warburg, O. and W. Christian, *Biochem. Z.*, **242**, 206 (1931); **254**, 438 (1932); **257**, 492 (1933); **263**, 228 (1933); *Naturwissenschaften*, **20**, 688, 980 (1932).
70. Warburg, O. and W. Christian, *Biochem. Z.*, **266**, 377 (1933).
71. Weygand, F., *Ber.*, **73**, 1259 (1940).

CHAPTER **4**

Pteroylglutamic Acid (Folic Acid)

PTERIDINES – PTEROYLGLUTAMIC ACID – Detection and isolation –
Sources of pteroylglutamic acid – Deficiency disease – Daily requirement – Structure – Synthesis – The SLR factor – Biosynthesis of
pteroylglutamic acid – Reduced forms of pteroylglutamic acid – The
citrovorum factor – Biological function of pteroylglutamic acid –
Analogues and antagonists of pteroylglutamic acid – BIBLIOGRAPHY

PTERIDINES[1,15]

PTEROYLGLUTAMIC ACID (1) contains a pteridine nucleus, and the
numbering of this ring system is shown in 2. The pteridine nucleus was
first recognized in the pigments of butterfly wings, but pteridines are not
confined to the insect world. Thus, xanthopterin (3) and biopterin (4)
are present in man.

Pteridines are usually synthesized from a diaminopyrimidine and
acetic acid or glyoxalic acid. Biopterin (4), which is a growth factor for
the protozoan *Crithidia fasciculata*[34,35], has been obtained[34] by the
condensation of 2,5,6-triamino-4-hydroxypyrimidine (5) and 5-deoxy-L-
arabinose. Purines can also be converted into pteridines[2] under very
mild conditions 6 → 9.

In general, pteridines are not very stable, and unless there are at least
two electron-donating substituents on the ring system, these compounds
are easily hydrolysed by acids and alkalis to pyrimidines or pyrazines.
The ultraviolet spectrum of pteridine is shown in Figure 4.1 (page 55).

PTEROYLGLUTAMIC ACID

Detection and isolation

In connexion with nutritional studies in man, animals and microorganisms, several apparently unrelated factors had been isolated in
various laboratories and for some time these substances presented a
somewhat confusing picture. However, once the structure of pteroylglutamic acid had been elucidated it was realized that it was the parent

compound of a number of biologically active substances. Thus Factor U, a chick growth factor[?], vitamin H, a nutritional factor for monkeys[?], vitamin B_c, a chick antianemic factor[?] and the liver $L.$ casei—eluate factor[?] were all shown to be forms of pteroylglutamic acid. Yeast "norit-eluate factor," moreover, was shown to be an "individual glutamic" conjugate of yeast "norite B_c conjugate[?]" proved to be pteroylhexaglutamylglutamic acid. The $S.$ faecalis casei R factor (SLR factor)[?] was shown[?] to be 10-N-formylpteroylglutamic acid.

Pteroylglutamic acid was first isolated in a crystalline form by Snell[?] and Stokstad[?].

Sources of pteroylglutamic acid

The richest sources of the vitamin in the animal kingdom are liver, kidney and yeast. In the plant kingdom asparagus, spinach, lemons, bananas and strawberries contain appreciable quantities.

Deficiency disease

Lack of pteroylglutamic acid in the diet is thought to be responsible for macrocytic anemia (that is a deficiency of normal polynuclear erythrocytes).

Daily requirement

It[?] has been estimated at 1-2 mg for the normal adult human, but daily doses of 15 mg have been administered therapeutically.

Structure

Structural studies actually began in 1943 with "yeast eluate factor," which is now known to be pteroylheptaglutamic acid, but the structure of pteroylglutamic acid also followed from this work.

Hydrolysis of the yeast $L.$ casei factor in the presence of air yielded[?] a deaminated amine, a fluorescent pigment, compound A. This substance A, $C_{18}H_{19}N_7O_6$, was shown to be devoid of O-methyl or N-methyl groups, but cleavage with acid indicated the presence of one carboxyl group and one enolic hydroxyl group. When this A was oxidized with chlorine water and the products dialysed, guanidine (10) was recognized among the products, thus showing the presence of a 2-aminopyrimidine skeleton in A. The partial structure 11, which can now be written for A,

(1)

(2)   (3)

(4)   (5)

(6)   (7)

(9)   (8)

compound of a number of biologically active substances. Thus, *Factor U*, a chick growth factor[54], *vitamin M*, a nutritional factor for monkeys[16], *vitamin B_C*, a chick antianemia factor[23] and the liver *Lactobacillus casei* factor[51] were all found to be identical with pteroylglutamic acid. Yeast *Lactobacillus casei* factor[25], however, was shown to be pteroyldiglutamyl-glutamic acid, and the yeast *vitamin B_C conjugate*[36] proved to be pteroyl-hexaglutamylglutamic acid. The *Streptococcus lactus* R factor (SLR factor) was shown[41] to be 10-*N*-formylpteroylglutamic acid.

Pteroylglutamic acid was first isolated in a crystalline form by Snell[30] and by Stokstad[53].

Sources of pteroylglutamic acid

The richest sources of the vitamin in the animal kingdom are liver, kidney and yeast; in the plant kingdom asparagus, spinach, lemons, bananas and strawberries contain appreciable quantities.

Deficiency disease

Lack of pteroylglutamic acid in the diet is thought to be responsible for macrocylic anemia (that is a deficiency of normal polynuclear erythrocytes).

Daily requirement

This has been estimated at 1–2 mg for the normal adult human, but daily doses of 15 mg have been administered therapeutically.

Structure[3,56,57]

Structural studies actually began with the yeast *L. casei* factor[25], which is now known to be pteroyldiglutamylglutamic acid, but the structure of pteroylglutamic acid also followed from this work.

Hydrolysis of the yeast *L. casei* factor in the presence of air yielded[56] a diazotizable amine and a fluorescent pigment, *compound A*. This substance A, $C_7H_5N_5O_3$, was shown to be devoid of *O*-methyl or *N*-methyl groups, but electrometric titration indicated the presence of one carboxyl group and one enolic hydroxyl group. When A was oxidized with chlorine water and then hydrolysed, guanidine (**10**) was recognized among the products, thus showing the presence of a 2-aminopyrimidine skeleton in A. The part-structure **11**, which can now be written for A,

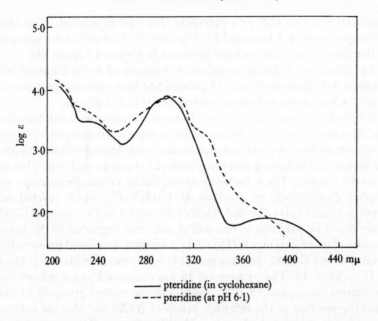

Figure 4.1. The ultraviolet spectrum of pteridine. [Reproduced, by permission, from S. F. Mason, *Chem. Soc. (London) Spec. Publ.*, No. 3, 143 (1955).]

$$
\begin{array}{c}
\text{H}_2\text{N} \quad \text{NH} \\
| \\
\text{C} \\
| \\
\text{NH}_2
\end{array}
$$

(10)

$$
\text{H}_2\text{N}
\begin{array}{c}
\text{N} \\
| \\
\text{N}
\end{array}
\begin{array}{l}
\text{—COOH} \\
\text{—OH} \\
\text{—C}_2\text{HN}_2
\end{array}
$$

(11)

3

suggested a purine (12) or a pteridine (13) type of nucleus. The ultraviolet spectrum of A favoured 13 (Figure 4.2). The ultraviolet spectrum of the yeast *L. casei* factor itself is shown in Figure 4.3 (page 58).

The product of decarboxylation of A appeared to be identical with 2-amino-4-hydroxypteridine (15), which had been prepared previously[58] from 2,4,5-triamino-6-hydroxypyrimidine (14) and glyoxal.

When the original yeast *L. casei* factor was treated with sulphur dioxide, cleavage occurred to yield an aromatic amine, which upon hydrolysis gave *p*-aminobenzoic acid and an α-amino acid. Microbiological assay of the amino acid indicated that three moles of glutamic acid were liberated from the vitamin. The second substance, isolated from the cleavage with sulphur dioxide, was an *aldehyde*, B, $C_7H_4N_5O_2$, which reacted with aqueous alkali to give one mole each of the acid A and a *compound C*. The latter could be oxidized to the acid A, and was degraded to the known 5-amino-2-methylpyrazine (16) using a method developed previously[62]. From this it followed that compound C is 17; the degradation is shown in 17 → 18 → 16. The structure of 16 was confirmed by a synthesis from the known compound 19. The position of the methyl group in 17 indicates the position of the aldehyde group of B (20) and also the carboxyl group in the acid A, which is thus 21. The structure 21 was proved by a synthesis[31] in which 2,4,5-triamino-6-hydroxypyrimidine (22) was condensed with ethyl α-bromo-β,β-diethoxypropionate (23). The latter compound had been prepared previously by Oroshnik[33], whereas the pyrimidine 22 may be prepared as shown in 24 + 25 → 26 → 22. The acid A has also been obtained from 22 and ethyl mesoxalate as shown in 22 → 27 → 28 → 21.

The structure 17 was also confirmed by synthesis[31]. The triaminopyrimidine 22 was condensed with methyl γ,γ-dimethoxyacetoacetate (29) to yield 30, oxidation of which yielded the acid A (21); decarboxylation of 30 gave 17. The isomeric compound 31 was also prepared from 17 and methylglyoxal. The required compound 29 was prepared from methyl dimethoxyacetate and methyl acetate.

When the yeast *L. casei* factor was hydrolysed[56] with alkali in the *absence* of air, no aromatic amine was produced, and no fluorescent pigment was observed, but after prolonged hydrolysis under these conditions two molecules of an α-amino acid and one molecule of a biologically active substance were formed. The latter was identified as the racemate of the liver *L. casei* factor. When this racemate was hydrolysed with alkali in the presence of air[56], an aromatic amine was formed, hydrolysis of which gave *p*-aminobenzoic acid. Hence, the aromatic amine must be

(12)   (13)

(14)   Glyoxal   (15)

(17)   1.NaOH/H$_2$O, pressure   2. H$^+$ (18) $-CO_2$ (16)

(19)   (20)   (21)

(22)   (23) $\longrightarrow$ 21

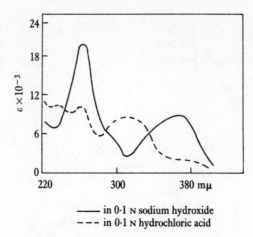

Figure 4.2. The ultraviolet spectrum of the acid
A (21). [Reproduced, by permission, from B. L.
Hutchings *et al.*, *J. Am. Chem. Soc.*, **70**, 2
(1948).]

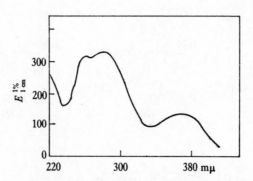

Figure 4.3. The ultraviolet spectrum of the
yeast *L. casei* factor (in 0·1 N sodium hydroxide). [Reproduced, by permission, from B. L.
Hutchings *et al.*, *J. Am. Chem. Soc.*, **70**, 7
(1948).]

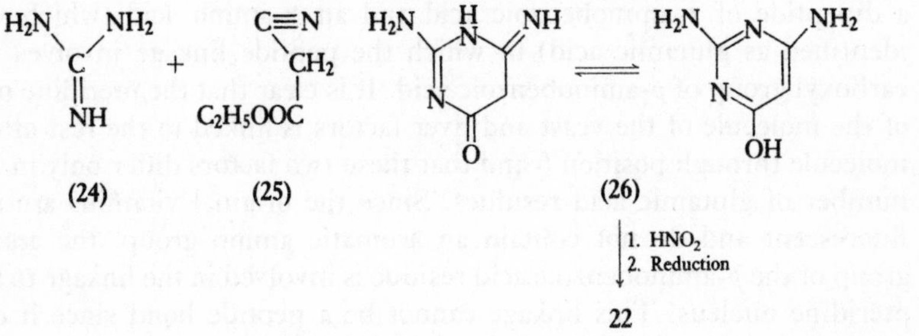
(24)
(25)
(26)
1. HNO2
2. Reduction
22

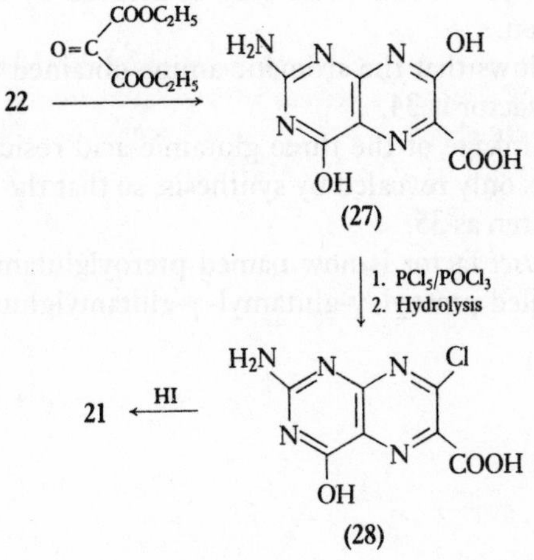
22
(27)
1. PCl5/POCl3
2. Hydrolysis
21
HI
(28)

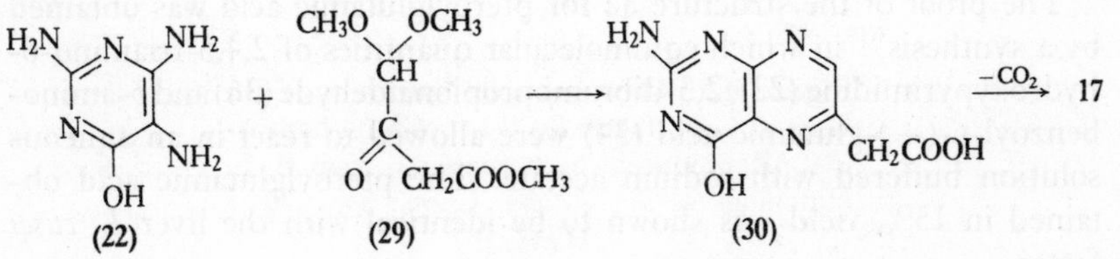
(22)
(29)
(30)
−CO2
17

a dipeptide of *p*-aminobenzoic acid and an α-amino acid (which was identified as glutamic acid) in which the peptide linkage involves the carboxyl group of *p*-aminobenzoic acid. It is clear that the pteridine part of the molecule of the yeast and liver factors is linked to the rest of the molecule through position 6 and that these two factors differ only in the number of glutamic acid residues. Since the original vitamins are not fluorescent and do not contain an aromatic amino group, the amino group of the *p*-aminobenzoic acid residue is involved in the linkage to the pteridine nucleus. This linkage cannot be a peptide bond since it can only be cleaved oxidatively. It was concluded[26] that a methylene group bridged the pteridine and peptide residues. Hence the structure of the liver *L. casei* factor is 32, and the yeast *L. casei* factor contains two more glutamic acid residues than this. It was found[31] that in the model system 33 the —CH_2—NH— bond could only be cleaved by hydrolysis in the presence of oxygen.

From 32 it follows that the aromatic amine obtained by hydrolysis of the liver *L. casei* factor is 34.

The mode of linkage of the three glutamic acid residues in the yeast *L. casei* factor was only revealed by synthesis, so that the structure of this factor can be written as 35.

The liver *L. casei* factor is now named pteroylglutamic acid, and the yeast factor is called pteroyl-γ-glutamyl-γ-glutamylglutamic acid.

Synthesis

The proof of the structure 32 for pteroylglutamic acid was obtained by a synthesis[61] in which equimolecular quantities of 2,4,5-triamino-6-hydroxypyrimidine (22), 2,3-dibromopropionaldehyde (36) and *p*-aminobenzoyl-L-(+)-glutamic acid (34) were allowed to react in an aqueous solution buffered with sodium acetate. The pteroylglutamic acid obtained in 15% yield was shown to be identical with the liver *L. casei* factor.

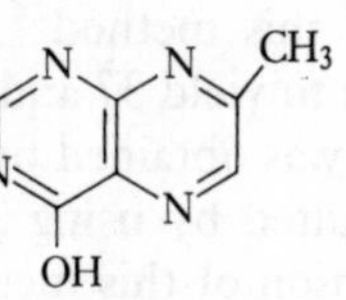

H₂N — pteridine ring with CH₃, OH

$$(31)$$

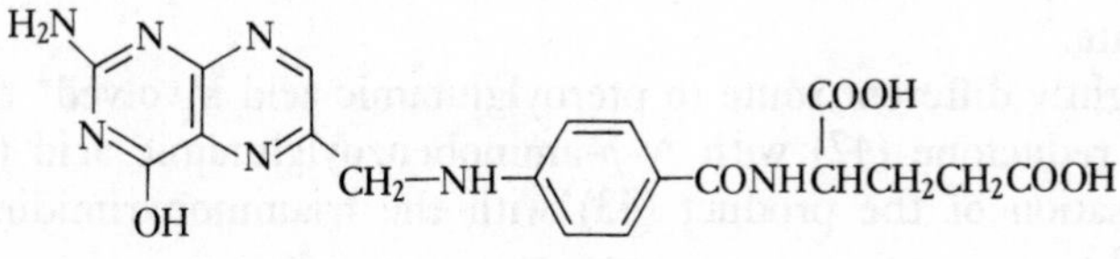

(32)

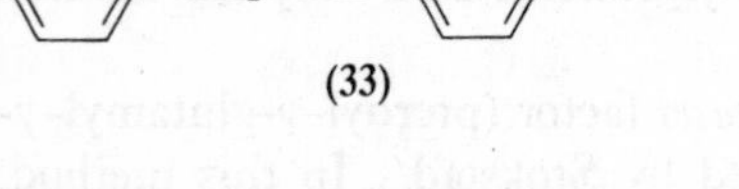

COOH structure: —CH₂—NH—⟨benzene⟩—CONHCHCH₂CH₂COOH

(33)

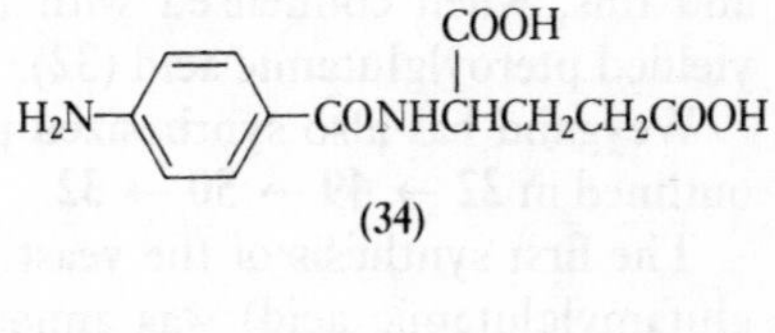

⟨benzene⟩—CH₂—NH—⟨benzene⟩—COOH

(34)

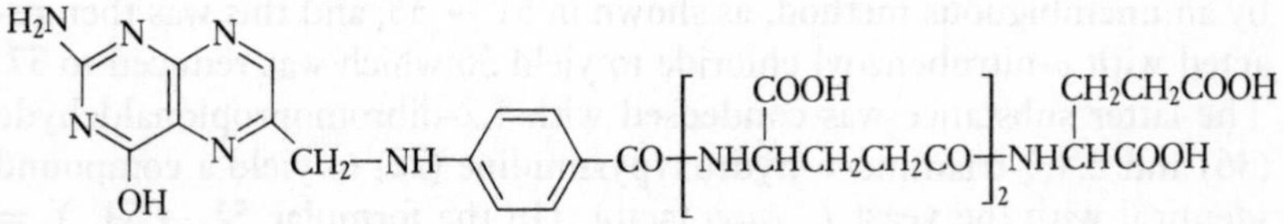

$$\text{H}_2\text{N}—\langle\text{benzene}\rangle—\text{CONHCHCH}_2\text{CH}_2\text{COOH}$$
with COOH

(35)

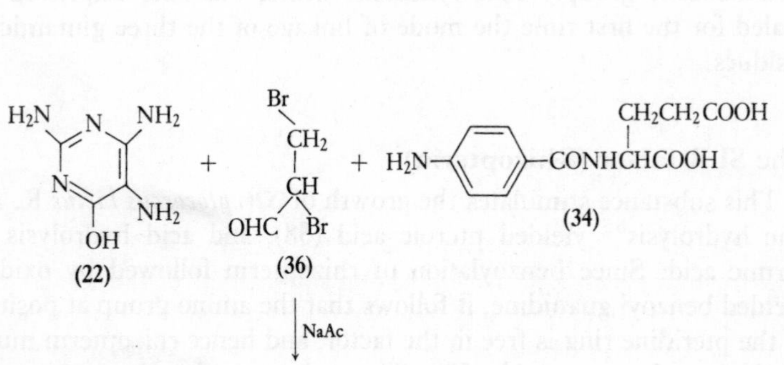

(22)   (36)

(34)

NaAc

32

In an improvement of this method[24], 2,3-dibromopropionaldehyde was reacted with pyridine to yield 37 and this was condensed with 22 to give 38. Pteroic acid (39) was obtained by condensing 38 with *p*-amino-benzoic acid, and 32 resulted by using 34 in place of *p*-aminobenzoic acid. In a slight modification of this method[6], the intermediate 38 was reduced with zinc in sodium hydroxide to yield 40, which was oxidized with hydrogen peroxide to 41; the latter was converted into 32 by side-chain halogenation followed by reaction with diethyl *N*-*p*-aminobenzoyl-glutamate.

A slightly different route to pteroylglutamic acid involved[4] the reac-tion of reductone (42) with *N*-*p*-aminobenzoylglutamic acid (34) and condensation of the product (43) with the triaminopyrimidine 22 to yield 32.

In an alternative approach to the synthesis of 32[49], a 2-amino-4-hydroxy-6-pteroyl derivative (48) was synthesized as shown in 44 → 48 and this, when condensed with *N*-*p*-aminobenzoylglutamic acid (34), yielded pteroylglutamic acid (32).

Weygand has also synthesized pteroylglutamic acid[63] by the method outlined in 22 → 49 → 50 → 32.

The first synthesis of the yeast *L. casei* factor (pteroyl-*γ*-glutamyl-*γ*-glutamylglutamic acid) was announced by Stokstad[7]. In this method, the tripeptide *γ*-glutamyl-*γ*-glutamylglutamic acid (55) was synthesized by an unambiguous method, as shown in 51 → 55, and this was then re-acted with *p*-nitrobenzoyl chloride to yield 56 which was reduced to 57. The latter substance was condensed with 1,2-dibromopropionaldehyde (36) and 2,4,5-triamino-6-hydroxypyrimidine (22) to yield a compound identical with the yeast *L. casei* factor. (In the formulae 51 → 54, Y = carbobenzoxy group.) This synthesis, which was later improved[8], re-vealed for the first time the mode of linkage of the three glutamic acid residues.

The SLR factor (Rhizopterin)

This substance stimulates the growth of *Streptococcus lactus* R. Alka-line hydrolysis[65] yielded pteroic acid (58), and acid hydrolysis gave formic acid. Since benzoylation of rhizopterin followed by oxidation yielded benzoyl guanidine, it follows that the amino group at position 2 of the pteridine ring is free in the factor, and hence rhizopterin must be 10-*N*-formylpteroic acid (59). The substance has been prepared[65] simply by heating pteroic acid with formic acid.

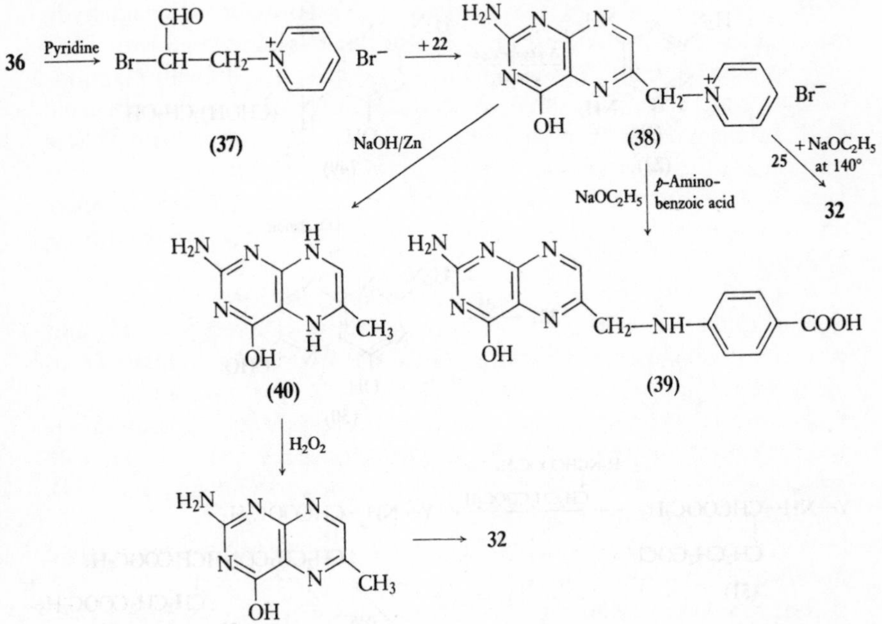

(37) (38) (39) (40) (41)

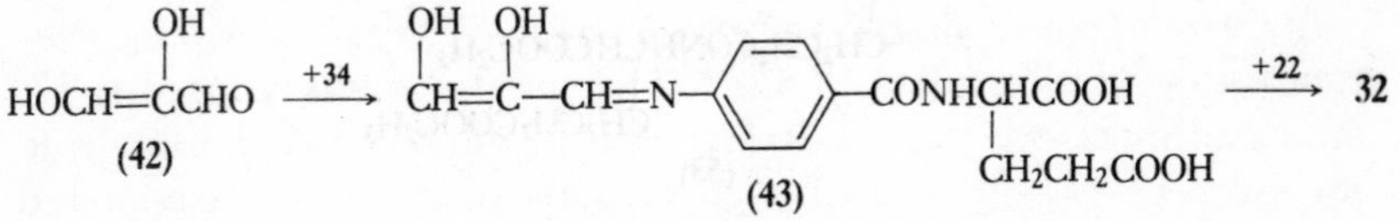

(42) (43)

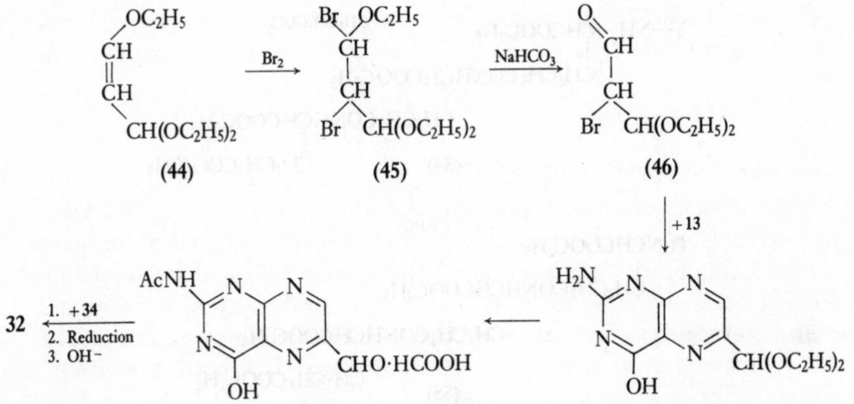

(44) (45) (46) (47) (48)

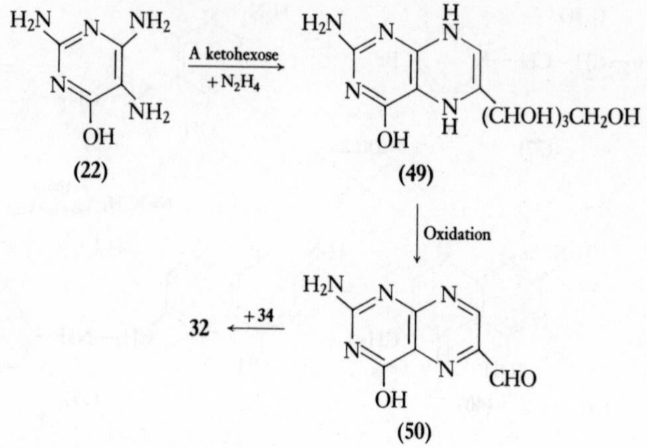

H_2N—[pyrimidine: NH_2, N, NH_2, OH]
(22)

$\xrightarrow[\text{+N}_2\text{H}_4]{\text{A ketohexose}}$

H_2N—[pteridine ring with H, N, N, H] $(CHOH)_3CH_2OH$, OH
(49)

$\downarrow$ Oxidation

H_2N—[pteridine ring] CHO, OH
(50)

$32 \xleftarrow{+34}$ (50)

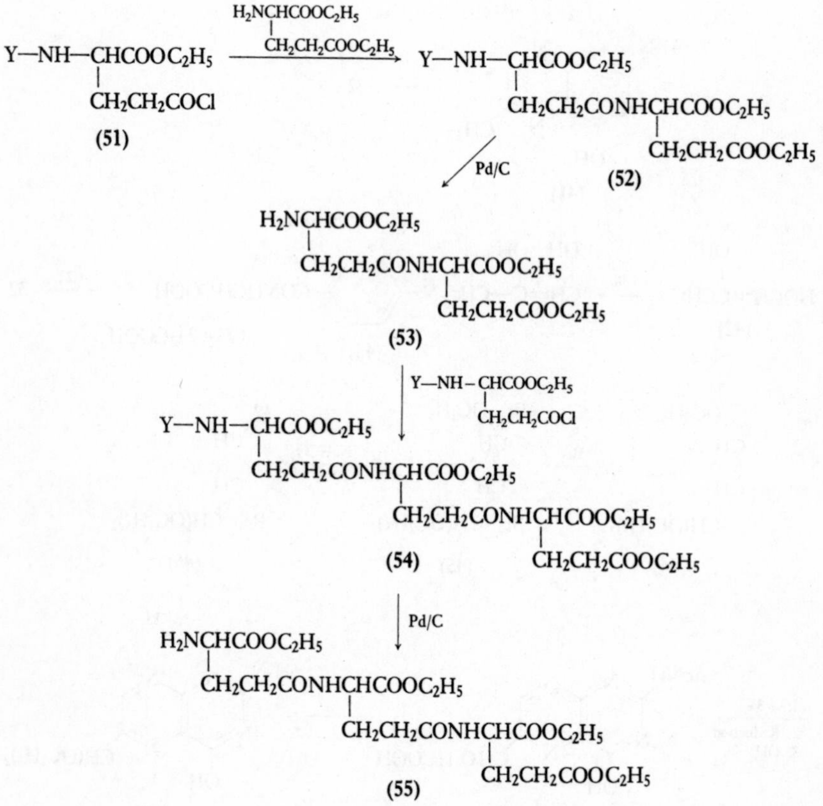

Y—NH—CHCOOC$_2$H$_5$ | CH$_2$CH$_2$COCl
(51)

$\xrightarrow[\text{CH}_2\text{CH}_2\text{COOC}_2\text{H}_5]{\text{H}_2\text{NCHCOOC}_2\text{H}_5}$

Y—NH—CHCOOC$_2$H$_5$ | CH$_2$CH$_2$CONHCHCOOC$_2$H$_5$ | CH$_2$CH$_2$COOC$_2$H$_5$
(52)

$\searrow$ Pd/C

H$_2$NCHCOOC$_2$H$_5$ | CH$_2$CH$_2$CONHCHCOOC$_2$H$_5$ | CH$_2$CH$_2$COOC$_2$H$_5$
(53)

$\downarrow$ Y—NH–CHCOOC$_2$H$_5$ | CH$_2$CH$_2$COCl

Y—NH—CHCOOC$_2$H$_5$ | CH$_2$CH$_2$CONHCHCOOC$_2$H$_5$ | CH$_2$CH$_2$CONHCHCOOC$_2$H$_5$ | CH$_2$CH$_2$COOC$_2$H$_5$
(54)

$\downarrow$ Pd/C

H$_2$NCHCOOC$_2$H$_5$ | CH$_2$CH$_2$CONHCHCOOC$_2$H$_5$ | CH$_2$CH$_2$CONHCHCOOC$_2$H$_5$ | CH$_2$CH$_2$COOC$_2$H$_5$
(55)

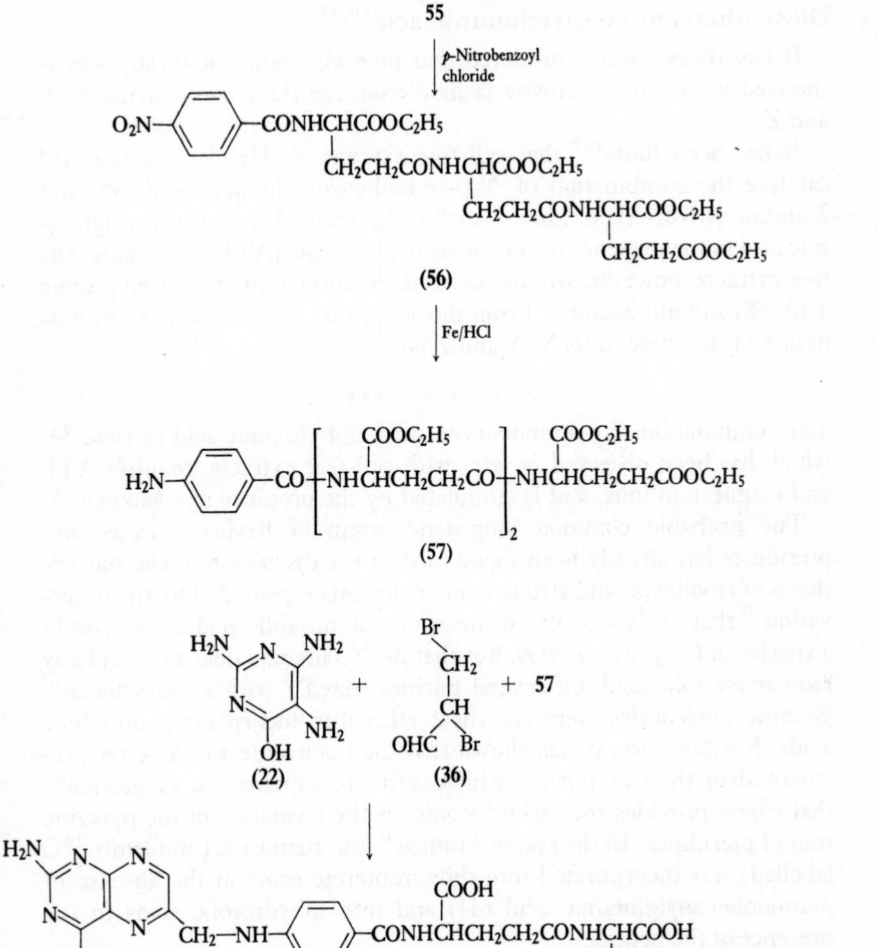

55

p-Nitrobenzoyl chloride

O_2N—⟨ ⟩—CONHCHCOOC$_2$H$_5$

CH$_2$CH$_2$CONHCHCOOC$_2$H$_5$

CH$_2$CH$_2$CONHCHCOOC$_2$H$_5$

CH$_2$CH$_2$COOC$_2$H$_5$

(56)

Fe/HCl

H_2N—⟨ ⟩—CO$\left[\text{NHCHCH}_2\text{CH}_2\text{CO}\right]_2$—NHCHCH$_2CH_2$COOC$_2H_5$

$\overset{|}{\text{COOC}_2\text{H}_5}$ $\overset{|}{\text{COOC}_2\text{H}_5}$

(57)

$\underset{\text{OH}}{H_2N\text{-pyrimidine-}NH_2, NH_2}$ **(22)** + $\underset{\text{OHC} \quad Br}{\overset{Br}{\text{CH}_2}\text{-CH}}$ **(36)** + **57**

H_2N—[pteridine]—CH$_2$—NH—⟨ ⟩—CONHCHCH$_2$CH$_2$CONHCHCOOH

OH   COOH

CH$_2$CH$_2$CONHCHCOOH

CH$_2$CH$_2$COOH

(35)

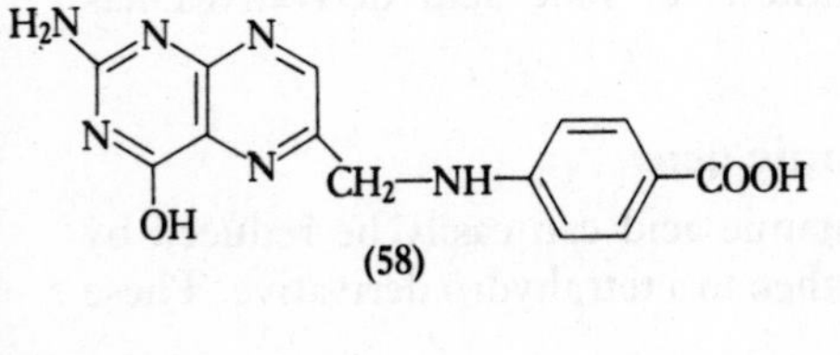

H_2N—[pteridine]—CH$_2$—NH—⟨ ⟩—COOH

OH

(58)

H_2N—[pteridine]—CH$_2$—N(CHO)—⟨ ⟩—COOH

OH

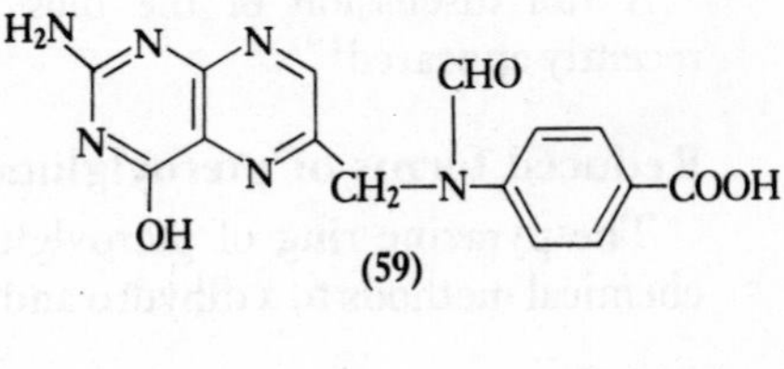

(59)

Biosynthesis of pteroylglutamic acid[19,37]

It has always been considered that pteroylglutamic acid (60) is synthesized *in vivo* in a stepwise fashion from the three components X, Y and Z.

It has been found[27] that cell-free extracts of *Mycobact. avium* will catalyse the combination of N-*p*-aminobenzoylglutamic acid (34) and 2-amino-4-hydroxypteridine-6-carboxylic acid (21) to form pterylglutamic acid in the presence of adenosine triphosphate (ATP). The same cell-free extracts, however, will not catalyse the formation of 60 from pteroic acid (58) and glutamate[27]. From this it appears that the order of combination of the three units X, Y and Z is

$$Z + Y \longrightarrow ZY \xrightarrow{X} ZYX$$

The combination of *p*-aminobenzoic acid and glutamic acid to yield 34, which has been observed *in vitro* with cell-free extracts, requires ATP and magnesium ions, and is stimulated by the presence of coenzyme A.

The probable common biogenetic origin of flavins, purines and pteridines has already been mentioned in the discussion of the biosynthesis of riboflavin, and strong support for this is provided by the observation[60] that 2-^{14}C-adenine is incorporated into folic acid derivatives in a species of *Coryne bacterium*, but that 8-^{14}C-adenine does not yield any radioactive folic acid. Of several purines tested[40] with *Escherichia coli*, guanine nucleotides were the most efficiently incorporated into folic acids. Furthermore, it was shown that the nucleotide was a better precursor than the free purine, which seems to support the suggestion[64] that ribose provides the carbon atoms for the formation of the pyrazine ring of pteridines. In the system studied[40] the guanosine (uniformly ^{14}C labelled) was incorporated into dihydropteroic acids in the absence of *p*-aminobenzoylglutamic acid (34) and into dihydrofolic acids in the presence of the peptide.

Evidence is accumulating[11,37] to suggest that the immediate pteridine precursor of folic acid is a 2-amino-3,4-dihydro-4-hydroxy-6-hydroxymethylpteridine (62), which arises from guanosine (61), and which condenses via its phosphate ester 63 with 34 to give dihydrofolic acid (64).

A full discussion of the biosynthesis of folic acid derivatives has recently appeared[19a].

Reduced forms of pteroylglutamic acid

The pyrazine ring of pteroylglutamic acid can easily be reduced by chemical methods to a dihydro and then to a tetrahydro derivative. These

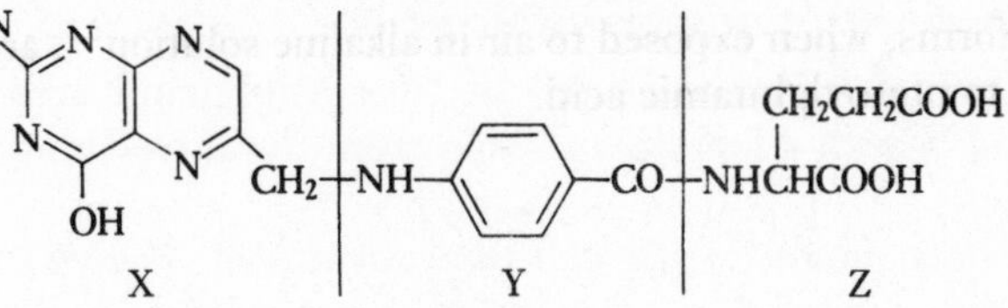

(60)

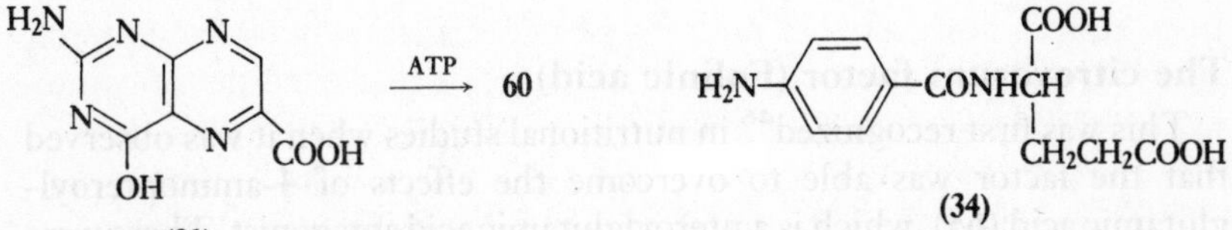

(21) $\xrightarrow{\text{ATP}}$ 60   (34)

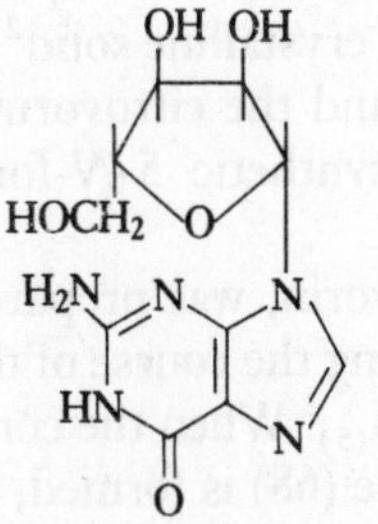

(61) 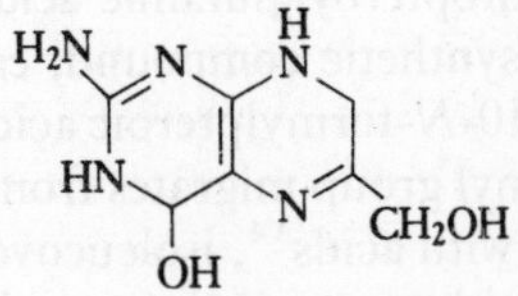   (62)

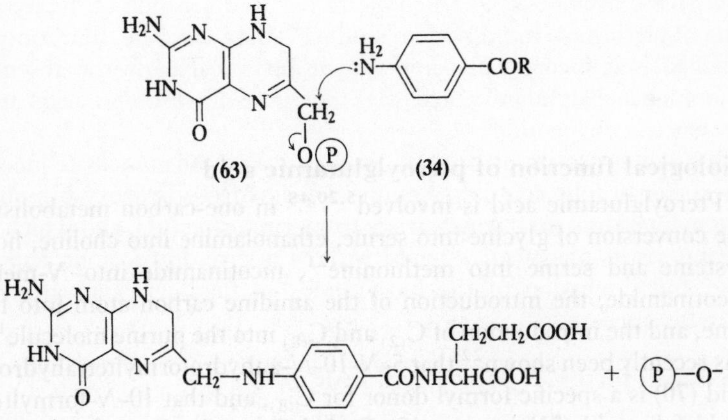

(63)   (34)

(64)   + $\text{P}-\text{O}^-$

reduced forms, when exposed to air in alkaline solution[32], are readily re-oxidized to pteroylglutamic acid.

The citrovorum factor (Folinic acid)

This was first recognized[46] in nutritional studies when it was observed that the factor was able to overcome the effects of 4-aminopteroyl-glutamic acid (65), which is a pteroylglutamic acid antagonist. There were indications that the new factor was closely related to pteroylglutamic acid[10], and it was eventually obtained as a crystalline solid[28]. The structure was investigated initially by May[29] and the citrovorum factor was finally shown[9,17] to be identical with synthetic 5-N-formyl-5,6,7,8-tetrahydropteroylglutamic acid (66).

The synthetic compound, called leucovorin, was prepared by reduction of 10-N-formylpteroic acid (67). During the course of this reduction the formyl group migrates from $N_{(10)}$ to $N_{(5)}$. When the compound 66 is treated with acids[14], isoleucovorin chloride (68) is formed, which, when boiled with water, is converted into anhydroleucovorin A (69).

Biological function of pteroylglutamic acid

Pteroylglutamic acid is involved[5,20,48] in one-carbon metabolism in the conversion of glycine into serine, ethanolamine into choline, homo-cysteine and serine into methionine[21], nicotinamide into N-methyl-nicotinamide, the introduction of the amidine carbon atom into histi-dine, and the introduction of $C_{(2)}$ and $C_{(8)}$ into the purine molecule[12]. It has recently been shown[22] that 5-N-10-N-anhydroformyltetrahydrofolic acid (70) is a specific formyl donor for $C_{(8)}$, and that 10-N-formyltetra-hydrofolic acid (71) is a specific formyl donor for $C_{(2)}$ of the purines. Other functions for pterolyglutamic acid have also been suggested[45].

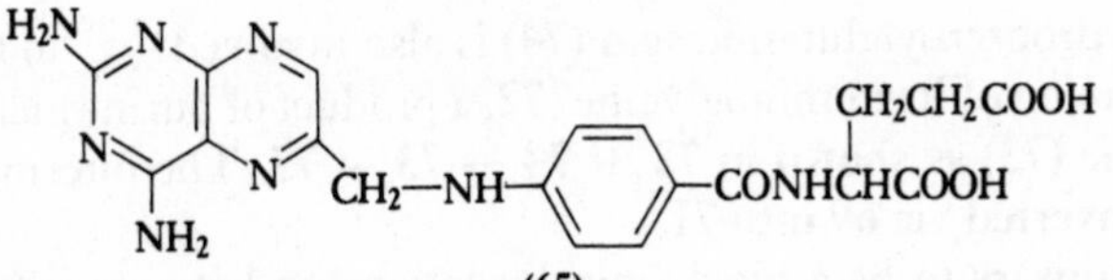

(65)

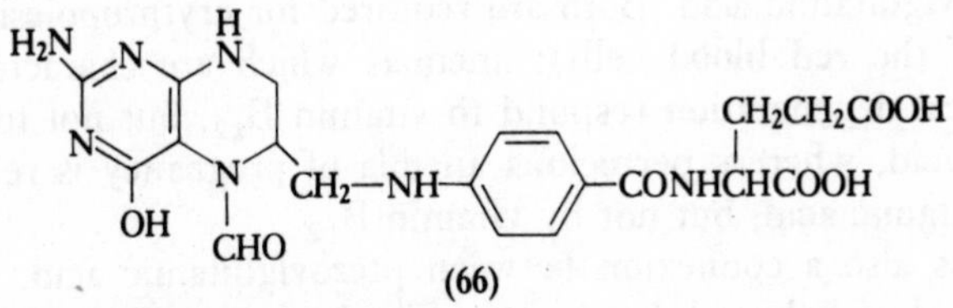

(66)

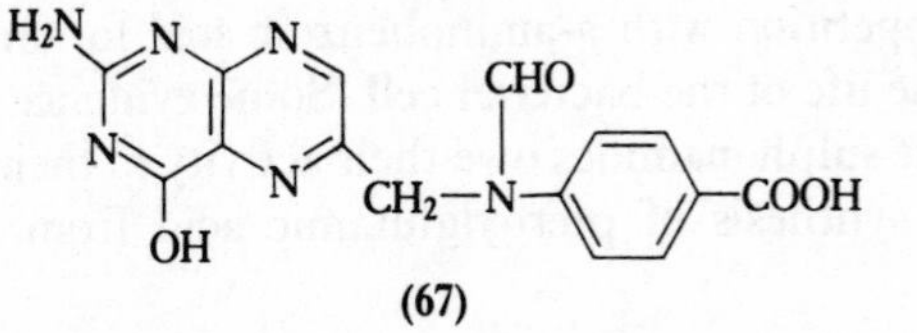

(67)

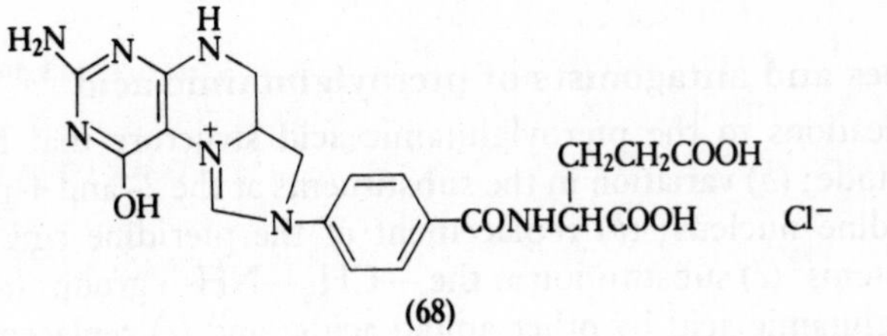

(68)

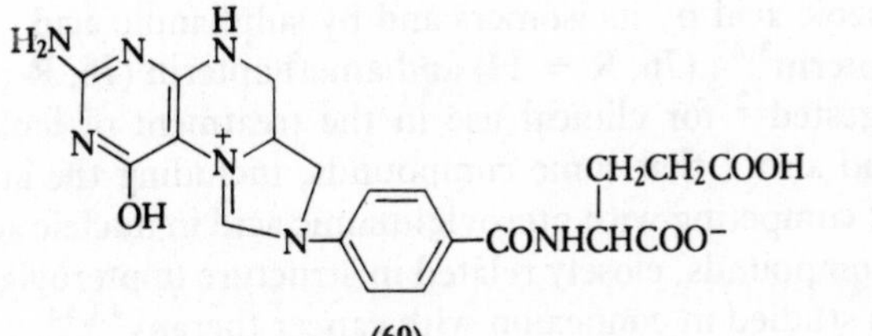

(69)

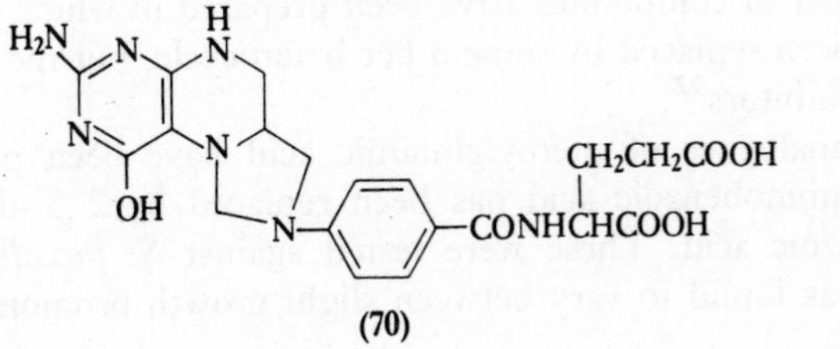

(70)

Tetrahydropteroylglutamic acid (74) is also involved[38,39] in the enzymic conversion of formiminoglycine (72, a product of purine metabolism) into glycine (73) as shown in $72 + 74 \rightarrow 73 + 75$. The intermediate 75 is then converted via 69 into 71.

There appears to be a biochemical relationship between vitamin B_{12} and pteroylglutamic acid. Both are required for erythropoiesis (manufacture of the red blood cells); anemias which are characterized by neurological degeneration respond to vitamin B_{12}, but not to pteroylglutamic acid, whereas pernicious anemia of pregnancy is relieved by pteroylglutamic acid, but not by vitamin B_{12}.

There is also a connexion between pteroylglutamic acid, p-aminobenzoic acid and the sulphonamides. The latter owe their antibacterial activity to competition with p-aminobenzoic acid for an enzyme system essential for the life of the bacterial cell. Some evidence is available[42] to suggest that the sulphonamides owe their activity to their ability to interfere with the synthesis of pteroylglutamic acid from p-aminobenzoic acid.

Analogues and antagonists of pteroylglutamic acid[13,50,59]

Modifications to the pteroylglutamic acid structure that have been made include: (a) variation in the substituents at the 2- and 4-position of the pteridine nucleus; (b) replacement of the pteridine ring by other cyclic systems; (c) substitution at the —CH_2—NH— group; (d) replacement of glutamic acid by other amino acids; and (e) replacement of p-aminobenzoic acid by its isomers and by sulphanilic acid.

Aminopterin[3,47] (76, R = H) and amethopterin (76, R = CH_3) have been suggested[52] for clinical use in the treatment of leukemia. It has been found also[18] that some compounds, including the above two, are capable of competing with pteroylglutamic acid in nucleic acid synthesis.

Some compounds, closely related in structure to pteroylglutamic acid, have been studied in connexion with cancer therapy[43,44].

A number of compounds have been prepared in which the pteridine ring has been replaced by some other heterocycle, but the products are growth inhibitors[42].

Some analogues of pteroylglutamic acid have been prepared[13] in which p-aminobenzoic acid has been replaced by 2′,5′-dihalogeno-p-aminobenzoic acid. These were tested against S. faccalis R and the activity was found to vary between slight growth promotion to strong inhibition.

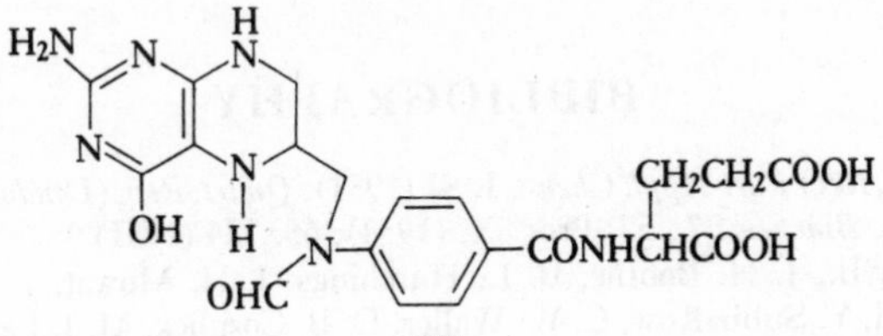

(71)

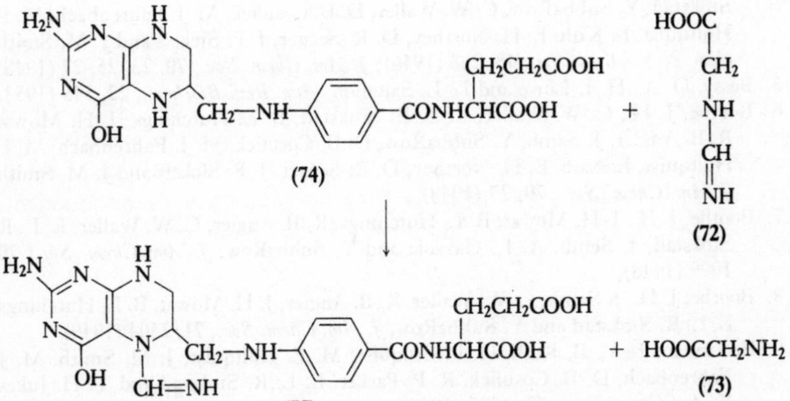

(74)

(72)

(75)

(73)

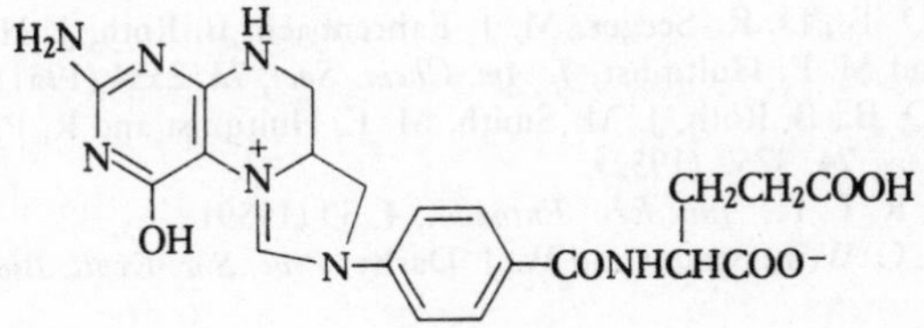

(69)

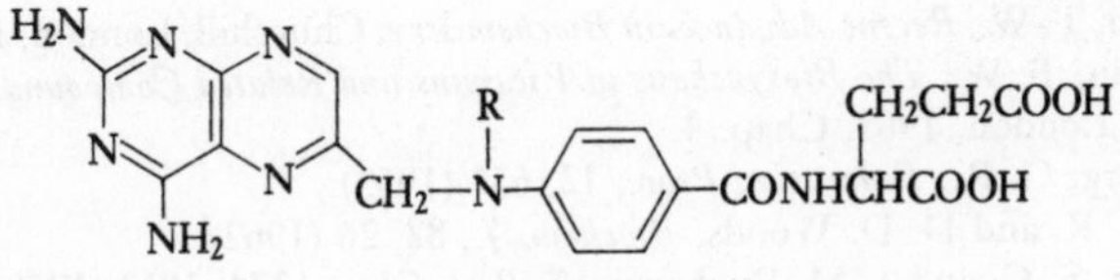

(76)

BIBLIOGRAPHY

1. Albert, A., *Rev. Pure Appl. Chem.*, 1, S1 (1951); *Quart. Rev. (London)*, 6, 197 (1952).
2. Albert, A., *Biochem. J.*, 57, Proc. X. (1954); 65, 124 (1957).
3. Angier, R. B., J. H. Boothe, B. L. Hutchings, J. H. Mowat, J. Semb, E. L. R. Stokstad, Y. SubbaRow, C. W. Waller, D. B. Cosulick, M. J. Fahrenbach, M. E. Hultquist, E. Kuh, E. H. Northey, D. R. Seeger, J. P. Sickels and J. M. Smith, *Science*, 103, 667 (1946).
4. Angier, R. B., J. H. Boothe, B. L. Hutchings, J. H. Mowat, J. Semb, E. L. R. Stokstad, Y. SubbaRow, C. W. Waller, D. B. Cosulick, M. J. Fahrenbach, M. E. Hultquist, E. Kuh, E. H. Northey, D. R. Seeger, J. P. Sickels and J. M. Smith, *Ann. N.Y. Acad. Sci.*, 48, 283 (1946); *J. Am. Chem. Soc.*, 70, 23, 25, 27 (1948).
5. Bessy, O. A., H. J. Lowe and L. L. Salomon, *Ann. Rev. Biochem.*, 22, 545 (1953).
6. Boothe, J. H., C. W. Waller, E. L. R. Stokstad, B. L. Hutchings, J. H. Mowat, R. B. Angier, J. Semb, Y. SubbaRow, D. B. Cosulick, M. J. Fahrenbach, M. E. Hultquist, E. Kuh, E. H. Northey, D. R. Seeger, J. P. Sickels and J. M. Smith, *J. Am. Chem. Soc.*, 70, 27 (1948).
7. Boothe, J. H., J. H. Mowat, B. L. Hutchings, R. B. Angier, C. W. Waller, E. L. R. Stokstad, J. Semb, A. L. Gazzola and Y. SubbaRow, *J. Am. Chem. Soc.*, 70, 1099 (1948).
8. Boothe, J. H., J. Semb, C. W. Waller, R. B. Angier, J. H. Mowat, B. L. Hutchings, E. L. R. Stokstad and Y. SubbaRow, *J. Am. Chem. Soc.*, 71, 2304 (1949).
9. Brockman, J. A., B. Roth, H. P. Broquist, M. E. Hultquist, J. M. Smith, M. J. Fahrenbach, D. B. Cosulick, R. P. Parker, E. L. R. Stokstad and T. H. Jukes, *J. Am. Chem. Soc.*, 72, 4325 (1950).
10. Broquist, H. F., E. L. R. Stokstad and T. H. Jukes, *J. Biol. Chem.*, 185, 399 (1950).
11. Brown, G. M., R. A. Weisman and D. A. Molnar, *J. Biol. Chem.*, 236, 2534 (1961).
12. Buchanan, J. M., *CIBA Symposium on Purines*, Churchill, London, 1957, p. 233.
13. Cosulick, D. B., D. R. Seeger, M. J. Fahrenbach, B. Roth, J. H. Mowat, J. M. Smith and M. E. Hultquist, *J. Am. Chem. Soc.*, 73, 2554 (1951).
14. Cosulick, D. B., B. Roth, J. M. Smith, M. E. Hultquist and R. P. Parker, *J. Am. Chem. Soc.*, 74, 3252 (1952).
15. Cromartie, R. I. T., *Ann. Rev. Entomol.*, 4, 59 (1959).
16. Day, P. L., C. W. Langston and W. J. Darby, *Proc. Soc. Exptl. Biol. Med.*, 38, 860 (1938).
17. Flynn, E. H., T. J. Bond, T. J. Bardos and W. Shive, *J. Am. Chem. Soc.*, 73, 1979 (1951).
18. Goldin, A., E. M. Greenspan, J. M. Venditti and E. B. Schoenbach, *J. Nat. Cancer Inst.*, 12, 987 (1952).
19. Goodwin, T. W., *Recent Advances in Biochemistry*, Churchill, London, 1960, p. 219.
19a. Goodwin, T. W., *The Biosynthesis of Vitamins and Related Compounds*, Academic Press, London, 1963, Chap. 4.
20. Greenberg, G. R., *Federation Proc.*, 12, 651 (1953).
21. Guest, J. R. and D. D. Woods, *Biochem. J.*, 82, 26 (1962).
22. Hartman, S. C. and J. M. Buchanan, *J. Biol. Chem.*, 234, 1812 (1959).
23. Hogan, A. G. and E. M. Parrott, *J. Biol. Chem.*, 128, xlvi (1939).

24. Hultquist, M. E., E. Kuh, D. B. Cosulick, M. J. Fahrenbach, E. H. Northey, D. R. Seeger, J. P. Sickels, J. M. Smith, R. B. Angier, J. H. Boothe, B. L. Hutchings, J. H. Mowat, J. Semb, E. L. R. Stokstad, Y. SubbaRow and C. W. Waller, *J. Am. Chem. Soc.*, **70**, 23 (1948).
25. Hutchings, B. L., E. L. R. Stokstad, N. Bohonos, N. H. Sloan and Y. SubbaRow, *J. Am. Chem. Soc.*, **70**, 1 (1948).
26. Hutchings, B. L., E. L. R. Stokstad, J. H. Mowat, J. H. Boothe, C. W. Waller, R. B. Angier, J. Semb and Y. SubbaRow, *J. Am. Chem. Soc.*, **70**, 10 (1948).
27. Katunuma, N., T. Shiota and H. Nocla, *J. Vitaminol.* (*Kyōto*), **3**, 77 (1957).
28. Keresztesy, J. C. and M. Silverman, *J. Am. Chem. Soc.*, **73**, 5510 (1951).
29. May, M., T. J. Bardos, F. L. Barger, M. Lansford, J. M. Ravel, G. L. Sutherland and W. Shive, *J. Am. Chem. Soc.*, **73**, 3067 (1951).
30. Mitchell, H. K., E. E. Snell and R. J. Williams, *J. Am. Chem. Soc.*, **63**, 2284 (1941).
31. Mowat, J. H., J. H. Boothe, B. L. Hutchings, E. L. R. Stokstad, C. W. Waller, R. B. Angier, J. Semb, D. B. Cosulick and Y. SubbaRow, *J. Am. Chem. Soc.*, **70**, 14 (1948).
32. O'Dell, B. L., J. M. Vanderbelt, E. S. Bloom and J. J. Pfiffner, *J. Am. Chem. Soc.*, **69**, 250 (1947).
33. Oroshnik, W. and P. E. Spoerri, *J. Am. Chem. Soc.*, **67**, 721 (1945).
34. Patterson, E. L., R. Milstrey and E. L. R. Stokstad, *J. Am. Chem. Soc.*, **78**, 5868 (1956).
35. Patterson, E. L., M. H. von Saltza and E. L. R. Stokstad, *J. Am. Chem. Soc.*, **78**, 5871 (1956).
36. Pfiffner, J. J., S. B. Binkley, E. S. Bloom and B. L. O'Dell, *J. Am. Chem. Soc.*, **69**, 1476 (1947).
37. Plaut, G. W. E., *Ann. Rev. Biochem.*, **30**, 409 (1961).
38. Rabinowitz, J. C. and W. E. Pricer, *J. Am. Chem. Soc.*, **78**, 4176 (1956).
39. Rabinowitz, J. C. and W. E. Pricer, *J. Am. Chem. Soc.*, **78**, 5702 (1956).
40. Reynolds, J. J. and G. M. Brown, *J. Biol. Chem.*, **237**, PC 2713 (1962).
41. Rickes, E. L., L. Chaiet and J. C. Keresztesy, *J. Am. Chem. Soc.*, **69**, 2749 (1947).
42. Robinson, F. A., *The Vitamin B Complex*, Chapman and Hall, London, 1951, p. 514.
43. Robinson, F. A., *The Vitamin B Complex*, Chapman and Hall, London, 1951, p. 518.
44. Robinson, F. A., *The Vitamin B Complex*, Chapman and Hall, London, 1951, p. 523.
45. Robinson, F. A., *The Vitamin B Complex*, Chapman and Hall, London, 1951, p. 526.
46. Sauberlich, H. E. and C. A. Baumann, *J. Biol. Chem.*, **176**, 165 (1948).
47. Seeger, D. R., J. M. Smith and M. E. Hultquist, *J. Am. Chem. Soc.*, **69**, 2567 (1947).
48. Shive, W., *Federation Proc.*, **12**, 639 (1953).
49. Sletzinger, M., R. Reinhold, J. Grier, M. Beacham and M. Tishler, *J. Am. Chem. Soc.*, **77**, 6365 (1955).
50. Smith, J. M., *New Jersey J. Pharm.*, **22**, No. 8, 15 (1949).
51. Snell, E. E. and W. H. Peterson, *J. Bact.*, **36**, 273 (1940).
52. Snell, E. E. and L. D. Wright, *Ann. Rev. Biochem.*, **19**, 277 (1950).
53. Stokstad, E. L. R., *J. Biol. Chem.*, **149**, 573 (1943).
54. Stokstad, E. L. R. and P. D. V. Manning, *J. Biol. Chem.*, **125**, 687 (1938).
55. Stokstad, E. L. R., B. L. Hutchings and Y. SubbaRow, *J. Am. Chem. Soc.*, **70**, 3 (1948).
56. Stokstad, E. L. R., B. L. Hutchings, J. H. Mowat, J. H. Boothe, C. W. Waller, R. B. Angier, J. Semb and Y. SubbaRow, *J. Am. Chem. Soc.*, **70**, 5 (1948).

57. Stokstad, E. L. R., B. L. Hutchings, J. H. Mowat, J. H. Boothe, C. W. Waller, R. B. Angier, J. Semb and Y. SubbaRow, *Ann. N.Y. Acad. Sci.*, 48, 269, 279 (1946).
58. Traube, W., *Ber.*, 33, 1371 (1900).
59. Thiersch, J. B. and F. S. Philips, *Am. J. Med. Sciences*, 217, 575 (1949).
60. Vieira, E. and E. Shaw, *J. Biol. Chem.*, 236, 2507 (1961).
61. Waller, C. W., B. L. Hutchings, J. H. Mowat, E. L. R. Stokstad, J. H. Boothe, R. B. Angier, J. Semb, Y. SubbaRow, D. B. Cosulick, M. J. Fahrenbach, M. E. Hultquist, E. Kuh, E. H. Northey, D. R. Seeger, J. P. Sickels and J. M. Smith, *J. Am. Chem. Soc.*, 70, 19 (1948).
62. Weijlard, J., M. Tishler and A. E. Erickson, *J. Am. Chem. Soc.*, 67, 802 (1945).
63. Weygand, F. and V. Schmied-Kowarzik, *Ber.*, 82, 333 (1949).
64. Weygand, F., H. Simon, G. Dahms, M. Waldschmidt, H. J. Schliep and H. Wacker, *Angew. Chem.*, 73, 402 (1961).
65. Wolf, D. E., R. C. Anderson, E. A. Kaczka, S. A. Harris, G. E. Arth, P. L. Southwick, R. Mozingo and K. Folkers, *J. Am. Chem. Soc.*, 69, 2753 (1947).

CHAPTER 5

The Vitamins B₆

INTRODUCTION – PYRIDOXINE – Occurrence and isolation – Sources –
Deficiency disease – Daily requirement – Properties – Structure –
Synthesis – PYRIDOXAL AND PYRIDOXAMINE – PYRIDOXAL PHOSPHATE –
BIOLOGICAL FUNCTION OF VITAMIN B₆ – Analogues of pyridoxine –
BIBLIOGRAPHY

INTRODUCTION

'VITAMIN B₆' refers to a group of very closely related compounds,
pyridoxine, pyridoxal and pyridoxamine, which, in the form of their
phosphates, are interconvertible *in vivo*.

PYRIDOXINE

Occurrence and isolation

Pyridoxine is widely distributed in the plant and animal kingdoms,
mainly chemically bound to proteins, with only a small proportion in the
free state. It was first isolated from rice bran[10,29,30], but has also been
obtained from rice[20,21,33] and from yeast[23].

Sources

Yeast and rice polishings are rich in vitamin B₆; foodstuffs such as
wheat, maize, fresh vegetables, eggs, meat and fish are also good sources.

Deficiency disease

Although vitamin B₆ has been detected in human urine, and presumably is of physiological importance[43], only recently was it demonstrated to be necessary for human life when a pyridoxine-responsible
anemia was reported[48]. Rats and chicks require the vitamin, but sheep
do not need an external supply since it is synthesized by the bacteria of
the rumen.

Deficiency of the vitamin causes a specific dermatitis (acrodynia) in rats, and growth is also inhibited. A detailed discussion of animal deficiency symptoms has been given by Robinson[42].

Daily requirement

This is very uncertain to establish for man, due to the lack of a specific observable deficiency disease, but 1–2 mg is recommended[39].

Properties

The free base is a colourless, optically inactive, crystalline solid, m.p. 160°, which is soluble in water. It is one of the most stable of the B group of vitamins.

Structure

The molecular formula of pyridoxine was established by analysis as $C_8H_{11}NO_3$; one C-methyl group and three active hydrogen atoms were also detected[47]. Preliminary tests showed that the nitrogen is basic, and indicated the absence of O-alkyl and of N-alkyl groups. The deep red colour produced with ferric chloride suggested the presence of a phenolic or enolic hydroxyl group, and the ultraviolet spectrum of pyridoxine (Figures 5.1 and 5.2) was found to be very similar to that of β-hydroxypyridines[25,47]. The Gibbs phenol test[6] with 2,6–dichloro-quinonechlorimine was positive[47], suggesting that the position *para* to the hydroxyl group is unsubstituted.

The formation of a triacetate[17,23] and a tribenzoate[47] indicated the presence of three hydroxyl groups. Treatment of pyridoxine with diazomethane yields[24] a mono-O-methyl ether, which forms a diacetate and which does not give a colour with ferric chloride. This monomethyl ether diacetate does not contain any reactive hydrogen atoms, so the basic nitrogen atom must be tertiary, and pyridoxine must contain one phenolic hydroxyl group and two alcoholic hydroxyl groups. The monomethyl ether does not react with lead tetraacetate, so the two alcoholic hydroxyl groups are not on adjacent carbon atoms.

The evidence outlined above can be summarized in the part-structure (1) for pyridoxine.

Pyridoxine is stable to both acidic and alkaline hydrolysis. Oxidation of pyridoxine monomethyl ether with neutral potassium permanganate yields a lactone $C_9H_9NO_3$, indicating[25] that the two aliphatic hydroxyl groups are 1,4 or 1,5 to each other. When pyridoxine monomethyl ether is oxidized with barium permanganate[26,27,47] a dicarboxylic acid,

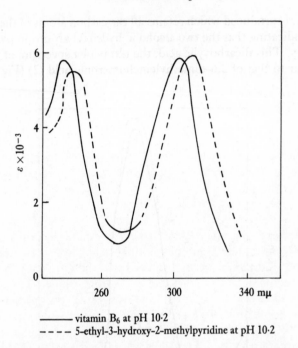

———— vitamin B$_6$ at pH 10·2
- - - - 5-ethyl-3-hydroxy-2-methylpyridine at pH 10·2

Figure 5.1. The ultraviolet spectrum of pyridoxine. [Reproduced, by permission, from R. A. Morton, *Application of Absorption Spectra to the Study of Vitamins, Hormones and Co-Enzymes*, 2nd ed., Hilger, London, 1942, p. 164.]

(1)

$C_9H_9NO_5$, is produced which retains all the carbon atoms of the original vitamin, indicating that the two alcoholic hydroxyl groups in pyridoxine are primary. This dicarboxylic acid, the ultraviolet spectrum of which is very similar to that of 2,6-dimethylcinchomeronic acid (2) (Figure 5.3),

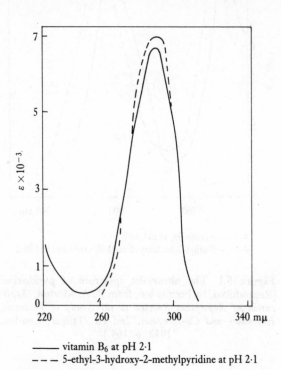

———— vitamin B_6 at pH 2·1
— — — 5-ethyl-3-hydroxy-2-methylpyridine at pH 2·1

Figure 5.2. The ultraviolet spectrum of pyridoxine. [Reproduced, by permission, from R. A. Morton, *Application of Absorption Spectra to the Study of Vitamins, Hormones and Co-Enzymes*, 2nd ed., Hilger, London, 1942, p. 167.]

is easily converted into an anhydride by treatment with acetic anhydride, so that the carboxyl groups are on adjacent carbon atoms. Since the dicarboxylic acid does not give a colour with ferrous sulphate, there is not a carboxyl group adjacent to the nitrogen in the α-position, and part-structure 3 can be written for the compound. The structure 4 was shown

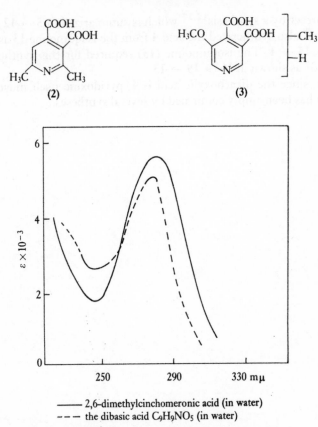

——— 2,6-dimethylcinchomeronic acid (in water)
- - - the dibasic acid $C_9H_9NO_5$ (in water)

Figure 5.3. The ultraviolet spectrum of a pyridoxine degradation product. [Reproduced, by permission, from R. A. Morton, *Application of Absorption Spectra to the Study of Vitamins, Hormones and Co-Enzymes*, 2nd ed., Hilger, London, 1942, p. 168.]

to be correct by a synthesis[12,27] which is summarized in $5 \rightarrow 12 \rightarrow 4$.

Kuhn[28] also synthesized the acid 4 from the isoquinoline 13 as shown in $13 \rightarrow 15 \rightarrow 4$. The isoquinoline (13) required for this synthesis was prepared[5] as shown in $16 \rightarrow 19 \rightarrow 13$.

Thus, since the dicarboxylic acid is 4, pyridoxine itself must be 20, and this has been amply confirmed by several syntheses.

Synthesis

The synthesis of Harris and Folkers[11,12] started from 21 and is shown in $21 \rightarrow 26 \rightarrow 20$.

In a modification of this synthesis[19], ethyl hydroxymethyleneoxalace-tate (28) was reacted with iminoacetylacetone (27) to yield 29 which was cyclized with sulphuric acid to the pyridine 30 and hydrolysed to 31. Application of the Schmidt reaction converted 31 into 32, reaction occurring with the acetyl group of 31 in preference to the acid or ester functions. Finally 32 was converted into 26 and thence to pyridoxine (20).

In a somewhat different approach[18,28] the isoquinoline 13 was converted into the acid 4 as indicated above, and pyridoxine (20) was produced from this as shown in $4 \rightarrow 33 \rightarrow 35 \rightarrow 20$.

Several other syntheses of pyridoxine have been described[15,32,40,49].

(5) + **(6)** → **(7)** (Piperidine)

(7) → **(8)** (HCl 120°)

(9) ← **(8)** (Fuming HNO$_3$ + H$_2$SO$_4$)

(10) ← **(9)** (POCl$_3$/PCl$_5$)

(10) → **(11)** (1. H$_2$/Pt 2. H$_2$/Pd/BaCO$_3$)

(11) → **(12)** (1. HNO$_2$ 2. CH$_2$N$_2$)

(12) → **(4)** (Ba(MnO$_4$)$_2$)

(13) → **(14)** (HNO$_3$)

(14) → **(15)** (Reduction)

(15) → **(4)** (KMnO$_4$)

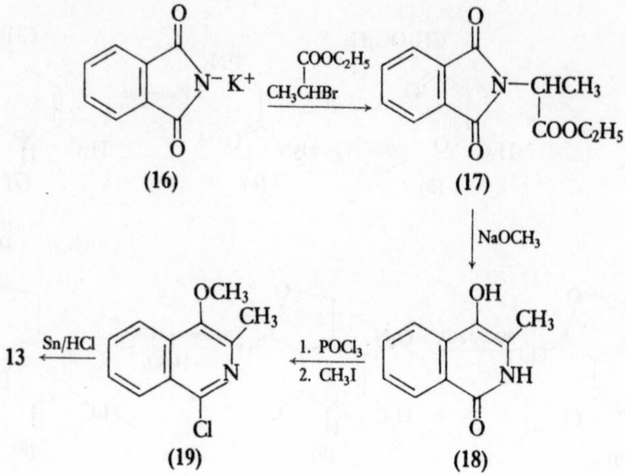

(16) (17) (18) (19)

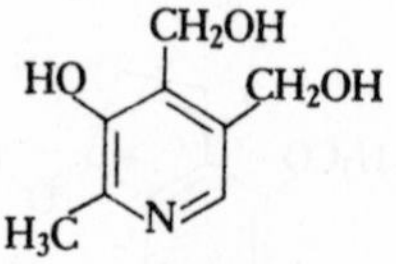

(20)

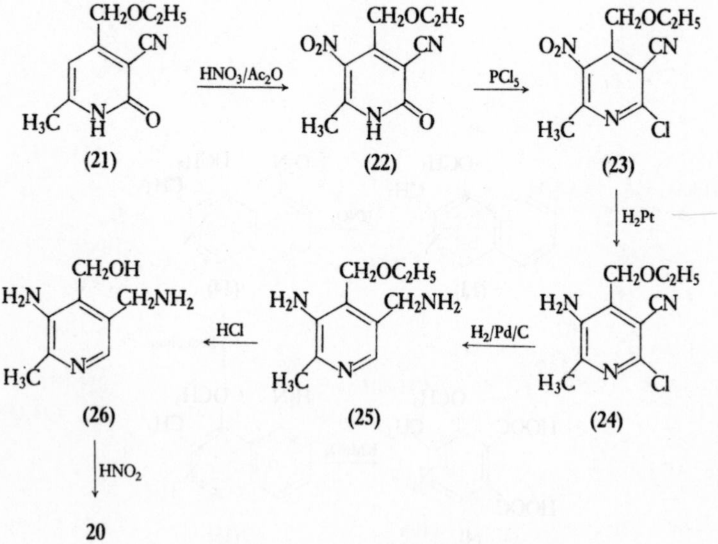

(21) (22) (23) (24) (25) (26)

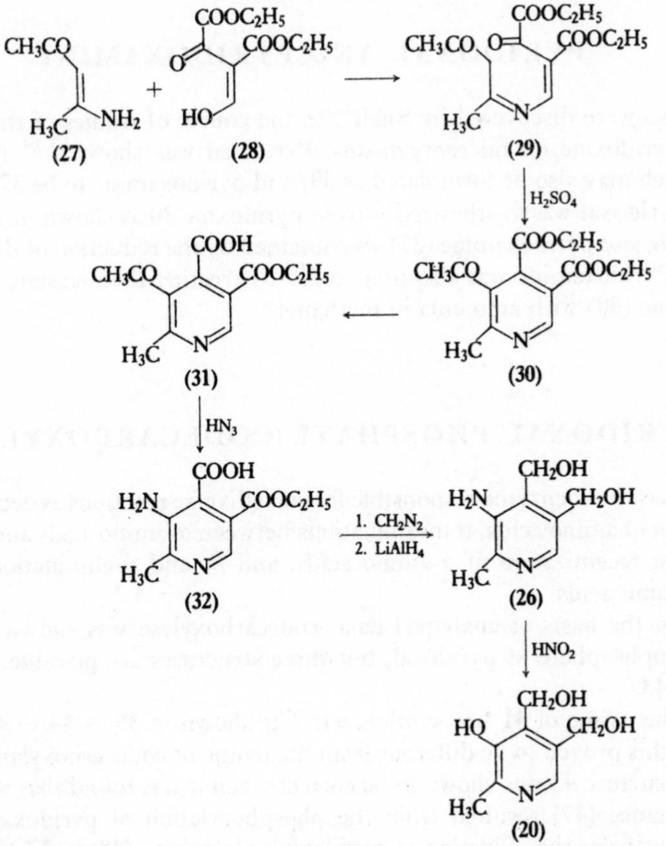

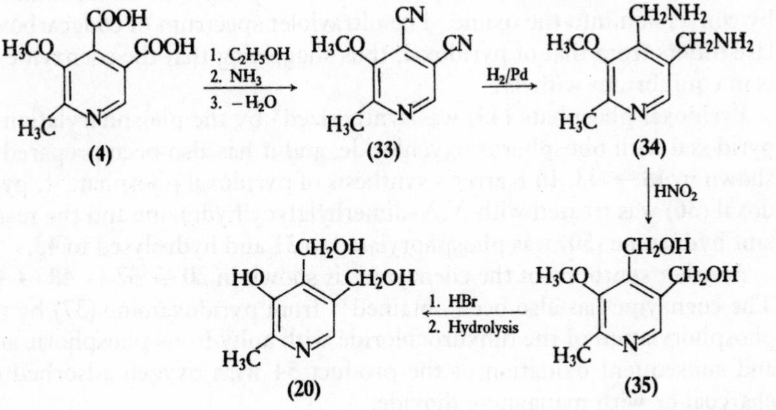

PYRIDOXAL AND PYRIDOXAMINE

These were discovered by Snell[44] in the course of studies of the effects of pyridoxine on microorganisms. Pyridoxal was shown[13,14] to be 36 (which may also be formulated as 39) and pyridoxamine to be 37.

Pyridoxal was synthesized[13] from pyridoxine 20 as shown in 20 → 38 → 36, and pyridoxamine (37) was obtained by the reduction of the oxime 38. Pyridoxamine was also prepared[13] by treating the diacetate of pyridoxine (40) with ammonia in methanol.

PYRIDOXAL PHOSPHATE (CODECARBOXYLASE)

This is the coenzyme responsible for such diverse reactions as decarboxylation of amino acids, transaminations between α-amino acids and α-keto acids, racemization of α-amino acids, and β- and γ-eliminations from α-amino acids.

On the basis of analytical data, codecarboxylase was shown to be a monophosphate of pyridoxal, but three structures are possible—41, 42 and 43.

The oxime of 41 was synthesized[16] as shown in 39 → 44 → 45 → 46 and this proved to be different from the oxime of codecarboxylase.

Structure 43 was shown to be correct when it was found that the same substance (47) resulted from the phosphorylation of pyridoxal oxime (38) as from the oxidation of pyridoxine phosphate (48) to 43, followed by conversion into the oxime. The ultraviolet spectrum of codecarboxylase differs from that of pyridoxal, thus suggesting that the coenzyme 43 is in equilibrium with 49.

Pyridoxal phosphate (43) was synthesized[9] by the phosphorylation of pyridoxal with phosphorus oxychloride, and it has also been prepared as shown in 48 → 43. In Karrer's synthesis of pyridoxal phosphate[51], pyridoxal (36) was treated with N,N-dimethylglycylhydrazine and the resultant hydrazone (50) was phosphorylated to 51 and hydrolysed to 43.

Another synthesis of the coenzyme[2] is shown in 20 → 52 → 48 → 43. The coenzyme has also been obtained[53] from pyridoxamine (37) by the phosphorylation of the dihydrochloride with anhydrous phosphoric acid and subsequent oxidation of the product 54 with oxygen adsorbed on charcoal or with manganese dioxide.

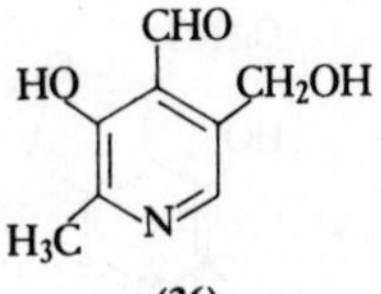

(36)

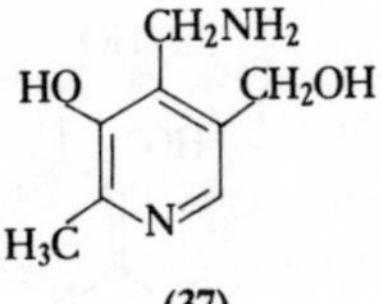

(37)

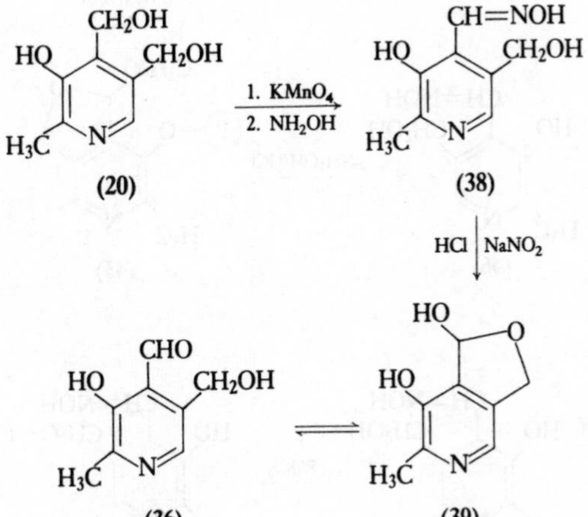

(20) →[1. KMnO$_4$][2. NH$_2$OH] (38)

HCl | NaNO$_2$

(36) ⇌ (39)

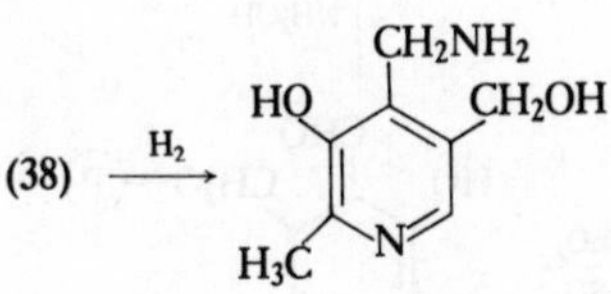

(38) →[H$_2$] (37) 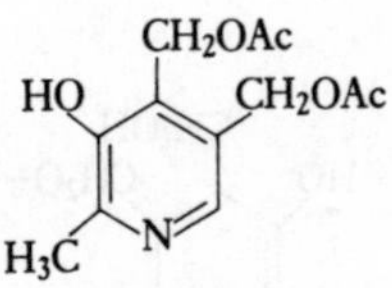   (40)

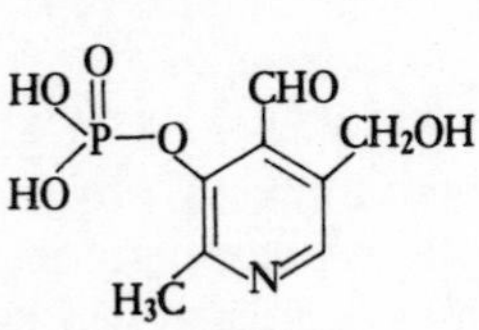

(41) 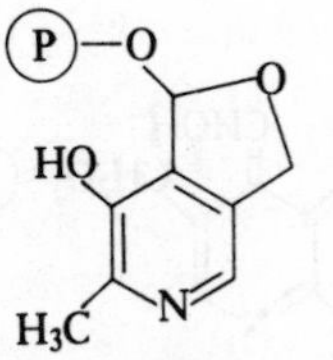   (42) 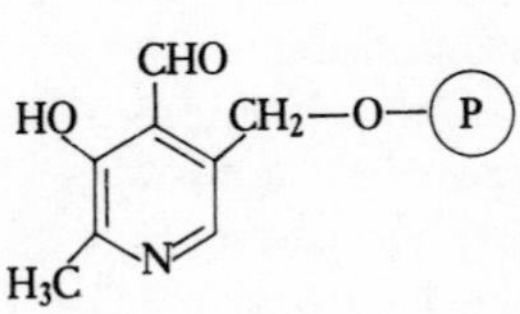   (43)

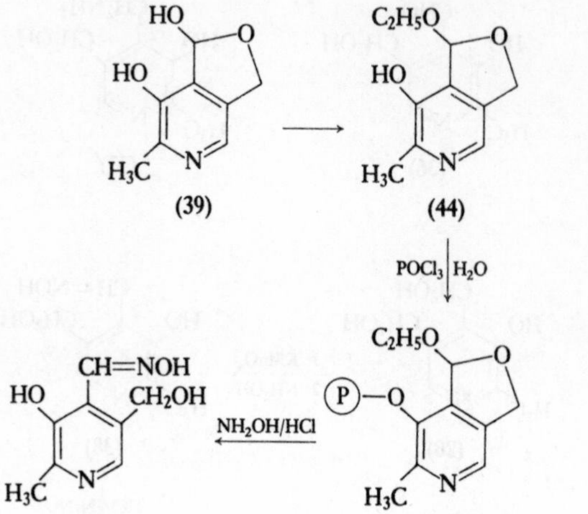

(39)

(44)

POCl₃ | H₂O

(46)

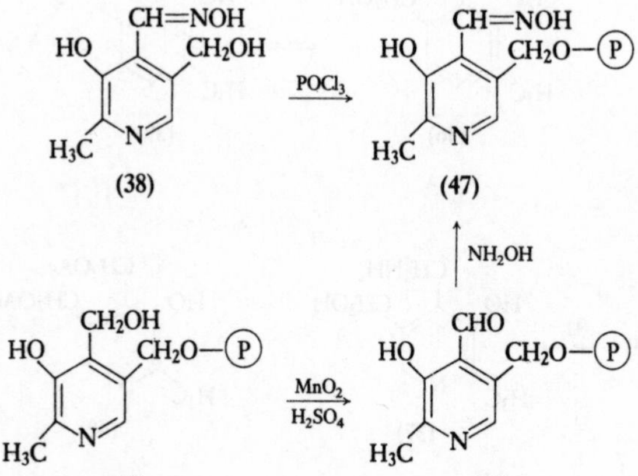

NH₂OH/HCl

(45)

(38)

POCl₃

(47)

NH₂OH

(48)

MnO₂, H₂SO₄

(43)

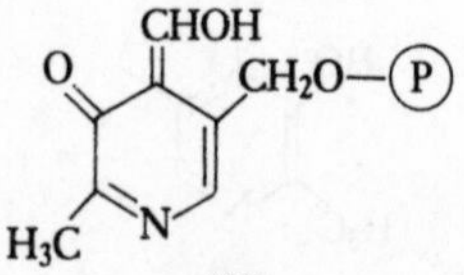

(49)

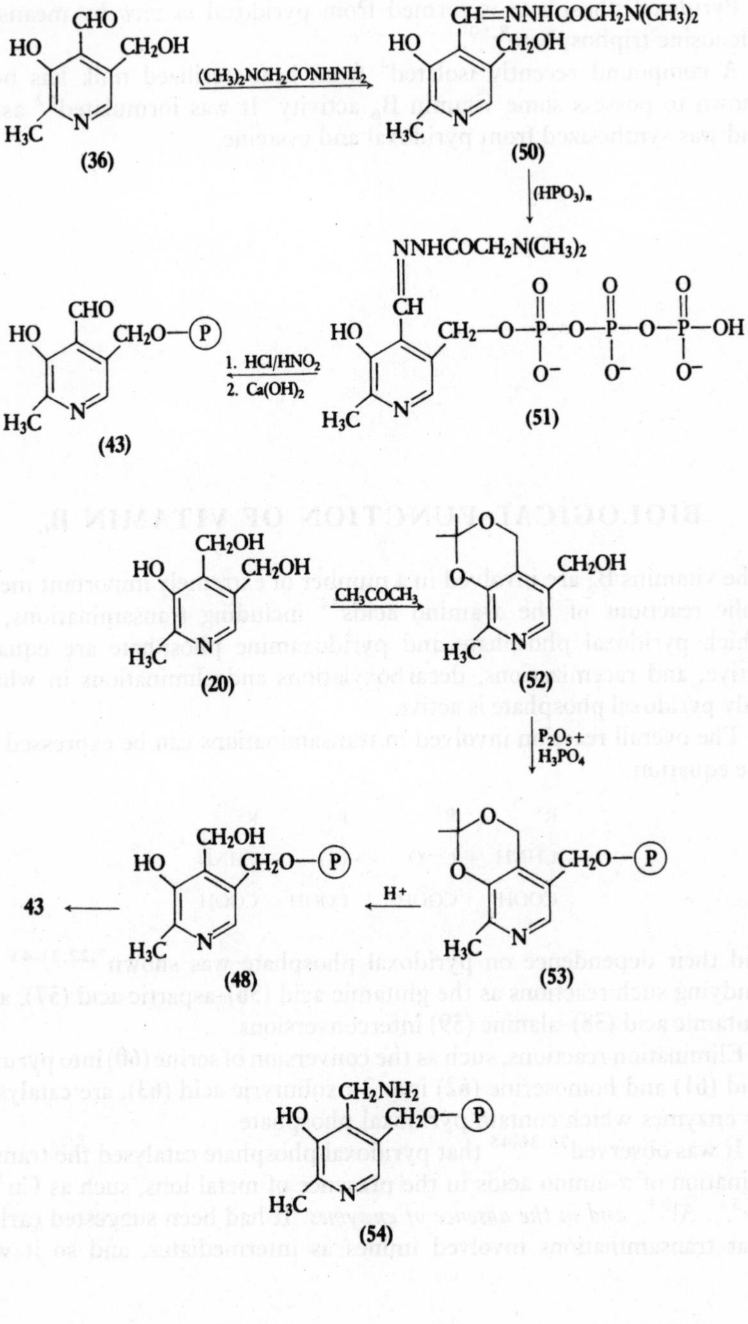

(36) → (CH$_3$)$_2$NCH$_2$CONHNH$_2$ → (50)

(50) → (HPO$_3$)$_n$ → (51)

(51) → 1. HCl/HNO$_2$ 2. Ca(OH)$_2$ → (43)

(20) → CH$_3$COCH$_3$ → (52)

(52) → P$_2$O$_5$ + H$_3$PO$_4$ → (53)

(53) → H$^+$ → (48)

(48) → 43

(54)

Pyridoxal phosphate is formed from pyridoxal *in vivo* by means of adenosine triphosphate[8,50].

A compound recently isolated[4] from heat-sterilized milk has been shown to possess some vitamin B_6 activity. It was formulated[52] as **55** and was synthesized from pyridoxal and cysteine.

BIOLOGICAL FUNCTION OF VITAMIN B_6

The vitamins B_6 are involved in a number of extremely important metabolic reactions of the α-amino acids[34] including transaminations, in which pyridoxal phosphate and pyridoxamine phosphate are equally active, and racemizations, decarboxylations and eliminations in which only pyridoxal phosphate is active.

The overall reaction involved in transaminations can be expressed by the equation

$$
\begin{array}{cccc}
\text{R}^1 & \text{R}^2 & \text{R}^1 & \text{R}^2 \\
| & | & | & | \\
\text{CHNH}_2 + \text{C}{=}\text{O} \longrightarrow \text{CO} & + \text{CHNH}_2 \\
| & | & | & | \\
\text{COOH} & \text{COOH} & \text{COOH} & \text{COOH}
\end{array}
$$

and their dependence on pyridoxal phosphate was shown[7,22,31,41] by studying such reactions as the glutamic acid (**56**)–aspartic acid (**57**), and glutamic acid (**58**)–alanine (**59**) interconversions.

Elimination reactions, such as the conversion of serine (**60**) into pyruvic acid (**61**) and homoserine (**62**) into 2-oxobutyric acid (**63**), are catalysed by enzymes which contain pyridoxal phosphate.

It was observed[35,36,45] that pyridoxal phosphate catalysed the transamination of α-amino acids in the presence of metal ions, such as Cu^{2+}, Fe^{3+}, Al^{3+}, *and in the absence of enzymes*. It had been suggested earlier that transaminations involved imines as intermediates, and so it was

$$\text{CH}_2\text{---S---S---CH}_2$$

HO   CH$_2$OH   HOCH$_2$ OH

H$_3$C   N   (55)   N   CH$_3$

$$\begin{array}{c} \text{NH}_2 \\ | \\ \text{HOOCCH}_2\text{CH}_2\text{CHCOOH} + \text{HOOCCH}_2\text{COCOOH} \\ \textbf{(56)} \end{array}$$

$$\rightleftharpoons$$

$$\begin{array}{c} \text{NH}_2 \\ | \\ \text{HOOCCH}_2\text{CH}_2\text{COCOOH} + \text{HOOCCH}_2\text{CHCOOH} \\ \textbf{(57)} \end{array}$$

$$\rightleftharpoons$$

$$\begin{array}{c} \text{NH}_2 \\ | \\ \text{HOOCCH}_2\text{CH}_2\text{CHCOOH} + \text{CH}_3\text{COCOOH} \\ \textbf{(58)} \end{array}$$

$$\rightleftharpoons$$

$$\begin{array}{c} \text{NH}_2 \\ | \\ \text{HOOCCH}_2\text{CH}_2\text{COCOOH} + \text{CH}_3\text{CHCOOH} \\ \textbf{(59)} \end{array}$$

$$\begin{bmatrix} \text{NH}_2 \\ | \\ \text{CH}_2\text{=CCOOH} \\ \\ \text{CH}_3\text{---C---COOH} \\ \| \\ \text{NH} \end{bmatrix}$$

$$\begin{array}{c} \text{NH}_2 \\ | \\ \text{HOCH}_2\text{CHCOOH} \longrightarrow \text{H}_2\text{O} + \\ \textbf{(60)} \end{array}$$

$\downarrow$ H$_2$O

$$\text{CH}_3\text{COCOOH} + \text{NH}_3$$
$$\textbf{(61)}$$

$$\begin{array}{c} \text{NH}_2 \\ | \\ \text{HOCH}_2\text{CH}_2\text{CHCOOH} \longrightarrow \text{H}_2\text{O} + \text{CH}_3\text{CH}_2\overset{\displaystyle\text{NH}}{\overset{\|}{\text{C}}}\text{COOH} \\ \textbf{(62)} \end{array}$$

$$\text{NH}_3 + \text{CH}_3\text{CH}_2\text{COCOOH} \quad \textbf{(63)}$$

postulated[1,37] that a metal chelate such as **64** was involved in these re-actions. The structure **64** is composed of one molecule each of pyridoxal, pyridoxamine, the amino acid, the corresponding α-keto acid and a metal ion. The transamination was then supposed to proceed as shown in **64** → **65** → products.

A detailed kinetic study of the reaction between pyridoxamine and pyruvic acid (to yield pyridoxal and alanine) has shown[3] that a Schiff base is rapidly formed, and the slow step involves the isomerization of this intermediate **66** → **67**.

A general mechanism has been proposed[37] to account for the variety of reactions of amino acids that are catalysed by pyridoxal or pyridoxamine. Thus, initially, a Schiff base **68** is formed from pyridoxal and the amino acid, which is stabilized by chelate formation (**69**). The succeeding re-actions of **69** then depend upon the ability of the electron-attracting groups in **69** to withdraw electrons from the region of the α-carbon of the original amino acid. For racemization of the amino acid, ionization of hydrogen on the α-carbon of **69** can occur to give **70**, with **71** and **72** as other canonical forms; finally recombination of a proton to **72**, followed by hydrolysis, would yield the racemic α-amino acid.

For transamination reactions, the chelate **69** loses a proton as before to yield **70**, which, in the form **73**, is then protonated and hydrolysed.

In decarboxylation of amino acids, the chelate **69** loses carbon dioxide to give **74**, and this, in the canonical form **75**, is protonated and hydro-lysed.

The chelate **69** can also react in other ways, depending upon the nature of the group R. Thus, if the original amino acid had been serine, then in **69**, R = CH_2OH, and in the complex **76** the bond *a* can break to yield formaldehyde and **70**, R = H. The latter compound can subse-quently be hydrolysed to yield pyridoxal and glycine, so that the overall reaction is

$$HOCH_2CHCOOH \longrightarrow HCHO + H_2NCH_2COOH$$
$$\underset{NH_2}{|}$$

The enzymic reactions that require the vitamins B_6 have been re-viewed[46].

Analogues of pyridoxine

The biological activity of vitamin B_6 seems to be a function of the molecule as a whole. A large number of analogues have been synthesized

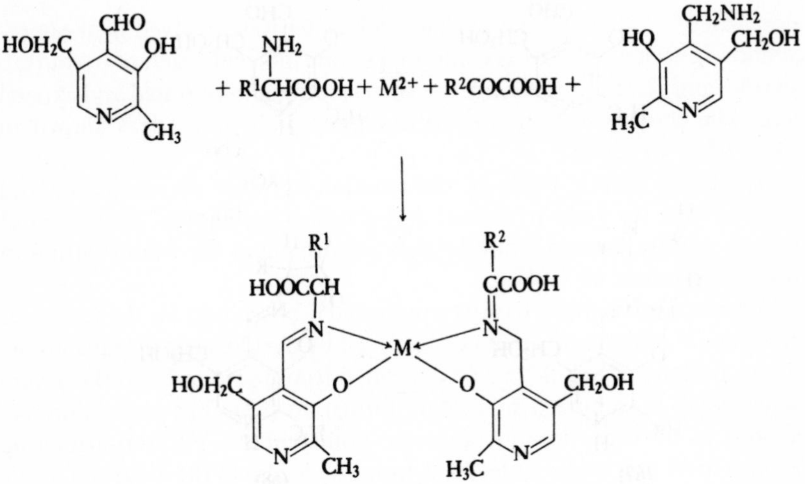

$$\text{(pyridoxal structure)} + R^1CHCOOH + M^{2+} + R^2COCOOH + \text{(pyridoxamine structure)}$$

(with NH_2 on $R^1CHCOOH$)

(64)

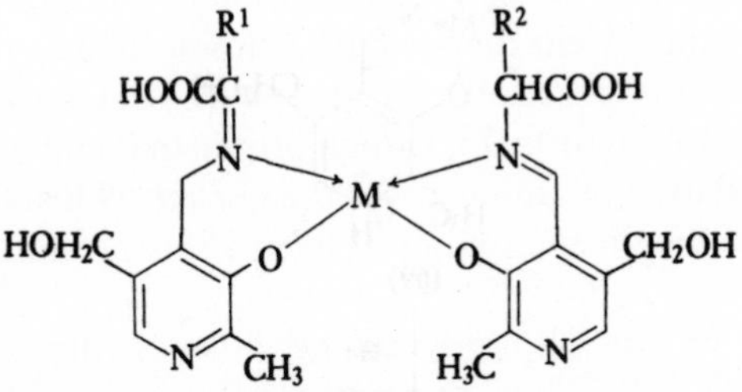

(65)

pyridoxamine + R^{1}COCOOH + M^{2+} + R^{2}CHCOOH + pyridoxal

(with NH_2 on R^{2}CHCOOH)

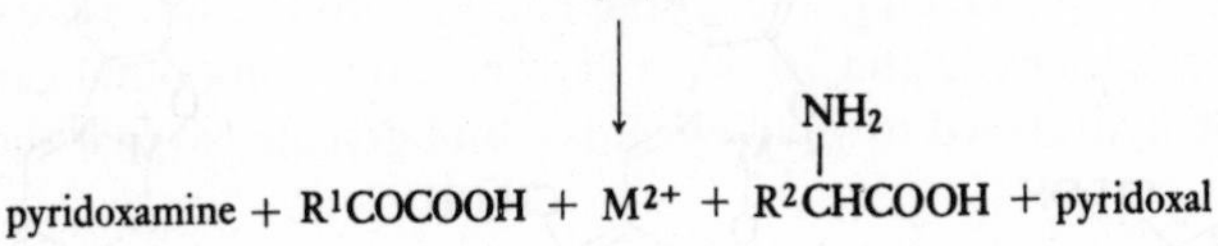

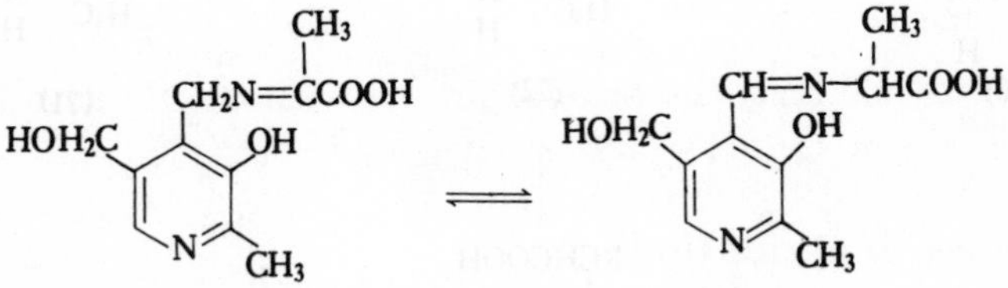

(66) ⇌ (67)

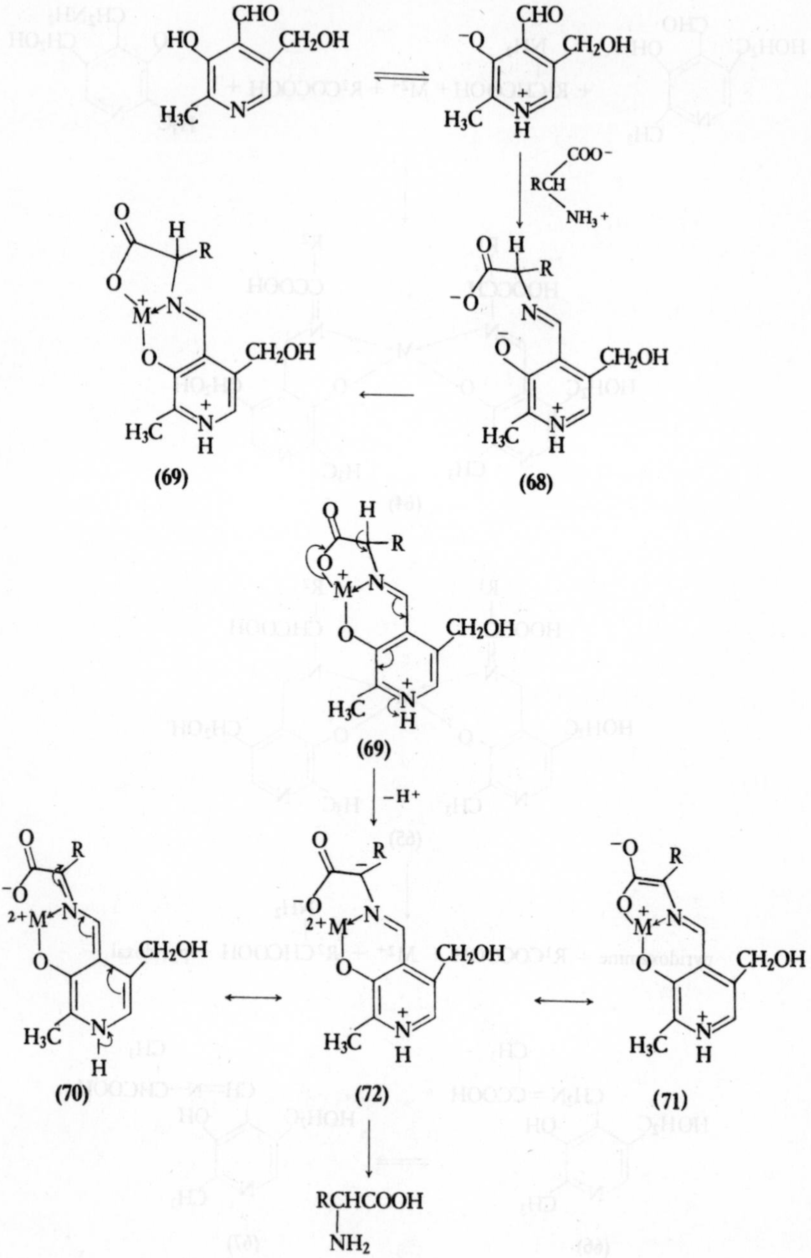

(69)   (68)

(69)

(70)   (72)   (71)

RCHCOOH
|
NH₂

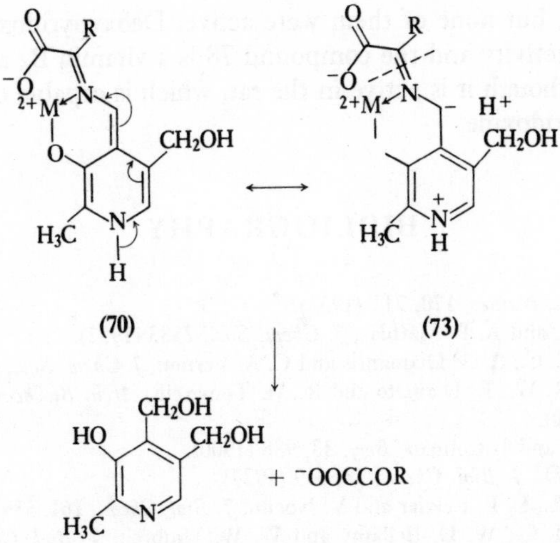

(70)   (73)

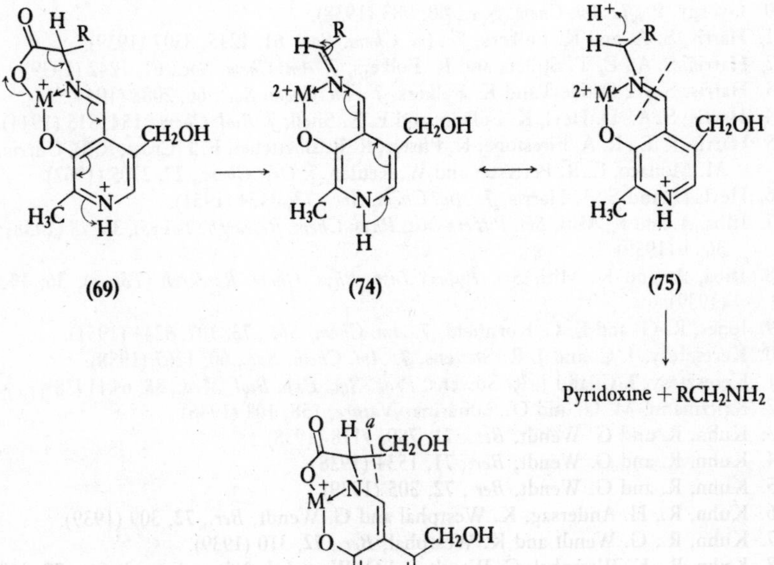

$$ + \; ^-OOCCOR $$

(69)   (74)   (75)

Pyridoxine + RCH₂NH₂

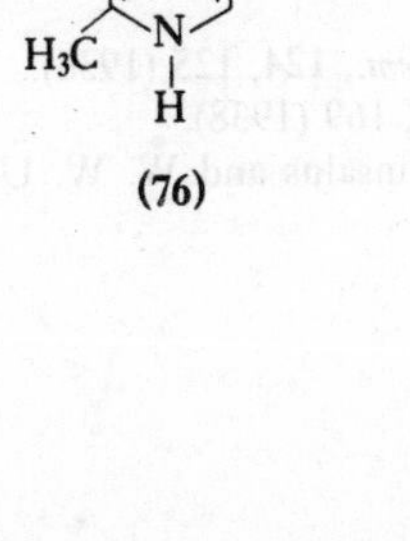

(76)

and tested[38], but none of them were active. Deoxypyridoxine (77) has antivitamin activity and the compound 78 is a vitamin B_6 antagonist in the chick, although it is active in the rat, which is capable of demethylating it to pyridoxine.

BIBLIOGRAPHY

1. Baddiley, J., *Nature*, 170, 711 (1952).
2. Baddiley, J. and A. P. Mathias, *J. Chem. Soc.*, 2583 (1952).
3. Banks, B. E. C., A. A. Diamantis and C. A. Vernon, *J. Chem. Soc.*, 4235 (1961).
4. Bernhart, R. W., E. D'amato and R. M. Tomarelli, *Arch. Biochem. Biophys.*, 88, 267 (1960).
5. Gabriel, S. and J. Colman, *Ber.*, 33, 988 (1900).
6. Gibbs, H. D., *J. Biol. Chem.*, 72, 649 (1927).
7. Green, D. E., L. F. Lelvier and V. Nocito, *J. Biol. Chem.*, 161, 559 (1945).
8. Gunsalus, I. C., W. D. Bellamy and W. W. Umbreit, *J. Biol. Chem.*, 155, 685 (1944).
9. Gunsalus, I. C., L. Struglia and D. I. O'Kane, *J. Biol. Chem.*, 194, 859 (1952).
10. György, P., *J. Am. Chem. Soc.*, 60, 983 (1938).
11. Harris, S. A. and K. Folkers, *J. Am. Chem. Soc.*, 61, 1245, 3307 (1939).
12. Harris, S. A., E. T. Stillers and K. Folkers, *J. Am. Chem. Soc.*, 61, 1242 (1939).
13. Harris, S. A., D. Heyl and K. Folkers, *J. Am. Chem. Soc.*, 66, 2088 (1944).
14. Harris, S. A., D. Heyl, K. Folkers and E. E. Snell, *J. Biol. Chem.*, 154, 315 (1944).
15. Harris, E. E., R. A. Firestone, K, Pfister, R. R. Boettcher, F. J. Cross, R. B. Currie, M. Monaco, E. R. Peterson and W. Reuter, *J. Org. Chem.*, 27, 2705 (1962).
16. Heyl, D. and S. A. Harris, *J. Am. Chem. Soc.*, 73, 3434 (1951).
17. Itiba, A. and K. Miti, *Sci. Papers Inst. Phys. Chem. Research (Tōkyō)*, 35, 73 (1938); 36, 1 (1939).
18. Itiba, A. and K. Miti, *Sci. Papers Inst. Phys. Chem. Research (Tōkyō)*, 36, 173 (1939).
19. Jones, R. G. and E. C. Kornfield, *J. Am. Chem. Soc.*, 73, 107, 5244 (1951).
20. Keresztesy, J. C. and J. R. Stevens, *J. Am. Chem. Soc.*, 60, 1267 (1938).
21. Keresztesy, J. C. and J. R. Stevens, *Proc. Soc. Exp. Biol. Med.*, 38, 64 (1938).
22. Kritzmann, M. G. and O. Samarina, *Nature*, 158, 104 (1946).
23. Kuhn, R. and G. Wendt, *Ber.*, 71, 780, 1118 (1938).
24. Kuhn, R. and G. Wendt, *Ber.*, 71, 1534 (1938).
25. Kuhn, R. and G. Wendt, *Ber.*, 72, 305 (1939).
26. Kuhn, R., H. Andersag, K. Westphal and G. Wendt, *Ber.*, 72, 309 (1939).
27. Kuhn, R., G. Wendt and K. Westphal, *Ber.*, 72, 310 (1939).
28. Kuhn, R., K. Westphal, G. Wendt and O. Westphal, *Naturwissenschaften*, 27, 469 (1939).
29. Lepkovsky, S., *J. Biol. Chem.*, 124, 125 (1938).
30. Lepkovsky, S., *Science*, 87, 169 (1938).
31. Lichstein, H. C., I. C. Gunsalus and W. W. Umbreit, *J. Biol. Chem.*, 161, 311 (1945).

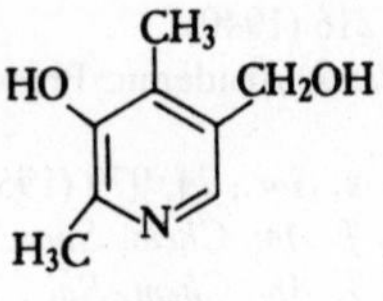

(77)

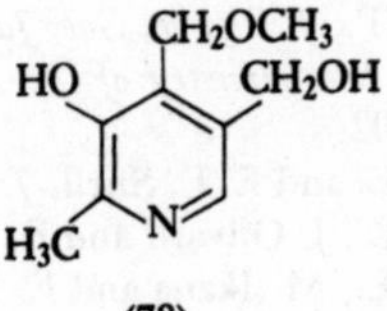

(78)

32. Matsui, M., A. Kobayashi and S. Watanabe, *Agr. Biol. Chem.* (*Tōkyō*), **25**, 240 (1961).
33. Matsukawa, T., *J. Pharm. Soc. Japan*, **60**, 216 (1940).
34. Meister, A., *Biochemistry of the Amino Acids*, Academic Press, New York, 1957, pp. 161, 202.
35. Metzler, D. E. and E. E. Snell, *J. Am. Chem. Soc.*, **74**, 979 (1952).
36. Metzler, D. E., J. Olivard and E. E. Snell, *J. Am. Chem. Soc.*, **76**, 644 (1954).
37. Metzler, D. E., M. Ikaua and E. E. Snell, *J. Am. Chem. Soc.*, **76**, 648 (1954).
38. Möller, E. F., *Z. Physiol. Chem.*, **260**, 246 (1939).
39. 'Recommended dietary allowances', *Natl. Acad. Sci.–Natl. Research Council Publ.*, No. 302 (1953).
40. Nielsen, J. T., N. Elming and N. Clauson-Kaas, *Acta Chem. Scand.*, **14**, 938 (1960).
41. O'Kane, D. E. and I. C. Gunsalus, *J. Biol. Chem.*, **170**, 425 (1947).
42. Robinson, F. A., *The Vitamin B Complex*, Chapman and Hall, London, 1951, p. 317.
43. Robinson, F. A., *The Vitamin B Complex*, Chapman and Hall, London, 1951, p. 322.
44. Snell, E. E., B. M. Guirard and R. J. Williams, *J. Biol. Chem.*, **143**, 519 (1942).
45. Snell, E. E., *J. Am. Chem. Soc.*, **67**, 194 (1945).
46. Snell, E. E., *Vitamins Hormones*, **16**, 77 (1958).
47. Stiller, E. T., J. C. Keresztesy and J. R. Stevens, *J. Am. Chem. Soc.*, **61**, 1237 (1939).
48. Stokstad, E. L. R., *Ann. Rev. Biochem.*, **31**, 451 (1962).
49. Suzuki, Y., *J. Pharm. Soc. Japan*, **81**, 792 (1961).
50. Umbreit, W. W., W. D. Bellamy and I. C. Gunsalus, *Arch. Biochem.*, **7**, 185 (1945).
51. Viscontini, M., C. Ebnother and P. Karrer, *Helv. Chim. Acta*, **34**, 1834 (1951).
52. Wendt, G. and F. W. Bernhart, *Arch. Biochem. Biophys.*, **88**, 270 (1960).
53. Wilson, A. N. and S. A. Harris, *J. Am. Chem. Soc.*, **73**, 4693 (1951).

CHAPTER 6

Nicotinamide and Nicotinic Acid
(The PP Factor)

NICOTINAMIDE AND NICOTINIC ACID – Isolation – Sources – Deficiency
disease – Daily requirement – Properties – Structure – Synthesis –
Biosynthesis – Biological function – Synthetic analogues of nicotinic
acid – BIBLIOGRAPHY

BOTH nicotinic acid and nicotinamide had been known for some time
before their biological significance was realized.

Isolation

Nicotinic acid was first isolated from yeast[8,9] and from rice bran[30,31].
Nicotinamide was first isolated[3] from liver concentrates, and was
shown[7,28] to be the pellagra-preventative (PP) factor.

Sources

Nicotinic acid (which is biologically equivalent to the amide) is widely
distributed in nature, but not usually in the free state; it is a constituent
of some very important coenzymes (see below under 'Biological function'). The richest sources of the vitamin are wheat germ, yeast and liver.
Barley, maize, oats and rice also contain appreciable amounts.

Deficiency disease

Deficiency of nicotinic acid (or nicotinamide) in man leads to a condition termed pellagra, and in dogs to blacktongue. Rats do not require
an external source of the vitamin. The pellagra is characterized[25] by
patches of dermatitis, thickening and abnormal pigmentation of the skin,
disfunction of the digestive and nervous systems, loss of memory, in-
sanity and ultimately death.

The disease is quite common in tropical countries, particularly
amongst people whose staple diet is maize.

97

Daily requirement

The average daily requirement for the normal healthy adult is 10–20 mg of nicotinamide.

Properties

Both the acid and the amide are crystalline solids, with typical ultraviolet spectra[16,20] (Figure 6.1).

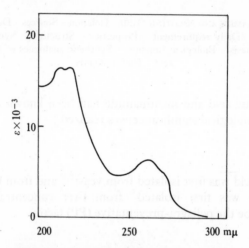

Figure 6.1. The ultraviolet spectrum of nicotinamide in water. [Reproduced, by permission, from H. R. Rosenberg, *The Chemistry and Physiology of the Vitamins*, Interscience, New York, 1945, p. 222.]

Structure

Nicotinic acid (2) was originally obtained[14] by the oxidation of nicotine (1) with nitric acid. The carboxyl group was shown to be at position 3 by the fact that pyridine-2,3-dicarboxylic acid yields nicotinic acid when decarboxylated, whereas pyridine-3,4-dicarboxylic acid yields a mixture of nicotinic and isonicotinic acids when similarly treated. The structure of nicotinic acid was proved beyond doubt[27] by the sequence shown in 3 → 7 → 2.

Synthesis

Nicotinamide was first obtained[4,23] by treating ethyl nicotinate with ammonia.

Nicotinic acid is still produced commercially by the oxidation of nicotine (1), and this is the preferred method. Other industrial methods include the oxidation of quinoline (obtained from coal-tar) followed by decarboxylation of the pyridine-2,3-dicarboxylic acid, and also the use of pyridine itself as a starting material: $8 \rightarrow 10 \rightarrow 2$.

Nicotinamide is prepared commercially[10] by treating the 3-cyano-pyridine (10) with alkali and hydrogen peroxide.

Biosynthesis

A fundamental observation made by Elvehjem and his colleagues[19] was that L-tryptophan (11) is converted into nicotinic acid in mammalian tissues; this would explain why symptoms of nicotinic acid deficiency in man can be relieved by the administration of L-tryptophan; it also explains why a maize diet leads to pellagra, for although maize contains some nicotinic acid, it is a very poor source of L-tryptophan. Thus pellagra must be assumed to be a disease associated with deficiency in the diet of both nicotinic acid and tryptophan.

The *in vivo* conversion of tryptophan into nicotinic acid is shown in $11 \rightarrow 18 \rightarrow 2$, and is fully discussed by Goodwin[11]. Tryptophan is first converted into N-formylkynurenine 12, oxidatively by an iron–porphyrin enzyme system; it then loses its formyl group to give kynurenine (13). The latter is hydroxylated to 14 under the influence of triphosphopyridine nucleotide, and then degraded to 3-hydroxyanthranilic acid (15) by a pyridoxal-dependent enzyme. Enzymic oxidation of 15 then yields 1-amino-4-formylbutadiene-1,2-dicarboxylic acid (16). Nicotinic acid (2) may be formed from 16 either by way of quinolinic acid (17) or through the compound 18. Evidence is now available[1] supporting the route $16 \rightarrow 17 \rightarrow 2$.

The biosynthesis of the vitamin in plants is not known, and in bacteria a route different to that in mammals is adopted. It has been found[29] that the carbon skeleton is built up from a C_3 unit (glycerol or its equivalent) and a C_4 dicarboxylic acid in such a way that one carboxyl group of the latter is lost and the other appears as the carboxyl group of the vitamin.

Biological function

Nicotinamide is concerned in the structures of two important hydrogen-transfer coenzymes. Coenzyme I (19) was first isolated from yeast and its structure was elucidated by degradation[5,6,26] and confirmed by

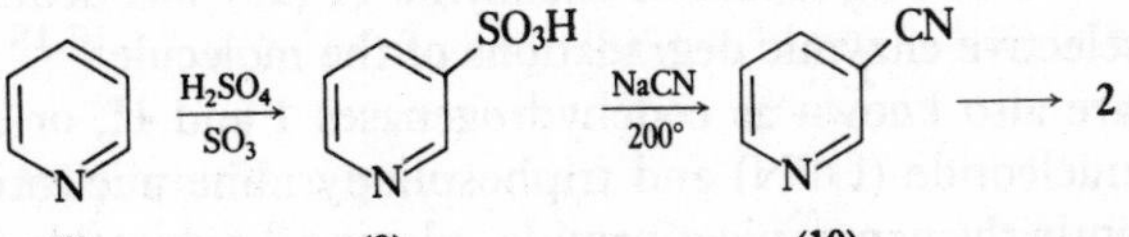

(8)   (9)   (10)   → 2

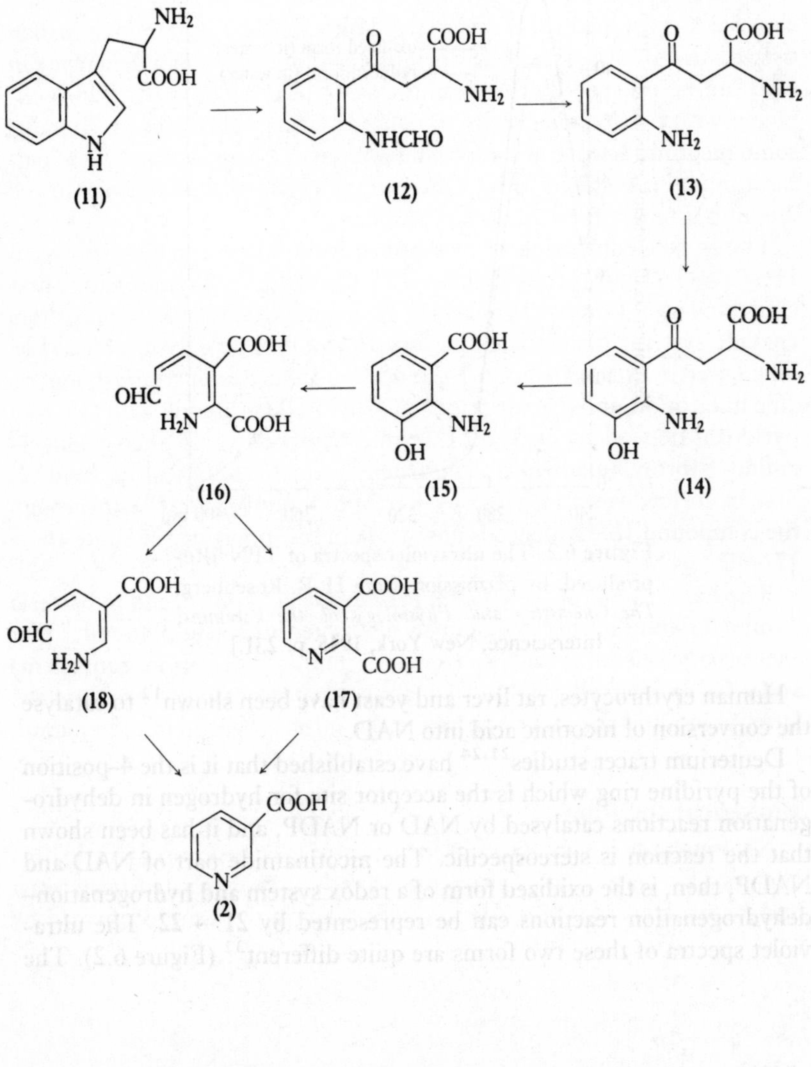

(11)   (12)   (13)

(16)   (15)   (14)

(18)   (17)

(2)

synthesis[13,15]. The structure of coenzyme II (20) was deduced from a study of selective enzymic degradations of the molecule[17,18]. These coenzymes are also known as codehydrogenases I and II, or diphosphopyridine nucleotide (DPN) and triphosphopyridine nucleotide (TPN). More recently the names nicotinamide–adenine dinucleotide (NAD) and nicotinamide–adenine dinucleotide phosphate (NADP) have been recommended[2]. Each of these two coenzymes can combine with a wide variety of proteins (apoenzymes) to give a number of enzymes, each of which is specific for a particular substrate.

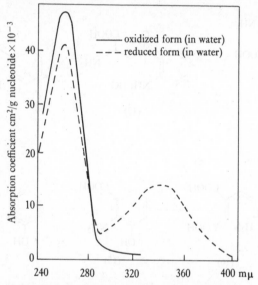

Figure 6.2. The ultraviolet spectra of TPN. [Reproduced, by permission, from H. R. Rosenberg, *The Chemistry and Physiology of the Vitamins*, Interscience, New York, 1945, p. 231.]

Human erythrocytes, rat liver and yeast have been shown[12] to catalyse the conversion of nicotinic acid into NAD.

Deuterium tracer studies[21,24] have established that it is the 4–position of the pyridine ring which is the acceptor site for hydrogen in dehydrogenation reactions catalysed by NAD or NADP, and it has been shown that the reaction is stereospecific. The nicotinamide part of NAD and NADP, then, is the oxidized form of a redox system and hydrogenation–dehydrogenation reactions can be represented by 21 → 22. The ultraviolet spectra of these two forms are quite different[32] (Figure 6.2). The

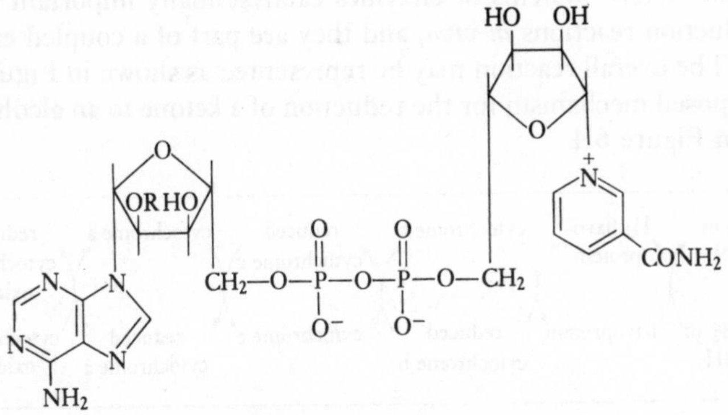

(19, R = H;
20, R = —O—P(=O)(OH)$_2$)

(21) (22)

NAD and NADP systems of enzymes catalyse many important oxidation–reduction reactions *in vivo*, and they are part of a coupled enzyme
system. The overall reaction may be represented as shown in Figure 6.3.

A proposed mechanism for the reduction of a ketone to an alcohol[22] is
shown in Figure 6.4.

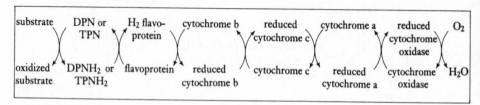

Figure 6.3.

Synthetic analogues of nicotinic acid

Compounds of the type **23** (where R = OC_2H_5, $NHCH_3$, $N(C_2H_5)_2$
and $NHCH_2COOH$) all show weak activity presumably because they are
hydrolysed *in vivo* to nicotinic acid. Trigonelline (**24**) is also active for
human pellagra but inactive against blacktongue. Quinolinic acid (**25**) is
also active, due to *in vivo* decarboxylation. The analogues **26** and **27** also
possess weak activity against human pellagra.

BIBLIOGRAPHY

1. Burns, J. J. and A. H. Conney, *Ann. Rev. Biochem.*, **29**, 413 (1960).
2. Dixon, M., *Nature*, **188**, 464 (1960); *Science*, **132**, 1548 (1960).
3. Elvehjem, C. A., R. J. Madden, F. M. Strong and D. W. Woolley, *J. Am. Chem. Soc.*, **59**, 1767 (1937).
4. Engler, C., *Ber.*, **27**, 1789 (1894).
5. von Euler, H., P. Karrer and B. Becker, *Helv. Chim. Acta*, **19**, 1060 (1936).
6. von Euler, H., F. Schlenk and R. Vestin, *Naturwissenschaften*, **25**, 318 (1937).
7. Fouts, P. J., O. M. Helmer, S. Lepkovsky and T. H. Jukes, *Proc. Soc. Exp. Biol. Med.*, **37**, 405 (1937).
8. Funk, C., *J. State Med.*, **20**, 341 (1912); *J. Physiol.*, **46**, 173 (1913).
9. Funk, C., *Brit. Med. J.*, **1**, 814 (1913).
10. Galat, A., *J. Am. Chem. Soc.*, **70**, 3945 (1948).
11. Goodwin, T. W., *Recent Advances in Biochemistry*, Churchill, London, 1960, p. 157.
12. Handler, P., *Proc. 4th Intern. Congr. Biochem.*, *Vienna, 1958*, Pergamon Press, London, 1959, Vol. II, p. 39.
13. Haynes, L. J., N. A. Hughes, G. W. Kenner and A. R. Todd, *J. Chem. Soc.*, 3727 (1957).

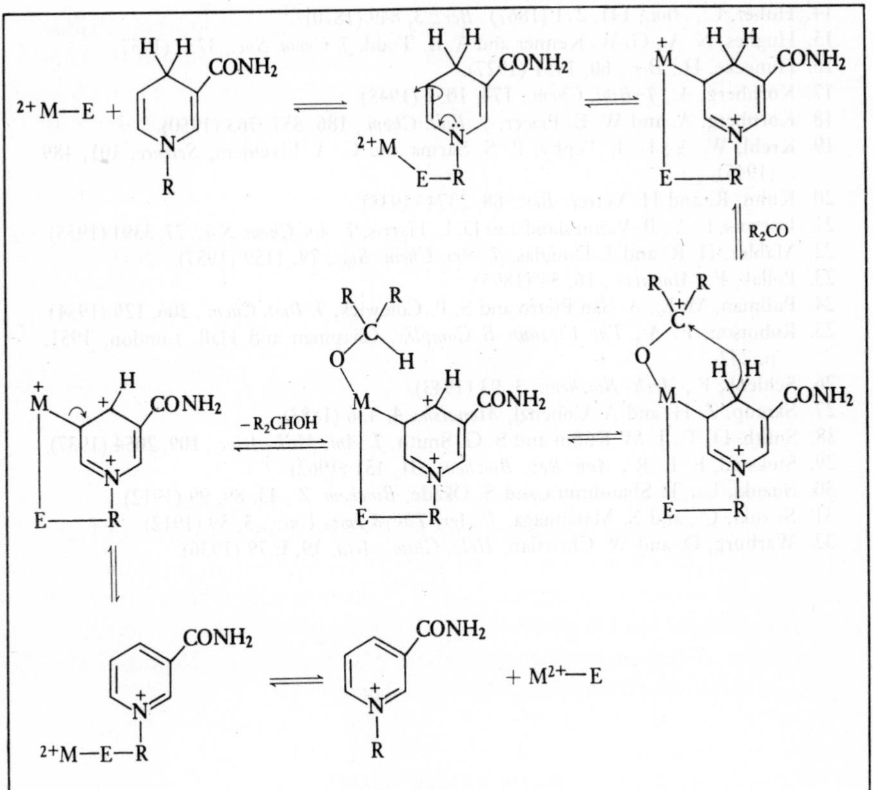

Figure 6.4.

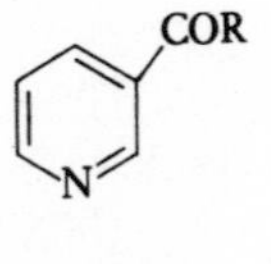

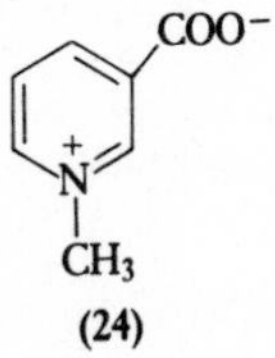

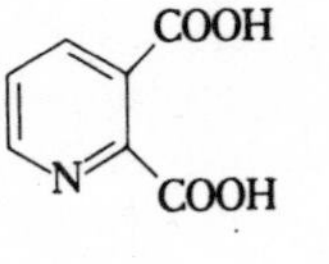

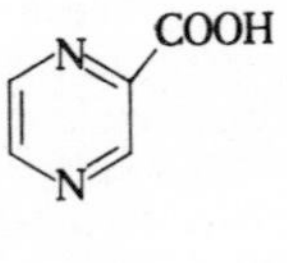

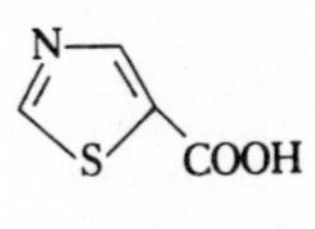

14. Huber, C., *Ann.*, **141**, 271 (1867); *Ber.*, **3**, 849 (1870).
15. Hughes, N. A., G. W. Kenner and A. R. Todd, *J. Chem. Soc.*, 3733 (1957).
16. Hunecke, H., *Ber.*, **60**, 1451 (1927).
17. Kornberg, A., *J. Biol. Chem.*, **174**, 1051 (1948).
18. Kornberg, A. and W. E. Pricer, *J. Biol. Chem.*, **186**, 557, 763 (1950).
19. Krehl, W. A., L. J. Tephy, P. S. Sarma and C. A. Elvehjem, *Science*, **101**, 489 (1945).
20. Kuhn, R. and H. Vetter, *Ber.*, **68**, 2374 (1935).
21. Loewus, F. A., B. Vennesland and D. L. Harris, *J. Am. Chem. Soc.*, **77**, 3391 (1955).
22. Mahler, H. R. and J. Douglas, *J. Am. Chem. Soc.*, **79**, 1159 (1957).
23. Pollak, F., *Monatsh.*, **16**, 53 (1895).
24. Pullman, M. E., A. San Pietro and S. P. Colewick, *J. Biol. Chem.*, **206**, 129 (1954).
25. Robinson, F. A., *The Vitamin B Complex*, Chapman and Hall, London, 1951, p. 242.
26. Schlenk, F., *Arch. Biochem.*, **3**, 93 (1943).
27. Skraup, Z. H. and A. Cobenzl, *Monatsh.*, **4**, 436 (1883).
28. Smith, D. T., J. M. Ruffin and S. G. Smith, *J. Am. Med. Assoc.*, **109**, 2054 (1937).
29. Stokstad, E. L. R., *Ann. Rev. Biochem.*, **31**, 451 (1962).
30. Suzuki, U., T. Shamimura and S. Okade, *Biochem. Z.*, **43**, 89, 99 (1912).
31. Suzuki, U., and S. Matsunaga, *J. Agr. Tōkyō Imp. Univ.*, **5**, 59 (1912).
32. Warburg, O. and W. Christian, *Helv. Chim. Acta*, **19**, E.79 (1936).

CHAPTER 7

Vitamin B$_{12}$ (Cyanocobalamin)

INTRODUCTION – Benzimidazoles – Porphyrins – VITAMIN B$_{12}$ – Discovery and isolation – Sources – Deficiency disease – Daily requirement – Properties – Structure – Nomenclature – Synthesis – Biosynthesis – Vitamin B$_{12}$ coenzymes – The biological function of vitamin B$_{12}$ – Analogues and antagonists – BIBLIOGRAPHY

INTRODUCTION

THE STRUCTURE of vitamin B$_{12}$ involves two heterocyclic systems, a benzimidazole and a modified porphyrin nucleus, now termed *corrin* (1).

Benzimidazoles[135]

In benzimidazole itself (2) the two nitrogen atoms are equivalent due to tautomerism, so that, in the absence of a nitrogen substituent, positions 4 and 7 and positions 5 and 6 are equivalent.

The benzimidazole ring system is usually synthesized from an *o*-phenylenediamine, the individual methods differing one from another in the mode by which the potential C$_2$ carbon fragment is introduced. Thus, 2-alkylbenzimidazoles may be prepared by the interaction of an *o*-phenylenediamine with an aliphatic acid. Derivatives of such acids, e.g. the nitrile or the imido ether, can also be used.

Benzimidazoles show weak acidic as well as weak basic properties. Alkylation affords, successively, the 1-alkyl- and the 1,3-dialkylbenzimidazoles. The ring system is quite stable towards oxidizing agents, with the benzene ring being eventually broken down before the heterocyclic ring.

Porphyrins[44,118]

The parent substance is porphin (3), which contains an eighteen-membered ring with a system of conjugated double bonds. X-ray diffraction studies have shown that this molecule is planar.

The aetioporphyrins are derivatives of 3 in which the positions 1 to 8 (the so-called beta positions) are substituted by methyl and ethyl groups.

Four isomers are possible, and these are known as aetioporphyrin I, II, III and IV (4 to 7) respectively.

The porphin derivatives are usually deep-red high-melting solids which are stable to heat and difficult to oxidize, although oxidation with chromic acid yields a mixture of maleimides. The absorption spectra of porphyrins are characteristic and can be correlated with structural features of the substituents[117]. The porphins form metallic derivatives of the type 8 with metals such as manganese, iron, copper and zinc, in which the metal ion is very firmly bound.

Four coproporphyrins (tetramethylporphintetrapropionic acids) are possible, corresponding to the aetioporphyrins with propionic acid residues in place of the ethyl groups. All four have been synthesized by conventional methods[11]. The related uroporphyrins I and III are octa-carboxylic acids, each of which can be decarboxylated to a coproporphyrin. Uroporphyrin I has been established by synthesis[91] to be 9 and uroporphyrin III is thus 10 (where A = acetic and P = propionic acid residue).

The chlorophylls are examples of 7,8-dihydro derivatives of the porphyrins which occur naturally, and more fully reduced porphyrins are also known[118].

VITAMIN B_{12}

Discovery and isolation[116]

In 1926 it was found[93] that the administration of whole liver to patients suffering from pernicious anemia resulted in a control of the disease and this discovery was so significant to medicine that it merited a Nobel prize award in 1934. Attempts were made in several laboratories to isolate the active principle from liver, and much of this early work has been reviewed[120]. The isolation studies were hampered by the lack of a chemical test to detect the active substance and by the lack of a suitable animal test. The results of fractionations could only be deduced by testing fractions on human patients suffering from pernicious anemia. The active substance, designated 'Vitamin B_{12}', was finally obtained in a crystalline state by Smith and his coworkers[111,112,115], by Folker's group[101] and later by Ellis[51]. Subsequently, crystalline vitamin B_{12} was obtained[102] from fermentations employing Streptomyces griseus, and this is now the commercial source of the vitamin.

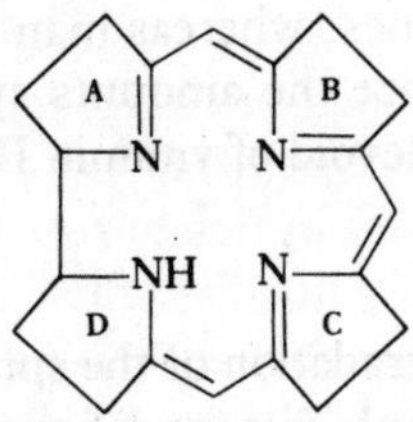

(1)

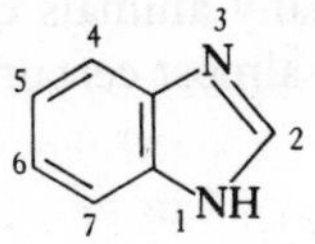

(2)

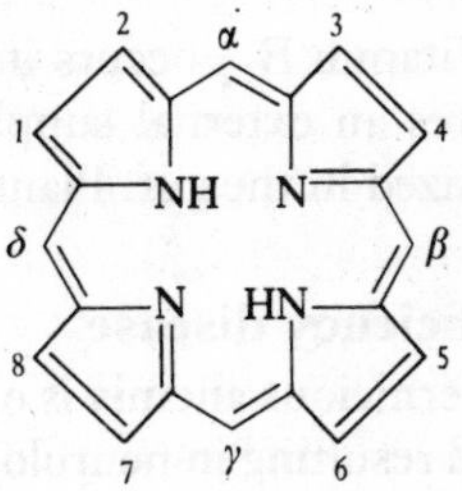

(3)

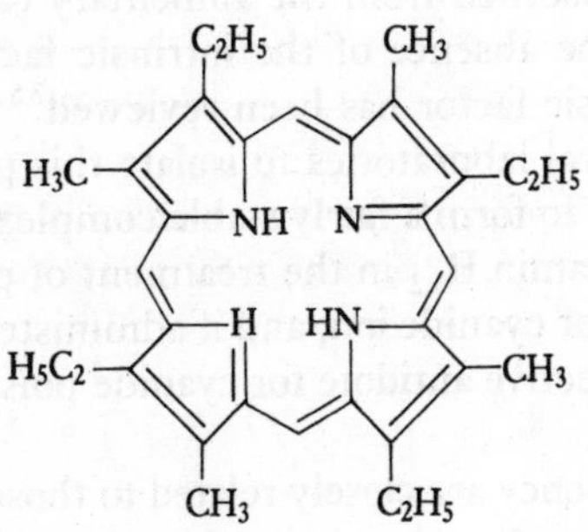

(4)

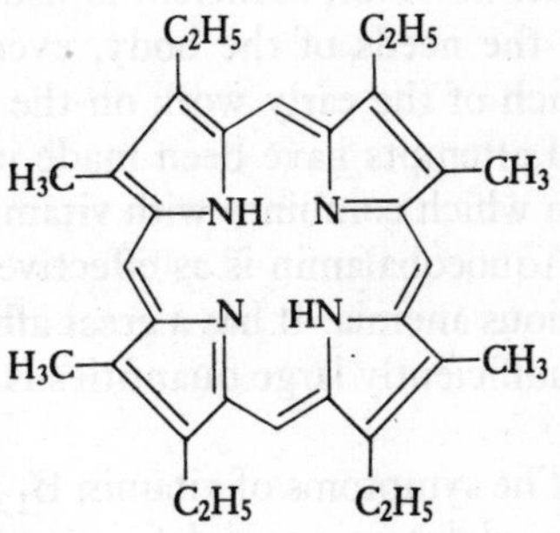

(5)

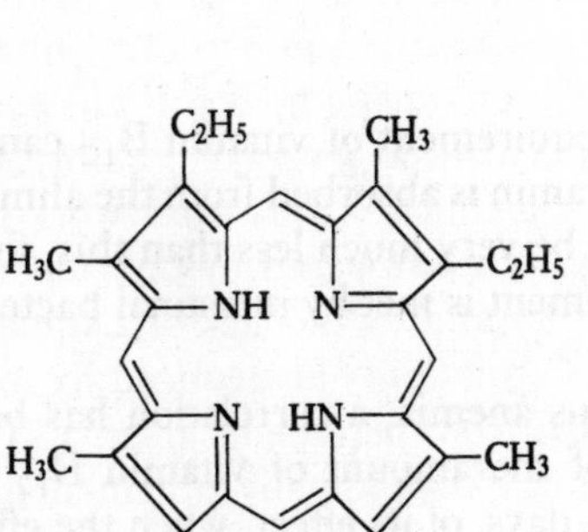

(6)

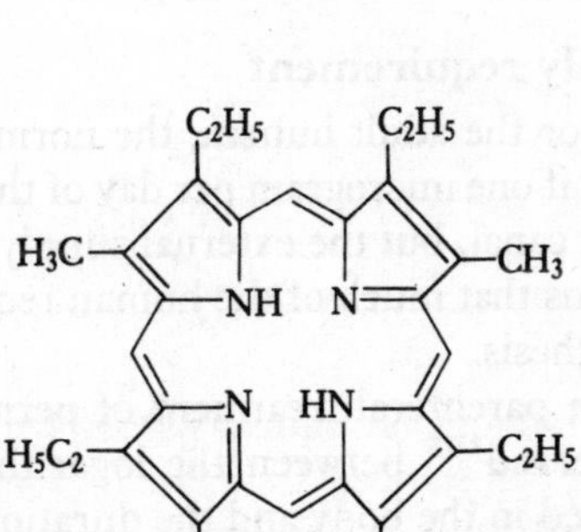

(7)

Sources

Vitamin B_{12} occurs in practically all animal tissues; whereas man requires an external supply, many animals can utilize the amounts synthesized in the gut. Plants are almost certainly all devoid of vitamin B_{12}.

Deficiency disease

Pernicious anemia is often accompanied by a degradation of the spinal cord resulting in neurological lesions. It is not a simple dietary deficiency disease due to the absence of vitamin B_{12}, but is due to a metabolic defect such that the vitamin is not assimilated through the alimentary canal. It has been established[34] that a gastric secretory substance, the 'intrinsic factor', is essential for the assimilation of vitamin B_{12} when the latter is administered orally on the microgram scale. On the milligram scale, however, sufficient is usually absorbed from the alimentary canal for the needs of the body, even in the absence of the intrinsic factor. Much of the early work on the intrinsic factor has been reviewed[35,105] and attempts have been made in several laboratories to isolate this protein which combines with vitamin B_{12} to form a fairly stable complex.

Aquocobalamin is as effective as vitamin B_{12} in the treatment of pernicious anemia. It has a great affinity for cyanide ion, and if administered in sufficiently large quantities is an effective antidote for cyanide poisoning.

The symptoms of vitamin B_{12} deficiency are closely related to those of pteroylglutamic acid deficiency (Chapter 4) and anemic patients respond to either vitamin. However, vitamin B_{12} is therapeutically beneficial for the neurological lesions, whereas pteroylglutamic acid is not.

Daily requirement

For the adult human, the normal requirement of vitamin B_{12} can be met if one microgram per day of the vitamin is absorbed from the alimentary canal, but the external supply can be very much less than this, for it seems that much of the human requirement is met by intestinal bacterial synthesis.

In parenteral treatment of pernicious anemia, a correlation has been observed[105] between the logarithm of the amount of vitamin B_{12} retained in the body and the duration, in days, of its effect, when the effect was based upon the maintenance of the serum vitamin level within the normal range. Under these conditions the concept of a fixed daily need for vitamin B_{12} may require modification.

(8)

(9)

(10)

Properties

Vitamin B_{12} (or cyanocobalamin) is soluble in water and crystallizes as deep red needles. It has no definite melting point, is laevorotatory, diamagnetic and exhibits a characteristic absorption spectrum (Figure 7.1[22,25]) with absorption maxima at 278, 361 and 550 mμ. The spectrum is essentially unaffected by a change in pH.

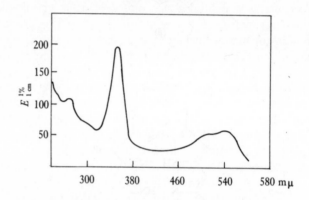

Figure 7.1. The ultraviolet spectrum of cyanocobalamin (in water). [Reproduced, by permission, from *J. Am. Chem. Soc.*, 73, 335 (1951).]

Structure

The structure of cyanocobalamin was deduced from a combination of physical and much chemical evidence, and the subject has been reviewed[67,69,72,81,104,129].

An ebullioscopic determination of the molecular weight in methanol gave a value of 1490 ± 150, whereas a value of 1360–1575 was deduced from early x-ray crystallographic data[71]. The uncertainty in this value was due mainly to variable hydration of the crystals. Elemental analysis of vitamin B_{12} indicated an approximate molecular formula of $C_{61-64} H_{86-92} N_{14} O_{13-14} P \cdot Co$[1,21,22]. The structure now accepted for the vitamin requires a formula of $C_{63} H_{88} N_{14} O_{14} P \cdot Co$ (which is in close agreement with the analysis[1] of the hexaperchlorate) and this corresponds to a molecular weight of 1355.

Cyanocobalamin is a weak polybasic acid which yields a hexaperchlorate[1]. The cobalt atom was shown[46,47,66,113,124] to be trivalent, and the stability of the complex, for example, to precipitating agents[86], to acid hydrolysis and to exchange with radio cobalt[4,18,55] indicated that the cobalt is firmly chemically bound. It was further demonstrated by potassium permanganate oxidation and by an infrared spectral examination[24] that the molecule of vitamin B$_{12}$ contains a cyanide group and that this grouping is directly linked to the cobalt atom. The cyanide group can be replaced by other anions. Thus, replacement by hydroxyl gives aquocobalamin (vitamin B$_{12a}$ or B$_{12b}$)[85,96,97]; it is a structure which incorporates a neutral water molecule, thus giving the whole molecule basic properties. When neutralized with hydrochloric acid the product is aquocobalamin chloride (rather than chlorocobalamin)[53]. The cyanide group may also be replaced by nitrite[2,113] to yield nitritocobalamin (vitamin B$_{12c}$), by bromide and by thiocyanate[24].

Early in the structural investigation a porphyrin-type of nucleus was assumed to be present since pyrroles were obtained on potash fusion of the vitamin[22] but the absorption spectrum is not that of a typical porphyrin; also oxidation did not yield either methylethylmaleimide or haematic acid (11) as would be expected from a porphyrin.

Most of the early knowledge concerning the structure of cyanocobalamin was obtained by an examination of the products of acid hydrolysis under a variety of conditions. The action of concentrated hydrochloric acid at 150° for several hours yielded ammonia (5–6 moles per mole of vitamin) from primary amide groups, phosphoric acid, a red cobalt-containing gum, a ninhydrin-reacting *substance A* (one mole per mole) and a *base B*. By an unsatisfactory method of analysis it was originally claimed[36] that two molecules of the substance A were produced, but it was subsequently[41] proved conclusively to be only one.

The substance A

This was isolated from the hydrolysate as a dibenzoate[3,41,230]. Analysis of the free amine (which was optically active) obtained by acid hydrolysis revealed a molecular formula of C$_3$H$_9$NO. The amine reacted with periodate to yield acetaldehyde and formaldehyde, so that its structure is that of 1-amino-2-propanol (12). This structure was confirmed, and the configuration of the molecule shown to be D$_g$-1-amino-2-propanol* by synthesis[130].

DL-Lactic acid (13) was resolved with morphine and the D$_g$-ethyl lactate (14) was converted into the amide and then reduced with lithium

---

* The subscript 'g' refers to glyceraldehyde as a configurational standard[123].

aluminium hydride to the amine, D_g-1-amino-2-propanol (15). The dibenzoate (16) of this amine was shown to be identical with the dibenzoate of substance A.

The base B

This was consistently obtained in 70% yield based upon one mole per mole of vitamin B_{12}. Analysis of the base B yielded a molecular formula of $C_9H_{10}N_2$. The compound, which is optically inactive, yielded 1·1 moles of acetic acid per mole in a Kuhn–Roth carbon-methyl group

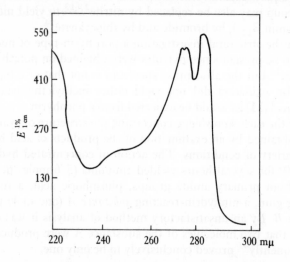

Figure 7.2. The ultraviolet spectrum of 5,6-dimethyl-benzimidazole. [Reproduced, by permission, from W. H. Sebrill and R. S. Harris, *The Vitamins: Chemistry, Physiology and Pathology*, Academic Press, New York, 1954, Vol. 1, p. 403.]

determination. Treatment of B with benzoyl chloride in aqueous alkali yielded 4,5-dibenzamido-1,2-dimethylbenzene (19) which was identified by comparison with a synthetic specimen. The base B was identified[8] as 5,6-dimethylbenzimidazole (18) by its ultraviolet absorption spectrum (Figure 7.2).

The structure 18 was confirmed by a synthesis[22,23] from 4,5-diamino-1,2-dimethylbenzene (17) and formic acid.

Less drastic conditions of hydrolysis (6 N hydrochloric acid at 100° for

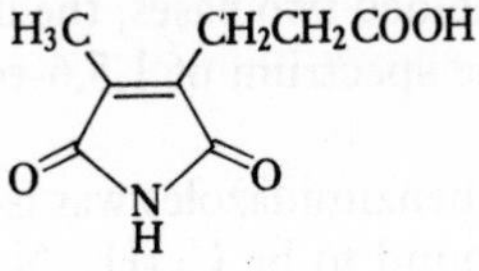

H$_3$C   CH$_2$CH$_2$COOH

CH$_2$NH$_2$
|
CHOH
|
CH$_3$

(11) 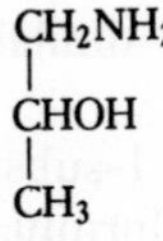   (12)

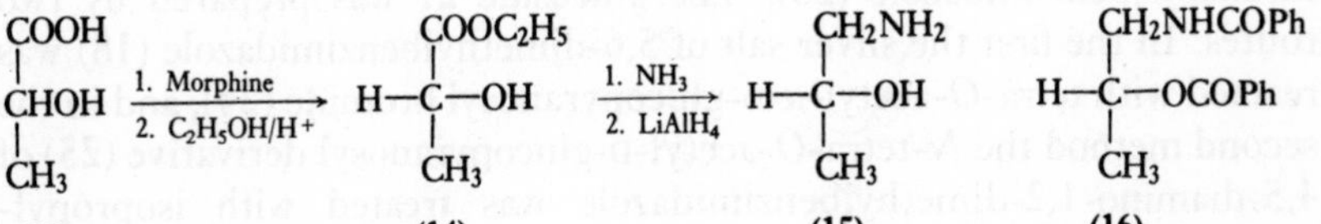

COOH
|
CHOH   1. Morphine
| 2. C$_2$H$_5$OH/H$^+$
CH$_3$

COOC$_2$H$_5$
|
H—C—OH
|
CH$_3$

1. NH$_3$
2. LiAlH$_4$

CH$_2$NH$_2$
|
H—C—OH
|
CH$_3$

CH$_2$NHCOPh
|
H—C—OCOPh
|
CH$_3$

(13)   (14)   (15)   (16)

H$_3$C   NH$_2$

H$_3$C   NH$_2$

HCOOH

H$_3$C   N

H$_3$C   N
|
H

PhCOCl
NaOH

H$_3$C   NHCOPh

H$_3$C   NHCOPh

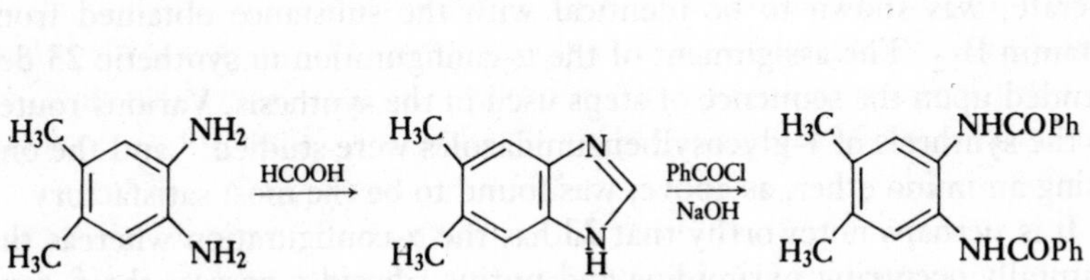

(17)   (18)   (19)

eight hours) of cyanocobalamin yielded two bases, the ultraviolet spectra of which were very similar[8] to the spectrum of 1,5,6-trimethylbenzimi-dazole.

The first of these 1-substituted benzimidazoles was isolated as a picrate and the molecular formula was found to be $C_{14}H_{18}N_2O_4 \cdot C_6H_3N_3O_7$. The base is dextrorotatory and gave a positive colour test for carbo-hydrate[77]. The glycosidic linkage is quite stable to acid hydrolysis; conditions which did break this link also decomposed the carbohydrate. The analysis, however, indicated a pentose rather than a hexose sugar, and the compound is different from the known[29] 5,6-dimethyl-1-ribityl-benzimidazole. The compound consumed one mole of periodate to yield a substance formulated[77] as 20, so that the sugar is in the furanose form. Similar oxidation of the model compound 1-β-D-glucopyranosyl-5,6-dimethylbenzimidazole (21) consumed two moles of periodate to give presumably 22, which is anomeric with 20. The structure of the first 1-substituted 5,6-dimethylbenzimidazole obtained by hydrolysis of vitamin B_{12} was thus[77] deduced to be that of 5,6-dimethyl-1-(α-D-ribo-furanosyl)benzimidazole (23). The glucoside 21 was prepared by two routes. In the first the silver salt of 5,6-dimethylbenzimidazole (18) was reacted with tetra-O-acetyl-α-D-glucopyranosyl bromide (24), and in the second method the N-tetra-O-acetyl-D-glucopyranosyl derivative (25) of 4,5-diamino-1,2-dimethylbenzimidazole was treated with isopropyl-formimino ether hydrochloride (26).

The structure 23 was confirmed by synthesis[78,82]. The synthesis of Folkers[78] used 4,5-dimethyl-2-nitro-N-(5'-trityl-D-ribofuranosyl)ani-line (27) as starting material, which itself was prepared by the interaction of 4,5-dimethyl-2-nitroaniline and 5-O-trityl-D-ribofuranose in ethanol solution in the presence of ammonium chloride. The compound 27 was hydrogenated on a palladium catalyst to the amine 28, which was then treated with ethylformimino ether hydrochloride, when ring closure occurred to yield the benzimidazole 29. The trityl group was removed from 29 by acid hydrolysis, and the product 23, which was isolated as the picrate, was shown to be identical with the substance obtained from vitamin B_{12}. The assignment of the α-configuration in synthetic 23 de-pended upon the sequence of steps used in the synthesis. Various routes to the synthesis of 1-glycosylbenzimidazoles were studied[70] and the one using an imino ether, as above, was found to be the most satisfactory.

It is perhaps noteworthy that 23 has the α-configuration whereas the naturally occurring pyrimidine and purine ribosides possess the β-con-figuration. The x-ray crystallographic investigation of cyanocobalamin

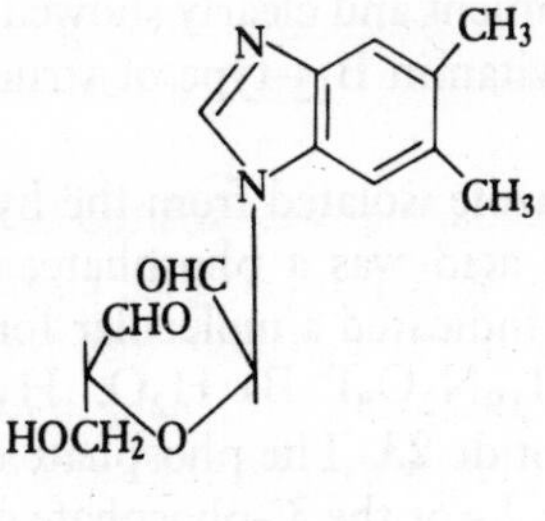

CH$_3$

CH$_3$

OHC
CHO

HOCH$_2$O

(20)

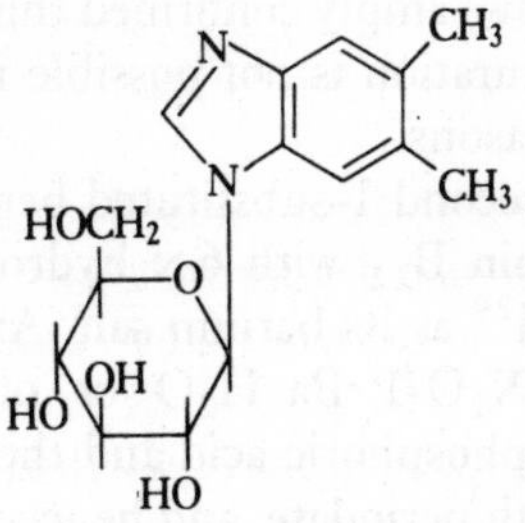

CH$_3$

CH$_3$

HOCH$_2$

O

OH

HO

HO

(21)

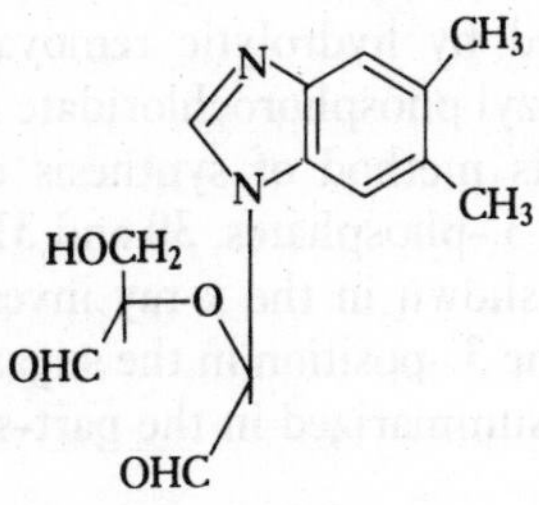

CH$_3$

CH$_3$

HOCH$_2$

OHC

OHC

O

(22)

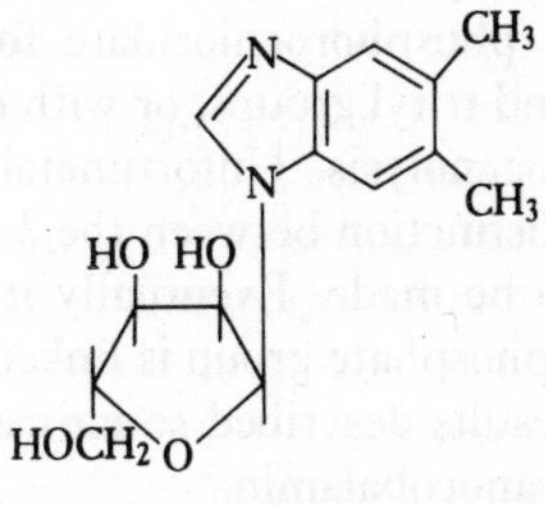

CH$_3$

CH$_3$

HO   HO

HOCH$_2$O

(23)

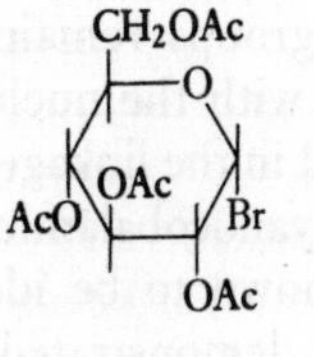

CH$_2$OAc

O

OAc

AcO   Br

OAc

(24)

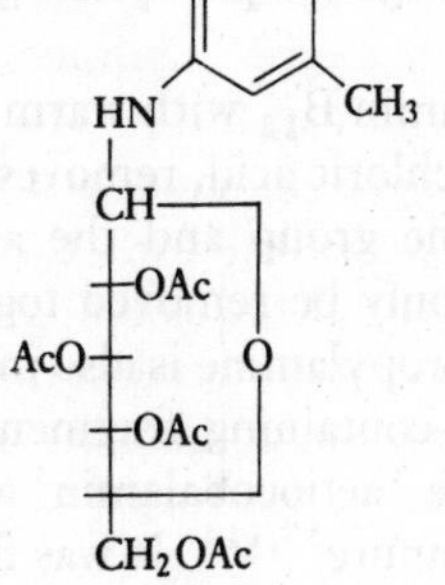

AcO

OAc

O

OAc

CH$_2$OAc

(25)

H$_2$N   CH$_3$

HN   CH$_3$

CH

OAc

O

OAc

CH$_2$OAc

NH·HCl

HC

OCH(CH$_3$)$_2$

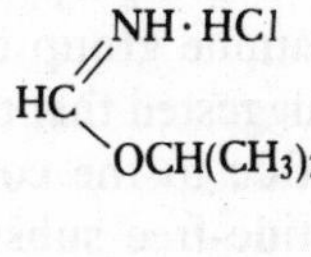

(26)

(see below) amply confirmed this assignment and clearly showed that the β-configuration is not possible in the vitamin B_{12}-type of structure for steric reasons.

The second 1-substituted benzimidazole isolated from the hydrolysis of vitamin B_{12} with 6 N hydrochloric acid was a phosphate, and was obtained[29] as its barium salt. Analysis indicated a molecular formula of $C_{14}H_{17}N_2O_7P \cdot Ba \cdot H_2O$ or of $C_{15}H_{19}N_2O_8P \cdot Ba \cdot H_2O$. Hydrolysis yielded phosphoric acid and the nucleotide 23. The phosphate does not react with periodate, and hence it is the 2'- or the 3'-phosphate of 23. By analogy with the course of hydrolysis of the ribonucleic acids[27], it was thought that the product isolated from the hydrolysis of vitamin B_{12} was a mixture of the 2'- and the 3'-phosphates derived from the 2',3'-cyclic phosphate, which has been prepared[17].

The phosphate has been synthesized[87] by treating 29 with either diphenyl phosphorochloridate followed by hydrolytic removal of the phenyl and trityl groups, or with dibenzyl phosphorochloridate followed by hydrogenolysis. Unfortunately, this method of synthesis does not allow a distinction between the 2'- and 3'-phosphates, 30 and 31 respectively, to be made. Eventually it was shown in the x-ray investigation that the phosphate group is linked to the 3'-position in the sugar.

The results described so far can be summarized in the part-structure 32 for cyanocobalamin.

Cyanocobalamin reacts with cyanide ions to yield a purple complex containing two cyanide groups[37,52,128], and an examination of the ultraviolet spectrum of this complex[9,10] suggested that the nitrogen at position 3 of the benzimidazole ring is coordinately attached to the cobalt atom. This link to cobalt can be broken without removing the benzimidazole nucleotide from the molecule, thus indicating that the nucleotide is linked in some way through the phosphate group to the cobalt-containing part of the molecule.

Brief hydrolysis of vitamin B_{12} with warm concentrated hydrochloric acid[3] or, better, with perchloric acid, removes the benzimidazole nucleotide, but the propylamine group and the amide groups remain. The propylamine group can only be removed together with the nucleotide. This suggested that the propylamine is also involved in the linkage of the nucleotide to the cobalt-containing fragment of cyanocobalamin. The nucleotide-free substance 'aetiocobalamin' was shown to be identical with 'factor B' of cow manure[57,114]. It was further demonstrated[3,12,20] that the aminopropanol group is linked by an amide group to the cobalt-containing moiety, so that the part-structure 32 can be expanded to 33.

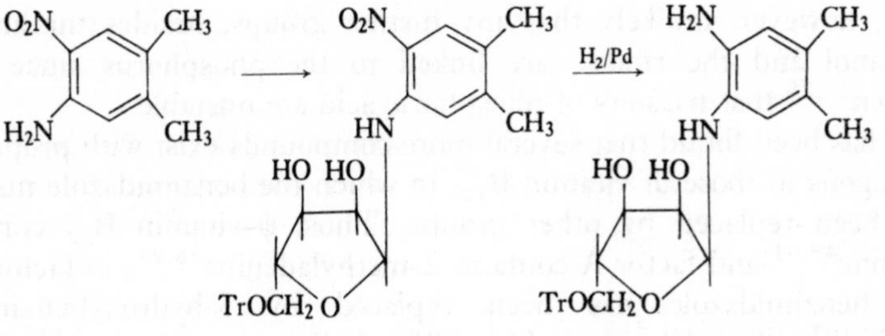

(27)   (28)

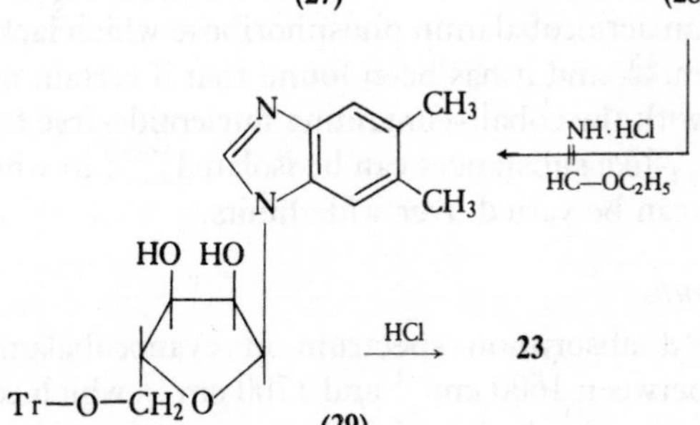

(29)

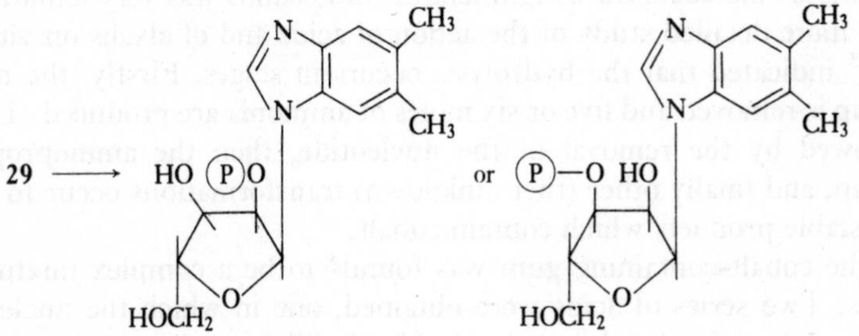

$\xrightarrow{\text{HCl}}$ 23

29 $\longrightarrow$

(30)   (31)

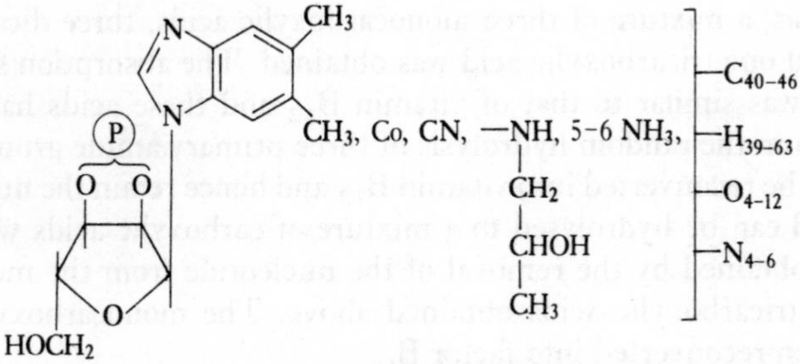

(32)

It is, however, unlikely that any further groups, besides the amino-propanol and the ribose, are linked to the phosphorus since it is known[27,28] that triesters of phosphoric acid are unstable.

It has been found that several more compounds exist with properties analogous to those of vitamin B_{12}, in which the benzimidazole nucleus has been replaced by other groups. Thus, ψ-vitamin B_{12} contains adenine[48,61] and factor A contains 2-methyladenine[58,95]; in factor III, the benzimidazole has been replaced by 5-hydroxybenzimida-zole[60,103,110], and in factor H by 2-methylmercaptoadenine[114]. Sewer sludge yields an aetiocobalamin phosphoribose which lacks the benzimi-dazole fragment[45], and it has been found that if certain microorganisms are provided with the cobalt-containing nucleotide-free fragment (factor B), vitamin B_{12}-like substances can be isolated[56,59] in which the nucleo-tide fragment can be varied over wide limits.

The amide groups

The infrared absorption spectrum of cyanocobalamin shows two broad bands between 1600 cm^{-1} and 1700 cm^{-1} which could be due[113] to unsubstituted and substituted amide groups respectively, but in such a complex molecule the assignment of these bands was very tentative.

A more detailed study of the action of acids and of alkalis on vitamin B_{12}[3] indicated that the hydrolysis occurs in stages. Firstly, the nitrile group is removed and five or six moles of ammonia are produced. This is followed by the removal of the nucleotide, then the aminopropanol group, and finally other (then unknown) transformations occur to yield the stable products which contain cobalt.

The cobalt-containing gum was found[3] to be a complex mixture of acids. Two series of acids were obtained, one in which the nucleotide group was retained and the other lacking it. The coordination state of the cobalt remains the same as in the vitamin itself. Under mild conditions of hydrolysis, a mixture of three monocarboxylic acids, three dicarboxylic acids and one tricarboxylic acid was obtained. The absorption spectrum of each was similar to that of vitamin B_{12} and these acids had clearly arisen from the random hydrolysis of three primary amide groups. Each acid can be reconverted into vitamin B_{12} and hence retain the nucleotide. Factor B can be hydrolysed to a mixture of carboxylic acids which can also be obtained by the removal of the nucleotide from the mono-, the di- and tricarboxylic acids obtained above. The monocarboxylic acids have been reconverted into factor B.

Hydrolysis of vitamin B_{12} in the presence of nitrous acid yields a

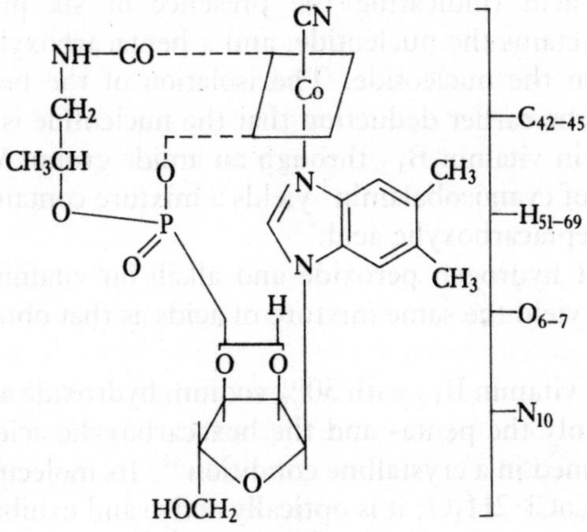

$$
\begin{array}{c}
\text{CN} \\
\text{NH—CO} \quad \text{Co} \\
\text{CH}_2 \\
\text{CH}_3\text{CH} \\
\text{O} \\
\text{P} \quad \text{CH}_3 \\
\text{O} \quad \text{CH}_3 \\
\text{N} \\
\text{H} \\
\text{O} \quad \text{O} \\
\text{O} \\
\text{HOCH}_2
\end{array}
$$

C$_{42-45}$

H$_{51-69}$

O$_{6-7}$

N$_{10}$

(33)

hexacarboxylic acid (indicating the presence of six primary amide groups) which retains the nucleotide, and a heptacarboxylic acid which does not contain the nucleotide. The isolation of the heptacarboxylic acid confirmed the earlier deduction that the nucleotide is linked to the cobalt complex in vitamin B_{12} through an amide group. Very vigorous acid hydrolysis of cyanocobalamin[3] yields a mixture containing a penta-, a hexa- and a heptacarboxylic acid.

The action of hydrogen peroxide and alkali on vitamin B_{12}[106] has been shown[3] to yield the same mixture of acids as that obtained by mild acid hydrolysis.

Hydrolysis of vitamin B_{12} with 30% sodium hydroxide at 150° for one hour yields mainly the penta- and the hexacarboxylic acids. The latter was finally obtained in a crystalline condition[31]. Its molecular formula is $C_{46}H_{60}N_6O_{13}CoCl \cdot 2H_2O$; it is optically active and exhibits an absorption spectrum very similar to that of the parent vitamin. This acid was subjected to an x-ray crystallographic examination (see below).

When vitamin B_{12} was treated for a short time with hot alkali[15,115] in the presence of air, a neutral, red crystalline substance was obtained as the major product which is very nearly indistinguishable from the starting material by physical methods, but which is biologically inactive. Further hydrolysis of this dehydrovitamin B_{12} yields the crystalline hexacarboxylic acid mentioned above.

Hence, a study of the hydrolysis of vitamin B_{12} showed the presence of six primary amide groups and a substituted amide group which links the nucleotide to the cobalt-containing nucleus.

The nucleus

The cobalt-containing mixture of acids obtained by the hydrolysis of vitamin B_{12}, when converted into the esters and oxidized[107] with dilute alkaline permanganate, yielded a mixture of eight simple acids. Four of these were identified[107] as oxalic, succinic, methylsuccinic and dimethylmalonic acids and later[63] one other was characterized as 3-carboxy-2,2-dimethyladipic acid. When the cobalt-containing hydrolysate itself was oxidized with sodium chromate in acetic acid[89], ($\pm$)-4-hydroxy-3,3-dimethyl-2,5-dioxopyrrolidine-4-propionic acid lactone (34) and ($\pm$)-3,3-dimethyl-2,5-dioxopyrrolidine-4-propionic acid (35) were identified among the products, whereas similar oxidation of vitamin B_{12} yielded 3,3-dimethyl-2,5-dioxopyrrolidine-4-propionamide (36) in addition to 34 and 35. When the hexacarboxylic acid was oxidized, the products included[121] the compound 37, which is now known to be derived from

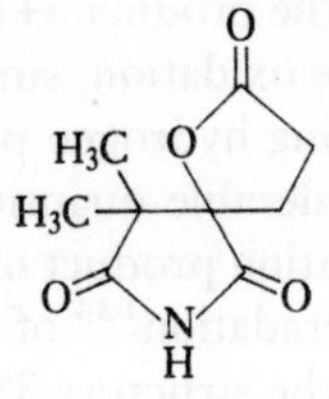

H$_3$C O

H$_3$C

O   N   O

H

(34)

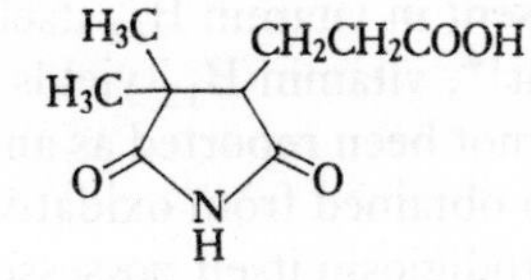

H$_3$C   CH$_2$CH$_2$COOH

H$_3$C

O   N   O

H

(35)

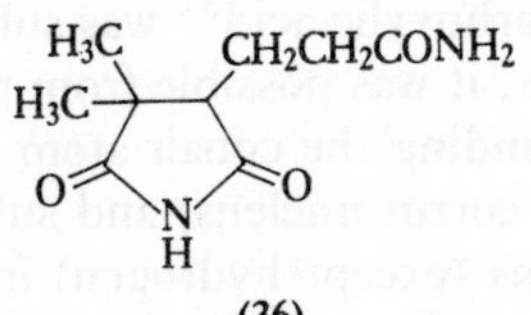

H$_3$C   CH$_2$CH$_2$CONH$_2$

H$_3$C

O   N   O

H

(36)

NH

H$_3$C   CH$_2$CH$_2$COOH

O   N   O

H

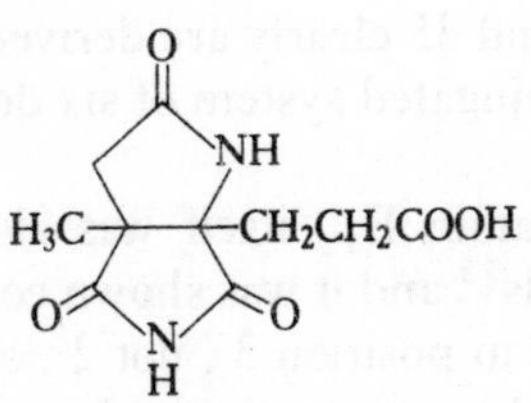

(37)

ring B of the vitamin. It is now known that the product 34 arises from an introduction of a hydroxyl group during the oxidation, since the lactone ring is not present in vitamin B_{12} itself. Using hydrogen peroxide as the oxidizing agent[14], vitamin B_{12} yields considerable quantities of oxamic acid. This has not been reported as an oxidation product of a porphyrin, but it has been obtained from oxidative degradation[134] of hydrogenated prodigiosin. Prodigiosin itself possesses[125] the structure 38, and this has been confirmed by synthesis[99].

The reactions of vitamin B_{12} with halogens have been studied by several workers[3,40,107]. With one mole of an N-chloroamide, a halogen-free compound is produced, which, although similar to the parent vitamin, possesses the properties of a lactone. Reaction with a second mole of chlorinating agent yields a purple chlorine-containing product, the shift in the absorption spectrum of which originally suggested that another double bond has been introduced into the molecule to extend the conjugated system. Further action of the N-chloroamide on vitamin B_{12} produces blue substances which contain two chlorine atoms.

The crystalline hexacarboxylic acid[31] was subjected to an x-ray crystallographic examination; it was possible from this, firstly, to show that the cyclic system surrounding the cobalt atom is a modified porphyrin (39)[25] (now termed the corrin nucleus) and subsequently to locate the positions of all the atoms (except hydrogen) in the compound[73]. The structure of the hexacarboxylic acid 40 followed from its known chemical properties. An additional ring is fused on to ring B, which from the x-ray evidence could be a lactone or a lactam; the latter was adopted since the ring is stable to alkali[14]. It was later found that vitamin B_{12} itself does not possess this lactam ring, so a hydroxyl group must be introduced into ring B, at a position activated by the adjacent $>C=N$ system, during the hydrolysis of the vitamin to the hexacarboxylic acid. The single carbon substituents revealed in the analysis of the x-ray diffraction data were formulated as methyl groups since all the oxygen and nitrogen required by the molecular formula could be accounted for in other groups. The oxidation products 34 and 35 clearly are derived from ring C. The x-ray evidence favoured a conjugated system of six double bonds, as shown in 40.

The structure of vitamin B_{12} itself was also investigated by x-ray crystallographic methods[75] and it was shown conclusively that the phosphate group is attached to position 3', not 2', of the ribose moiety, that the lactam ring attached to ring B in the hexacarboxylic acid 40 is not present, that in the vitamin the nitrile group occupies the position

(38)

(39)

(40)

occupied by the chlorine atom in **40**, and that the nucleotide occupies the position taken up by the nitrile group in **40**. All the atoms, except hydrogen, of the vitamin were located and identified in the x-ray work, and the structure **41** may now be written for cyanocobalamin. In this structure the nitrile and benzimidazole groups are on the opposite sides of the cobalt atom; the atoms of the nucleus surrounding the cobalt are almost planar and the plane of the benzimidazole ring is nearly at right angles to the plane of the nucleus. The atoms directly attached to the cobalt are arranged in an almost regular octahedron; the ribose group turns back towards a position nearly parallel with the nucleus. All the acetamide groups project towards the nitrile group and all the propionamide groups project towards the benzimidazole group. Using the chemically deduced configurations of the sugar and the propanolamine as references, it was possible also from the x-ray evidence to allot the absolute stereochemistry of the vitamin molecule.

The only doubtful feature of **41** was the number of double bonds in the nucleus, for on the x-ray evidence it was not possible to distinguish between five and six[74] double bonds. Six were preferred[75] and a further round of calculations confirmed this; such a structure would allow resonance between the canonical forms **42–45**, of which **44** is preferred. Such a structure leaves the cobalt with a unit positive charge, which is balanced by a negative charge on a phosphate oxygen to give a neutral molecule. This is in agreement with the x-ray evidence which clearly showed only the ribose and the propanolamine residues attached to the phosphate.

Chemical evidence originally suggested that additional double bonds were introduced into the vitamin B_{12} molecule by chlorination[3,40] and hence favoured five double bonds in the molecule. The deepening of colour on chlorination has now been found[15] to be due to a change in the coordination sphere and to substitution effects, and not to an increase in conjugation. Theoretical calculations on the visible and ultraviolet spectrum of the vitamin also support[94] a structure with six double bonds.

Since the rates of hydrolysis of completely β-substituted amides is greatly reduced[32,33], the structure **41** for cyanocobalamin readily explains the results of hydrolysis, for two of the acetamide groups (those on rings A and B) are completely β-substituted, and the one on ring D is partially hindered.

Dehydrovitamin B_{12} differs from vitamin B_{12} itself only in the existence of a lactam ring attached to ring B, and its part-structure is shown in **46**, the remainder being the same as **41**.

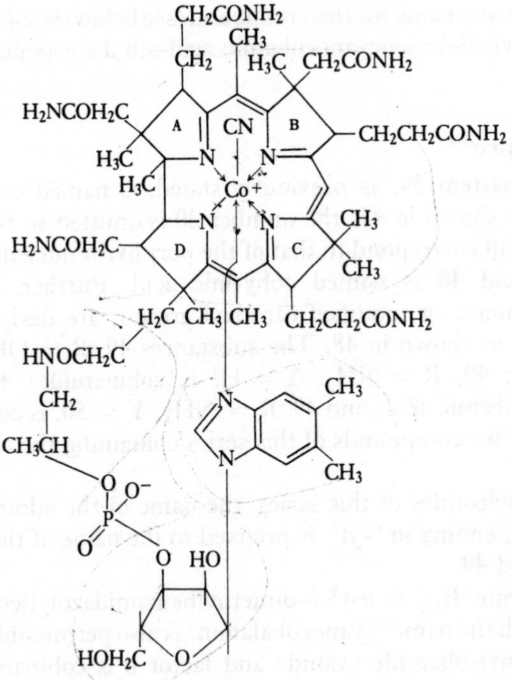

(41)

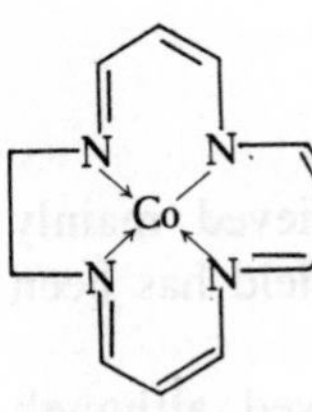

(42) 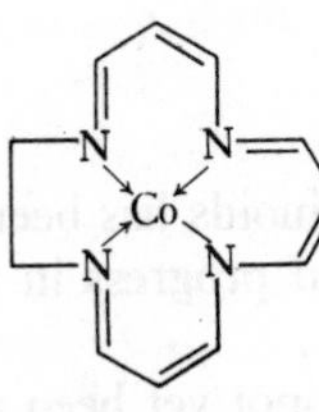   (43) 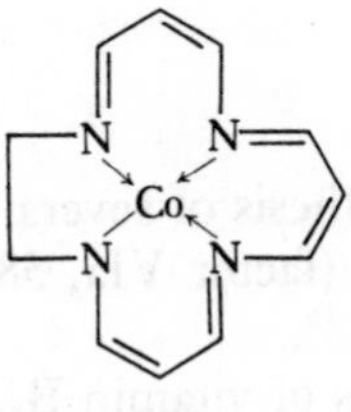   (44) 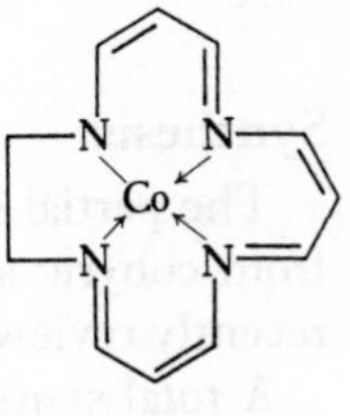   (45)

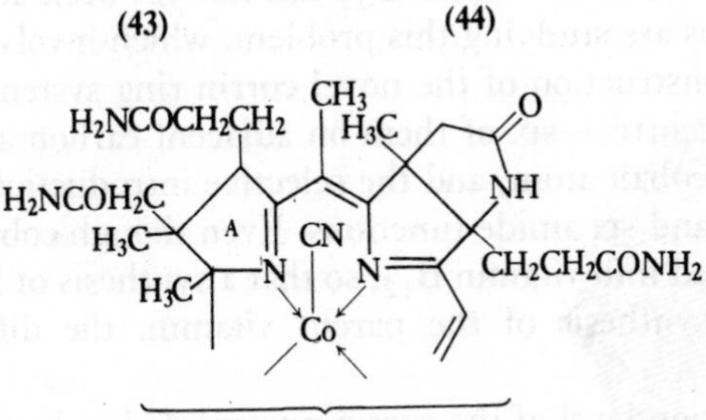

(46)

The systematic name for this compound (see below) is α-(5,6-dimethyl-benziminazoyl)-9-aminocyanocobamic acid-a,b,d,e,g-pentaamide-c-lac-tam.

Nomenclature[80]

The ring system **39**, as previously stated, is named corrin, and the numbering is shown in **47**; the number 20 is omitted so that the corrin numbering will correspond to that of the porphyrin nucleus. The hepta-carboxylic acid **48** is named cobyrinic acid. Further, the terminal —COOH groups, or modified carboxyl groups, are designated by the letters a to g as shown in **48**. The substances **49**, R = OH, Y = H, is cobinic acid; **49**, R = NH$_2$, Y = H, is cobinamide; **49**, R = OH, Y = **50**, is cobamic acid; and **49**, R = NH$_2$, Y = **50**, is cobamide. The generic name for compounds of this series containing the corrin nucleus is 'corrinoid'.

For the nucleotides of this series, the name of the additional hetero-cyclic radical, ending in '-yl', is prefixed to the name of the appropriate moiety **48** and **49**.

Thus vitamin B$_{12}$ is α-(5,6-dimethylbenzimidazolyl)cobamide cya-nide, although the name 'cyanocobalamin' is also permissible. ψ-Vitamin B$_{12}$ is α-adenylcobamide cyanide and factor B is cobinamide chloride cyanide. Vitamin B$_{12b}$ may be termed 'aquocobalamin', and vitamin B$_{12c}$ 'nitritocobalamin'.

Synthesis

The partial synthesis of several corrinoids has been achieved, mainly from cobyric acid (factor VIa, **58**), and progress in this field has been recently reviewed[13a].

A total synthesis of vitamin B$_{12}$ has not yet been achieved, although several groups are studying this problem, which involves amongst other things the construction of the novel corrin ring system containing nine asymmetric centres—six of them on adjacent carbon atoms—the intro-duction of a cobalt atom, and the selective introduction of one free car-boxyl group and six amide functions. Even though cobyric acid (**58**) has been converted into vitamin B$_{12}$, so that a synthesis of **58** becomes equi-valent to a synthesis of the parent vitamin, the difficulties are still formidable.

The oxidation level of the corrin nucleus **47** lies between the levels of pyrrolines and pyrroles, and one approach[17] to the construction of the

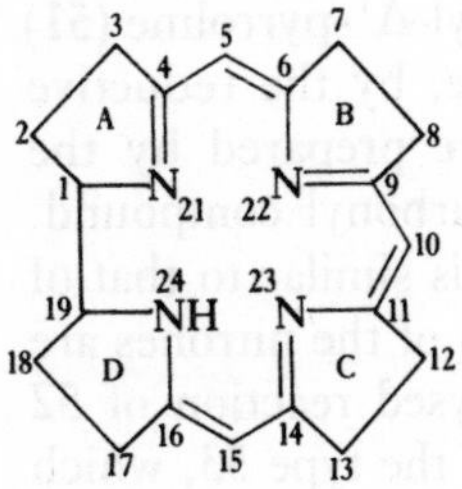

(47)

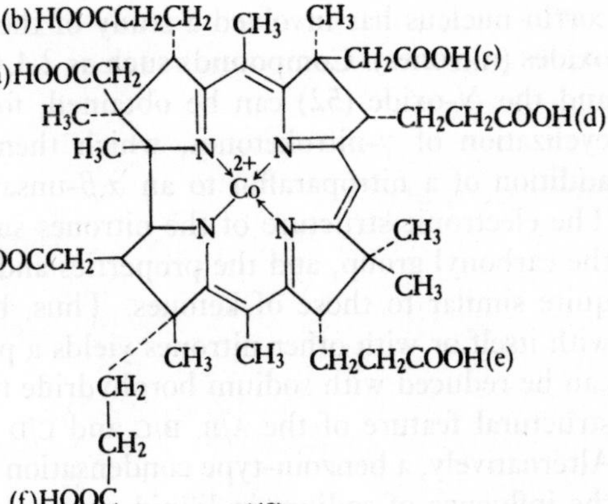

(b) $HOOCCH_2CH_2$ CH_3 CH_3
CH_2COOH (c)
(a) $HOOCCH_2$
H_3C
H_3C
CH_2CH_2COOH (d)
Co^{2+}
CH_3
CH_3
(g) $HOOCCH_2$
CH_3 CH_3 CH_2CH_2COOH (e)
CH_2
CH_2
(f) $HOOC$

(48)

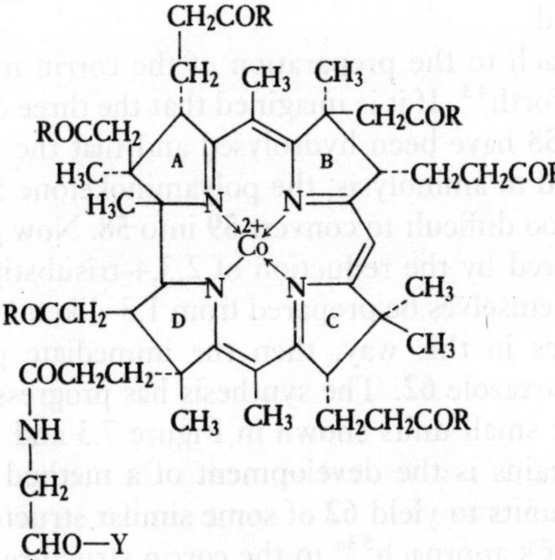

CH_2COR
CH_2 CH_3 CH_3
CH_2COR
$ROCCH_2$
H_3C
H_3C
CH_2CH_2COR
Co^{2+}
CH_3
$ROCCH_2$
CH_3
$COCH_2CH_2$
CH_3 CH_3 CH_2CH_2COR
NH
CH_2
CHO—Y
CH_3

(49)

O^-
P
O O OH
OH
$HOCH_2$

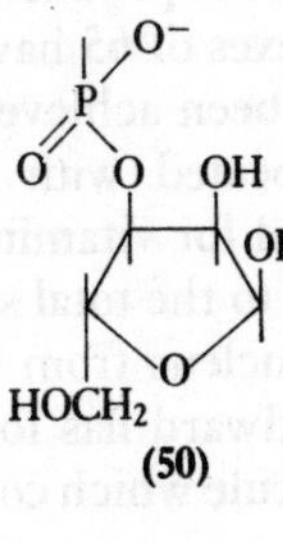

(50)

corrin nucleus has involved a study of the properties of 1-pyrroline-1-oxides (nitrones). Compounds such as 2,4,4-trimethyl-Δ^1-pyrroline (51) and the N-oxide (52) can be obtained, for example, by the reductive cyclization of γ-nitroketones, which themselves are prepared by the addition of a nitroparaffin to an α,β-unsaturated carbonyl compound. The electronic structure of the nitrones such as 52 is similar to that of the carbonyl group, and the properties and reactions of the nitrones are quite similar to those of ketones. Thus, base-catalysed reaction of 52 with itself or with other nitrones yields a product of the type 53, which can be reduced with sodium borohydride to 54 and dehydrated to 55, a structural feature of the A/B, B/C and C/D ring linkages of corrin (47). Alternatively, a benzoin-type condensation of a nitrone such as 56 under the influence of sodium in liquid ammonia yields 57, which is characteristic of the A/D ring linkage of corrin.

No further work on this method of approach to the synthesis of corrin has been published.

Another approach to the preparation of the corrin nucleus has been outlined by Cornforth[43]. If it is imagined that the three carbon–nitrogen double bonds of 58 have been hydrolysed and that the A/D ring linkage has been subjected to aminolysis, the polyaminoketone 59 would result. It should not be too difficult to convert 59 into 58. Now β-aminoketones (61) can be prepared by the reduction of 2,3,4-trisubstituted isoxazoles (60), which can themselves be prepared from 1,3-diketones. If use can be made of isoxazoles in this way, then the immediate precursor of 59 would be the triisoxazole 62. The synthesis has progressed as far as the preparation of the small units shown in Figure 7.3 and the outstanding problem that remains is the development of a method for the linking together of these units to yield 62 of some similar structure.

In Eschenmoser's approach[53a] to the corrin structure, use is made of the properties of imido esters for the formation of carbon–carbon bonds. The synthesis of the two intermediates 63 and 64 is described, but when these two were reacted together, the product was 65 and not the cyclized product 66. Some metal complexes of 65 have been prepared. Of course when the final ring closure has been achieved in this model system, the entire synthesis has to be repeated with the much more difficultly accessible intermediates required for vitamin B_{12} itself.

In Woodward's approach[130a] to the total synthesis of the vitamin, it is hoped to build up the corrin nucleus from the three components indicated schematically in 67. Woodward has focused attention on the preparation of that part of the molecule which contains the A/D ring junction,

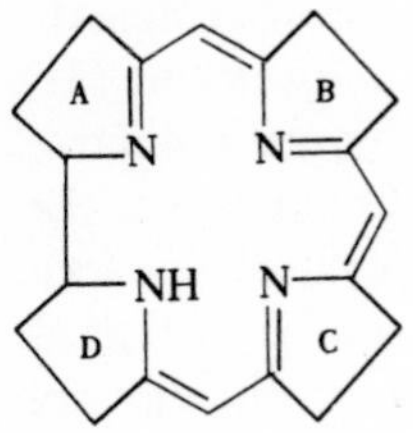

(47)

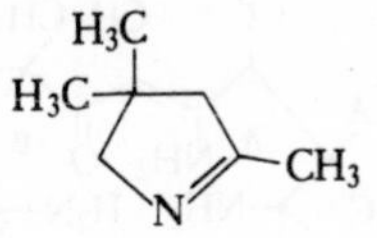

(51)

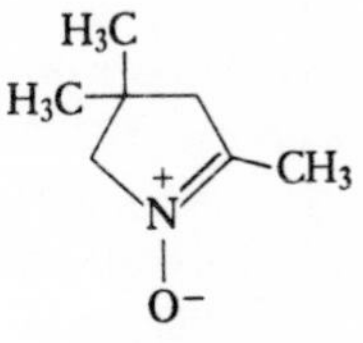

(52)

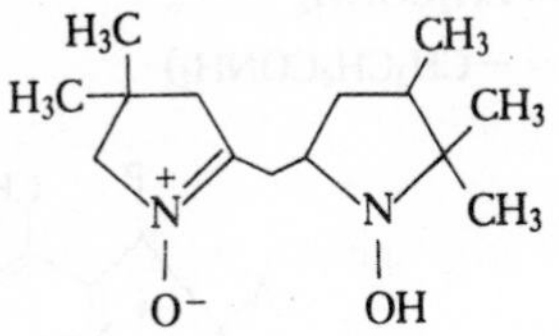

(53)

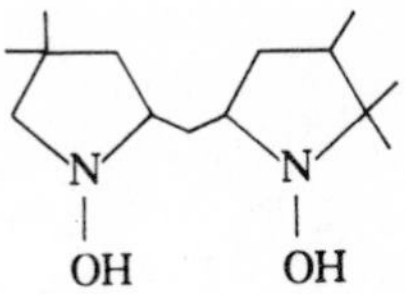

(54)

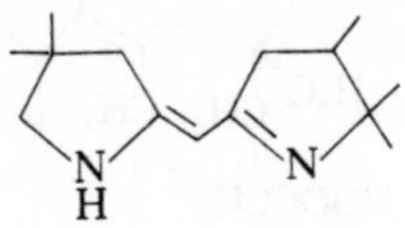

(55)

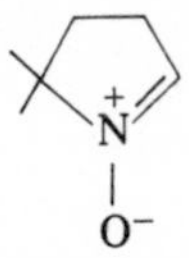

(56)

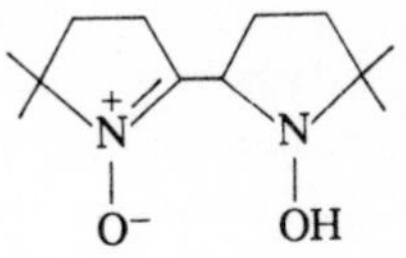

(57)

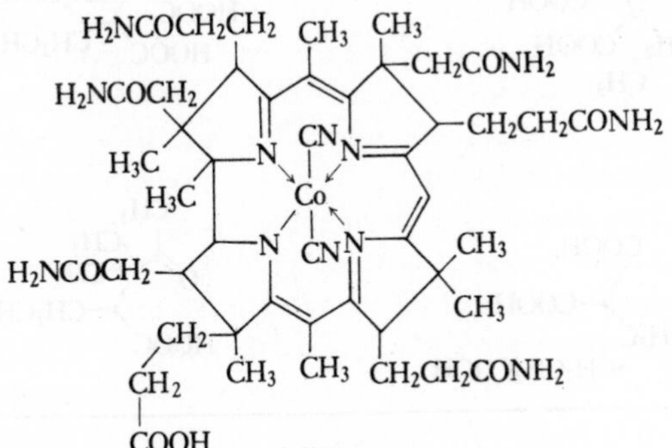

(58)

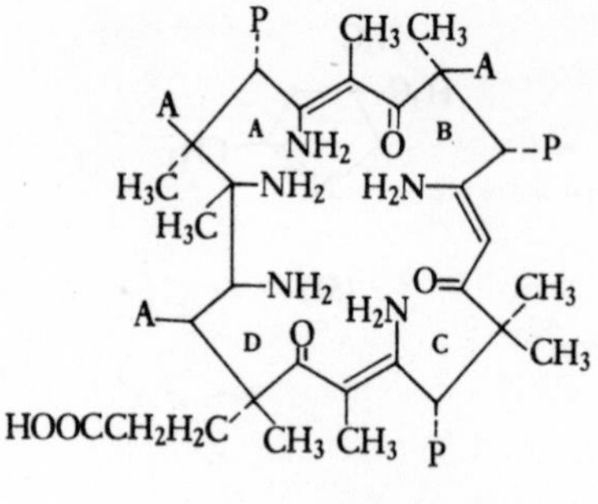

(59, A = CH₂CONH₂

P = —CH₂CH₂CONH₂)

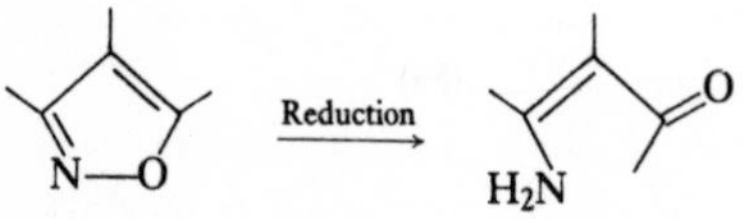

(60)   Reduction   (61)

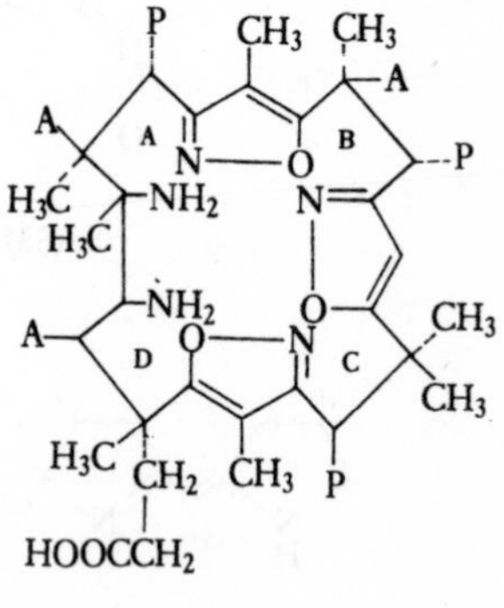

(62)

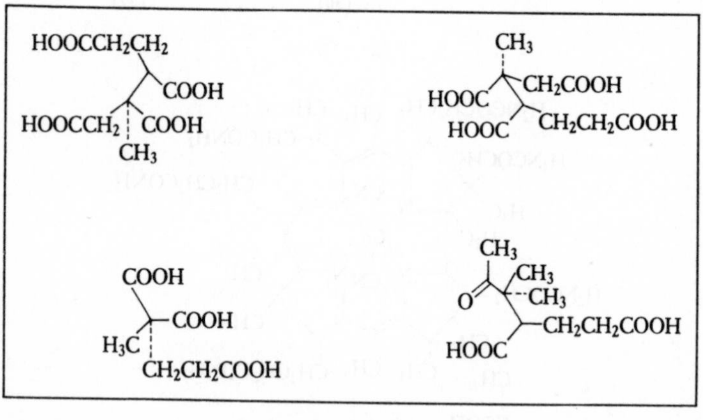

Figure 7.3.

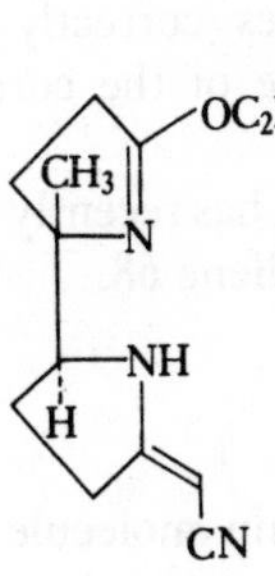

(63)

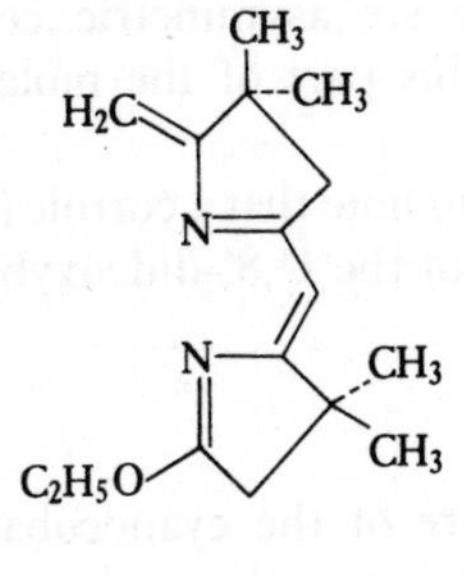

(64)

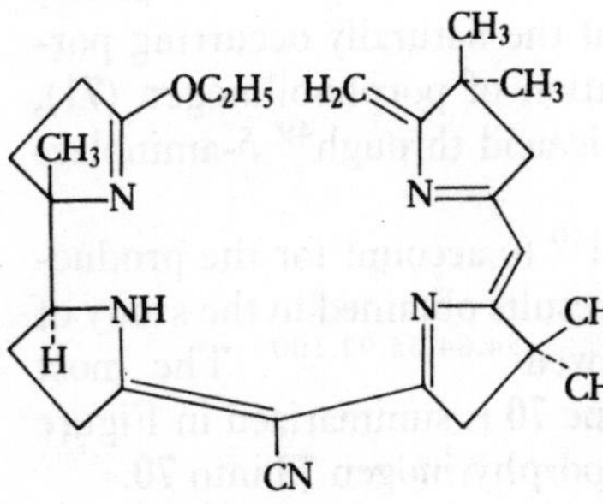

(65)

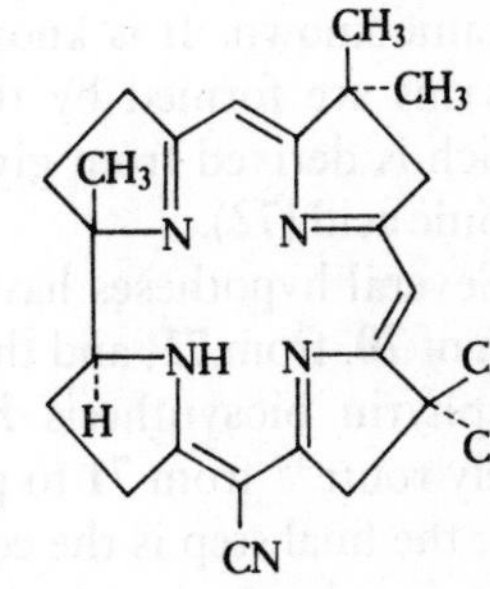

(66)

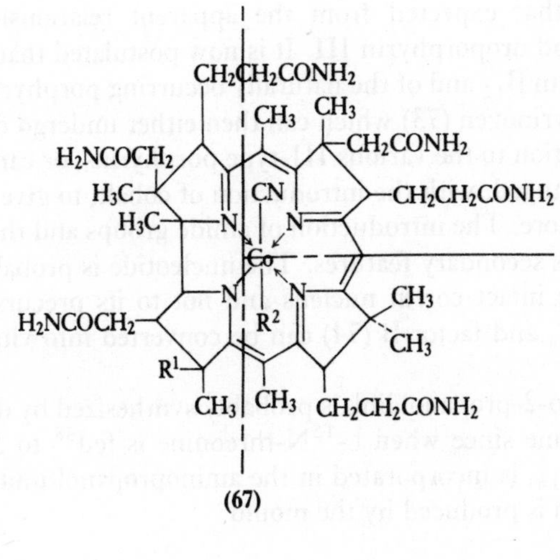

(67)

together with the six asymmetric centres correctly substituted and oriented. So far this part of the molecule of the corrin has not been obtained.

It is interesting to note that a corrole (69) has recently been obtained[83a] by the irradiation of the 1′,8′-dideoxybiladiene 68.

Biosynthesis

A notable feature of the cyanocobalamin molecule (41) is that the acetamide and propionamide residues are arranged around the nucleus in the same way as the acetic acid and propionic acid residues of uroporphyrin III (70), and a close connexion between corrin and porphyrin biosynthesis was envisaged immediately the structure of vitamin B_{12} became known. It is known[26,38,49,64] that the naturally occurring porphyrins are formed by the self-condensation of porphobilinogen (71), which is derived from glycine and succinic acid through[49] δ-aminolaevulinic acid (72).

Several hypotheses have been advanced[30] to account for the production of 70, from 71, and the experimental results obtained in the study of porphyrin biosynthesis have been reviewed[54,64,65,92,100]. The most likely route[30] from 71 to porphyrins of type 70 is summarized in Figure 7.4; the final step is the conversion of uroporphyrinogen 73 into 70.

It has been shown that $1,4\text{-}^{14}C\text{-}\delta$-aminolaevulinic acid[42,108] and radioactive porphobilinogen[126] are incorporated into vitamin B_{12}, and the distribution of radiocarbon between the amide groups and the nucleus[42] is that expected from the apparent relationship between vitamin B_{12} and uroporphyrin III. It is now postulated that the biosynthesis of vitamin B_{12} and of the naturally occurring porphyrins proceeds to a uroporphyrinogen (73) which can then either undergo decarboxylation and oxidation to the various III-type porphyrins, or can be methylated and rearranged, with the introduction of cobalt, to give the vitamin B_{12} chromophore. The introduction of amide groups and the nucleotide are regarded as secondary features. The nucleotide is probably attached directly to the intact corrin nucleus and not to its precursor, because both factor V_{1a} and factor B (74) can be converted into vitamin B_{12} *in vivo*.

The 1-amino-2-propanol link is probably synthesized by decarboxylation of threonine since when L-^{15}N-threonine is fed[88] to *Streptomyces griseus*, the $N_{(15)}$ is incorporated in the aminopropanol unit of the vitamin B_{12} which is produced by the mould.

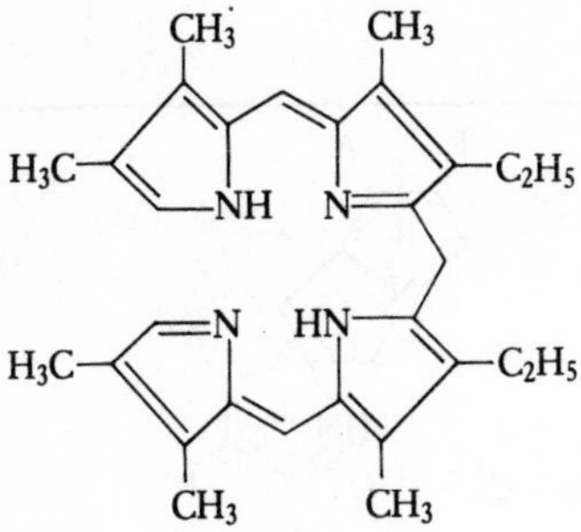

(68)

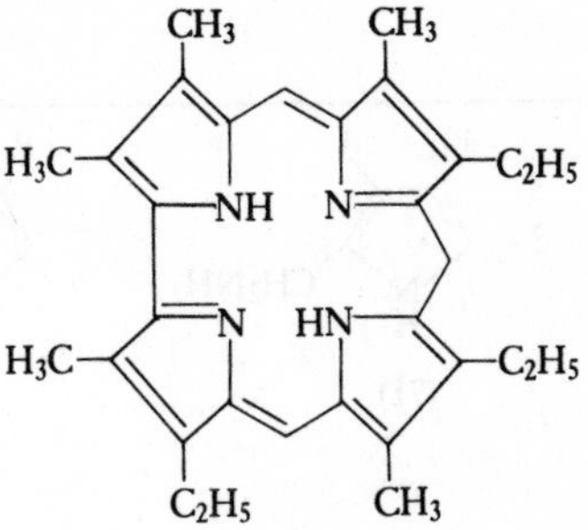

(69)

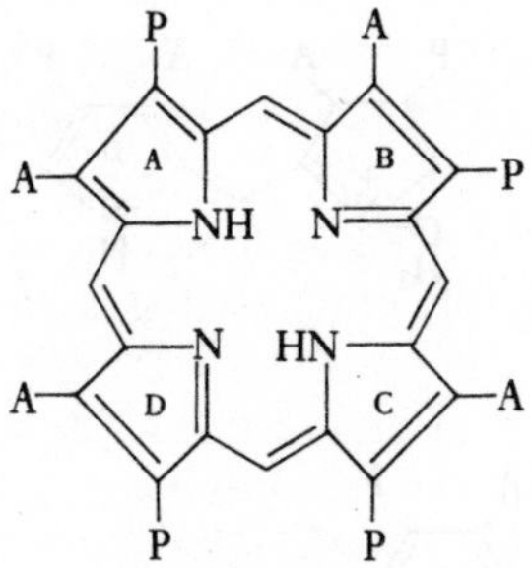

(70)

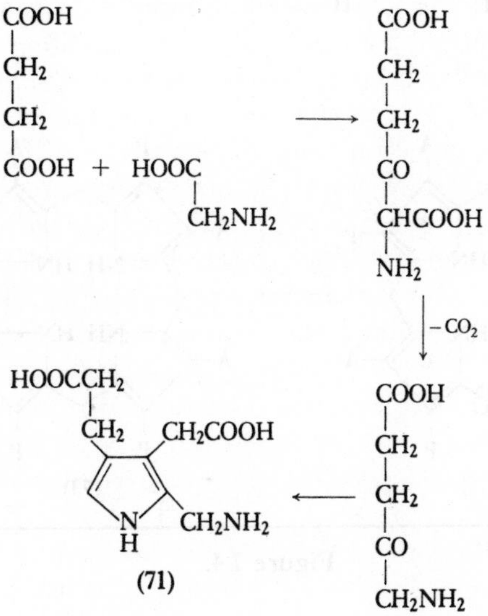

(71)

(72)

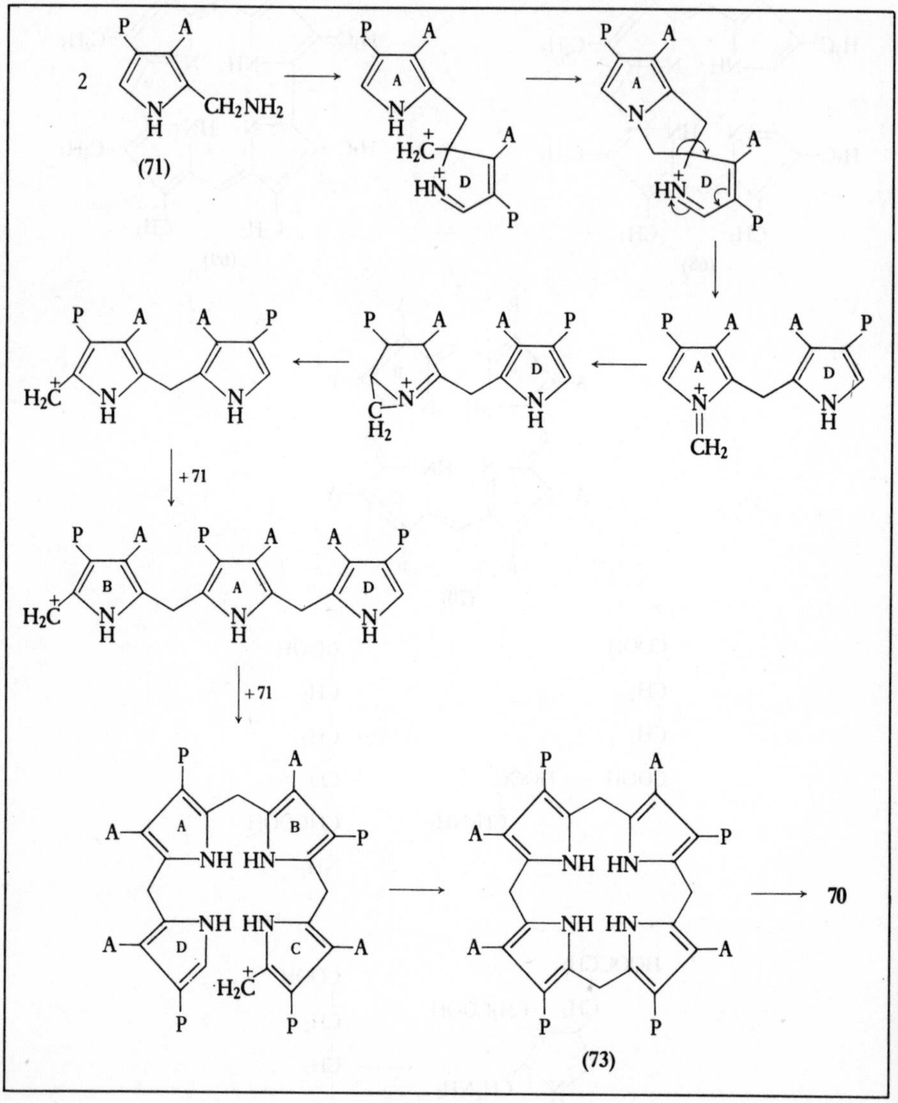

Figure 7.4.

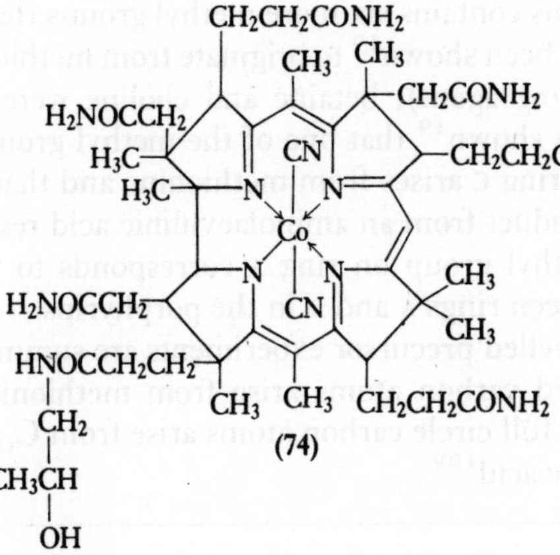

$CH_2CH_2CONH_2$

CH_3 CH_3

H_2NOCCH_2 $-CH_2CONH_2$

H_3C-

H_3C CN $-CH_2CH_2CONH_2$

Co

N   N

H_2NOCCH_2 N   N CH_3

CN CH_3

$HNOCCH_2CH_2$ CH_3 CH_3 $CH_2CH_2CONH_2$

CH_2

CH_3CH

OH

(74)

The corrin nucleus contains six more methyl groups than the porphyrins, and these have been shown[19] to originate from methionine (a known biological methylating agent); betaine and choline were not so incorporated. It was also shown[19] that one of the methyl groups of the *gem*-dimethyl group on ring C arises from methionine and that the other is a decarboxylation product from an aminolaevulinic acid residue. Further, the bridgehead methyl group on ring A corresponds to the methylene bridge carbon between rings A and D in the porphyrins.

The results of labelled precursor experiments are summarized in 75[98] in which the starred carbon atoms arise from methionine, as already mentioned, and the full circle carbon atoms arise from $C_{(1)}$ or from $C_{(4)}$ of δ-aminolaevulinic acid[109].

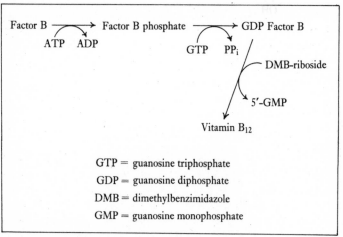

Figure 7.5. The biosynthesis of vitamin B_{12}.

Two new vitamin B_{12}-like factors have recently been described[119]. One is a guanosine-5'-pyrophosphate ester of factor B in which ribose is linked to position 9 of guanine, and the other is a guanosine-3'-phosphate ester of factor B in which ribose is linked to position 7 of guanine. It is postulated[119] that these factors are involved in the biosynthesis of vitamin B_{12} in a way indicated in Figure 7.5.

Vitamin B_{12} coenzymes

Once it was realized that vitamin B_{12}, in addition to being the antipernicious anemia factor, it also a member of the B group of vitamins, a search was made for a vitamin B_{12}-containing enzyme or coenzyme.

(75)

(76)

(77)

Such substances were first recognized as a result of a study of the enzymic conversion of glutamate into β-methylaspartate by *Clostridium tetanomorphum*[88]. The coenzyme was finally obtained as an orange solid, which could not be crystallized. The compound was found to be unstable to light, and when treated with cyanide ions the dicyano form of vitamin B_{12} was formed, adenine (76) also being detected. The coenzyme itself was found to contain an adenine and a sugar in addition to the vitamin B_{12} structure, and the cyanide grouping of cyanocobalamin was concluded to be absent from the coenzyme.

.Later, other analogues of this coenzyme containing benzimidazole, 5,6-dimethylbenzimidazole, 2,6-diaminopurine, 5(6)-methylbenzimidazole, 5(6)-trifluoromethylbenzimidazole, 5(6)-aminobenzimidazole or 5(6)-nitrobenzimidazole in place of the adenine were obtained[6,122] by growing *Clostridium tetanomorphum* or *Propionibacterium arabinosim* in the presence of the appropriate bases. The benzimidazole and the 5,6-dimethylbenzimidazole analogues were obtained in a crystalline form. The sugar obtained by cleavage of the coenzyme was identified as 77, but was thought to be an artefact[76]. This structure was confirmed by a synthesis[83] shown in 78 → 80 → 77.

The structure of the 5,6-dimethylbenzimidazole analogue of the coenzyme has been deduced[90] by x-ray crystallography. It is assumed that the natural adenine-containing coenzyme has an analogous structure and may be written as 81.

A partial synthesis of 81 has been reported recently[82a] in which aquocobalamin was first reduced with sodium borohydride and then reacted with 2′,3′-*O*-isopropylidene-5′-tosyladenosine. After removal of the protecting groups by hydrolysis and purification the product was found to be identical with the vitamin B_{12} coenzyme. Analogues of this structure in which the adenine is replaced by a wide variety of other groups were prepared by similar methods[83a].

Some chemical reactions of the coenzymes have also been studied[83] and are compatible with the structure 81.

The biological function of vitamin B_{12}

Vitamin B_{12} is an essential growth factor for some animals (and is identical with the 'animal protein factor') and also for some microorganisms. It appears to be involved in the reduction of disulphide groups and in the biosynthesis of labile methyl groups in such compounds as methionine and choline, but is probably not concerned in transmethylation reactions. Two very important functions of vitamin B_{12}-containing

$$ClCH_2-\overset{\overset{\displaystyle O}{|}}{CH}-CH_2 \xrightarrow{C_2H_2} HC{\equiv}CCH{=}CHCH_2OH$$

$$\underset{(78)}{} \qquad\qquad\qquad \underset{(79)}{}$$

$$\downarrow HCO_3H$$

$$\underset{\underset{(77)}{}}{CH_2{=}CH-\overset{\overset{\displaystyle H}{|}}{\underset{\underset{\displaystyle OH}{|}}{C}}-\overset{\overset{\displaystyle H}{|}}{\underset{\underset{\displaystyle OH}{|}}{C}}-CHO} \xleftarrow[\text{2. OH}^-]{\text{1. H}_2/\text{Pd}/\text{CaCO}_3} HC{\equiv}C-\overset{\overset{\displaystyle H}{|}}{\underset{\underset{\underset{\displaystyle OHC}{|}}{\displaystyle O}}{C}}-\overset{\overset{\displaystyle H}{|}}{\underset{\underset{\underset{\displaystyle H}{|}}{\displaystyle O}}{C}}-CH_2OH$$

$$\underset{(80)}{}$$

(81)

enzymes are the catalysis of the L-glutamic acid to L-β-methylaspartic acid[5] and the succinylcoenzyme A to methylmalonylcoenzyme A[7,50,68] rearrangements. The former has only been observed so far in microorganisms, but the latter occurs in animals as well as in microorganisms, and is an essential step in the formation and utilization of propionate.

Labelling experiments have shown that in the isomerization of glutamic acid (82), $C_{(3)}$ becomes the β-methyl group of β-methylaspartic acid (83), $C_{(4)}$ becomes the tertiary carbon atom and $C_{(5)}$ remains a carboxyl group. A carbanion mechanism 82 → 85 → 89 has been proposed[79] in which the charge of the cobalt atom helps to stabilize the carbanion. The intermediate cyclopropane derivative (86) would have to be opened by attack by the enzyme (E) followed by attack by ammonia to retain the L-configuration in the product. An objection to this mechanism is that it involves a primary carbanion.

The isomerization of methylmalonylcoenzyme A (90) to succinylcoenzyme A (91) has been shown[50] to involve the rearrangement of the thiol ester group since methylmalonyl-2-^{14}C-coenzyme A is converted into succinyl-3-^{14}C-coenzyme A, and not into succinyl-2-^{14}C-coenzyme A. A carbanion mechanism 92 → 95 has been suggested[79] for this reaction; a free-radical process 97 → 100 has also been proposed[50] (p. 145).

Analogues and antagonists[116]

Woolley[132] found that the addition of 4,5-diamino-1,2-dichlorobenzene to cultures of *Bacillus megatherium* inhibited the production of cyanocobalamin, whereas 4,5-diamino-1,2-dimethylbenzene stimulated its production. A series of analogues of diaminodimethylbenzene were synthesized[131,133] and tested; the results have been summarized by Jukes and Williams[84].

The three crystalline monocarboxylic acids which may be obtained by hydrolysis of vitamin B_{12} can be converted into substituted amides by reaction with amines (or amino acids). Some of these compounds (for example that derived from phenylethylamine) show antivitamin B_{12} activity.

BIBLIOGRAPHY

1. Alicino, J. F., *J. Am. Chem. Soc.*, 73, 4051 (1951).
2. Anslow, K. W., S. Ball, W. B. Emery, K. H. Fantes, E. L. Smith and A. D. Walker, *Chem. Ind. (London)*, 574 (1950); 939 (1951).

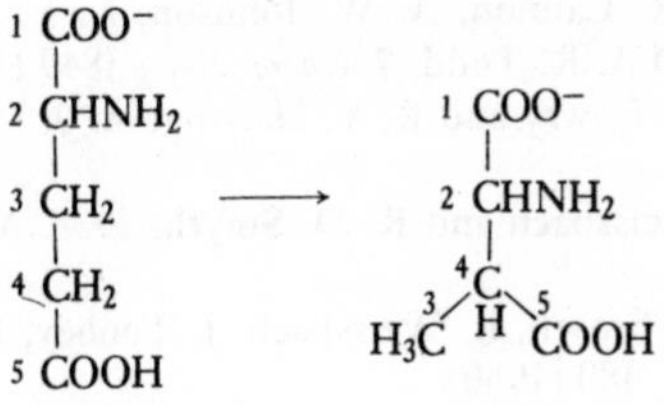

$$
\begin{array}{c}
\text{1 COO}^- \\
| \\
\text{2 CHNH}_2 \\
| \\
\text{3 CH}_2 \\
| \\
\text{4 CH}_2 \\
| \\
\text{5 COOH} \\
(82)
\end{array}
\longrightarrow
\begin{array}{c}
\text{1 COO}^- \\
| \\
\text{2 CHNH}_2 \\
| \\
\text{4C} \\
\text{H}_3\text{C}^3 \quad \text{H}^5\text{COOH} \\
(83)
\end{array}
$$

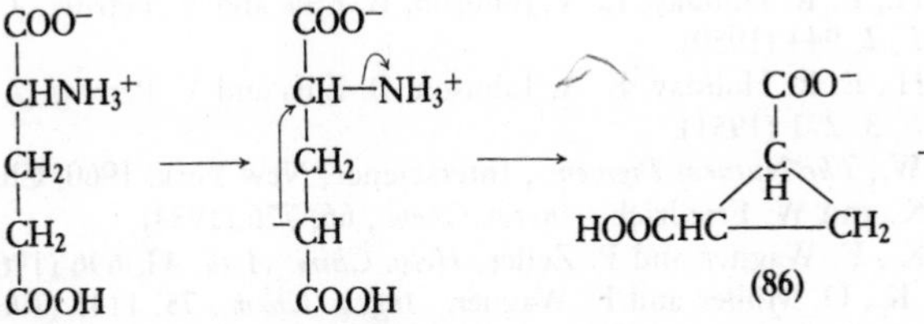

$$
\begin{array}{c}
\text{COO}^- \\
| \\
\text{CHNH}_3^+ \\
| \\
\text{CH}_2 \\
| \\
\text{CH}_2 \\
| \\
\text{COOH} \\
(82)
\end{array}
\longrightarrow
\begin{array}{c}
\text{COO}^- \\
| \\
\text{CH} \quad \text{NH}_3^+ \\
| \\
\text{CH}_2 \\
| \\
^-\text{CH} \\
| \\
\text{COOH} \\
(85)
\end{array}
\longrightarrow
\begin{array}{c}
\text{COO}^- \\
| \\
\text{C} \\
\text{H} \\
\text{HOOCHC}\text{———}\text{CH}_2 \\
(86)
\end{array}
+ \text{NH}_3
$$

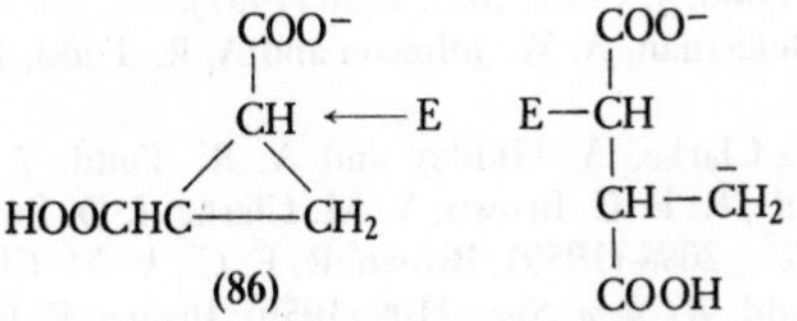

$$
\begin{array}{c}
\text{COO}^- \\
| \\
\text{CH} \quad \longleftarrow \text{E} \\
\text{HOOCHC}\text{———}\text{CH}_2 \\
(86)
\end{array}
\qquad
\begin{array}{c}
\text{COO}^- \\
| \\
\text{E—CH} \\
| \\
\text{CH—CH}_2 \\
| \\
\text{COOH} \\
(87)
\end{array}
$$

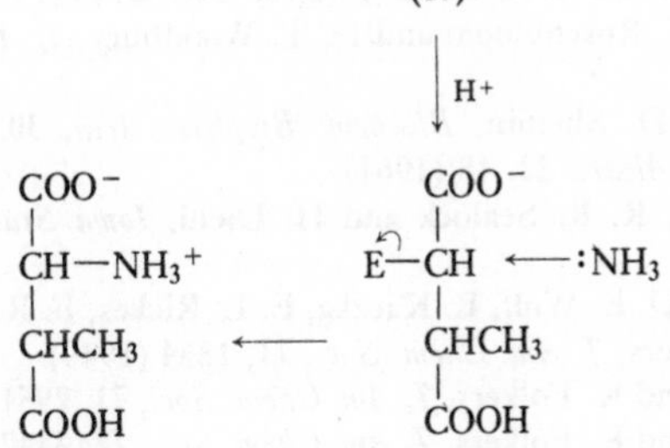

$$
\Big\downarrow \text{H}^+
$$

$$
\begin{array}{c}
\text{COO}^- \\
| \\
\text{CH—NH}_3^+ \\
| \\
\text{CHCH}_3 \\
| \\
\text{COOH} \\
(89)
\end{array}
\longleftarrow
\begin{array}{c}
\text{COO}^- \\
| \\
\text{E—CH} \quad \longleftarrow :\text{NH}_3 \\
| \\
\text{CHCH}_3 \\
| \\
\text{COOH} \\
(88)
\end{array}
$$

$$
\begin{array}{c}
\text{CO—SCoA} \\
| \\
\text{H}_3\text{C—}\overset{*}{\text{C}}\text{HCOOH} \\
(90)
\end{array}
\qquad
\begin{array}{c}
\text{CO—SCoA} \\
| \\
\overset{*}{\text{C}}\text{H}_2\text{CH}_2\text{COOH} \\
(91)
\end{array}
$$

144   THE CHEMISTRY OF THE VITAMINS

3. Armitage, J. B., J. R. Cannon, A. W. Johnson, L. F. J. Parker, E. L. Smith, W. H. Stafford and A. R. Todd, *J. Chem. Soc.*, 3849 (1953).

4. Baldwin, R. R., J. R. Lowry and R. V. Harrington, *J. Am. Chem. Soc.*, 73, 4968 (1951).

5. Barker, H. A., H. Weissbach and R. D. Smyth, *Proc. Nat. Acad. Sci. U.S.*, 44, 1093 (1958).

6. Barker, H. A., R. D. Smyth, R. Weissbach, J. Toohey, Ladd and B. E. Volcani, *J. Biol. Chem.*, 235, 480 (1960).

7. Beck, W. S. and S. Ochoa, *J. Biol. Chem.*, 232, 931 (1958).

8. Beaven, G. H., E. R. Holiday, E. A. Johnson, B. Ellis, P. Mamalis, V. Petrow and B. Sturgeon, *J. Pharm. Pharmacol.*, 1, 957 (1949).

9. Beaven, G. H., E. R. Holiday, E. A. Johnson, B. Ellis and V. Petrow, *J. Pharm. Pharmacol.*, 2, 944 (1950).

10. Beaven, G. H., E. R. Holiday, E. A. Johnson, B. Ellis and V. Petrow, *J. Pharm. Pharmacol.*, 3, 271 (1951).

11. Bentley, K. W., *The Natural Pigments*, Interscience, New York, 1960, Chap. 6.

12. Bernhauer, K. and W. Friedrich, *Angew. Chem.*, 66, 776 (1954).

13. Bernhauer, K., F. Wagner and P. Zeller, *Helv. Chim. Acta*, 43, 696 (1960).

13a. Bernhauer, K., O. Müller and F. Wagner, *Angew. Chem.*, 75, 1145 (1963).

14. Bonnett, R., J. R. Cannon, A. W. Johnson, I. O. Sutherland, A. R. Todd and E. L. Smith, *Nature*, 176, 328 (1955).

15. Bonnett, R., J. R. Cannon, V. M. Clarke, A. W. Johnson, F. J. Parker, E. L. Smith and A. R. Todd, *J. Chem. Soc.*, 1158 (1957).

16. Bonnett, R., J. G. Buchanan, A. W. Johnson and A. R. Todd, *J. Chem. Soc.*, 1168 (1957).

17. Bonnett, R., V. M. Clarke, A. Giddey and A. R. Todd, *J. Chem. Soc.*, 2087 (1959); Bonnett, R., R. F. C. Brown, V. M. Clarke, I. O. Sutherland and A. R. Todd, *J. Chem. Soc.*, 2094 (1959); Brown, R. F. C., V. M. Clarke, I. O. Sutherland and A. R. Todd, *J. Chem. Soc.*, 2109 (1959); Brown, R. F. C., V. M. Clarke, M. Lamchen and A. R. Todd, *J. Chem. Soc.*, 2116 (1959).

18. Boos, R. N., C. Rosenbloom and D. T. Woodbury, *J. Am. Chem. Soc.*, 73, 5446 (1951).

19. Bray, R. and D. Shemin, *Biochem. Biophys. Acta*, 30, 647 (1959); Bray, R., *Dissertation Abstr.*, 22, 48 (1961).

20. Brierly, J. M., R. R. Sealock and H. Diehl, *Iowa State Coll. J. Sci.*, 29, 141 (1954).

21. Brink, N. G., D. E. Wolf, E. Kaczka, E. L. Rickes, F. R. Koninszy, T. R. Wood and K. Folkers, *J. Am. Chem. Soc.*, 71, 1854 (1949).

22. Brink, N. G. and K. Folkers, *J. Am. Chem. Soc.*, 71, 2951 (1949).

23. Brink, N. G. and K. Folkers, *J. Am. Chem. Soc.*, 72, 4442 (1950).

24. Brink, N. G., F. A. Kuehl and K. Folkers, *Science*, 112, 354 (1950).

25. Brink, C., D. C. Hodgkin, J. Lindsay, J. Pickworth, J. H. Robertson and J. G. White, *Nature*, 174, 1169 (1954).

26. Brockman, P. E. and C. H. Gray, *Biochem. J.*, 54, 22 (1953).

27. Brown, D. M. and A. R. Todd, *J. Chem. Soc.*, 52 (1952).

28. Brown, D. M., D. I. Magrath and A. R. Todd, *J. Chem. Soc.*, 4396 (1955).

29. Buchanan, J. G., A. W. Johnson, J. A. Mills and A. R. Todd, *J. Chem. Soc.*, 2845 (1950).

$$
\begin{array}{c}
\text{COO}^- \\
| \\
\text{CH}_2 \\
| \\
\text{CH}_2 \\
| \\
\text{COS—CoA} \\
\textbf{(92)}
\end{array}
\longrightarrow
\begin{array}{c}
\text{COO}^- \\
| \\
-\text{CH} \\
| \\
\text{CH}_2 \\
\diagdown \\
\text{C} \\
\diagup \diagdown \\
\text{O} \quad \text{SCoA} \\
\textbf{(93)}
\end{array}
\longrightarrow
\begin{array}{c}
\text{COO}^- \\
| \\
\text{CH} \\
\diagup \diagdown \\
\text{CH}_2 \\
| \\
\text{C} \\
\diagup \diagdown \\
-\text{O} \quad \text{SCoA} \\
\textbf{(94)}
\end{array}
$$

$$
\begin{array}{c}
\text{COO}^- \\
| \\
\text{CHCH}_3 \\
| \\
\text{COS—CoA} \\
\textbf{(96)}
\end{array}
\longleftarrow
\begin{array}{c}
\text{COO}^- \\
| \\
\text{CH—CH}_2{}^- \\
| \\
\text{COS—CoA} \\
\textbf{(95)}
\end{array}
$$

$$
\begin{array}{c}
\text{COOH} \\
| \\
\text{CHCH}_3 \\
| \\
\text{COS—CoA} \\
\textbf{(97)}
\end{array}
\xrightarrow{\text{Co}^{3+}}
\begin{array}{c}
\text{COOH} \\
| \\
\text{CH\.{C}H}_2 \\
| \\
\text{COS—CoA} \\
\textbf{(98)}
\end{array}
+ \text{H}^+ + \text{Co}^{2+}
$$

$$
\begin{array}{c}
\text{COOH} \\
| \\
\text{CH}_2 \\
| \\
\text{CH}_2 \\
| \\
\text{COS—CoA} \\
\textbf{(100)}
\end{array}
\xleftarrow[\text{H}^+]{\text{Co}^{2+}}
\begin{array}{c}
\text{COOH} \\
| \\
\text{\.{C}H—CH}_2 \\
| \\
\text{COS—CoA} \\
\textbf{(99)}
\end{array}
$$

30. Bullock, E., A. W. Johnson, E. Markham and K. B. Shaw, *J. Chem. Soc.*, 1430 (1958); *Nature*, 185, 607 (1960).
31. Cannon, J. R., A. W. Johnson and A. R. Todd, *Nature*, 174, 1168 (1954).
32. Cason, J. and H. J. Wolfhager, *J. Org. Chem.*, 14, 155 (1949).
33. Cason, J., C. Gastaldo, D. L. Glusker, J. Allinger and L. B. Ash, *J. Org. Chem.*, 18, 1129 (1953).
34. Castle, W. B., *Am. J. Med. Sci.*, 178, 748 (1929).
35. Castle, W. B., *New Engl. J. Med.*, 249, 603 (1953).
36. Chargaff, E., C. Levine, C. Green and J. Kveam, *Experientia*, 6, 229 (1950).
▶37. Conn, J. B., S. L. Norman and T. G. Wartman, *Science*, 113, 658 (1951).
38. Cookson, G. H. and C. Rimington, *Nature*, 171, 875 (1953).
39. Cookson, G. H. and C. Rimington, *Biochem. J.*, 57, 476 (1954).
40. Cooley, G., B. Ellis, V. Petrow, G. H. Beaven, E. R. Holiday and E. A. Johnson, *J. Pharm. Pharmacol.*, 3, 271 (1951).
41. Cooley, G., M. T. Davies, B. Ellis, V. Petrow and B. Sturgeon, *J. Pharm. Pharmacol.*, 5, 257 (1953).
42. Corcoran, J. W. and D. Shemin, *Biochem. Biophys. Acta*, 25, 661 (1957).
43. Cornforth, J. W., *Symp. Nitrogen Heterocyclic Chem.*, Hatfield, England, 1962.
44. Corwin, A. H. in *Organic Chemistry* (Ed. by H. Gilman), Vol. II, 2nd ed., Wiley, New York, 1943, p. 1260.
★45. Delling, H. and K. Bernhauer, *Arch. Biochem. Biophys.*, 69, 74 (1957).
46. Diehl, H., R. W. Vander Haar and R. R. Sealock, *J. Am. Chem. Soc.*, 72, 5312 (1950).
47. Diehl, H., J. I. Morrison and R. R. Sealock, *Experientia*, 7, 60 (1951).
48. Dion, H. W., D. G. Calkins and J. J. Pfiffner, *J. Am. Chem. Soc.*, 74, 1108 (1952).
49. Dresel, E. I. B. and J. E. Falk, *Nature*, 172, 1185 (1953).
▾50. Eggerer, H., P. Overath, F. Lynen and E. R. Stadtman, *J. Am. Chem. Soc.*, 82, 2643 (1960); *Biochem. Z.*, 333, 1 (1960).
51. Ellis, B., V. Petrow and G. F. Snook, *J. Pharm. Pharmacol.*, 1, 60 (1949).
52. Ellis, B., V. Petrow, G. H. Beaven, E. R. Holiday and E. A. Johnson, *J. Pharm. Pharmacol.*, 2, 735 (1950).
53. Ellis, B. and V. Petrow, *J. Pharm. Pharmacol.*, 4, 152 (1952).
53a. Eschenmoser, A., Congress Lectures, *XIXth Intern. Congr. Pure Applied Chem.*, London, 1963, Butterworth, London, 1963, p. 297.
54. Falk, J. A. and C. Remington, *Ann. Rep. Progr. Chem.* (*Chem. Soc. London*), 47, 280 (1950).
55. Fantes, K. H., J. E. Page, L. F. J. Parker and E. L. Smith, *Proc. Roy. Soc. Ser. B*, 136, 592 (1949).
56. Fantes, K. H. and C. H. O'Callaghan, *Biochem. J.*, 59, 79 (1955).
57. Ford, J. E. and J. W. G. Porter, *Biochem. J.*, 51, V (1952).
58. Ford, J. E. and J. W. G. Porter, *Brit. J. Nutr.*, 7, 326 (1953).
★59. Ford, J. E., E. S. Holdsmith and S. K. Kon, *Biochem. J.*, 59, 86 (1955).
60. Friedrich, W. and K. Bernhauer, *Ber.*, 89, 2030 (1956).
61. Friedrich, W. and K. Bernhauer, *Ber.*, 89, 2507 (1956).
62. Friedrich, W., G. Cross, K. Bernhauer and P. Zeller, *Helv. Chim. Acta*, 43, 704 (1960).
63. Garkers, C. F., H. Schmid and P. Karrer, *Helv. Chim. Acta*, 38, 1490 (1955).

64. Gibson, K. D., M. Mathew, A. Neuberger and G. H. Tait, *Nature*, **192**, 204 (1961).
65. Goodwin, T. W., *Recent Advances in Biochemistry*, Churchill, London, 1960, p. 166.
66. Grun, F. and R. Menasse, *Experientia*, **6**, 263 (1950).
67. Harris, R. S., G. F. Marrian and K. V. Thimann, *Vitamins Hormones*, **12**, 1 (1954).
68. Hegre, C. S., S. J. Miller and M. D. Lane, *Biochem. Biophys. Acta*, **56**, 538 (1962).
69. Heinrich, H. C., *Vitamin B$_{12}$ and Intrinsic Factor*, Enke, Stuttgart, 1957.
70. Heyl, D., E. C. Chase, C. H. Shunk, M. V. Moore, G. A. Emerson and K. Folkers, *J. Am. Chem. Soc.*, **76**, 1355 (1954).
71. Hodgkin, D. C., M. W. Porter and R. C. Spiller, *Proc. Roy. Soc. (London), Ser. B*, **136**, 609 (1949).
72. Hodgkin, D. C., A. W. Johnson and A. R. Todd, *Chem. Soc. (London), Spec. Publ.*, No. 3, 109 (1955).
73. Hodgkin, D. C., J. Kanyor, J. Lindsay, M. Mackay, J. Pickworth, J. H. Robertson, C. B. Shoemaker, J. G. White, R. J. Prosen and K. N. Trueblood, *Nature*, **176**, 325 (1955).
74. Hodgkin, D. C., J. Kamper, M. Mackay, J. Pickworth, K. N. Trueblood and J. G. White, *Nature*, **178**, 64 (1956).
75. Hodgkin, D. C., J. Kamper, J. Lindsay, M. Mackay, J. Pickworth, J. H. Prosen and K. N. Trueblood, *Proc. Roy. Soc. (London), Ser. A*, **242**, 228 (1957); *Fortschr. Chem. Org. Naturstoffe*, **15**, 167 (1958).
76. Hogenkamp, H. P. C. and H. A. Barker, *J. Biol. Chem.*, **236**, 3097 (1961).
77. Holly, F. W., C. H. Shunk, E. W. Peel, J. J. Cahill and K. Folkers, *J. Am. Chem. Soc.*, **72**, 1866 (1950).
78. Holly, F. W., C. H. Shunk, E. W. Peel, J. Cahill, J. B. Lavigne and K. Folkers, *J. Am. Chem. Soc.*, **74**, 4521 (1952).
79. Ingraham, L. L., *Biochemical Mechanisms*, Wiley, New York, 1962.
80. IUPAC, Commission on the Nomenclature of Biological Chemistry, *J. Am. Chem. Soc.*, **82**, 5575 (1960).
81. Johnson, A. W., *Sci. Progr. (London)*, **38**, 97 (1950); **44**, 81 (1956).
82. Johnson, A. W., G. W. Miller, J. A. Mills and A. R. Todd, *J. Chem. Soc.*, 3061 (1953).
82a. Johnson, A. W., L. Mervyn, N. Shaw and E. L. Smith, *J. Chem. Soc.*, 4146 (1963).
83. Johnson, A. W. and N. Shaw, *J. Chem. Soc.*, 4608 (1962).
83a. Johnson, A. W. and I. T. Kay, *Proc. Chem. Soc.*, 89 (1964).
84. Jukes, T. H. and W. L. Williams in *The Vitamins: Chemistry, Physiology and Pathology*, Vol. I (Ed. by W. H. Sebrell and R. S. Harris), Academic Press, New York, 1954, p. 488.
85. Kaczka, E., D. E. Wolf and K. Folkers, *J. Am. Chem. Soc.*, **71**, 1514 (1949).
86. Kaczka, E., D. E. Wolf, F. A. Kuehl and K. Folkers, *J. Am. Chem. Soc.*, **73**, 3569 (1951).
87. Kaczka, E. A., D. Heyl, W. H. Jones and K. Folkers, *J. Am. Chem. Soc.*, **74**, 5549 (1952).
88. Krasna, A. I., C. Rosenbloom and D. B. Sprinson, *J. Biol. Chem.*, **225**, 745 (1957).
89. Kuehl, F. A., C. H. Shunk and K. Folkers, *J. Am. Chem. Soc.*, **77**, 251 (1955).
90. Lenhart, P. G. and D. C. Hodgkin, *Nature*, **192**, 937 (1961).

148   THE CHEMISTRY OF THE VITAMINS

91. MacDonald, S. F. and R. J. Stedman, *Can. J. Chem.*, **32**, 896 (1954).
92. Maitland, P., *Quart. Rev. (London)*, **4**, 45 (1950).
93. Minot, G. R. and W. P. Murphy, *J. Am. Med. Assoc.*, **87**, 470 (1926).
94. Orgel, L. E. in a private communication quoted by Hodgkin in ref. 75.
95. Pfiffner, J. J., D. G. Calkins and H. W. Dion, *Fed. Proc.*, **13**, 274 (1954); **90**, 465 (1957).
96. Pierce, J. V., A. C. Page, E. L. R. Stokstad and T. H. Jukes, *J. Am. Chem. Soc.*, **71**, 2952 (1949).
97. Pierce, J. V., A. C. Page, E. L. R. Stokstad and T. H. Jukes, *J. Am. Chem. Soc.*, **72**, 2615 (1950).
98. Plaut, G. W. E., *Ann. Rev. Biochem.*, **30**, 409 (1961).
99. Rapoport, H. and K. G. Holden, *J. Am. Chem. Soc.*, **84**, 635 (1962).
100. Remington, C., *Ann. Rep. Progr. Chem. (Chem. Soc., London)*, **51**, 312 (1954).
101. Rickes, E. L., N. G. Brink, F. R. Koninszy, T. R. Wood and K. Folkers, *Science*, **107**, 396 (1948).
102. Rickes, E. L., N. G. Brink, F. R. Koninszy, T. R. Wood and K. Folkers, *Science*, **108**, 634 (1948).
103. Robinson, F. M., I. M. Miller, J. F. McPherson and K. Folkers, *J. Am. Chem. Soc.*, **77**, 5192 (1955).
104. Sebrell, W. H. and R. S. Harris, *The Vitamins: Chemistry, Physiology and Pathology*, Vol. I, Academic Press, New York, 1954, p. 395.
105. *2nd European Symp. Vitamin B₁₂ and Intrinsic Factor, Hamburg, 1961*, Enke, Stuttgardt, 1962.
106. Schindler, O., *Helv. Chim. Acta*, **34**, 101 (1951).
107. Schmid, H., A. Ebnother and P. Karrer, *Helv. Chim. Acta*, **36**, 65 (1953).
108. Shemin, D., J. W. Corcoran, C. Rosenbloom and I. M. Miller, *Science*, **124**, 272 (1956).
109. Shemin, D., J. W. Corcoran, C. Rosenbloom and I. M. Miller, *Science*, **124**, 272 (1956); Corcoran, J. W. and D. Shemin, *Biochem. Biophys. Acta*, **25**, 661 (1957).
110. Shunk, C. H., F. M. Robinson, J. F. McPherson, M. M. Gasser and K. Folkers, *J. Am. Chem. Soc.*, **78**, 3228 (1956).
111. Smith, E. L. and L. F. J. Parker, *Biochem. J.*, **43**, viii (1948).
112. Smith, E. L., *Nature*, **161**, 638 (1948).
113. Smith, E. L., K. H. Fantes, S. Ball, J. G. Walker, W. B. Emery, W. K. Anslow and A. D. Walker, *Biochem. J.*, **52**, 389 (1952).
114. Smith, E. L., *Biochem. J.*, **56**, xxxiv (1954).
115. Smith, E. L., *Biochem. Soc. Symp. Vitamin B₁₂, Cambridge*, 1955.
116. Smith, E. L., *Vitamin B₁₂*, Methuen, London, 1960.
117. Stern, A. and H. Wenderlein, *Z. Physik. Chem. (Leipzig)*, **A175**, 405 (1936); A. Stern and F. Pruckner, *Z. Physik. Chem. (Leipzig)*, **A180**, 321 (1937).
118. Stevens, T. S., in *Chemistry of Carbon Compounds* (Ed. by E. H. Rodd), Vol. IV^B, Elsevier, Amsterdam, 1959, p. 1119.
119. Stokstad, E. L. R., *Ann. Rev. Biochem.*, **31**, 451 (1962).
120. SubbaRow, Y., A. B. Hastings and M. Elkin, *Vitamins Hormones*, **3**, 237 (1948).
121. Todd, A. R., *Vitamin B₁₂, Osterr. Chemiker-Zeitung*, **58**, 113 (1957).
122. Toohey, J., D. Perlman and H. A. Barker, *J. Biol. Chem.*, **236**, 2119 (1961).
123. Vickery, H. B., *J. Biol. Chem.*, **169**, 237 (1947).
124. Wallmann, J. C., B. B. Cunningham and M. Calvin, *Science*, **113**, 55 (1951).

125. Wasserman, H., J. E. McKeon, L. Smith and P. Forgione, *J. Am. Chem. Soc.*, 82, 506 (1960).

126. Watson, C. J., *Arch. Internal Med.*, 99, 323 (1957).

127. Weissbach, H., J. Toohey and H. A. Barker, *Proc. Nat. Acad. Sci. U.S.*, 45, 521 (1959).

128. Wijmenga, H. G., W. L. C. Veer and J. Lens, *Biochem. Biophys. Acta*, 6, 229 (1950).

129. Williams, R. T., *Biochem. Soc. Symp. Vitamin B$_{12}$, Cambridge, 1955*, No. 13.

130. Wolf, D. E., W. H. Jones, J. Valient and K. Folkers, *J. Am. Chem. Soc.*, 72, 2820 (1950).

130a. Woodward, R. B., *Chem. Soc. Anniversary Meeting, Birmingham, 1964*.

131. Woolley, D. W. and A. Pringle, *Federation Proc.*, 10, 272 (1951).

132. Woolley, D. W., *Proc. Soc. Exp. Biol. Med.*, 75, 745 (1950); *J. Exp. Med.*, 93, 13 (1951).

133. Woolley, D. W. and A. Pringle, *J. Biol. Chem.*, 194, 729 (1952).

134. Wrede, F. and A. Rothaas, *Z. Physiol. Chem.*, 215, 75; 219, 267 (1933).

135. Wright, J. B., *Chem. Rev.*, 48, 397 (1951).

CHAPTER 8

Pantothenic Acid (Vitamin B₃)

PANTOTHENIC ACID – Detection and isolation – Occurrence – Deficiency
disease – Daily requirement – Properties – Structure – Synthesis –
Biosynthesis – Biological function – Analogues of pantothenic acid –
BIBLIOGRAPHY

Detection and isolation

DURING the early work on thiamine it was noted that an additional factor was present in the extracts being studied which was necessary for the proper growth and health of pigeons. Later, a growth factor for yeast was detected[22] which was called pantothenic acid, or filtrate factor (since it remained in the filtrate after removal of pyridoxine from yeast or liver extracts with Fuller's earth). At about the same time evidence was obtained[5,6] for the existence of a chicken antidermatitis factor. It was subsequently shown that the chicken factor[11,27] and a lactic acid bacteria factor[17] were both identical with pantothenic acid, and with the pigeon factor.

Pantothenic acid was first obtained in a pure state from yeast[25] and from liver[14,25] extracts.

Occurrence

Pantothenic acid is widely distributed, mainly in a combined form. The best sources are liver, yeast, egg yolk, and fresh vegetables.

Deficiency disease

A deficiency disease in man due to lack of pantothenic acid is virtually unknown. Deficiency has been induced by administration of ω-methylpantothenic acid (which is a pantothenic acid antagonist) to volunteers, who developed burning sensations, muscle weakness, abdominal disorders and depression as the result.

Deficiency symptoms in animals are well defined but vary with the species. Pantothenic acid is a vitamin for chickens (who suffer from a specific dermatitis in the absence of the compound) and for rats (where growth would otherwise be retarded and a depigmentation of the fur would occur).

Daily requirement

This is unknown for man, but the requirement has been estimated at 10 mg. Definite evidence has been obtained that pantothenic acid is synthesized by the intestinal flora in man.

Properties

Pantothenic acid is a pale yellow viscous oil which is optically active and is sensitive to heat, to acids and to bases. The compound shows mainly acidic, but also some basic properties.

Structure[23,24]

Analysis established a molecular formula of $C_9H_{17}NO_5$ for pantothenic acid, and an active hydrogen determination indicated the presence of two hydroxyl groups. These cannot be on adjacent carbon atoms, however, since pantothenic acid does not react with periodic acid or with lead tetraacetate. Preliminary tests indicated the absence of double bonds, carbonyl groups, primary amino groups and aromatic rings. A carboxyl group was shown to be present since pantothenic acid yields a methyl ester when treated with diazomethane.

Alkaline hydrolysis of pantothenic acid yields β-alanine (1)[19] and also[14,26] an acid, pantoic acid, $C_6H_{12}O_4$, which readily forms a γ-lactone, pantolactone. Thus, pantoic acid must possess a hydroxyl group on a carbon γ to the carboxyl group, and since treatment of pantoic acid with sulphuric acid yields formic acid and carbon monoxide there must be a second hydroxyl group α to the carboxyl group. Part-structure (2) can thus be written for this acid.

Acid hydrolysis of pantothenic acid yields pantolactone directly. A Kuhn–Roth determination on this product indicated two carbon-methyl groups and these were shown to be attached to the same carbon atom when acetone was isolated from the products of oxidation of pantolactone with barium permanganate.

When pantolactone is treated with methylmagnesium bromide followed by lead tetraacetate, an aldehyde is obtained which gives the known[20] 3-hydroxy-2,2-dimethylpropionic acid (3) upon oxidation.

6

Thus the aldehyde obtained by glycol cleavage must be 4 and the product of the action of methylmagnesium bromide on pantolactone is 5. From this it follows that pantolactone is 6 and pantoic acid is 7.

Now pantoic acid (7) and β-alanine (1) contain all the carbon atoms of the original pantothenic acid, and since these two fragments were obtained by hydrolysis, the vitamin must be 8. This molecule contains one asymmetric centre which has been[8] related to the D_g-series by the use of Hudson's hydrazide rule of isorotation[9]. This rule, which is used for allotting configurations of α-hydroxy acids, states that the difference in optical rotation between the hydrazide and the parent acid is positive for a D-configuration at the α-carbon atom and negative for an L-configuration. Thus, natural dextrorotatory pantothenic acid can be represented by the Fischer projection 9 and the enantiomer (which is available by synthesis) is 10.

Synthesis[13,15,18]

Folkers and his coworkers[18] achieved a total synthesis of the optically active pantothenic acid by first preparing and resolving pantolactone (6), and reacting each isomer separately with β-alanine. Only the dextrorotatory pantothenic acid is biologically active.

Pantolactone has been prepared[7,12,15,18] by condensing isobutraldehyde (11) with formaldehyde to yield 3-hydroxy-2,2-dimethylpropanal (12), which upon reaction with hydrogen cyanide followed by hydrolysis yielded pantolactone (6) via the acid 7. The racemic product was resolved via its quinine salt.

β-Alanine (1) may be prepared by a variety of methods, but one of the favoured ones for the industrial-scale production of pantothenic acid involves the catalytic hydrogenation[21] of ethyl cyanoacetate followed by hydrolysis.

$H_2NCH_2CH_2COOH$

(1)

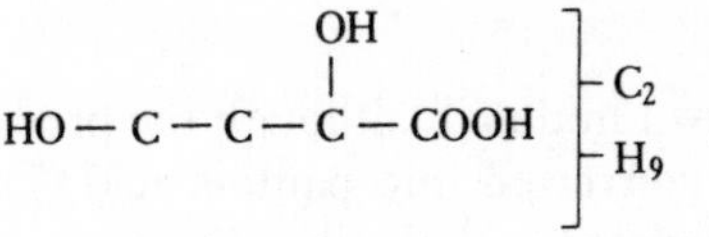

$$HO-C-C-\overset{\overset{\displaystyle OH}{|}}{C}-COOH \left.\right]^{C_2}_{H_9}$$

(2)

$$HO-CH_2-\overset{\overset{\displaystyle CH_3}{|}}{\underset{\underset{\displaystyle CH_3}{|}}{C}}-COOH$$

(3)

$$HO-CH_2-\overset{\overset{\displaystyle CH_3}{|}}{\underset{\underset{\displaystyle CH_3}{|}}{C}}-CHO$$

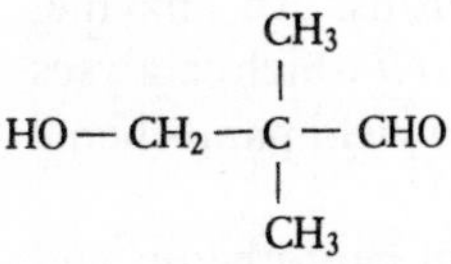

(4)

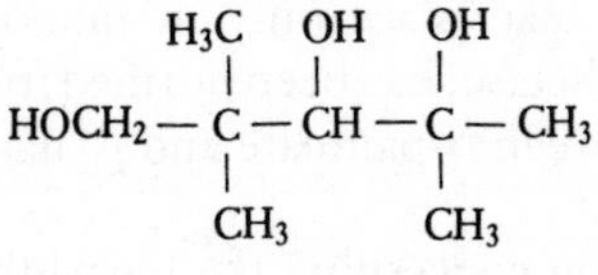

$$HOCH_2-\overset{\overset{\displaystyle H_3C}{|}}{\underset{\underset{\displaystyle CH_3}{|}}{C}}-\overset{\overset{\displaystyle OH}{|}}{CH}-\overset{\overset{\displaystyle OH}{|}}{\underset{\underset{\displaystyle CH_3}{|}}{C}}-CH_3$$

(5)

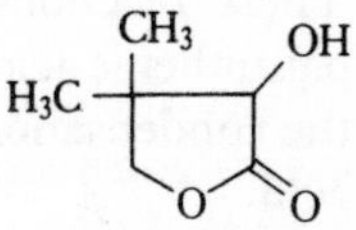

(6)

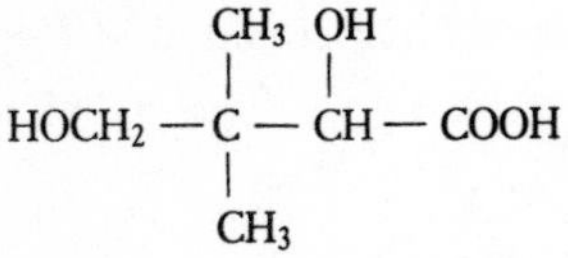

$$HOCH_2-\overset{\overset{\displaystyle CH_3}{|}}{\underset{\underset{\displaystyle CH_3}{|}}{C}}-\overset{\overset{\displaystyle OH}{|}}{CH}-COOH$$

(7)

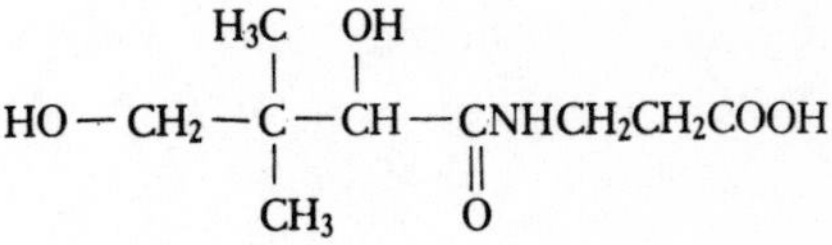

$$HO-CH_2-\overset{\overset{\displaystyle H_3C}{|}}{\underset{\underset{\displaystyle CH_3}{|}}{C}}-\overset{\overset{\displaystyle OH}{|}}{CH}-\underset{\underset{\displaystyle O}{||}}{C}NHCH_2CH_2COOH$$

(8)

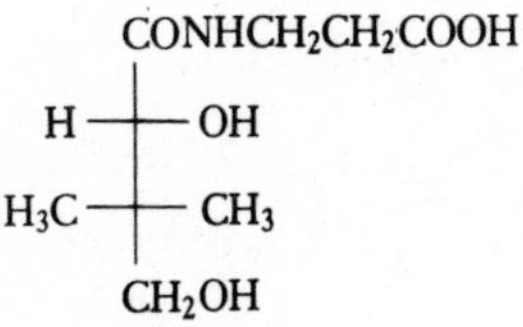

CONHCH$_2$CH$_2$COOH

H —— OH

H$_3$C —— CH$_3$

CH$_2$OH

(9)

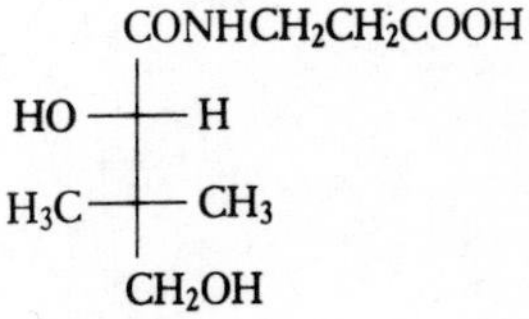

CONHCH$_2$CH$_2$COOH

HO —— H

H$_3$C —— CH$_3$

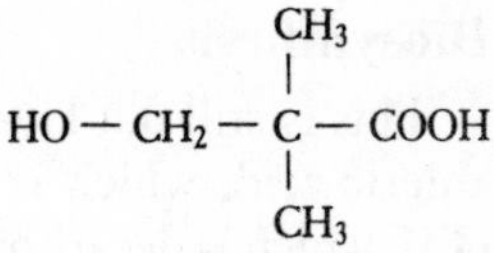

CH$_2$OH

(10)

$$\overset{\displaystyle H_3C}{\underset{\displaystyle H_3C}{\diagdown}}CHCHO \xrightarrow[K_2CO_3]{HCHO} HOCH_2-\overset{\overset{\displaystyle CH_3}{|}}{\underset{\underset{\displaystyle CH_3}{|}}{C}}-CHO$$

(11)   (12)

resolution with quinine ←

(6)

1. NaHSO$_3$
2. KCN
3. Hydrolysis

$$\left[HO-CH_2-\overset{\overset{\displaystyle CH_3}{|}}{\underset{\underset{\displaystyle CH_3}{|}}{C}}-\overset{\overset{\displaystyle OH}{|}}{CH}COOH \right]$$

(7)

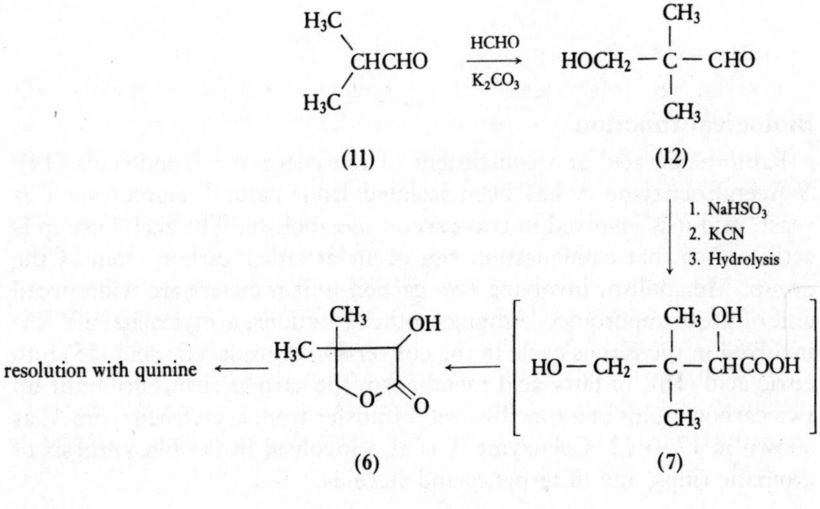

Biosynthesis

This is still not known in detail, although the precursors are[10] 2-oxo-valeric acid, which is converted into pantoic acid (7), and aspartic acid (13), which is decarboxylated to β-alanine. These two substances, pantoic acid and β-alanine, then condense together to yield pantothenic acid. These reactions can take place only in microorganisms. An enzyme, pantothenic acid synthetase, has been purified from *E. coli* which catalyses the condensation between D-pantoate and β-alanine to yield pantothenic acid.

The present position concerning the biosynthesis of pantothenic acid has recently been summarized by Goodwin[7a].

Biological function

Pantothenic acid is a constituent of the coenzyme A molecule (14). *S*-Acetylcoenzyme A has been isolated from natural sources such as yeast[4] and it is involved in two-carbon metabolism. The acetyl group is activated so that condensation can occur at either carbon atom of the group. Metabolism involving two carbon unit transfers are widespread and of great importance. Amongst other reactions, acetylcoenzyme A is involved in the Krebs cycle in the conversion of oxalacetic acid (15) into citric acid (16); in fatty acid metabolism the carbon chains are built up two carbon atoms at a time by acetyl transfer from acetylcoenzyme A, as shown in 17 → 22. Coenzyme A is also involved in the biosynthesis of aromatic rings, and of terpenes and steroids.

COOH
|
CH₂
| $-CO_2 \longrightarrow$ COOH
CH₂NH₂ |
| CH₂
COOH |
                                    CH₂NH₂

(13)   (1)

(14)

COOH   COOH
| |
C=O $\xrightarrow{CH_3COS—CoA}$ HO—C—CH₂COOH
| |
CH₂   CH₂
| |
COOH   COOH

(15)   (16)

$CoA—SCOCH_3 + CH_3COS—CoA \longrightarrow CH_3COCH_2COS—CoA$

(17)   (18)

OH
|
$CH_3CH=CHCOS—CoA \longleftarrow CH_3CHCH_2COS—CoA$

(20)   (19)

$CH_3CH_2CH_2COS—CoA \xrightarrow{CH_3COS—CoA} CH_3CH_2CH_2COCH_2COS—CoA \longrightarrow$ etc.

(21)   (22)

The biosynthesis of coenzyme A itself was originally thought[10] to involve the condensation of pantothenic acid with cysteine, to yield 23, followed by decarboxylation to 24 and then phosphorylation to panto-theine-4'-phosphate (25). The latter was considered to then condense with adenine triphosphate (26) to yield 27, followed by phosphorylation to coenzyme A (14). However, conclusive evidence has now established[2,3] that pantothenic acid is first converted into the 4'-phosphate which condenses with cysteine to yield 4'-phosphopantothenylcysteine, and this is then decarboxylated to 25, from which coenzyme A is obtained as before. These reactions from pantothenic acid to coenzyme A can occur in microorganisms and in mammals.

Analogues of pantothenic acid

Several analogues of this vitamin have been prepared and their biological activity examined[16]. The molecule seems to be quite specific, and even simple esters of pantothenic acid (which would be expected to be easily hydrolysed *in vivo* to pantothenic acid) are inactive (in bacteria). Some of the synthetic analogues have about 1% of the activity of *d*-pantothenic acid, but one (pantoyltaurine, 28) is a growth inhibitor in microorganisms; presumably these synthetic analogues are built up into coenzyme A-like substances which are inactive[1].

Most of the synthetic analogues have been prepared by condensing β-alanine with various γ-lactones, for example compounds such as 29 to

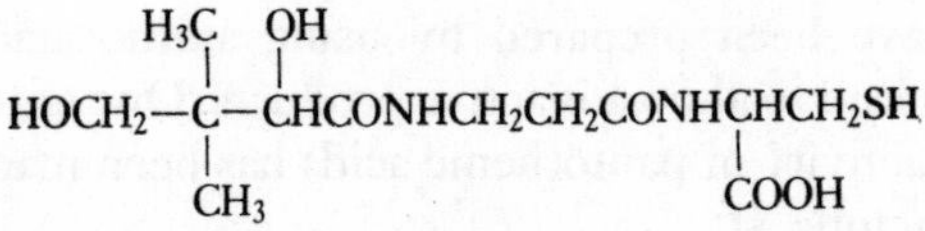

$$\underset{\underset{CH_3}{|}}{\overset{\overset{H_3C}{|}\ \ \overset{OH}{|}}{HOCH_2-C-CHCONHCH_2CH_2CONHCHCH_2SH}}\underset{COOH}{}$$

(23)

$$\bigg\downarrow -CO_2$$

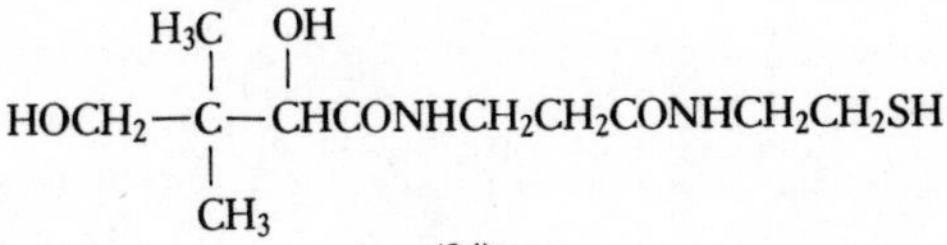

$$\underset{\underset{CH_3}{|}}{\overset{\overset{H_3C}{|}\ \ \overset{OH}{|}}{HOCH_2-C-CHCONHCH_2CH_2CONHCH_2CH_2SH}}$$

(24)

$$\underset{\underset{CH_3}{|}}{\overset{\overset{H_3C}{|}\ \ \overset{OH}{|}}{\underset{HO}{\overset{HO\ \ O}{P}}-O-CH_2-C-CHCONHCH_2CH_2CONHCH_2CH_2SH}}$$

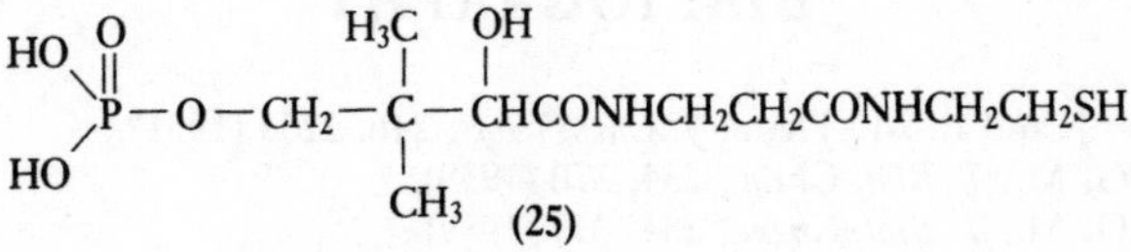

(25)

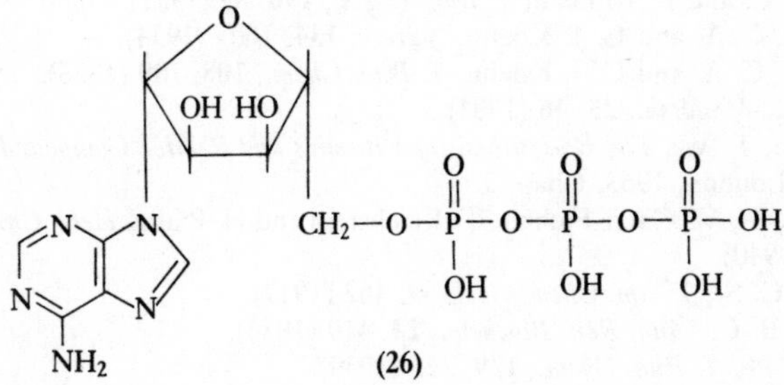

(26)

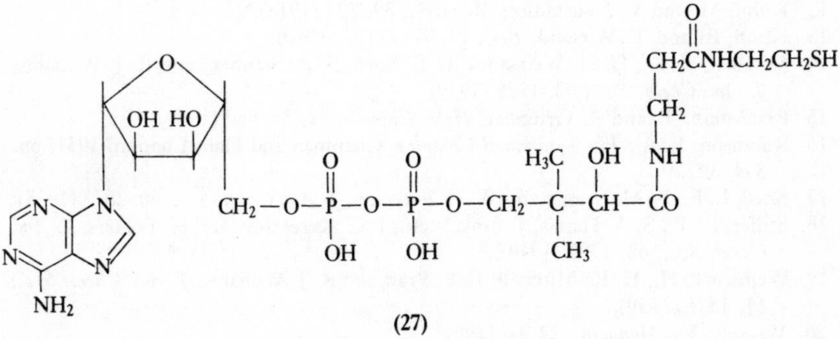

(27)

$$\bigg\downarrow$$

14

31, and some have been prepared by using amino acids other than β-alanine, but all lead to almost inactive products. One of the most active analogues (25% activity of pantothenic acid) has been made from β-alanine and the γ-lactone 31.

BIBLIOGRAPHY

1. Baddiley, J. and E. M. Thain, *J. Chem. Soc.*, 246, 2253 (1951).
2. Brown, G. M., *J. Biol. Chem.*, 234, 370 (1959).
3. Brown, G. M., *J. Biol. Chem.*, 234, 379 (1959).
4. Chou, T. C. and F. Lipman, *J. Biol. Chem.*, 196, 89 (1952).
5. Elvehjem, C. A. and C. J. Koehn, *Nature*, 134, 1007 (1934).
6. Elvehjem, C. A. and C. J. Koehn, *J. Biol. Chem.*, 108, 709 (1935).
7. Glaser, E., *Monatsh.*, 25, 46 (1904).
7a. Goodwin, T. W., *The Biosynthesis of Vitamins and Related Compounds*, Academic Press, London, 1963, Chap. 5.
8. Grussner, A., M. Gatzi-Fichter, T. Reichstein and H. Pfaltz, *Helv. Chim. Acta*, 23, 1276 (1940).
9. Hudson, C. S., *J. Am. Chem. Soc.*, 39, 462 (1917).
10. Johnson, B. C., *Ann. Rev. Biochem.*, 24, 419 (1955).
11. Jukes, T. H., *J. Biol. Chem.*, 129, 225 (1939).
12. Kohn, M. and V. Neustadler, *Monatsh.*, 39, 293 (1918).
13. Kuhn, R. and T. Wieland, *Ber.*, 73, 971, 1134 (1940).
14. Mitchell, H. K., H. H. Weinstock, E. E. Snell, S. R. Stanbery and R. J. Williams, *J. Am. Chem. Soc.*, 62, 1776 (1940).
15. Reichstein, T. and A. Grussner, *Helv. Chim. Acta*, 23, 650 (1940).
16. Robinson, F. A., *The Vitamin B Complex*, Chapman and Hall, London, 1951, pp. 394, 397.
17. Snell, E. E., F. M. Strong and W. H. Peterson, *J. Am. Chem. Soc.*, 60, 2825 (1938).
18. Stiller, E. T., S. A. Harris, J. Finkelstein, J. C. Keresztesy and K. Folkers, *J. Am. Chem. Soc.*, 62, 1785 (1940).
19. Weinstock, H., H. K. Mitchell, E. F. Pratt and R. J. Williams, *J. Am. Chem. Soc.*, 61, 1421 (1939).
20. Wessely, L., *Monatsh.*, 22, 66 (1901).
21. Weygand, F., *Ber.*, 74, 256 (1941).
22. Williams, R. J., C. M. Lyman, G. H. Goodyear, T. H. Truesdail and D. Holaday, *J. Am. Chem. Soc.*, 55, 2912 (1933).
23. Williams, R. J., W. A. Mosher and E. Rohrmann, *Biochem. J.*, 30, 2036 (1936).

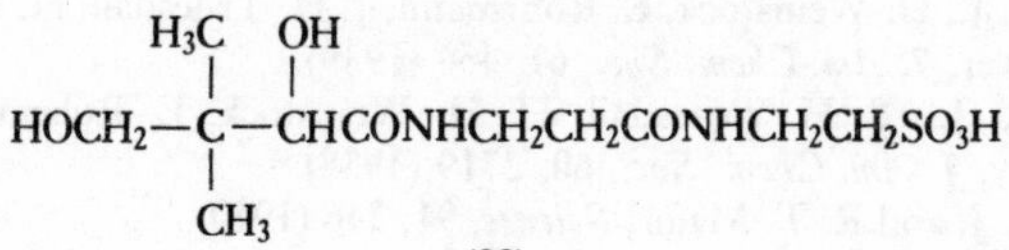
H3C OH
HOCH2—C—CHCONHCH2CH2CONHCH2CH2SO3H
CH3

(28)

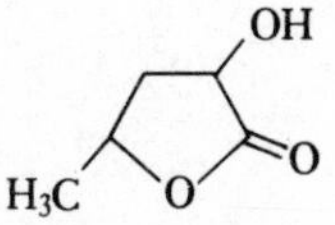
OH
O
H3C
O

(29)

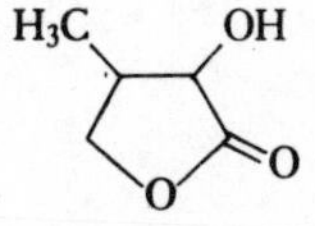
H3C
OH
O
O

(30)

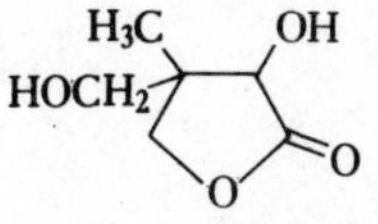
H3C
OH
HOCH2
O
O

(31)

24. Williams, R. J., H. Weinstock, E. Rohrmann, J. H. Truesdail, H. K. Mitchell and C. E. Meyer, *J. Am. Chem. Soc.*, 61, 454 (1939).
25. Williams, R. J., T. H. Truesdail, H. H. Weinstock, E. Rohrmann and C. H. McBurney, *J. Am. Chem. Soc.*, 60, 2719 (1938).
26. Williams, R. J. and R. T. Major, *Science*, 91, 246 (1940).
27. Woolley, D. W., H. A. Waisman and C. A. Elvehjem, *J. Biol. Chem.*, 129, 573 (1939).

CHAPTER 9

Biotin (Vitamin H)

BIOTIN – Isolation – Sources – Deficiency disease – Daily requirement
– Properties – Structure – Stereochemistry of biotin – Synthesis of
biotin – The synthesis of desthiobiotin – Biosynthesis of biotin –
Analogues of biotin – The biochemical function of biotin – Complex
biotins – BIBLIOGRAPHY

INDEPENDENT investigations were being conducted simultaneously in
a number of laboratories upon a yeast growth factor termed 'bios', upon
'coenzyme R'[1], a growth and respiration factor for certain bacteria, and
upon a rat nutrition factor termed 'vitamin H'. It was subsequently
realized[24] that all three investigations were dealing with the same substance, namely biotin.

Isolation

Biotin was first isolated[43], as a crystalline methyl ester, from egg-yolk,
and was subsequently obtained in a pure form from liver[23] and from
milk[51]. It has been claimed[46,47] that the substance isolated from egg-
yolk is very similar to, but not identical with, that obtained from liver.
Kögl termed this second substance (from egg-yolk) α-biotin, and suggested that the factor isolated from liver be called β-biotin. However
Folkers[20] considers that the existence of two biotins is very doubtful. In
this book the term biotin will be used[40] and refers to Kögl's β-biotin.

Sources

The richest sources of biotin are egg-yolk, liver and yeast. In animals
and in yeasts it is present in a bound form, but in the free state in plants.
Biotin is a member of the vitamin B complex.

Deficiency disease

In man, biotin can be synthesized by the intestinal bacteria, so that a
true deficiency disease is virtually unknown. It is believed that deficiency
of biotin causes a dermatitis, loss of hair and progressive paralysis.
Biotin is a growth factor for rats, yeast and some microorganisms.

Green plants seem to require it for the fixation of carbon dioxide, whereas animal cells need it during the course of decarboxylation and deamination reactions[48,49]. It is certainly involved in the biological synthesis of oleic acid.

Daily requirement

This is almost impossible to assess since it can be synthesized in the intestine. Estimates range from 150–300γ for an average adult, whereas Williams[63] suggests 0·25 mg. Volunteer subjects who were made biotin-deficient quickly recovered normal health upon injection with 75–300γ per day of biotin.

Properties

Biotin crystallizes from water in fine needles, m.p. 230° (decomp.). It is soluble in dilute aqueous alkali, sparingly soluble in dilute mineral acids, and is optically active.

Structure

The molecular formula of biotin was established as $C_{10}H_{16}N_2O_3S$[59], and electrometric titration[60] indicated the presence of one carboxyl group. The compound was also found to be very feebly basic—so weak, in fact, that biotin can be crystallized as such from strongly acidic solutions. Biotin reacts with diazomethane to yield a monomethyl ester, identical with the ester isolated from natural sources.

Treatment of biotin with hydrogen iodide indicated the absence of O-, N- or S-methyl groups. In an attempted van Slyke amino group determination[13] no nitrogen was evolved. Hydrolysis of biotin occurred under drastic conditions, according to the equation[33,44]

$$C_{10}H_{16}N_2O_3S + H_2O \xrightarrow[Ba(OH)_2]{HCl \text{ or}} CO_2 + C_9H_{18}N_2O_2S$$

to yield an optically active diaminocarboxylic acid A. Biotin was re-formed[52] from the acid A when it was treated with phosgene, thus indicating a cyclic urea-type of structure in biotin. No distinction was possible between a five- and six-membered ring. The evidence so far can be summarized in the part-structure 1.

The sulphur atom of biotin seemed to be quite stable since hydrogen sulphide was not evolved upon treatment with zinc dust and hydrochloric acid, and no sulphate was formed after treatment of biotin with bromine. Oxidation of biotin with cold potassium permanganate or with hydrogen peroxide in acetic acid yielded a sulphone $C_{10}H_{16}N_2O_5S$[33,45];

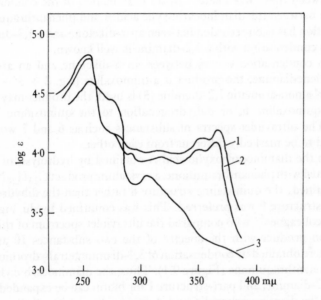

(1)

Curve 1 — phenanthraquinonediamino acid from biotin
(in ethanol)
Curve 2 — phenanthraquinonethiophene (11) (in
ethanol)
Curve 3 — phenanthraquinonethiophene (10) (in
ethanol)

Figure 9.1. The ultraviolet spectra of some quinoxaline derivatives. [Reproduced, by permission, from D. B. Melville, *Vitamins Hormones*, **2**, 55 (1944).]

this indicated the presence of a thioether linkage. No double bonds could be detected in biotin, so that, from an examination of the molecular formula together with part-structure 1, it was concluded that the sulphur must be part of a ring[45]. Hence biotin must contain two rings and a side-chain. The size of the sulphur-containing ring was unknown at this point.

Now, drastic hydrolysis of biotin sulphone[52] yielded the sulphone of the diaminocarboxylic acid A, since reaction of this substance with phosgene regenerated biotin sulphone. Hence, under the conditions of the hydrolysis of biotin to the acid A, the sulphur-containing part of the molecule remains unchanged.

The urea ring was thought to be five- or six-membered, and a distinction between these was made[34] by an examination of the condensation reaction between the diaminocarboxylic acid A and phenanthraquinone. No reaction has been recorded between an α-diketone and a 1,3-diamine, whereas condensation with a 1,2-diamine is well known.

When condensation occurs between an α-diketone and an aromatic o-phenylenediamine, the product is a quinoxaline (e.g. 2 + 3 → 4). If, however, a non-aromatic 1,2-diamine (5) is used, the product may be the dihydroquinoxaline 6, or dehydrogenation to the quinoxaline 7 may occur. The ultraviolet spectra of substances such as 6 and 7 would be expected to be markedly different from each other.

When the diaminocarboxylic acid A obtained by hydrolysis of biotin was reacted with phenanthraquinone, a crystalline product $C_{23}H_{20}N_2O_2S$ was obtained; the quinoxaline structure 8 rather than the dihydroquin-oxaline structure 9 was preferred. This was confirmed by du Vigneaud and his colleagues[42] who compared the ultraviolet spectrum of this condensation product with the spectra of the two substances 10 and 11, which were obtained by condensation of 3,4-diaminotetrahydrothiophene with phenanthraquinone (Figure 9.1). Thus, the diaminocarboxylic acid A is a 1,2-diamine, and part-structure 1 for biotin can be expanded to 12.

After the diaminocarboxylic acid A was oxidized with alkaline potassium permanganate or with concentrated nitric acid[32,35], adipic acid was isolated from the reaction mixture. This could have arisen either from an aliphatic side-chain in biotin, in which case the carboxyl group of the vitamin would appear as one of the carboxyl groups of adipic acid, or from a six-carbon ring, in which case neither of the carboxyl groups of adipic acid corresponds to the one originally present in biotin. Biotin methyl ester was degraded[35] by the Curtius method to the amine, and the product 13 was hydrolysed to a triamine (14) which was then oxidized.

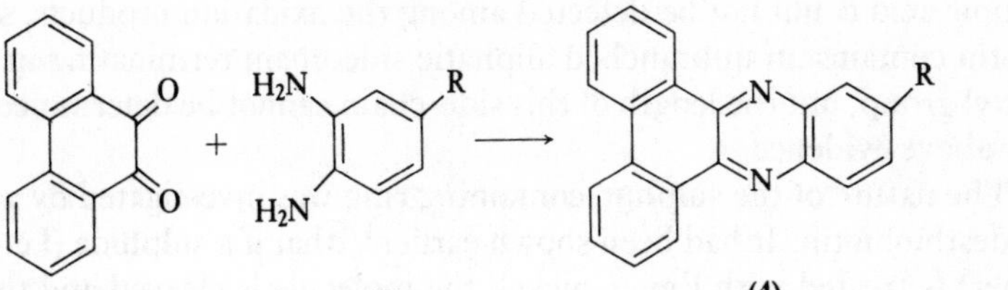

(2) + (3) $\longrightarrow$ (4)

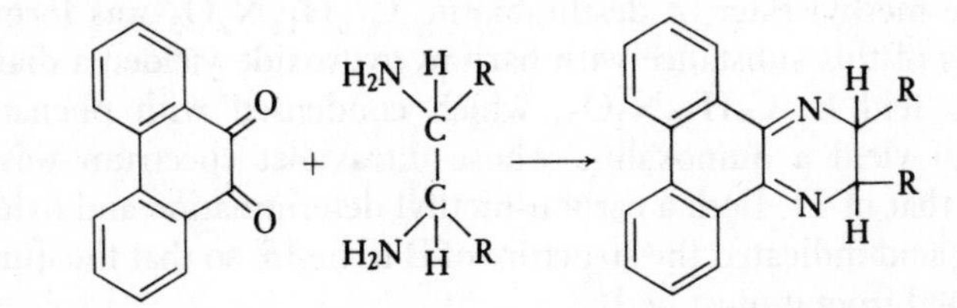

(2) + (5) $\longrightarrow$ (6)

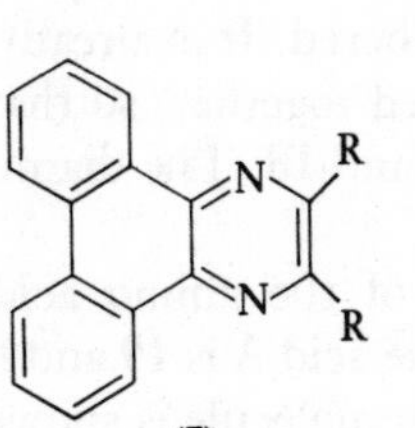

(7)

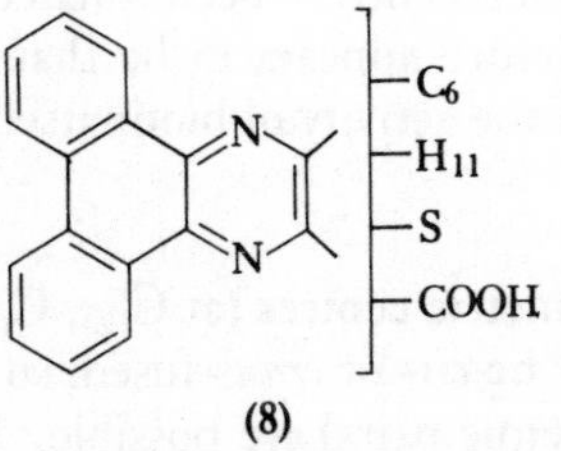

(8)

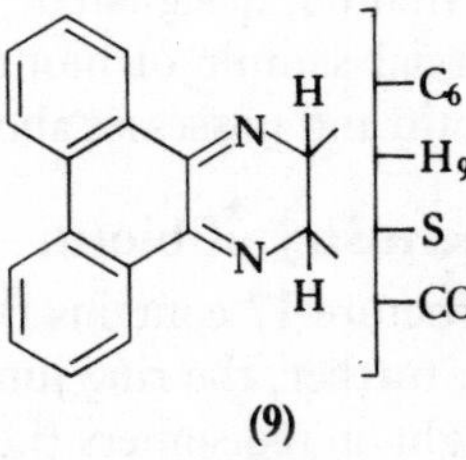

$$\left[\begin{array}{l} -C_6 \\ -H_{11} \\ -S \\ -COOH \end{array} \right]$$

(9)

$$\left[\begin{array}{l} -C_6 \\ -H_9 \\ -S \\ -COOH \end{array} \right]$$

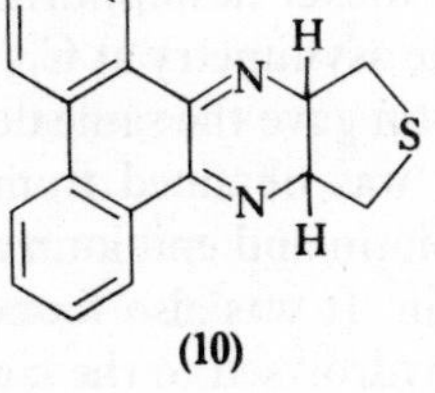

(10)

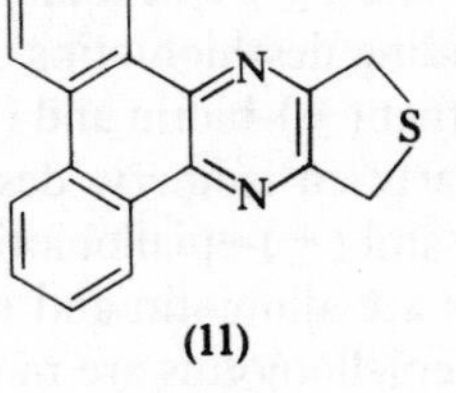

(11)

Adipic acid could not be detected among the oxidation products, so that biotin contains an unbranched aliphatic side-chain terminating in a carboxyl group, but the length of this side-chain cannot be determined from the above evidence.

The nature of the sulphur-containing ring was investigated by a study of desthiobiotin. It had been shown earlier[11] that if a sulphide (i.e. a thio ether) is treated with Raney nickel, the molecule is cleaved and the sulphur is removed. When biotin methyl ester was treated with Raney nickel, the methyl ester of desthiobiotin, $C_{10}H_{18}N_2O_3$ was formed[61]. Hydrolysis of this substance with barium hydroxide yielded a diaminocarboxylic acid B, $C_9H_{20}N_2O_2$, which condensed with phenanthraquinone to yield a quinoxaline whose ultraviolet spectrum was very similar to that of 11. Both a carbon-methyl determination and oxidation to pimelic acid indicated the structure of B to be 15, so that the quinoxaline obtained from it must be 16.

Now, from the structure of B the sulphur-containing ring of biotin could be five- or six-membered. It is already clear that the sulphur ring and the urea ring are fused together, so that the most likely structures possible for biotin are 17 and 18. The diaminocarboxylic acid A is thus either 19 or 20.

Hofmann degradation of the amino acid A[53] yielded δ-thienyl-2-valeric acid (21), so that the acid A is 19 and biotin itself is 17. The numbering system of the biotin molecule is shown in 17.

Kögl claims that α-biotin has the structure 22.

A new vitamin, designated γ-biotin, has recently[41] been isolated from a commercial sample of biotin. Its structure appears to be that of N-phenylbiotin and possesses about 80% of the activity of biotin itself.

Stereochemistry of biotin

The structure 17 contains three asymmetric centres (at $C_{(2)}$, $C_{(3)}$ and $C_{(4)}$) and, further, the ring junction may be cis- or trans-fused, so that a total of eight stereoisomers (i.e. four racemic pairs) are possible. All the racemates have been synthesized[8,22]: ($\pm$)-biotin, ($\pm$)-epibiotin, ($\pm$)-allobiotin and ($\pm$)-epiallobiotin. Raney nickel desulphurization to the corresponding desthiobiotins destroys the asymmetry at $C_{(2)}$. It was observed[31] that ($\pm$)-biotin and ($\pm$)-epibiotin gave the same desthiobiotin, and similarly an isomeric desthiobiotin was obtained from both ($\pm$)-allobiotin and ($\pm$)-epiallobiotin. Thus biotin and epibiotin are epimeric at $C_{(2)}$, as are allobiotin and epiallobiotin. It was also found[31] that the allo- and epiallobiotins are more easily hydrolysed to the corresponding

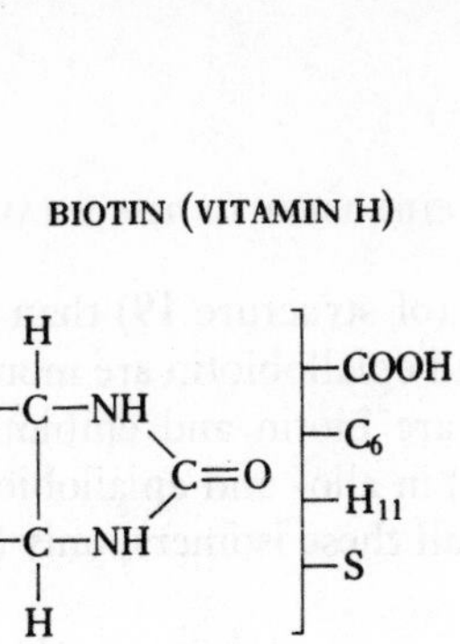

(12)

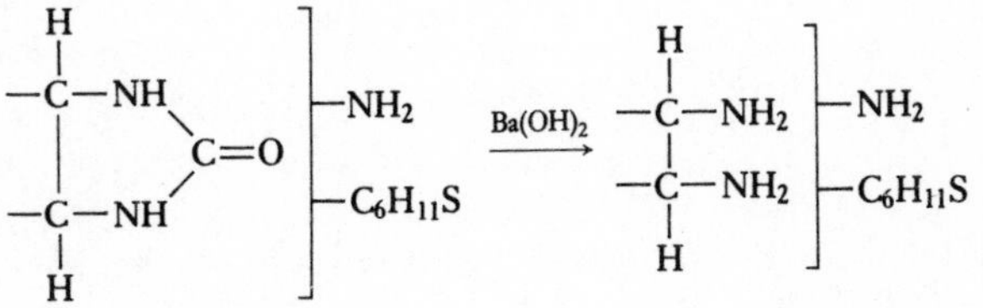

(13) $\xrightarrow{\text{Ba(OH)}_2}$ (14)

$H_2N-\overset{\displaystyle H}{\underset{\displaystyle H}{\overset{|}{\underset{|}{C}}}}-CH_3$

$H_2N-C-CH_2(CH_2)_4COOH$

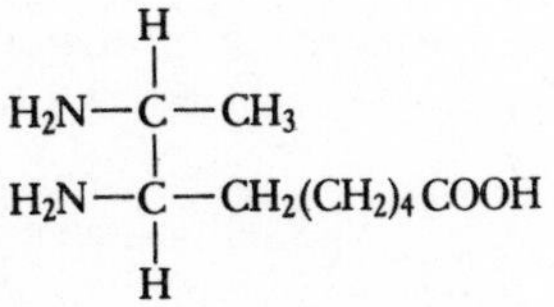

(15)

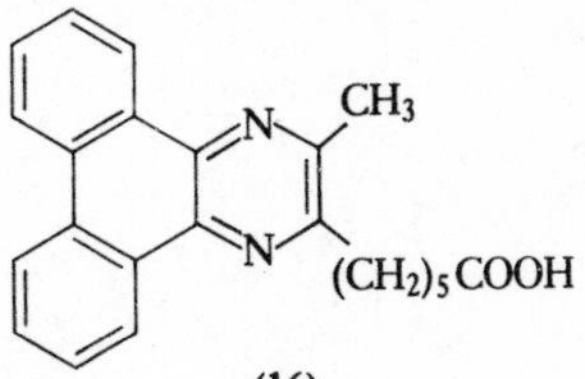

(16)

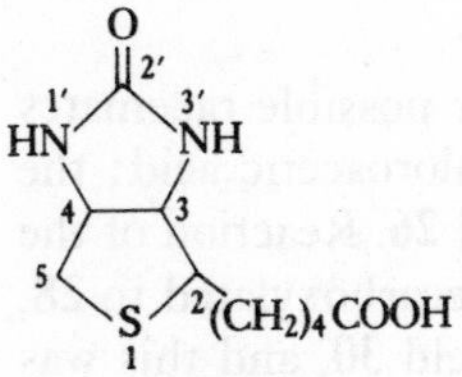

(17)

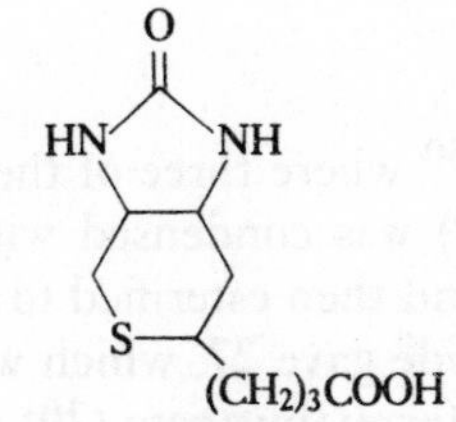

(18)

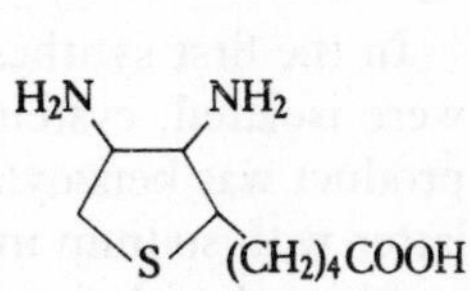

(19)

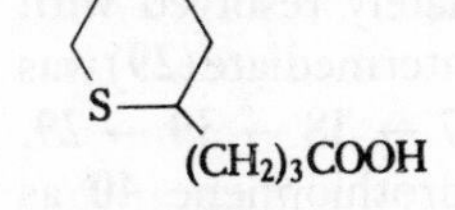

(20)

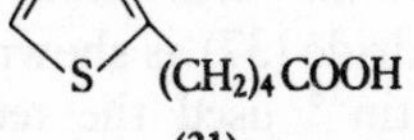

(21)

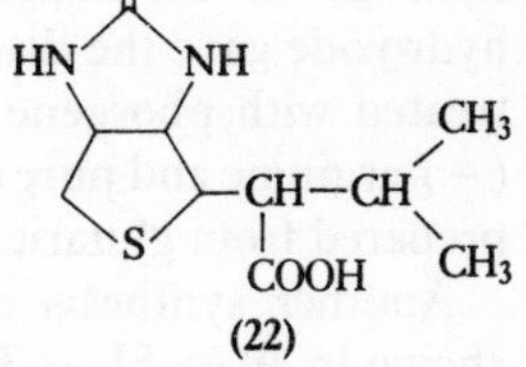

(22)

diaminocarboxylic acids (of structure 19) than are biotin and epibiotin. Conversely, allobiotin and epiallobiotin are more difficult to reform from these amino acids than are biotin and epibiotin. This means that the rings are *trans*-fused (23) in allo- and epiallobiotin, and *cis*-fused (24) in biotin and epibiotin. Of all these isomers, only (+)-biotin is biologically active.

Synthesis of biotin

In the first synthesis[26-30] where three of the four possible racemates were isolated, cysteine (25) was condensed with chloroacetic acid; the product was benzoylated and then esterified to yield 26. Reaction of the latter with sodium methoxide gave 27, which was decarboxylated to 28, condensed with methyl γ-formylbutyrate (29) to yield 30, and this was converted into the oxime 31. The latter was reduced with zinc dust and acetic acid to a mixture of 32 and 33, which was further reduced with hydrogen to the mixture of isomers 34. Hydrolysis of 34 with barium hydroxide gave the diaminocarboxylic acid 35, and this yielded 36 when treated with phosgene. The product (36) was ultimately resolved with (−)-arginine and pure (+)-biotin was isolated. The intermediate (29) was prepared from glutaric anhydride (37) as shown in 37 → 38 → 39 → 29.

Another synthesis of biotin[28] used the tetrahydrothiophene 40 as shown in 40 → 51 → 36 (p. 171).

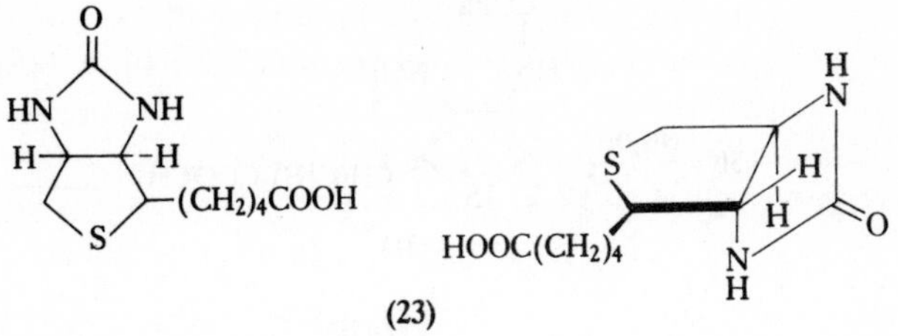

(23)

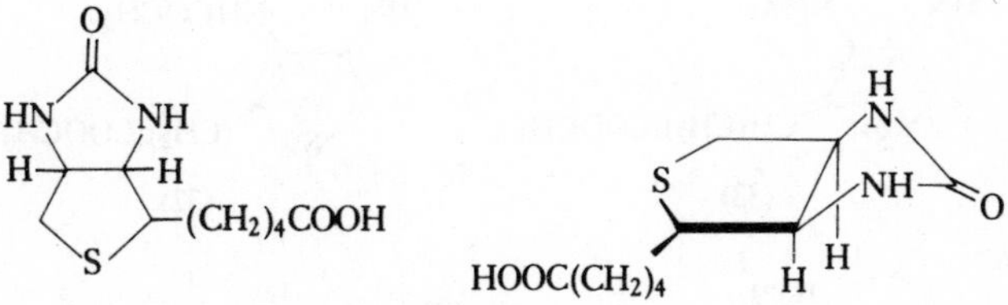

(24)

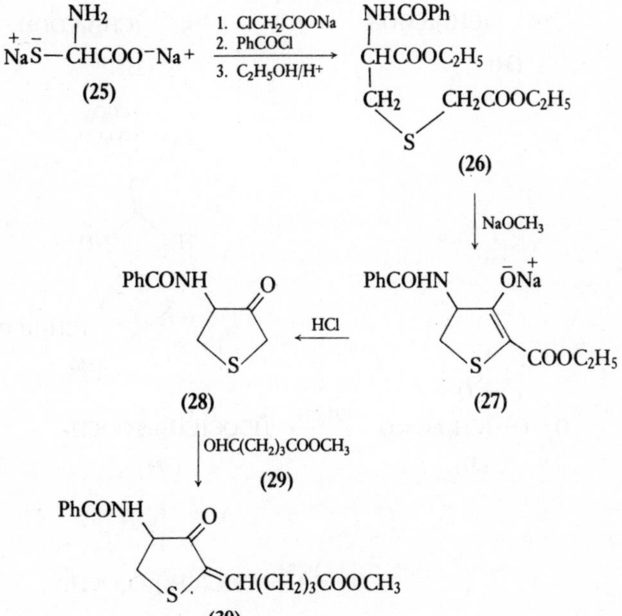

(25) (26) (27) (28) (29) (30)

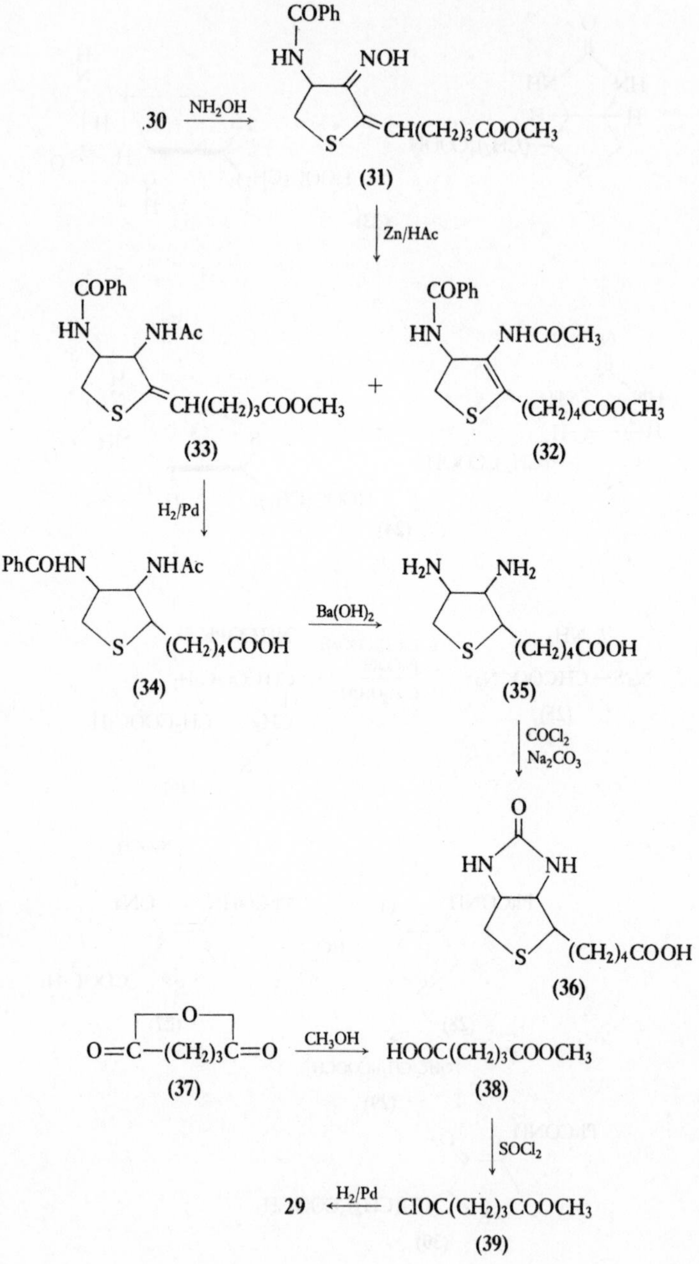

$$30 \xrightarrow{\text{NH}_2\text{OH}}$$

(31)

COPh
HN   NOH
└─ ┐
   S ═CH(CH$_2$)$_3$COOCH$_3$

| Zn/HAc

(33)

COPh
HN   NHAc

S ═CH(CH$_2$)$_3$COOCH$_3$

+

(32)

COPh
HN   NHCOCH$_3$

S (CH$_2$)$_4$COOCH$_3$

| H$_2$/Pd

(34)

PhCOHN   NHAc

S (CH$_2$)$_4$COOH

$\xrightarrow{\text{Ba(OH)}_2}$

(35)

H$_2$N   NH$_2$

S (CH$_2$)$_4$COOH

| COCl$_2$
| Na$_2$CO$_3$

(36)

O
‖
HN   NH

S (CH$_2$)$_4$COOH

(37)

O=C—(CH$_2$)$_3$C=O (with —O— bridge) $\xrightarrow{\text{CH}_3\text{OH}}$ HOOC(CH$_2$)$_3$COOCH$_3$

(38)

| SOCl$_2$

(39)

$29 \xleftarrow{\text{H}_2/\text{Pd}}$ ClOC(CH$_2$)$_3$COOCH$_3$

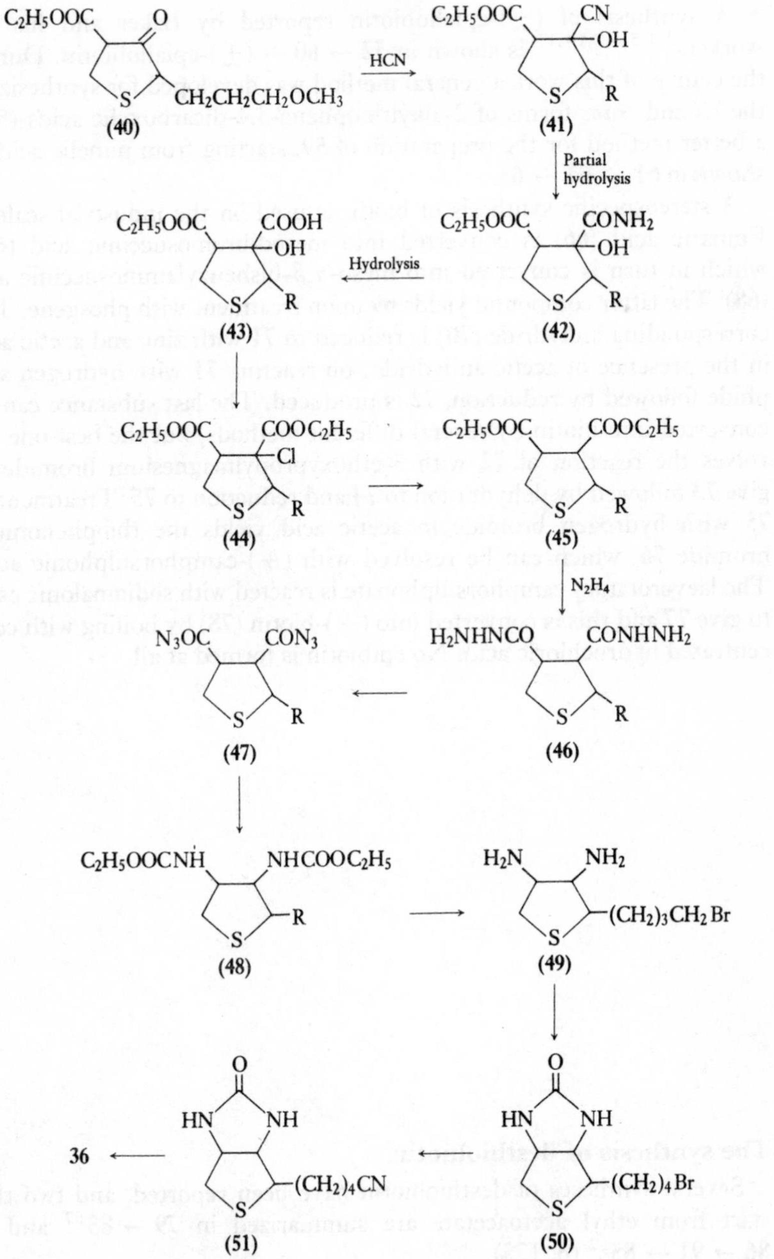
C_2H_5OOC
O
S
$CH_2CH_2CH_2OCH_3$
(40)
HCN
C_2H_5OOC
CN
OH
S
R
(41)
Partial hydrolysis
C_2H_5OOC
COOH
OH
S
R
(43)
Hydrolysis
C_2H_5OOC
$CONH_2$
OH
S
R
(42)
C_2H_5OOC
$COOC_2H_5$
Cl
S
R
(44)
C_2H_5OOC
$COOC_2H_5$
S
R
(45)
N_2H_4
N_3OC
CON_3
S
R
(47)
H_2NHNCO
$CONHNH_2$
S
R
(46)
C_2H_5OOCNH
$NHCOOC_2H_5$
S
R
(48)
H_2N
NH_2
S
$(CH_2)_3CH_2Br$
(49)
O
HN
NH
S
$(CH_2)_4CN$
(51)
36
O
HN
NH
S
$(CH_2)_4Br$
(50)

A synthesis of (±)-epiallobiotin reported by Baker and his co-workers[3,4,5,6,7,14,15] is shown in **52 → 60 →** (±)-epiallobiotin. During the course of this work a general method was developed for synthesizing the *cis* and *trans* forms of 2-alkylthiophene-3,4-dicarboxylic acids (**59**); a better method for the preparation of **59**, starting from pimelic acid, is shown in **61 → 64 → 65**.

A stereospecific synthesis of biotin is used on the industrial scale[21]. Fumaric acid (**66**) is converted into mesodibromosuccinic acid (**67**), which in turn is converted into meso-α,β-bisbenzylaminosuccinic acid (**68**). The latter compound yields **69** upon treatment with phosgene. The corresponding anhydride (**70**) is reduced to **71** with zinc and acetic acid in the presence of acetic anhydride; on reacting **71** with hydrogen sulphide followed by reduction, **72** is produced. The last substance can be converted into biotin by several different methods, but the best one involves the reaction of **72** with 3-ethoxypropylmagnesium bromide to give **73** followed by dehydration to **74** and reduction to **75**. Treatment of **75** with hydrogen bromide in acetic acid yields the thiophenonium bromide **76**, which can be resolved with (+)-camphorsulphonic acid. The laevorotatory camphorsulphonate is reacted with sodiomalonic ester to give **77** and this is converted into (+)-biotin (**78**) by boiling with concentrated hydrochloric acid. No epibiotin is formed at all.

The synthesis of desthiobiotin

Several syntheses of desthiobiotin have been reported, and two that start from ethyl acetoacetate are summarized in **79 → 85**[17] and in **86 → 91 → 85**[12] (p. 175).

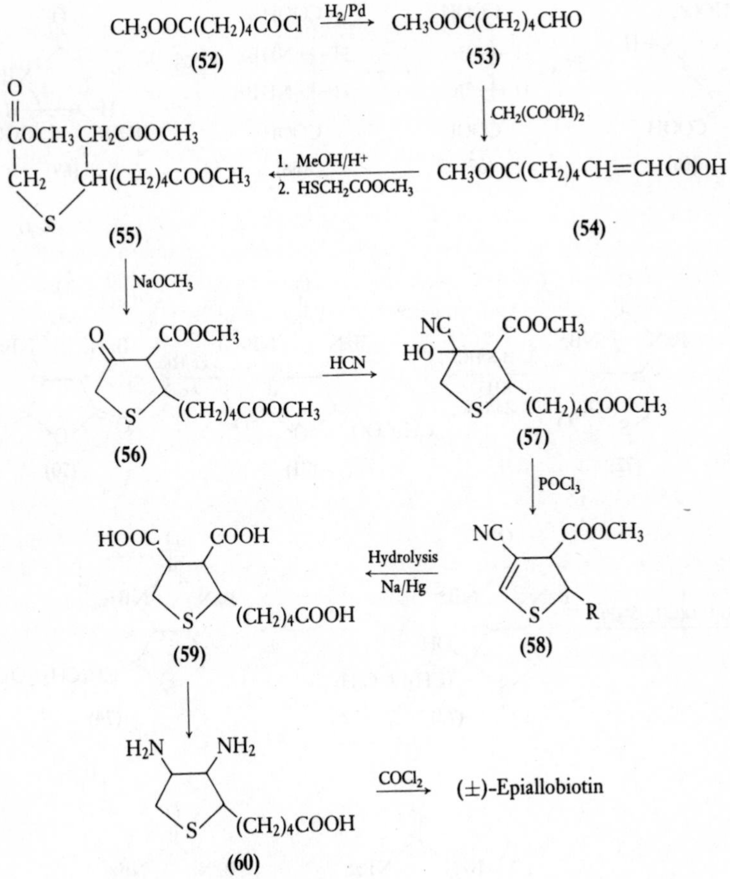

$$CH_3OOC(CH_2)_4COCl \xrightarrow{H_2/Pd} CH_3OOC(CH_2)_4CHO$$

(52)   (53)

$$\downarrow CH_2(COOH)_2$$

$$CH_3OOC(CH_2)_4CH{=}CHCOOH$$

(54)

(55) $\xrightarrow[\text{2. HSCH_2COOCH_3}]{\text{1. MeOH/H^+}}$

(55)

$$\downarrow NaOCH_3$$

(56) $\xrightarrow{HCN}$ (57)

$$\downarrow POCl_3$$

(59) $\xleftarrow[\text{Na/Hg}]{\text{Hydrolysis}}$ (58)

$$\downarrow$$

(60) $\xrightarrow{COCl_2}$ (±)-Epiallobiotin

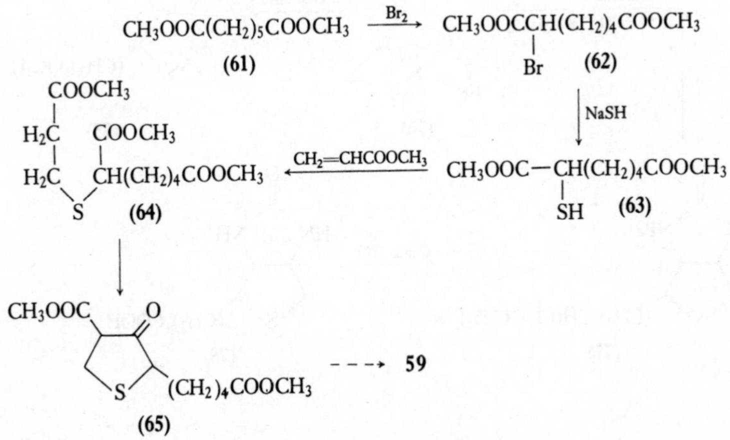

$$CH_3OOC(CH_2)_5COOCH_3 \xrightarrow{Br_2} CH_3OOCCH(CH_2)_4COOCH_3$$

(61) $\underset{Br}{|}$ (62)

$$\downarrow NaSH$$

(64) $\xleftarrow{CH_2{=}CHCOOCH_3}$ $CH_3OOC{-}CH(CH_2)_4COOCH_3$

                              $\underset{SH}{|}$ (63)

$$\downarrow$$

(65) $- - \rightarrow$ 59

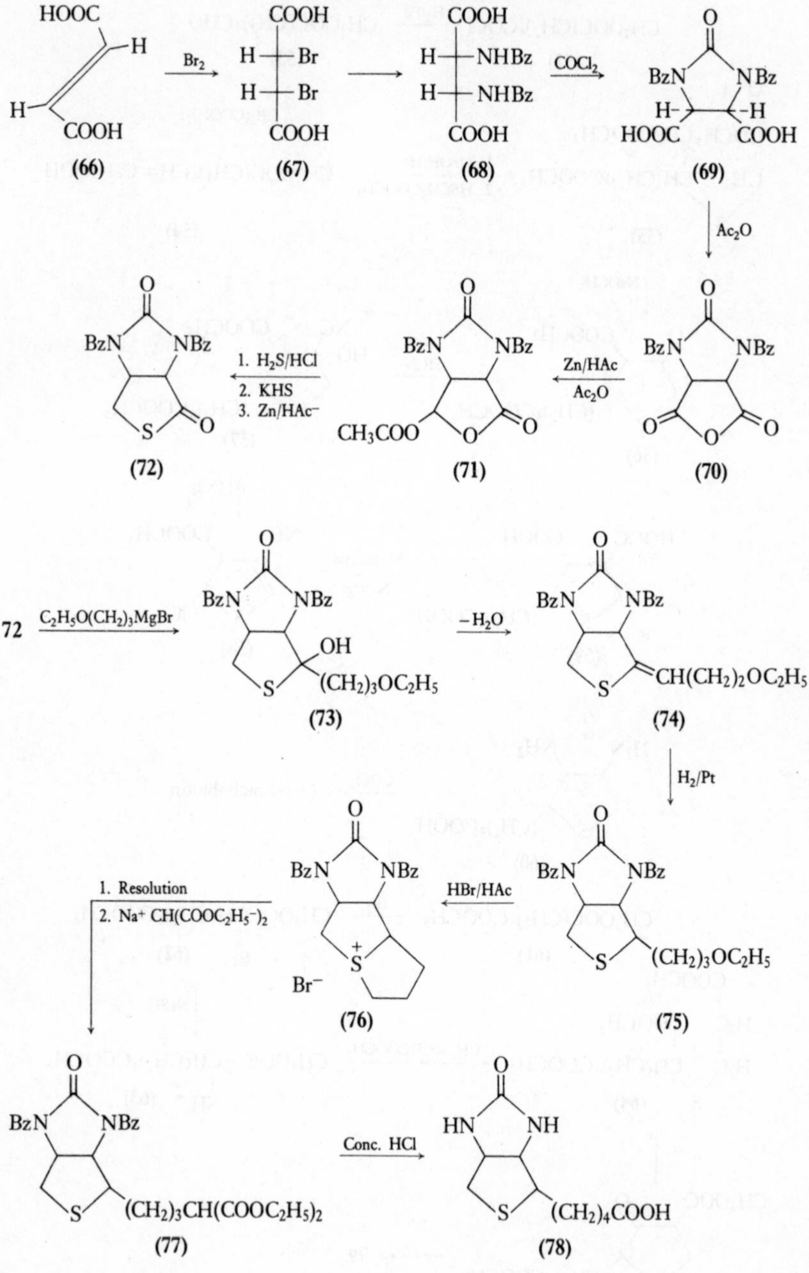

(66)
Br₂
(67)
(68)
COCl₂
(69)
Ac₂O
(70)
Zn/HAc
Ac₂O
(71)
1. H₂S/HCl
2. KHS
3. Zn/HAc⁻
(72)
72
C₂H₅O(CH₂)₃MgBr
(73)
−H₂O
(74)
H₂/Pt
(75)
HBr/HAc
(76)
1. Resolution
2. Na⁺ CH(COOC₂H₅⁻)₂
(77)
Conc. HCl
(78)

$$CH_3COCH_2COOC_2H_5 \xrightarrow{HNO_2} CH_3\underset{\underset{NOH}{\|}}{C}OC-COOC_2H_5 \xrightarrow{H_2/Pt} CH_3COCHCOOC_2H_5$$

$$(79) \qquad\qquad (80) \qquad\qquad \underset{NH_2}{|}$$
$$\qquad\qquad\qquad\qquad\qquad\qquad (81)$$

$$\downarrow KCNO$$

Structure (83) ← NaOH ← Structure (82), with ClOC(CH₂)₄COOC₂H₅ reacting to form (84)

$$\xrightarrow{\substack{1.\ Pt/H_2 \\ 2.\ Hydrolysis}}$$ Structure (85)

$$[CH_3CO\bar{C}HCOOC_2H_5]Na^+ \xrightarrow{Br(CH_2)_5COOC_2H_5} \underset{\underset{(CH_2)_5COOC_2H_5}{|}}{CH_3COCHCOOC_2H_5}$$

$$(86) \qquad\qquad\qquad\qquad\qquad (87)$$

$$\downarrow KOH$$

$$CH_3CO\underset{\underset{NNHPh}{\|}}{C}(CH_2)_5COOH \xleftarrow{PhN_2^+\ Cl^-} CH_3COCH_2(CH_2)_5COOH$$

$$(89) \qquad\qquad\qquad\qquad\qquad (88)$$

$$\downarrow H_2/Pd$$

$$CH_3CO\underset{\underset{NH_2}{|}}{C}H(CH_2)_5COOH \xrightarrow{KCNO} \text{Structure (91)} \xrightarrow{H_2/Pt} 85$$

$$(90) \qquad\qquad\qquad\qquad\qquad (91)$$

Biosynthesis of biotin

It has been found[56] that *Penicillium chrysogenum 62078* can synthesize desthiobiotin, and the amount produced is increased by the addition of pimelic acid; this adds support to the belief that desthiobiotin is an intermediate in the biosynthesis of biotin.

Analogues of biotin[25,55]

Of the eight possible stereoisomers of biotin, only (+)-biotin possesses biological activity. Desthiobiotin is active in some microorganisms, but not in others, and it was found that the former group of organisms is able to convert desthiobiotin into biotin. Oxybiotin (**98**) is an analogue with the sulphur of biotin replaced by oxygen. It has been synthesized[16,37,38,39] by the method summarized in **92 → 98**.

Oxybiotin can replace biotin in metabolic reactions, and it has been shown[36] that it is not converted *in vivo* into biotin, so that the sulphur atom of biotin is not essential for activity.

Several other analogues of biotin have been synthesized and biologically tested[25,55]. It has been found that increasing or decreasing the length of the side-chain leads to growth inhibitors. The compounds 2-γ-hydroxypropyl-2′-oxoimidazolidino[4′,5′-c]thiophene (**99**) and (±)-tetradehydrobiotin (**100**) are inactive, and that (±)-oxybiotinsulphonic acid (**101**, R = SO_3H) and the thiol **101**, R = SH^2, are biotin antagonists for some microorganisms.

The biochemical function of biotin[57]

Evidence has recently been obtained[62] that biotin functions in the form **102** and transfers a carboxyl group to some acceptor molecule (for example coenzyme A) to give **103** and the carboxylated acceptor (malonylcoenzyme A). The reverse reaction (**103 → 102**) can be brought about by treatment with bicarbonate.

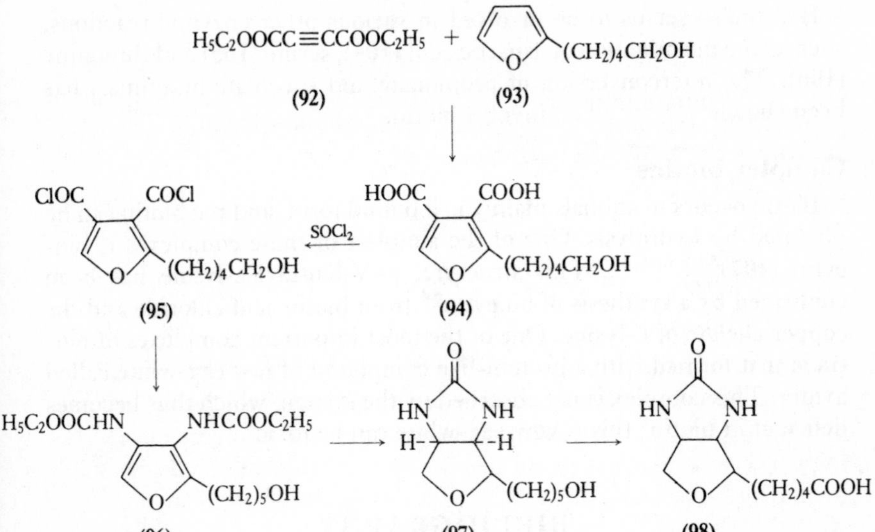

(92) (93) (94) (95) (96) (97) (98)

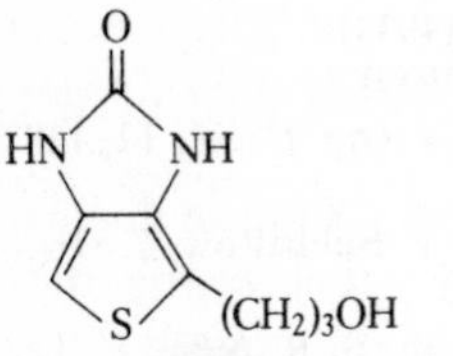

(99)

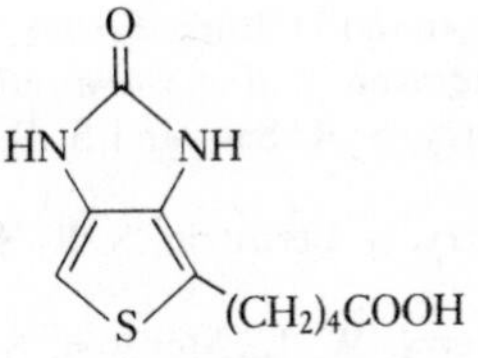

(100)

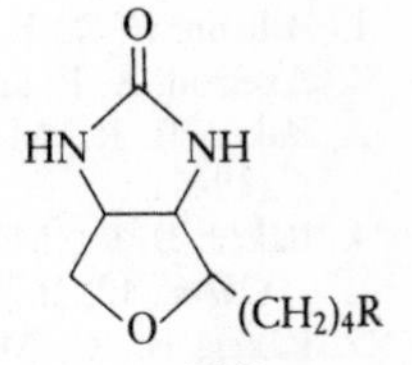

(101)

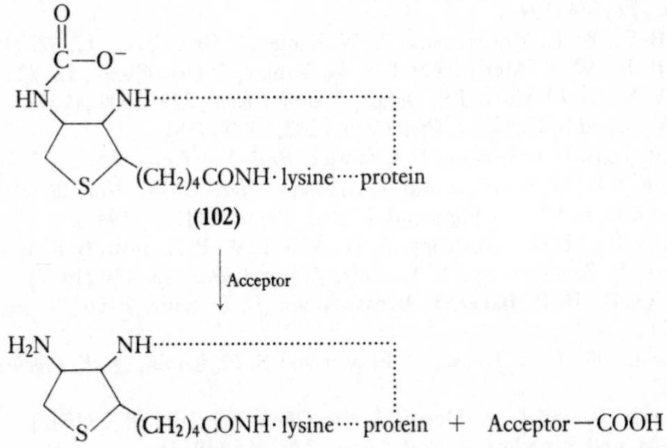

(102) (103)

Biotin also seems to be involved in various other enzymic reactions, such as the deamination of aspartic acid (104), serine (105) and threonine (106). The interconversion of propionate and succinate in animals has been shown[9,10,18,19,58] to involve biotin.

Complex biotins

Biotin occurs in animals mainly in a bound form, and the biotin can be liberated by hydrolysis. One of the simplest of these complexes is bio-cytin (107)[54,65,66,67]. This structure, ε-N-biotinyl-L-lysine has been confirmed by a synthesis of biocytin[64] from biotin acid chloride and the copper chelate of L-lysine. One of the most important complexes of biotin is that formed with a protein-like compound of raw egg-white called avidin. This complex is not absorbed by the system, which thus becomes deficient in biotin; this is why egg-white can be toxic.

BIBLIOGRAPHY

1. Allison, F. E., E. R. Hoover and D. Burk, *Science*, **78**, 217 (1933).
2. Axelrod, A. F. and K. Hofmann, *J. Biol. Chem.*, **180**, 525 (1949).
3. Baker, B. R., M. V. Querry, S. R. Safir and S. Bernstein, *J. Org. Chem.*, **12**, 138 (1947).
4. Baker, B. R., M. V. Querry, S. Bernstein, S. R. Safir and Y. SubbaRow, *J. Org. Chem.*, **12**, 167 (1947).
5. Baker, B. R., M. V. Querry, W. L. McEwen, S. Bernstein, S. R. Safir, L. L. Dorfman and Y. SubbaRow, *J. Org. Chem.*, **12**, 186 (1947).
6. Baker, B. R., M. V. Querry, S. R. Safir, W. L. McEwen and S. Bernstein, *J. Org. Chem.*, **12**, 174 (1947).
7. Baker, B. R., W. L. McEwen and W. N. Kinley, *J. Org. Chem.*, **12**, 322 (1947).
8. Baker, B. R., W. L. McEwen and W. N. Kinley, *J. Org. Chem.*, **12**, 323 (1947).
9. Beck, W. S., M. Flavin and S. Ochoa, *J. Biol. Chem.*, **229**, 1009 (1957).
10. Beck, W. S. and S. Ochoa, *J. Biol. Chem.*, **232**, 931 (1958).
11. Bougault, J., E. Cattelain and P. Chabrier, *Bull. Soc. Chim. France*, **7**, 781 (1940).
12. Bourquin, J. P., O. Schnider and A. Grussner, *Helv. Chim. Acta*, **28**, 528 (1945).
13. Brown, G. B. and V. du Vigneaud, *J. Biol. Chem.*, **141**, 85 (1941).
14. Brown, G. B., M. D. Armstrong, A. W. Moyer, W. P. Anslow, B. R. Baker, M. V. Querry, S. Bernstein and S. R. Safir, *J. Org. Chem.*, **12**, 160 (1947).
15. Brown, G. B., B. R. Baker, S. Bernstein and S. R. Safir, *J. Org. Chem.*, **12**, 155 (1947).
16. Duschinsky, R., L. A. Dolan, D. Flower and S. H. Rubin, *Arch. Biochem.*, **6**, 480 (1945).
17. Duschinsky, R. and L. A. Dolan, *J. Am. Chem. Soc.*, **67**, 2079 (1945).
18. Flavin, M. and S. Ochoa, *J. Biol. Chem.*, **229**, 965 (1957).
19. Flavin, M., H. Castro-Mendoza and S. Ochoa, *J. Biol. Chem.*, **229**, 981 (1957).

COOH
|
CH₂
|
CHNH₂
|
COOH
(104)

COOH
|
CHNH₂
|
CH₂OH
(105)

COOH
|
CHNH₂
|
CHOH
|
CH₃
(106)

$$\text{(CH}_2\text{)}_4\text{CONH(CH}_2\text{)}_4\overset{\overset{\displaystyle NH_2}{|}}{\text{CH}}\text{COOH}$$
(107)

20. Folkers, K., *Medicinal Chemistry* (Ed. by A. Burger), 2nd ed., Interscience, New York, 1960, Chap. 10.
21. Goldberg, M. W. and L. H. Sternback, *U.S. Pat.*, 2,489,232–2,489,238 (1949).
22. Grussner, A., J. P. Bourquin and O. Schnider, *Helv. Chim. Acta*, 28, 517 (1945).
23. Gyorgy, P., R. Kuhn and E. Lederer, *J. Biol. Chem.*, 131, 745 (1939).
24. Gyorgy, P., D. B. Melville, D. Burk and V. du Vigneaud, *Science*, 91, 243 (1940).
25. Gyorgy, P., *The Vitamins: Chemistry, Physiology and Pathology* (Ed. by W. H. Sebrell and R. S. Harris), Academic Press, New York, 1954, p. 563.
26. Harris, S. A., D. E. Wolf, R. Mozingo and K. Folkers, *Science*, 97, 447 (1943).
27. Harris, S. A., D. E. Wolf, R. Mozingo, R. C. Anderson, G. E. Arth, N. R. Easton, D. Heyl, A. N. Wilson and K. Folkers, *J. Am. Chem. Soc.*, 66, 1756 (1944).
28. Harris, S. A., N. R. Easton, D. Heyl, A. N. Wilson and K. Folkers, *J. Am. Chem. Soc.*, 66, 1757 (1944).
29. Harris, S. A., R. Mozingo, D. E. Wolf, A. N. Wilson, G. E. Arth and K. Folkers, *J. Am. Chem. Soc.*, 66, 1800 (1944).
30. Harris, S. A., D. E. Wolf, R. Mozingo, G. E. Arth, R. C. Anderson, N. R. Easton and K. Folkers, *J. Am. Chem. Soc.*, 67, 2096 (1945).
31. Harris, S. A., R. Mozingo, D. E. Wolf, A. N. Wilson and K. Folkers, *J. Am. Chem. Soc.*, 67, 2102 (1945).
32. Hofmann, K., D. B. Melville and V. du Vigneaud, *J. Am. Chem. Soc.*, 63, 3237 (1941).
33. Hofmann, K., D. B. Melville and V. du Vigneaud, *J. Biol. Chem.*, 141, 207 (1941).
34. Hofmann, K., G. W. Kilner, D. B. Melville, V. du Vigneaud and H. H. Darby, *J. Biol. Chem.*, 145, 503 (1942).
35. Hofmann, K., D. B. Melville and V. du Vigneaud, *J. Biol. Chem.*, 144, 513 (1942).
36. Hofmann, K. and T. Winnick, *J. Biol. Chem.*, 160, 449 (1945).
37. Hofmann, K., *J. Am. Chem. Soc.*, 67, 694 (1945).
38. Hofmann, K., *J. Am. Chem. Soc.*, 67, 1459 (1945).
39. Hofmann, K., *Brit. Pats.*, 615,901 (1945); 615,908 (1946); 615,909 (1946); 617,260 (1946).
40. International Union Pure Applied Chemistry (Commission on Nomenclature of Biological Chemistry), *J. Am. Chem. Soc.*, 82, 5575 (1960).
41. Jansen, A. B. A. and P. J. Stokes, *J. Chem. Soc.*, 4909 (1962).
42. Kilner, G. W., M. D. Armstrong, G. B. Brown and V. du Vigneaud, *J. Biol. Chem.*, 145, 495 (1942).
43. Kögl, F. and B. Tönnis, *Z. Physiol. Chem.*, 242, 43 (1936).
44. Kögl, F. and L. Pons, *Z. Physiol. Chem.*, 269, 61 (1941).
45. Kögl, F. and T. J. de Man, *Z. Physiol. Chem.*, 269, 81 (1941).
46. Kögl, F. and E. J. ten Ham, *Naturwissenschaften*, 31, 208 (1943).
47. Kögl, F. and E. J. ten Ham, *Z. Physiol. Chem.*, 279, 140 (1943).
48. Landy, M., van R. Potter and C. A. Elvehjem, *J. Biol. Chem.*, 169, 451 (1947).
49. Lichstein, H. C. and W. W. Umbreit, *J. Biol. Chem.*, 170, 329 (1947).
50. Lichstein, H. C., *Vitamins Hormones*, 9, 27 (1951).
51. Melville, D. B., K. Hofmann, E. Hague and V. du Vigneaud, *J. Biol. Chem.*, 142, 615 (1942).
52. Melville, D. B., K. Hofmann and V. du Vigneaud, *J. Biol. Chem.*, 145, 101 (1942).
53. Melville, D. B., A. W. Moyer, K. Hofmann and V. du Vigneaud, *J. Biol. Chem.*, 146, 487 (1942).

54. Peck, R. L., D. E. Wolf and K. Folkers, *J. Am. Chem. Soc.*, **74**, 1999 (1952).
55. Robinson, F. A., *The Vitamin B Complex*, Chapman and Hall, London, 1951, p. 446.
56. Tatum, E. L., *J. Biol. Chem.*, **160**, 455 (1945).
57. Terroine, T., *Vitamins Hormones*, **18**, 1 (1960).
58. Tietz, A. and S. Ochoa, *J. Biol. Chem.*, **234**, 1394 (1959).
59. du Vigneaud, V., K. Hofmann, D. B. Melville and J. R. Rachele, *J. Biol. Chem.*, **140**, 643 (1941).
60. du Vigneaud, V., K. Hofmann, D. B. Melville and J. R. Rachele, *J. Biol. Chem.*, **140**, 763 (1941).
61. du Vigneaud, V., D. B. Melville, K. Folkers, D. E. Wolf, R. Mozingo, J. C. Keresztesy and S. A. Harris, *J. Biol. Chem.*, **146**, 475 (1942).
62. Waite, M. and S. J. Wakil, *J. Biol. Chem.*, **238**, 81 (1963).
63. Williams, R. J., *J. Am. Med. Assoc.*, **119**, 1 (1942).
64. Wolf, D. E., J. Valiant and K. Folkers, *J. Am. Chem. Soc.*, **73**, 4142 (1951).
65. Wolf, D. E., J. Valiant, R. L. Peck and K. Folkers, *J. Am. Chem. Soc.*, **74**, 2002 (1952).
66. Wright, L. D., E. L. Cresson, H. R. Skeggs, R. L. Peck, D. E. Wolf, T. R. Wood, J. Valiant and K. Folkers, *Science*, **114**, 635 (1951).
67. Wright, L. D., E. L. Cresson, H. R. Skeggs, T. R. Wood, R. L. Peck, D. E. Wolf and K. Folkers, *J. Am. Chem. Soc.*, **72**, 1048 (1950); **74**, 1996 (1952).

CHAPTER 10

Lipoic Acid (6-Thiotic Acid)

LIPOIC ACID – Structure – Synthesis – Biochemical function –
BIBLIOGRAPHY

SNELL was able to show[24] that the growth factor for *Tetrahymena geleii* present in liver extracts[6,11], the acetate-replacing factor for *Lactobacillus casei* present in yeast extracts[7] and the pyruvate-oxidation factor for *Streptococcus faecalis* present in yeast[13] were one and the same substance. The compound was first isolated in a pure state[17] from liver and was named α-lipoic acid.

No deficiency disease has been observed in man.

Structure[21]

The analysis of lipoic acid established[4,15] a molecular formula of $C_8H_{14}O_2S_2$. The compound was found to be optically active, and to be an acid (pK_a 5·0). A Kuhn–Roth determination indicated the absence of carbon-methyl groups.

When lipoic acid was treated with Raney nickel, n-octanoic acid (1) was formed, whereas mild reduction of the vitamin yielded a substance containing two sulphydryl groups. Hence lipoic acid is a cyclic disulphide of octanoic acid.

The size of the sulphur-containing ring was revealed by synthesis[5] and the structure of lipoic acid was thus established as 2, 5-[3-(1,2-dithiolanyl)]pentanoic acid.

Synthesis

Several syntheses of lipoic acid have been reported[5,10,20,23,25]. The first one[10] was ambiguous because of the rearrangements that occurred in one or more of the intermediates, thus not helping to establish the structure of the substance. In this synthesis, 4-(α-tetrahydrofuranyl)-butanoic acid (3) was reacted with thiourea and hydrobromic acid to

$CH_3(CH_2)_6COOH$

(1)

(CH$_2$)$_4$COOH attached to a ring S—S

(2)

O attached to ring (CH$_2$)$_3$COOH

(3)

→ [reagents: $S=C(NH_2)_2$, HBr]

$$HN=C(NH_2)-S-(CH_2)_x-CH-(CH_2)_yCOOH$$
with S below the CH, and $H_2NC=NH$ attached

(4)

↓

$$HS-(CH_2)_x-CH-(CH_2)_yCOOH$$
$$SH$$

(5)

yield a diisothiouronium salt (4), which was hydrolysed to a dimercapto-octanoic acid (5). The latter, on oxidation with iodine, formed a cyclic disulphide (6) which was identical with (±)-lipoic acid. It was found that when 3 was treated with hydrobromic acid alone, the δ-lactone 7 was formed, which readily isomerized to the γ-lactone 8; treatment of the latter with thiourea and acid gave the compound 4. In the formulae 4 → 8, $x + y = 6$. The starting material 3 was prepared from furfural as shown in 9 → 12 → 3.

The first unambiguous synthesis which established the structure 2 for lipoic acid[5] is shown in 13 → 18 → 2.

The synthesis of the compound 19 has also been described[5] and it was shown to be different from lipoic acid.

The above method of synthesis was later modified[25] and improved yields were obtained of the racemic lipoic acid. This synthesis is shown in 14 → 20 → 23 → 18 → 2. Further modifications[20] of this general scheme were subsequently reported.

A rather different approach which also gives good yields of lipoic acid[23] is shown in 24 → 29 → 2 (p. 186).

The (±)-lipoic acid which results from these syntheses has been resolved[2] through the cinchonidine salt. However, both isomers of lipoic acid have also been obtained synthetically by resolution of a suitable intermediate[1,2,26]. For example[26], (±)-7-carbethoxy-3-thioacetoxyheptanoic acid (30) was resolved, and each isomer carried through the remainder of the synthesis, which involved hydrolysis, introduction of a second —SH group and oxidation.

The dextro- and laevorotatory forms of 31, obtained from 30 by hydrolysis, have been related[12] to (+)-3-methyloctane-1,8-dioic acid (32) whose configuration is known. It was concluded[12] that (−)-3-mercaptooctanedioic acid (31) possesses the same configuration as (+)-3-methyloctanedioic acid (32), and since (−)-31 is the intermediate which ultimately yields the biologically active (+)-lipoic acid, the absolute configuration of (+)-lipoic acid must be as shown in 33 (p. 187).

Biochemical function[9,22]

It has been shown[8,14,16,18,19] that lipoic acid is involved, together with thiamine and coenzyme A, in the enzymic oxidation of pyruvate to acetate, and the subsequent participation of acetate in the citric acid cycle. It has already been shown (in the discussion of the biological function of thiamine given in Chapter 2) how the anion 34 can arise by interaction of pyruvate with thiamine. If this anion now reacts with lipoic

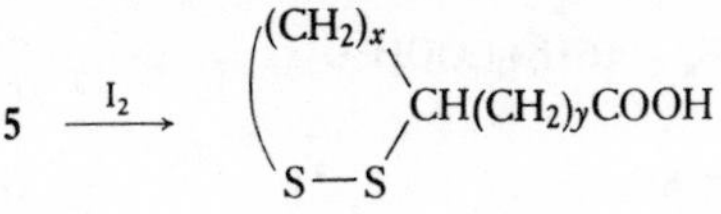

(6)

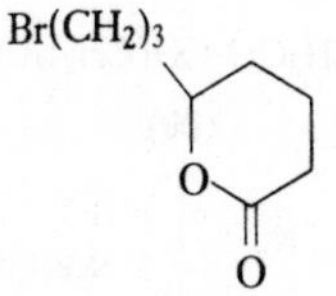

(7)

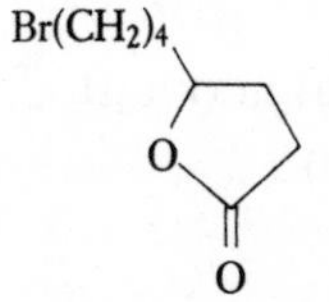

(8)

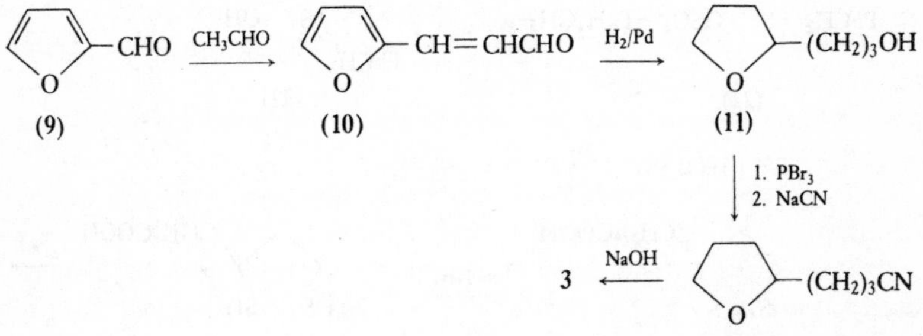

(9) (10) (11) (12)

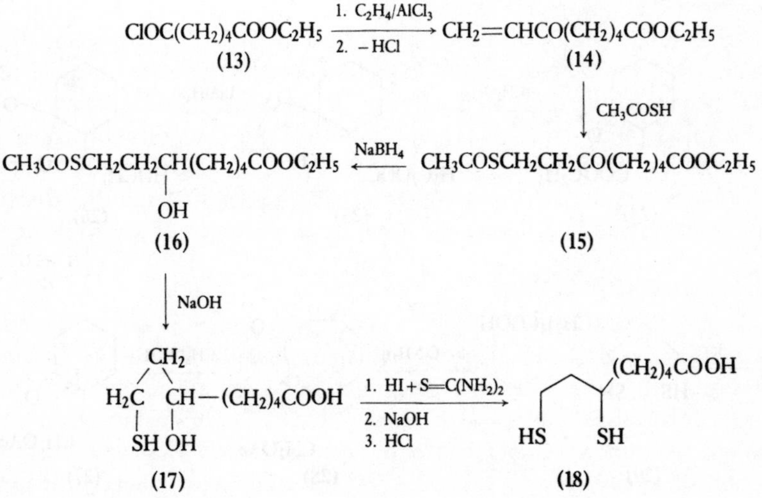

(13) (14) (15) (16) (17) (18)

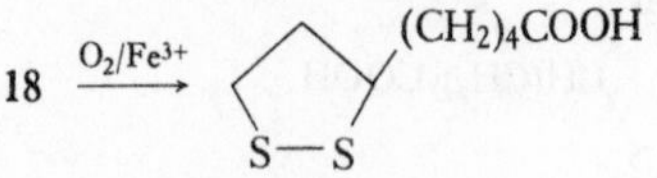

$$18 \xrightarrow{O_2/Fe^{3+}}$$

(2)

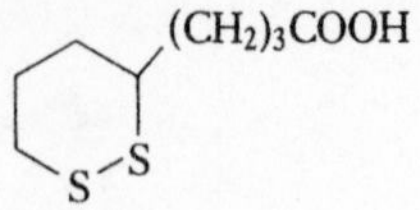

(19)

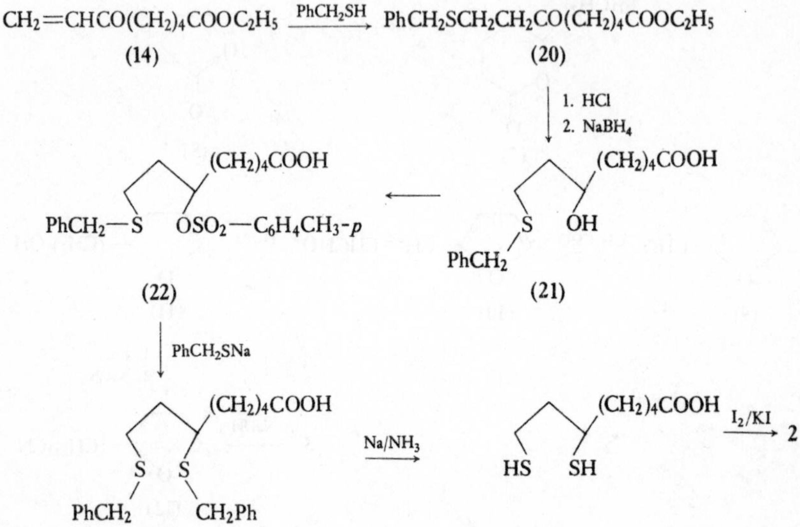

$$CH_2{=}CHCO(CH_2)_4COOC_2H_5 \xrightarrow{PhCH_2SH} PhCH_2SCH_2CH_2CO(CH_2)_4COOC_2H_5$$

(14)   (20)

1. HCl
2. NaBH$_4$

(22)

(21)

PhCH$_2$SNa

(23)

$$\xrightarrow{Na/NH_3}$$

(18)

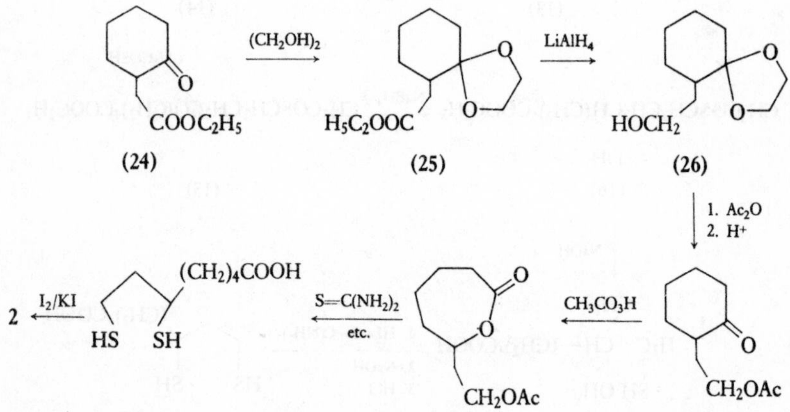

$$\xrightarrow{I_2/KI} 2$$

(24)

$$\xrightarrow{(CH_2OH)_2}$$

(25)

$$\xrightarrow{LiAlH_4}$$

(26)

1. Ac$_2$O
2. H$^+$

$$2 \xleftarrow{I_2/KI}$$

(29)

$$\xleftarrow[\text{etc.}]{S{=}C(NH_2)_2}$$

(28)

$$\xleftarrow{CH_3CO_3H}$$

(27)

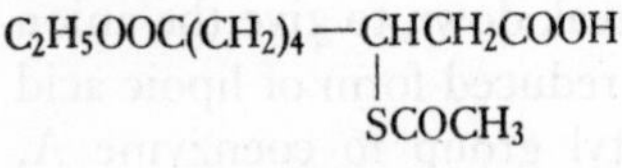
C2H5OOC(CH2)4—CHCH2COOH
SCOCH3

(30)

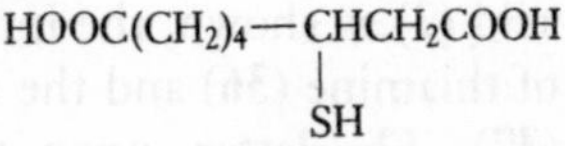
HOOC(CH2)4—CHCH2COOH
SH

(31)

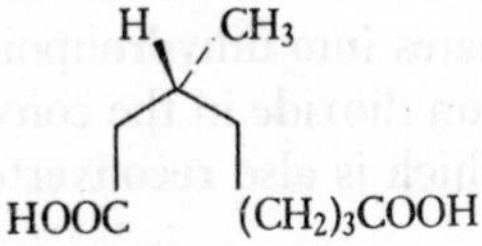
H
CH3
HOOC
(CH2)3COOH

(32)

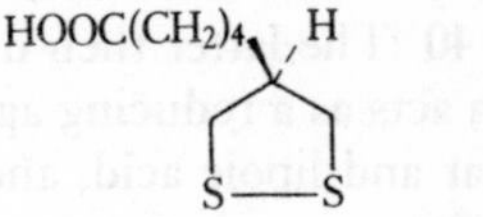
HOOC(CH2)4
H
S
S

(33)

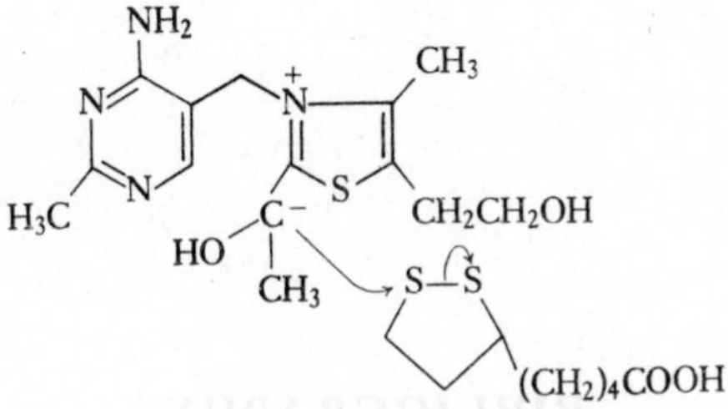
NH2
CH3
N
N
H3C
S
CH2CH2OH
C−
HO
CH3
S–S
(CH2)4COOH

(34) (2)

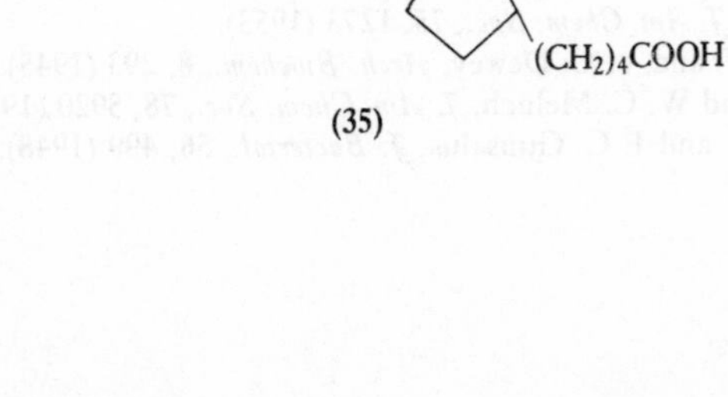
NH2
CH3
N
N
H3C
S
H—O
C
CH2CH2OH
CH3
S
SH
(CH2)4COOH

(35)

acid (2) as shown, the intermediate 35 can break down to give the anion of thiamine (36) and the monoacetate of the reduced form of lipoic acid (37). The latter, upon transferring its acetyl group to coenzyme A, yields acetylcoenzyme A and the reduced form of lipoic acid (38) which is reconverted into 2 by a diphosphopyridine nucleotide enzyme system.

(+)-Lipoic acid is also involved[3] in the conversion of light energy into chemical energy during photosynthesis. It is postulated that lipoic acid (2) is converted into the diradical 39 which reacts with water to form 40. The latter then disproportionates into dihydrolipoic acid (38), which acts as a reducing agent for carbon dioxide in the conversion into a sugar and lipoic acid, and into 41, which is also reconverted to lipoic acid (2).

BIBLIOGRAPHY

1. Acker, D. S., U.S. Pat., 2,792,406 (1957).
2. Acker, D. S. and W. J. Wayne, J. Am. Chem. Soc., 79, 6483 (1957).
3. Barltrop, J. A., P. M. Hayes and M. Calvin, J. Am. Chem. Soc., 76, 4348 (1954).
4. Brockman, J. A., E. L. R. Stokstad, E. L. Patterson, J. V. Pierce, M. E. Macchi and F. P. Day, J. Am. Chem. Soc., 74, 1868 (1952).
5. Bullock, M. W., J. A. Brockman, E. L. Patterson, J. V. Pierce, M. H. von Saltza, F. Sanders and E. L. R. Stokstad, J. Am. Chem. Soc., 76, 1828 (1954).
6. Dewey, V. C., Proc. Soc. Exp. Biol. Med., 46, 482 (1941).
7. Guirard, B. M., E. E. Snell and R. J. Williams, Arch. Biochem., 9, 361 (1946).
8. Gunsalus, I. C., L. Struglia and D. I. O'Kane, J. Biol. Chem., 194, 859 (1952).
9. Gunsalus, I. C., J. Vitaminol. (Kyōto), 4, 52 (1958).
10. Hornberger, C. S., R. F. Heitmiller, I. C. Gunsalus, G. H. F. Schnakenberg and L. J. Reed, J. Am. Chem. Soc., 75, 1273 (1953).
11. Kidder, G. W. and V. C. Dewey, Arch. Biochem., 8, 293 (1945).
12. Mislow, K. and W. C. Meluch, J. Am. Chem. Soc., 78, 5920 (1956).
13. O'Kane, D. J. and I. C. Gunsalus, J. Bacteriol., 56, 499 (1948).

$$(36) \quad + \quad (37)$$

$$\downarrow \text{CoA}$$

$$\text{Acetylcoenzyme A} \quad + \quad (38)$$

$$\downarrow \text{DPN}$$

$$(2)$$

$$(2) \xrightarrow[\text{chlorophyll}]{h\nu} (39)$$

$$\downarrow H_2O$$

$$(40) \longleftarrow (41)$$

$$(41) \downarrow$$

$$2 + H_2O_2$$

$$(40) \downarrow$$

$$(38) \xrightarrow[CO_2]{TPN} 2 + \text{a sugar}$$

14. Patterson, E. L., J. A. Brockman, F. P. Day, J. V. Pierce, M. E. Macchi, C. E. Hoffman, C. T. O. Fong, E. L. R. Stokstad and T. J. Jukes, *J. Am. Chem. Soc.*, 73, 5919 (1951).
15. Pierce, J. V. and M. E. Macchi, *J. Am. Chem. Soc.*, 76, 1827 (1954).
16. Reed, L. J. and B. G. De Busk, *J. Am. Chem. Soc.*, 73, 5920 (1951).
17. Reed, L. J., B. G. De Busk, I. C. Gunsalus and C. S. Hornberger, *Science*, 114, 93 (1951).
18. Reed, L. J., *Physiol. Rev.*, 33, 544 (1953).
19. Reed, L. J. and B. G. De Busk, *J. Am. Chem. Soc.*, 75, 1261 (1953).
20. Reed, L. J. and Ching-I Niu, *J. Am. Chem. Soc.*, 77, 416 (1955).
21. Reed, L. J., *Advan. in Enzymol.*, 18, 319 (1957).
22. Reed, L. J., *Vitamins Hormones*, 20, 1 (1962).
23. Segre, A., R. Viterbo and G. Parisi, *J. Am. Chem. Soc.*, 79, 3503 (1957).
24. Snell, E. E. and H. P. Broquist, *Arch. Biochem.*, 23, 326 (1949).
25. Soper, Q. F., W. E. Buting, J. E. Cochran and A. Pohland, *J. Am. Chem. Soc.*, 76, 4109 (1954).
26. Walton, E., A. F. Wagner, F. W. Bachelor, L. H. Peterson, F. W. Holly and K. Folkers, *J. Am. Chem. Soc.*, 77, 5144 (1955).

CHAPTER 11

Vitamin C (L-Ascorbic Acid)

INTRODUCTION – VITAMIN C – Isolation – Occurrence – Deficiency
disease – Daily requirement – Structure – Synthesis – Biosynthesis –
Analogues of L-ascorbic acid – The biological function of L-ascorbic
acid – BIBLIOGRAPHY

INTRODUCTION

THE DISEASE called scurvy has been known from ancient times, and in
the eighteenth century its cause was traced to a lack of fresh fruit and
vegetables in the diet. Lemon juice in particular was found to be an
effective cure provided that the disease was not too far advanced. In
early attempts to isolate the antiscorbutic factor[14,44], active concentrates
were obtained from lemons and some of the properties of the compound
or compounds were investigated even though pure material was not
available. It was shown[14,44] that the substance is a water-soluble
organic compound which does not contain nitrogen and is probably
related to the sugars. It was found that the compound is a strong reducing agent and the oxidized form (now known as dehydroascorbic acid)
retains the antiscorbutic activity.

VITAMIN C

Isolation

Szent-Györgyi[38,39] isolated a crystalline, optically active compound
of molecular formula $C_6H_8O_6$ from orange juice which he named
'hexuronic acid'. Later the antiscorbutic factor was isolated[41] from
lemon juice and subsequently was found to be identical with hexuronic
acid.

Occurrence

Vitamin C is distributed widely in both the plant and animal kingdoms,
either as such (plants) or in equilibrium with dehydroascorbic acid

(animals and plants). The richest sources of the compound are rose hips, pine needles, West Indian cherry, liver, milk, fruits and green vegetables.

Deficiency disease

The first symptoms of ascorbic acid deficiency are usually weakness, easy fatigue and listlessness, followed by shortage of breath and aching in the bones. As the scurvy becomes worse the skin becomes dry and rough. Haemorrhage occurs in the muscles, causing a typical bruised appearance on the skin. In severe deficiency the gums swell and bleed very easily and the teeth become loose. Ultimately convulsions and death occur.

Daily requirement

This depends somewhat on the degree of physical exertion, but for the normal healthy adult 75–100 mg are recommended[29].

Ascorbic acid is practically non-toxic.

Structure[12,15,20,28,35]

L-Ascorbic acid is a white crystalline solid of molecular formula $C_6H_8O_6$, and is optically active. It liberates carbon dioxide from sodium bicarbonate to form the salt $C_6H_7O_6Na$. Ascorbic acid forms a 2,4-dinitrophenylhydrazone, but the colour is not restored to Schiff's reagent; it gives an intense colour with ferric chloride. Upon treatment with acids, ascorbic acid is easily converted into furfural, and catalytic hydrogenation of the compound[27] yields L-idonic acid (indicating the presence of one double bond). Thus, ascorbic acid possesses an unbranched chain of six carbon atoms and is closely related to the sugars. It is a powerful reducing agent, much more so than sugars such as D-glucose.

Ascorbic acid can be converted[10] into a tetraacetate, thus indicating the presence of four hydroxyl groups in the molecule, but two of these are of a different character because acetylation of ascorbic acid under mild conditions[5,9] yields a diacetate. The remaining two hydroxyl groups can be methylated with diazomethane[23,24]. These two methyl groups are stable to alkali, indicating[20] that they are probably enolic.

When ascorbic acid itself is treated with an excess of diazomethane, a dimethyl ether is produced, which, when treated with one equivalent of sodium hydroxide, forms a sodium salt without the loss of a methyl group, showing that a lactone ring is present in the molecule. The dimethylascorbic acid yields a monoisopropylidene derivative with acetone[24,26] and it also forms a monotrityl derivative[43]. Hence, the two free hydroxyl groups of dimethylascorbic acid are normal alcoholic hydroxyl groups, and one of these is primary.

In the cold ascorbic acid reacts immediately with one mole of chlorine, bromine or iodine[20] to yield dehydroascorbic acid, $C_6H_6O_6$, and two equivalents of hydrogen halide. Halogen is not added to the molecule. This oxidation may be reversed by hydrogen iodide or by hydrogen sulphide.

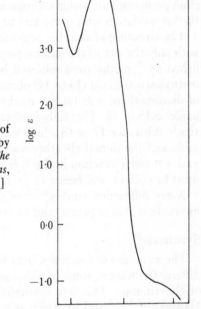

Figure 11.1. The ultraviolet spectrum of ascorbic acid (in water). [Reproduced, by permission, from H. R. Rosenberg, *The Chemistry and Physiology of the Vitamins*, Interscience, New York, 1945, p. 294.]

Dehydroascorbic acid does not yield furfural when treated with acids, and *it is not acidic*. This observation—that a strongly acidic compound (ascorbic acid) yields an almost neutral substance when mildly oxidized —strongly suggested that the enediol system 1 is present in ascorbic acid. Dehydroascorbic acid was shown to possess the properties typical of a γ-lactone[15].

The ultraviolet spectrum of ascorbic acid (Figure 11.1) is closely similar to the spectrum of dihydroxymaleic acid (2), which is also easily oxidized to a dehydro compound (3).

Since it was shown above that ascorbic acid contains a lactone ring, the evidence so far described may be summarized in the part-structure 4. This structure expresses the acidic properties, the unsaturation and the reducing properties of the molecule. In one or other of its possible tautomeric forms (5 or 6), the typical carbonyl properties are explained.

When dehydroascorbic acid is oxidized with iodine in alkaline solution, oxalic acid is formed, so that the part-structure 7 may be written for the compound. Since the positions of the carboxyl groups indicates the position of the enediol grouping of ascorbic acid itself, part-structure 4 may be expanded to 8. Oxidation of ascorbic acid itself with acidified potassium permanganate yields L-threonic acid (9), which was identified by its further oxidation with nitric acid to L-tartaric acid (10).

The structure of ascorbic acid may thus now be expanded to 11 or 12 with only the size of the lactone ring in doubt. This last point was established by[20] methylation followed by oxidation. The neutral 2,3-di-O-methylascorbic acid (13 or 14) obtained from ascorbic acid by the action of diazomethane was further methylated with methyl iodide and silver oxide to 15 or 16. This fully methylated compound was ozonized to the single substance 17 or 18 which was treated with ammonia to yield oxamide and the dimethyl-L-threonamide (19 or 20). Since this substance gave a positive reaction in the Weerman test for α-hydroxyamides[11], 19 must be correct, and hence 11 for L-ascorbic acid itself.

X-ray diffraction studies[6,7,8] of L-ascorbic acid have shown that the molecule is almost planar, and its structure is as shown in 21 (p. 197).

Synthesis[36]

The structure of L-ascorbic acid has been amply confirmed by several different syntheses, some of which are used for the industrial production of the vitamin. The first synthesis was announced independently by Haworth[1,3,16,17] and by Reichstein[33,34].

In Haworth's synthesis, D-galactose (22) was converted into the diisopropylidene derivative (23) which was oxidized with potassium permanganate to 24. Sulphuric acid removed the blocking groups to yield D-galacturonic acid (25). This was reduced with sodium amalgam to L-galactonic acid (26) which was subjected to the Weerman degradation to yield L-lyxose (27). The derived osazone of 27 was hydrolysed with benzaldehyde to form L-xylosone (or L-lyxosone) (28) and the latter compound was treated with hydrogen cyanide to give 29. Hydrolysis of this

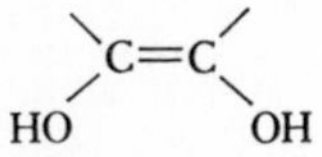

(1)

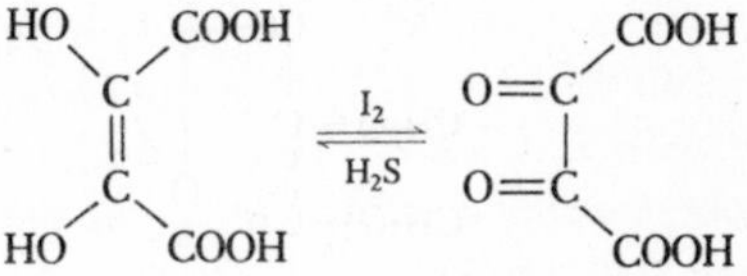

(2)

(3)

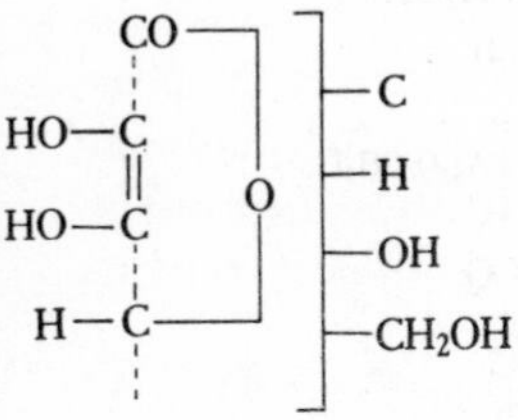

(4)

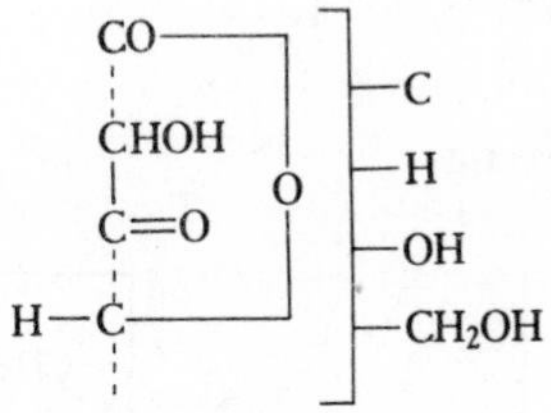

(5)

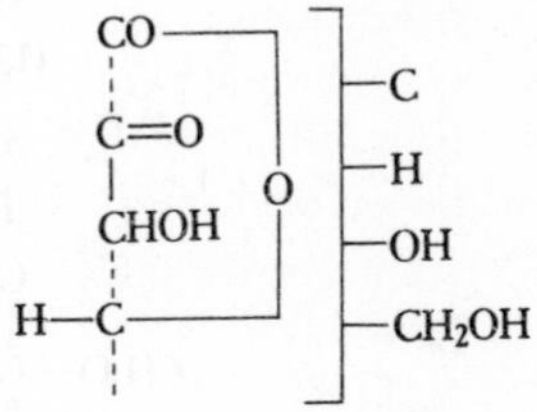

(6)

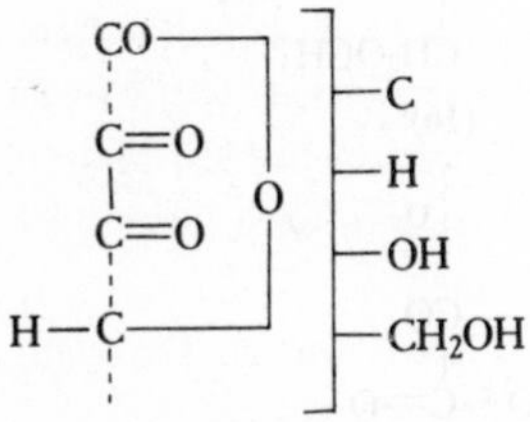

(7)

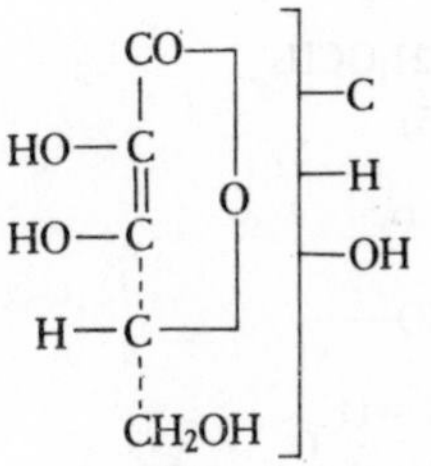

(8)

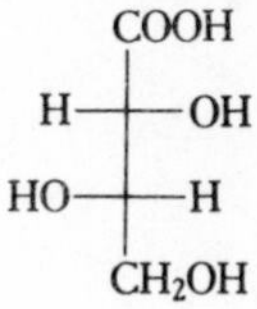

(9)

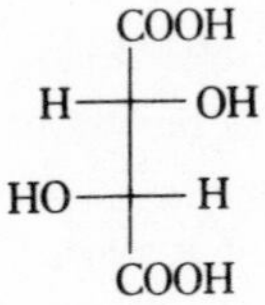

(10)

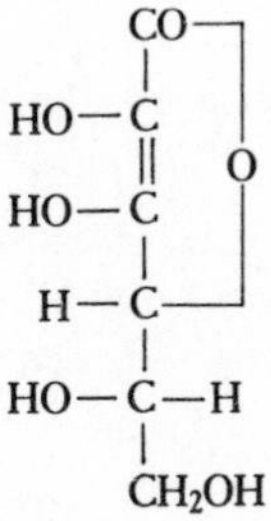

(11)

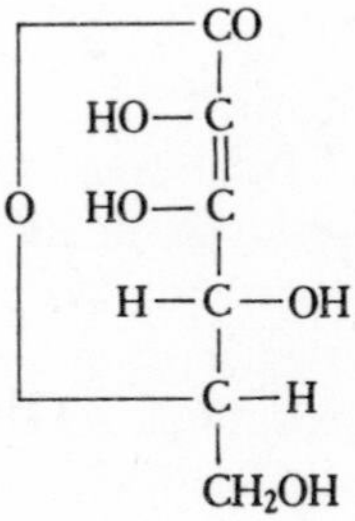

(12)

```
        CO──┐                         ┌──CO
CH₃O─C    │                    CH₃O─C
      ‖     O               O  CH₃O─C
CH₃O─C    │                          ‖
      │                              │
   H─C──┘                      H─C─OH
      │                            │
 HO─C─H                           C─H
      │                            │
   CH₂OH                         CH₂OH
    (13)                          (14)
```

$$\downarrow \text{Ag}_2\text{O}/\text{CH}_3\text{I} \qquad\qquad \downarrow \text{Ag}_2\text{O}/\text{CH}_3\text{I}$$

```
        CO──┐                         ┌──CO
CH₃O─C    │                    CH₃O─C
      ‖     O               O  CH₃O─C
CH₃O─C    │                          ‖
      │                              │
   H─C──┘                      H─C─OCH₃
      │                            │
CH₃O─C─H                          C─H
      │                            │
  CH₂OCH₃                       CH₂OCH₃
    (15)                          (16)
```

$$\downarrow \text{O}_3 \qquad\qquad\qquad \downarrow \text{O}_3$$

```
        CO──┐                         ┌──CO
CH₃O─C=O    │                 CH₃O─C=O
CH₃O─C=O    O              O  CH₃O─C=O
   H──┘   │                    H───┐
CH₃O──┤─H │                       │─OCH₃
      │                            │─H
  CH₂OCH₃                       CH₂OCH₃
    (17)                          (18)
```

$$\downarrow \text{NH}_3 \qquad\qquad\qquad \downarrow \text{NH}_3$$

```
    CONH₂                         CONH₂
  H──┤─OH                      H──┤─OCH₃
CH₃O──┤─H                     HO──┤─H
  CH₂OCH₃                       CH₂OCH₃
    (19)                          (20)
```

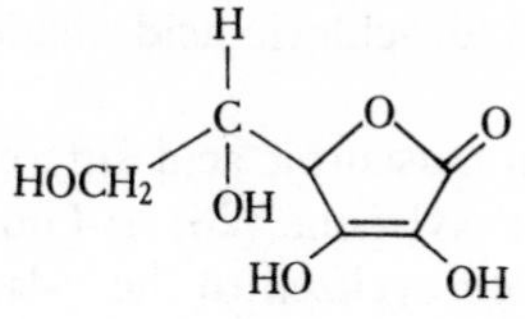

(21)

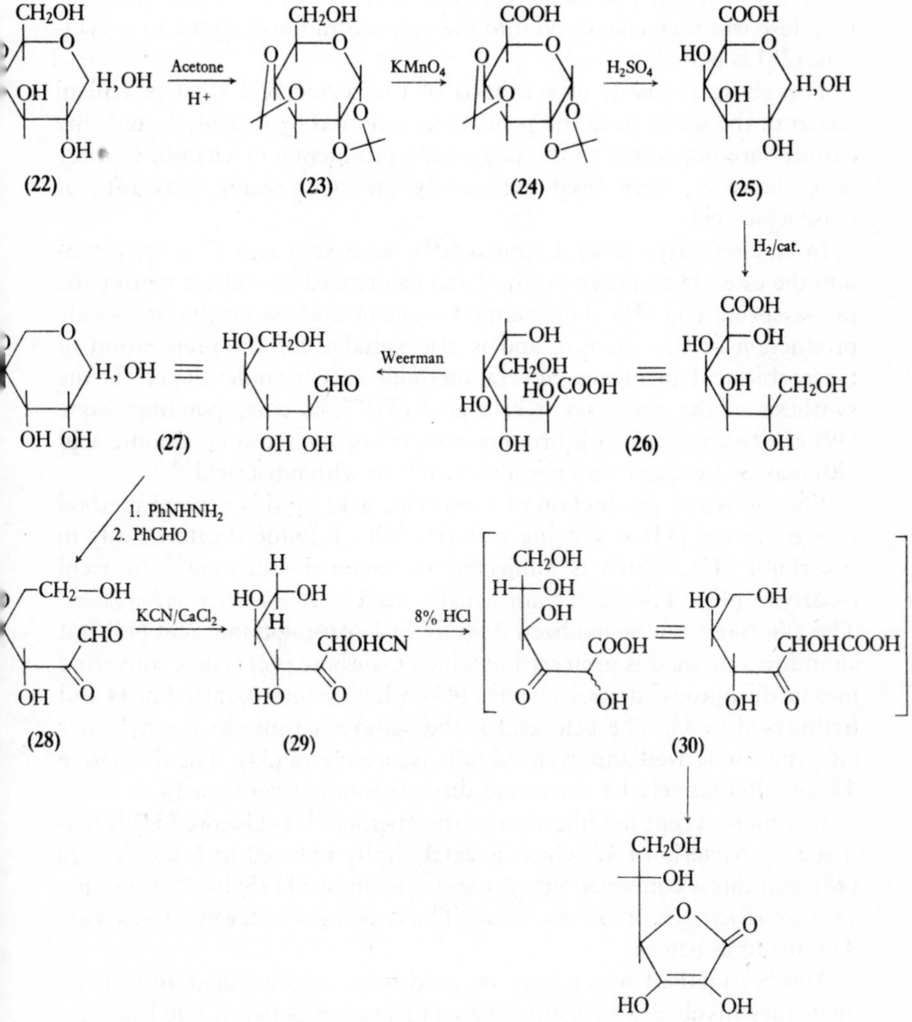

(22)   Acetone / H+   (23)   KMnO$_4$ (24)   H$_2$SO$_4$ (25)

H$_2$/cat.

(27) $\equiv$ Weerman   (26)

1. PhNHNH$_2$
2. PhCHO

(28)   KCN/CaCl$_2$ (29)   8% HCl   (30)

(31)

hydroxynitrile with 8% hydrochloric acid yielded L-ascorbic acid (31) via the intermediate 30.

Reichstein's synthesis of L-ascorbic acid differed from the above in the method used to prepare L-xylosone (28). D-Glucose (32) was oxidized with nitric acid to 33 which cyclized to the γ-lactone 34. Reduction of this lactone with sodium amalgam yielded L-gulonic acid (35), the calcium salt of which was oxidized to L-xylose (36) with Fenton's reagent. L-Xylose was then converted into the osazone and hydrolysed to L-xylosone (28) as before.

The above methods of synthesis of L-ascorbic acid (that is Kiliani ascent of the series from the pentosone, followed by hydrolysis and ring closure) are not suited to the large-scale production of vitamin C; they have, however, been used extensively for synthesizing analogues of L-ascorbic acid.

In an alternative general approach[36], the α-keto acid 37 is converted into the ester 38 and then cyclized and isomerized by sodium methoxide to L-ascorbic acid (31). This method is one of the best for the large-scale production of the vitamin, and is also suitable for the preparation of L-ascorbic acid analogues. Several methods have been developed for the synthesis of the necessary α-keto acid (37). The corresponding osone (39) can be oxidized with bromine water[30] or the required aldonic acid (40) may be oxidized with chromic acid[32] or with nitric acid[18].

The industrial production of L-ascorbic acid by this general method uses D-glucose (32) as starting material. This is reduced catalytically to D-sorbitol (41), which is subjected to bacterial oxidation[42] to yield L-sorbose (42). The bacterium usually used is *Acetobacter suboxydans*. The L-sorbose can be oxidized directly to 2-oxo-L-gulonic acid (45) but an indirect method is preferred in which L-sorbose (42) is first converted into its diisopropylidene derivative (43), which is then oxidized to 44 and hydrolysed to 45. The keto acid is then converted into its methyl ester (46) and isomerized and cyclized to L-ascorbic acid (31). The derivative 45 can alternatively be converted directly into L-ascorbic acid.

In a more recent modification of this method[21], D-glucose (32) is oxidized by bacteria to 47 which is catalytically reduced to L-idonic acid (48), and this is converted into 2-oxo-L-gulonic acid (45) by *Pseudomonas sp.*, *Acetobacter sp.* or *Aerobacter sp.* The remainder of the synthesis from 45 remains as before.

Another method which may be used for L-ascorbic acid and for its analogues involves a benzoin-type condensation between ethyl glyoxalate or ethyl mesoxalate and an aldotetrose. Thus, L-ascorbic acid itself

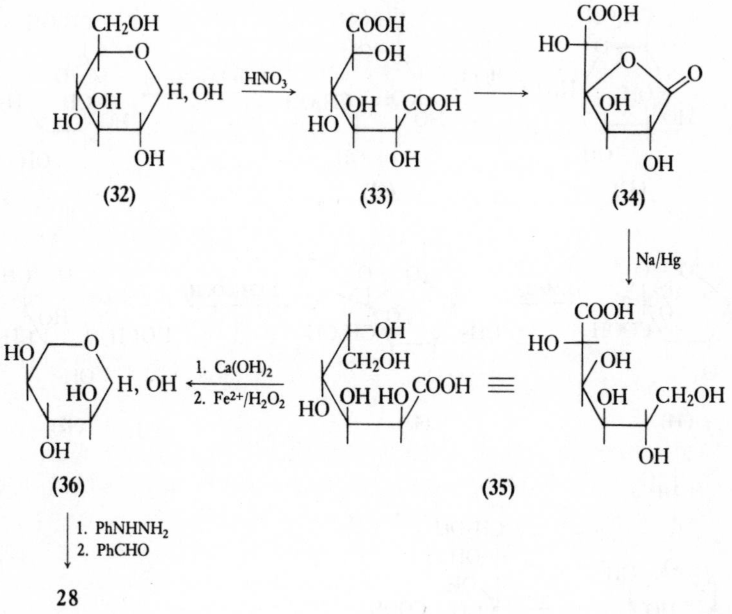

CH$_2$OH

HO

OH

H, OH

OH

(32)

$\xrightarrow{\text{HNO}_3}$

COOH

OH

HO

OH

COOH

OH

(33)

$\longrightarrow$

COOH

HO

O

O

OH

OH

(34)

$\downarrow$ Na/Hg

HO

O

HO

H, OH

OH

(36)

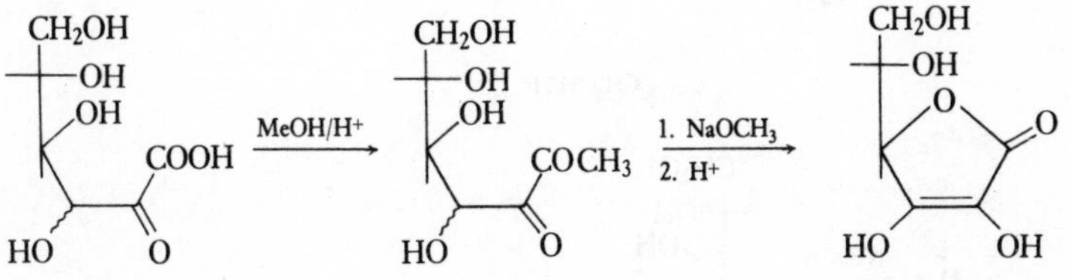

$\xleftarrow[\text{2. Fe}^{2+}/\text{H}_2\text{O}_2]{\text{1. Ca(OH)}_2}$

OH

CH$_2$OH

HO

OH HO

COOH

(35)

$\equiv$

COOH

HO

OH

OH

CH$_2$OH

OH

1. PhNHNH$_2$
2. PhCHO

28

CH$_2$OH

OH

OH

COOH

HO

O

(37)

$\xrightarrow{\text{MeOH/H}^+}$

CH$_2$OH

OH

OH

COCH$_3$

HO

O

(38)

$\xrightarrow[\text{2. H}^+]{\text{1. NaOCH}_3}$

CH$_2$OH

OH

O

O

HO

OH

(31)

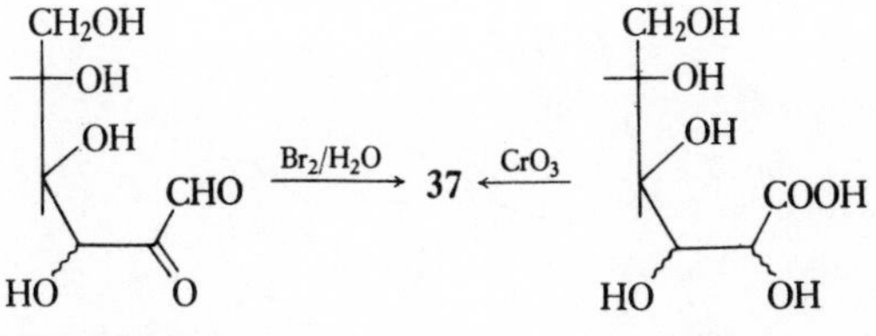

CH$_2$OH

OH

OH

CHO

HO

O

(39)

$\xrightarrow{\text{Br}_2/\text{H}_2\text{O}}$ 37 $\xleftarrow{\text{CrO}_3}$

CH$_2$OH

OH

OH

COOH

HO

OH

(40)

H₂/Pd
Bacterial oxidation
2 CH₃COCH₃
KMnO₄
H⁺
CH₃OH/H⁺
NaOCH₃
31
(32)
(41)
(42)
(43)
(44)
(45)
(46)

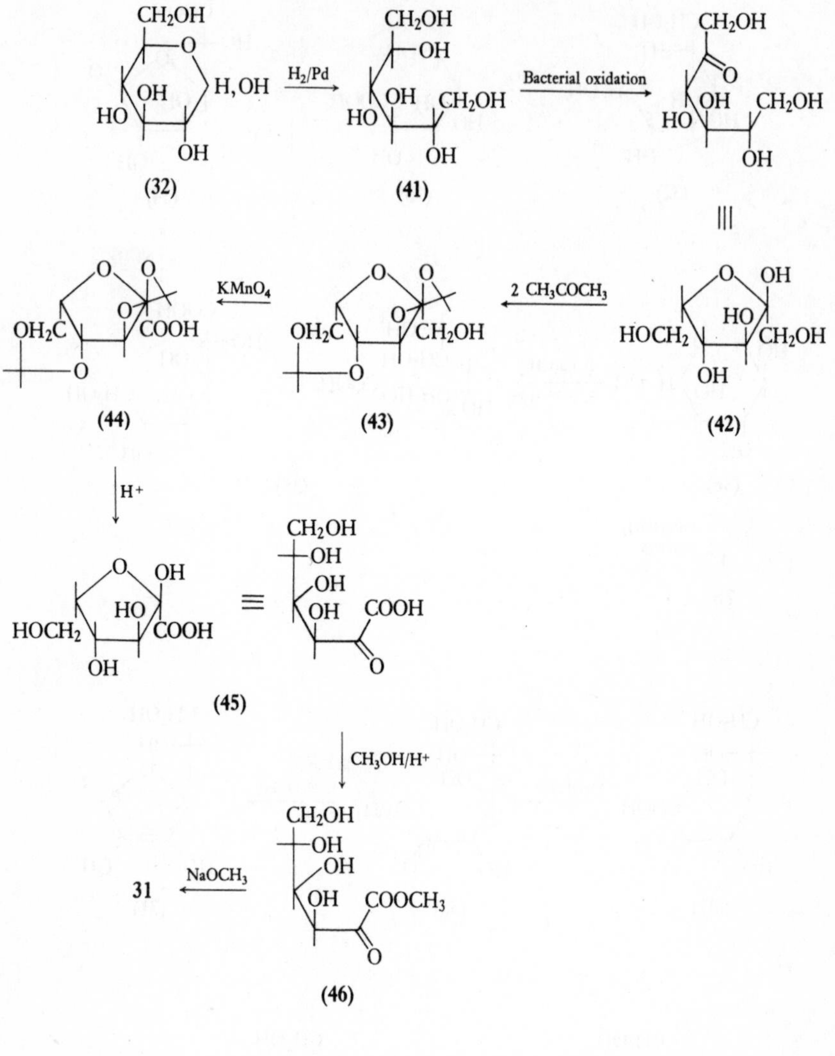

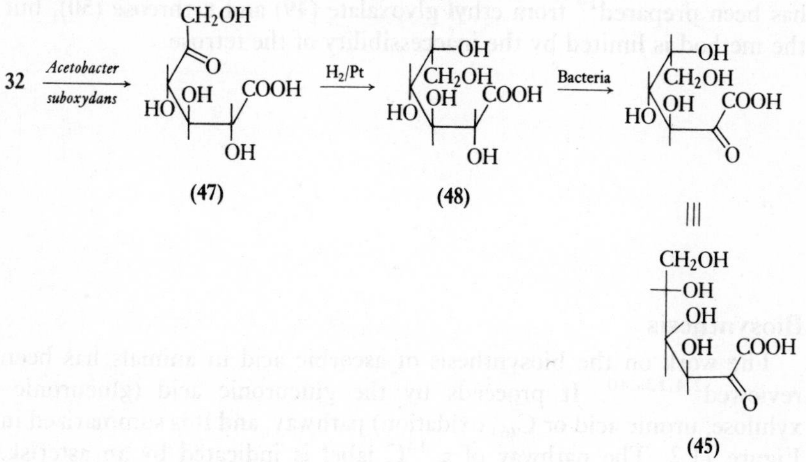

32 $\xrightarrow[\text{suboxydans}]{\text{Acetobacter}}$ (47) $\xrightarrow{\text{H}_2/\text{Pt}}$ (48) $\xrightarrow{\text{Bacteria}}$

(47)

(48)

$|||$

(45)

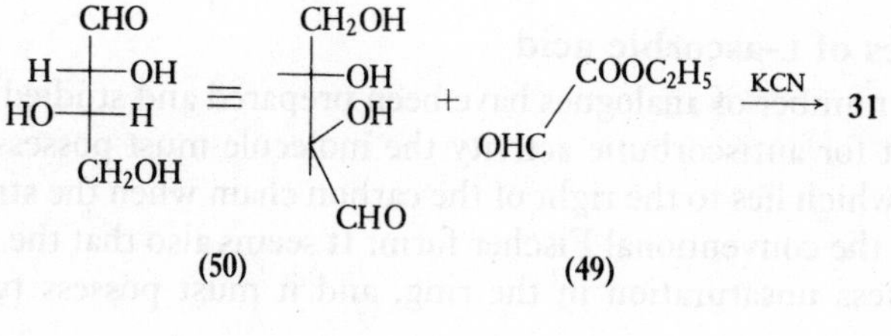

(50) $\equiv$ (49) $+$ $\xrightarrow{\text{KCN}}$ 31

has been prepared[19] from ethyl glyoxalate (49) and L-threose (50), but the method is limited by the inaccessibility of the tetrose.

Biosynthesis

The work on the biosynthesis of ascorbic acid in animals has been reviewed[2,4,13a,40]. It proceeds by the glucuronic acid (glucuronic-xylulose, uronic acid or $C_{(6)}$ oxidation) pathway, and it is summarized in Figure 11.2. The pathway of a ^{14}C label is indicated by an asterisk. D-Glucose (32) is oxidized to D-glucuronic acid (51), and this is reduced to L-gulonic acid (52), which is the precursor of ascorbic acid (31), via L-gulonolactone (53) and 2-oxo-L-gulonolactone (54), and of L-xylulose (56) via 3-oxo-L-gulonic acid (55). The L-xylulose (55) is converted through xylitol (57) and D-xylulose (58) into D-xylulose-5-phosphate (59), and the latter is reconverted into D-glucose (32) by the pentose phosphate pathway[13].

Man is able to carry out all the steps in this scheme except the conversion of L-gulonolactone (53) into ascorbic acid.

The route for the biosynthesis of ascorbic acid in plants is still not clear.

Analogues of L-ascorbic acid

A large number of analogues have been prepared and studied[37], and it seems that for antiscorbutic activity the molecule must possess a γ-lactone ring which lies to the right of the carbon chain when the structure is written in the conventional Fischer form. It seems also that the molecule must possess unsaturation in the ring, and it must possess two enolic

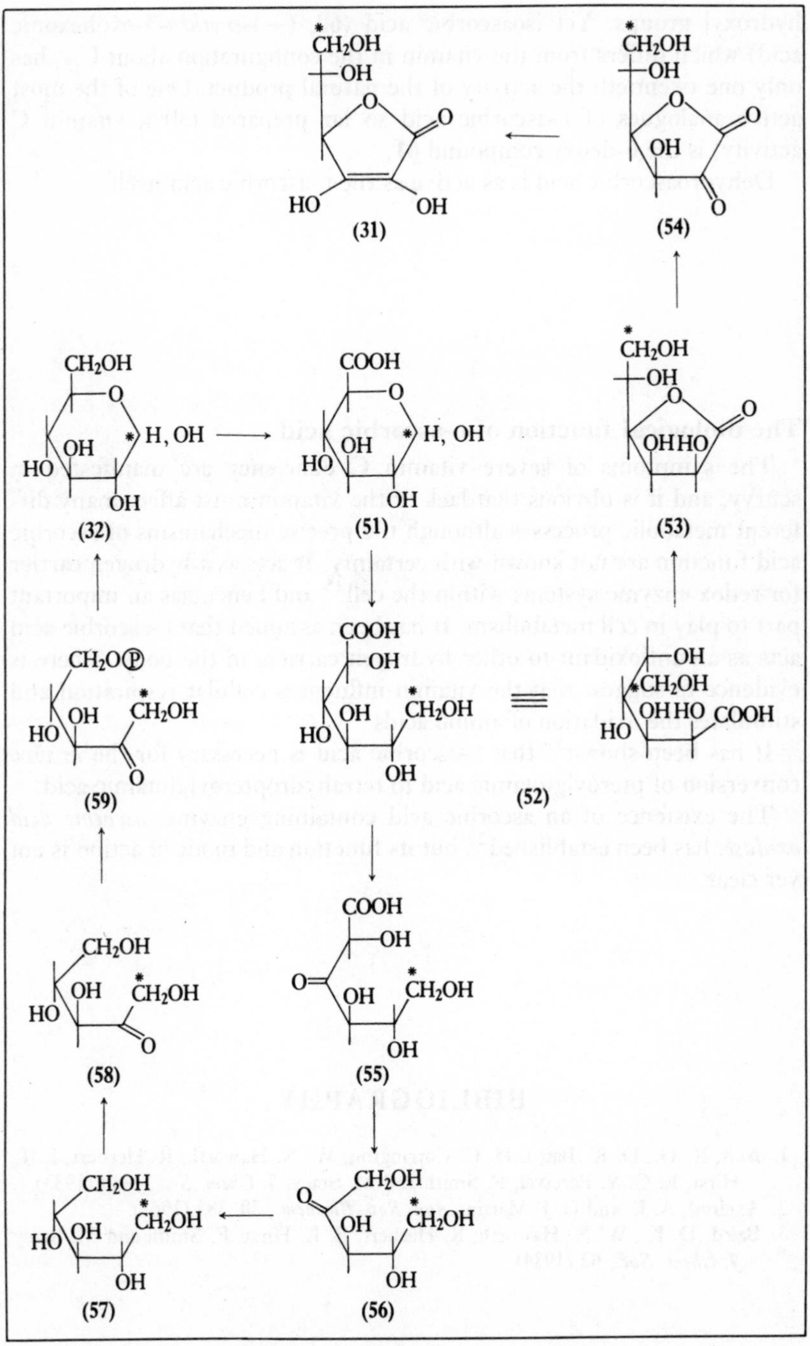

Figure 11.2. The biosynthesis of vitamin C.

hydroxyl groups. Yet isoascorbic acid (**60**, (+)-*erythro*-3-oxohexonic acid) which differs from the vitamin in the configuration about $C_{(5)}$ has only one twentieth the activity of the natural product. One of the most active analogues of L-ascorbic acid so far prepared (30% vitamin C activity) is the 6-deoxy compound **61**.

Dehydroascorbic acid is as active as the L-ascorbic acid itself.

The biological function of L-ascorbic acid

The symptoms of severe vitamin C deficiency are manifested in scurvy, and it is obvious that lack of the vitamin must affect many different metabolic processes although the precise mechanisms of ascorbic acid function are not known with certainty. It acts as a hydrogen carrier for redox enzyme systems within the cell[25] and hence has an important part to play in cell metabolism. It has been assumed that L-ascorbic acid acts as an antioxidant to other hydrogen carriers in the body. There is evidence to suggest that the vitamin influences cellular respiration and stimulates the oxidation of amino acids.

It has been shown[31] that L-ascorbic acid is necessary for the *in vivo* conversion of pteroylgiutamic acid to tetrahydropteroylglutamic acid.

The existence of an ascorbic acid containing enzyme, *ascorbic acid oxidase*, has been established[22] but its function and mode of action is not yet clear.

BIBLIOGRAPHY

1. Ault, R. G., D. K. Baird, H. C. Corrington, W. N. Haworth, R. Herbert, E. L. Hirst, E. G. V. Percival, F. Smith and M. Stacy, *J. Chem. Soc.*, 1419 (1933).
2. Axelrod, A. E. and C. J. Martin, *Ann. Rev. Biochem.*, **30**, 383 (1961).
3. Baird, D. K., W. N. Haworth, R. Herbert, E. L. Hirst, F. Smith and M. Stacy, *J. Chem. Soc.*, 62 (1934).

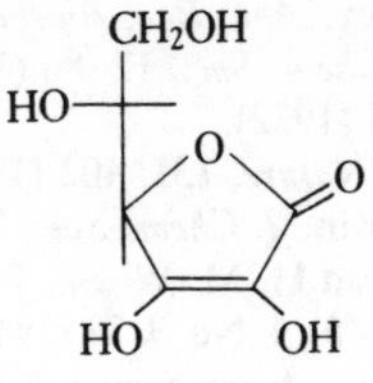

$$\text{CH}_2\text{OH}$$

(60)

$$\text{CH}_3$$

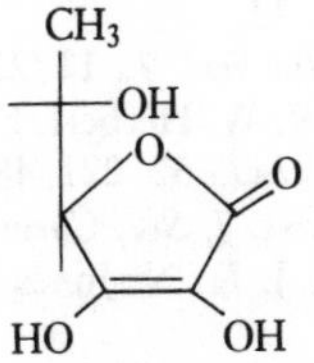

(61)

4. Burns, J. J. and A. H. Conney, *Ann. Rev. Biochem.*, **29**, 413 (1960).
5. Ching-Hao Kau, *J. Chinese Chem. Soc.*, **17**, 86 (1950).
6. Cox, E. G., *Nature*, **130**, 205 (1932).
7. Cox, E. G. and E. L. Hirst, *Nature*, **131**, 402 (1933).
8. Cox, E. G. and T. H. Goodwin, *J. Chem. Soc.*, 769 (1936).
9. Creighton, M., W. Wenner and H. M. Wuest, *J. Org. Chem.*, **13**, 613 (1948).
10. Devyatuin, V. A., *Khim. Ref. Zh.*, **4**, No. 9, 71 (1941); *Chem. Abstr.*, **38**, 2789 (1944).
11. Dyke, S. F., *The Carbohydrates*, Interscience, New York, 1960, p. 16.
12. von Euler, E. and E. Klussman, *Arkiv Kemi Mineral. Geol.*, **B11**, No. 7 (1933); *Chem. Abstr.*, **27**, 2180 (1933).
13. Goodwin, T. W., *Recent Advances in Biochemistry*, Churchill, London, 1960, Chap. II.
13a. Goodwin, T. W., *The Biosynthesis of Vitamins and Related Compounds*, Academic Press, London, 1963, Chap. 11.
14. Harden, A. and S. S. Zilva, *Biochem. J.*, **12**, 259 (1918).
15. Haworth, W. N., E. L. Hirst, R. W. Herbert, E. G. V. Percival, R. J. W. Reynolds and F. Smith, *J. Soc. Chem. Ind.*, **52**, 221, 482 (1933).
16. Haworth, W. N. and E. L. Hirst, *J. Soc. Chem. Ind.*, **52**, 645 (1933).
17. Haworth, W. N., E. L. Hirst, J. K. N. Jones and F. Smith, *J. Chem. Soc.*, 1192 (1934).
18. Haworth, W. N., E. L. Hirst, J. K. N. Jones and F. Smith, *Brit. Pat.*, 443,901 (1937).
19. Helferich, B. and O. Peters, *Ber.*, **70**, 465 (1937).
20. Herbert, R. W., E. L. Hirst, E. G. V. Percival, R. J. W. Reynolds and F. Smith, *J. Chem. Soc.*, 1270 (1933).
21. Hori, I. and T. Nakatani, *J. Ferment. Technol.*, **31**, 72 (1953).
22. James, W. O. and D. Boulter, *New Phytologist*, **54**, 1 (1955).
23. Karrer, P., H. Saloman, K. Schopp and R. Morf, *Helv. Chim. Acta*, **16**, 181 (1933); *Biochem. Z.*, **258**, 4 (1933).
24. Karrer, P., G. Schwarzonbach and K. Schopp, *Helv. Chim. Acta*, **16**, 302 (1933).
25. Mapson, M. A., *The Vitamins: Chemistry, Physiology and Pathology* (Ed. by W. H. Sebrell and R. S. Harris), Academic Press, New York, 1954, Vol. I, p. 211.
26. Micheel, F. and K. Kraft, *Z. Physiol. Chem.*, **215**, 215 (1933).
27. Micheel, F. and K. Kraft, *Z. Physiol. Chem.*, **218**, 280 (1933).
28. Micheel, F. and K. Kraft, *Z. Physiol. Chem.*, **222**, 235 (1933).
29. *Nat. Acad. Sci.–Nat. Res. Council Publ.*, No. 302 (1953).
30. Neuberg, C. and T. Kitasato, *Biochem. Z.*, **183**, 485 (1927).
31. Nichol, C. A. and A. D. Welch, *Proc. Soc. Exp. Biol. Med.*, **74**, 52 (1950).
32. Pasternak, R. and P. P. Regua, *U.S. Pat.*, 2,153,311 (1939).
33. Reichstein, T., A. Grussner and R. Oppenauer, *Helv. Chim. Acta*, **16**, 1019 (1933).
34. Reichstein, T., A. Grussner and R. Oppenauer, *Helv. Chim. Acta*, **21**, 561 (1938).
35. Rosenberg, H. R., *Chemistry and Physiology of the Vitamins*, Interscience, New York, 1945.
36. Smith, F., in *The Vitamins: Chemistry, Physiology and Pathology* (Ed. by W. H. Sebrell and R. S. Harris), Academic Press, New York, 1954, Vol. I, p. 188.
37. Smith, F., in *The Vitamins: Chemistry, Physiology and Pathology* (Ed. by W. H. Sebrell and R. S. Harris), Academic Press, New York, 1954, Vol. I, p. 198.
38. Svirbely, J. L. and A. Szent-Györgyi, *Biochem. J.*, **27**, 279 (1933).

39. Szent-Györgyi, A., *Biochem. J.*, **22**, 1387 (1928).
40. Touster, O., *Ann. Rev. Biochem.*, **31**, 407 (1962).
41. Waught, W. A. and C. G. King, *J. Biol. Chem.*, **97**, 325 (1932).
42. Wells, P. A., J. J. Stubbs, L. B. Lockwood and E. T. Roe, *Ind. Eng. Chem.*, **29**, 1385 (1937); *U.S. Pat.*, 2,121,533 (1938).
43. Wilson, W. J., *J. Chem. Soc.*, 829 (1937).
44. Zilva, S. S., *Biochem. J.*, **17**, 416 (1923); **18**, 186 (1924); **19**, 589 (1925).

CHAPTER 12

The Vitamins A

INTRODUCTION – Carotenoids – THE VITAMINS A – Detection and isolation – Sources – Deficiency disease – Daily requirement – Nomenclature – VITAMIN A₁ – Structure – Synthesis – The stereochemistry of
the retinols – Synthetic analogues of retinol – Anhydrovitamin A –
VITAMIN A₂ – Structure – Synthesis – The isomers of dehydroretinol –
THE RETINALS – THE VITAMINS A AND VISION – PROVITAMINS A –
Biosynthesis – BIBLIOGRAPHY

INTRODUCTION

VITAMIN A₁ (retinol, 1) is closely related in structure to the carotenoids, the most common members of this group being lycopene (2), α-carotene (3), β-carotene (4) and γ-carotene (5). Each of these substances possesses an α-ionone (6), β-ionone (7) or ψ-ionone (8) residue.

ψ-Ionone (8) may be obtained from the condensation of acetone and the monoterpene citral (9); when treated with acids 8 cyclizes to a mixture of α-ionone (6) and β-ionone (7). The structures of α- and β-ionone are readily deduced by a study of the oxidation products. Thus, whereas α-ionone (6) yields initially isogeronic acid (10), then β,β-dimethyladipic acid (11) and finally α,α-dimethylglutaric acid (12), β-ionone (7) produces geronic acid (13), then α,α-dimethyladipic acid (14) and finally 12.

Carotenoids[53]

The carotenoids themselves are yellow to orange pigments which occur widely in plants and animals. They may be regarded as polyiso-prenes linked head-to-tail, except in the 'centre' of the molecule where the tail-to-tail linkage is quite characteristic. About eighty of these sub-stances are now known and the structures have been determined for about half of them. The general methods that are available for the deter-mination of structure of carotenoids include: (a) the determination of the molecular weight by the Rast method or by x-ray diffraction studies; (b) the determination of the number of double bonds either

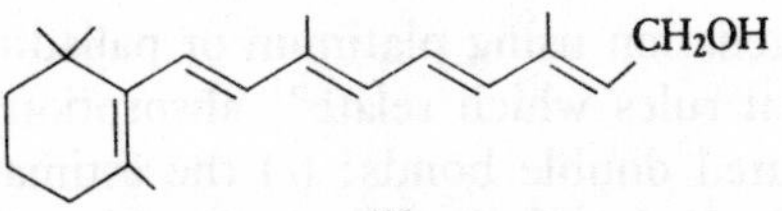

(1)

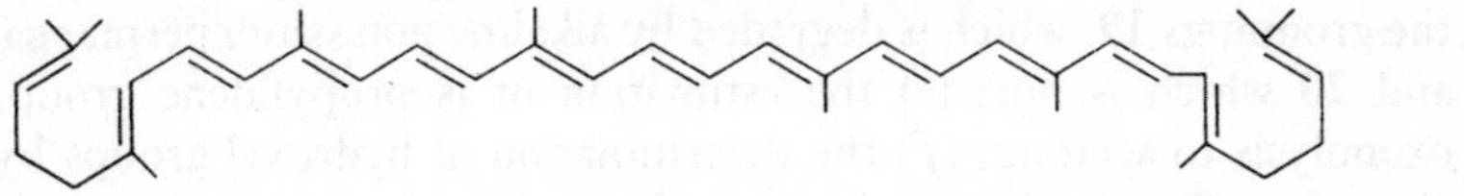

(2)

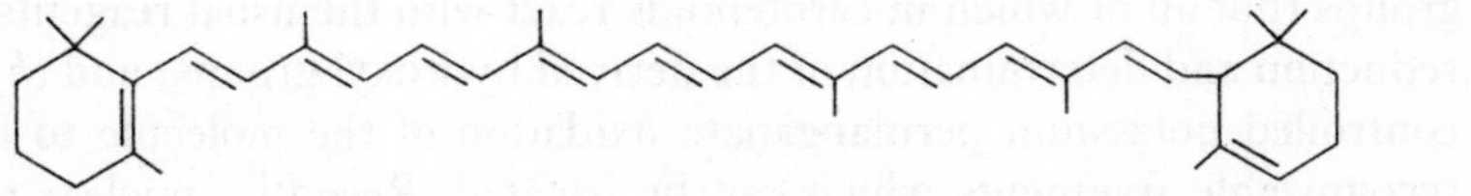

(3)

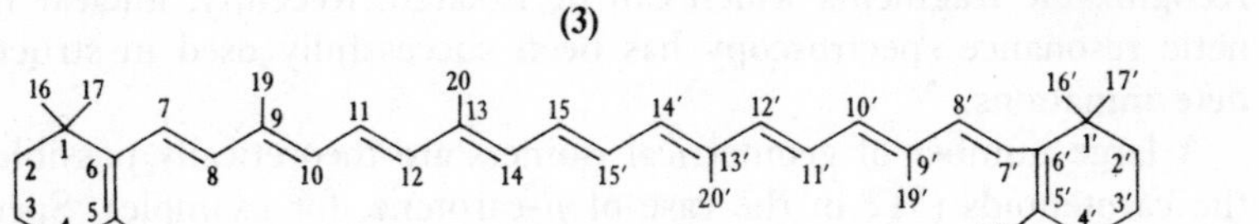

(4)

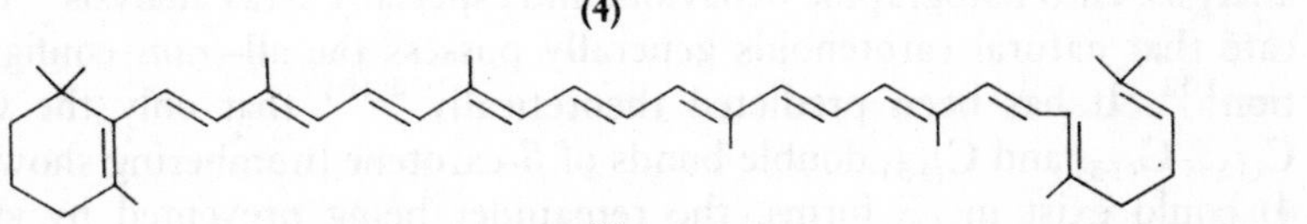

(5)

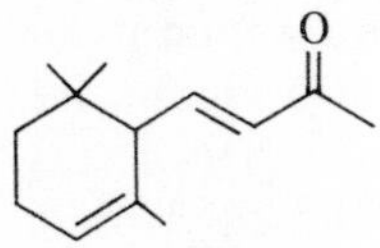

(6)

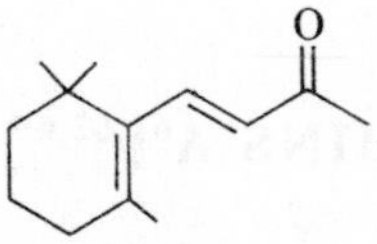

(7)

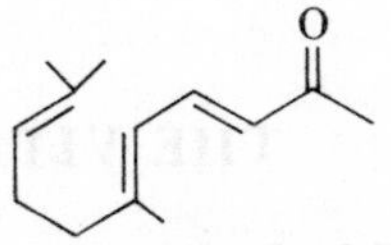

(8)

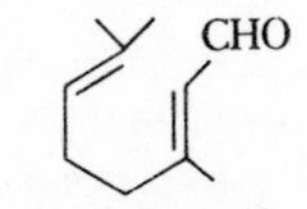

(9)

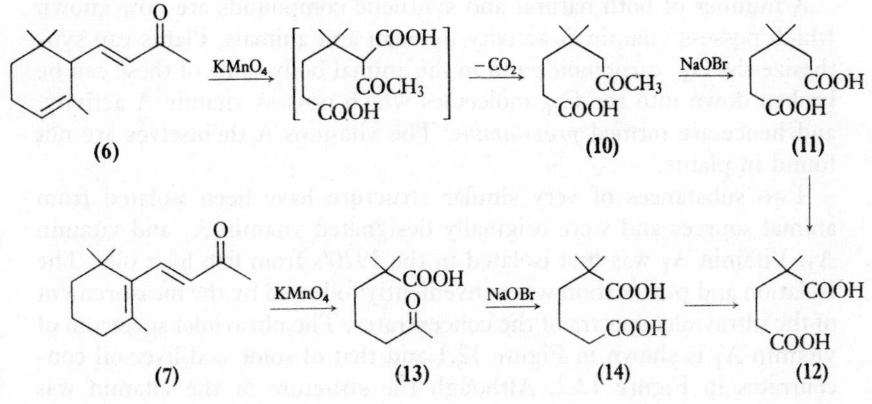

(6)　KMnO$_4$　[COOH COCH$_3$ COOH]　$-CO_2$　(10) COCH$_3$ COOH　NaOBr　(11) COOH COOH

(7)　KMnO$_4$　(13)　NaOBr　(14) COOH COOH　(12) COOH COOH

by catalytic hydrogenation using platinum or palladium catalysts or by the use of empirical rules which relate[61] absorption maxima with the number of conjugated double bonds; (c) the estimation of side-chain methyl groups by the Kuhn–Roth procedure; (d) the distinction between the groupings **19**, which is degraded by alkaline potassium permanganate and **20** which is not; (e) the estimation of isopropylidene groups by ozonolysis to acetone; (f) the determination of hydroxyl groups by the Zerewitinoff active hydrogen method; (g) the determination of carbonyl groups (not all of which in carotenoids react with the usual reagents) by reduction and determination of the derived hydroxyl groups; and (h) the controlled potassium permanganate oxidation of the molecule to large recognizable fragments which can be isolated. Recently, nuclear magnetic resonance spectroscopy has been successfully used in structural determinations.

A large number of geometrical isomers are theoretically possible for the carotenoids (512 in the case of β-carotene, for example). Spectral analysis, chromatographic behaviour and especially x-ray analysis[57] indicate that natural carotenoids generally possess the all-*trans* configuration[102]. It has been predicted theoretically[74,101] that only the $C_{(9)}$, $C_{(11)}$, $C_{(13)}$ and $C_{(15)}$ double bonds of β-carotene (numbering shown in **4**) could exist in *cis* forms, the remainder being prevented by steric hindrance.

THE VITAMINS A[61,62,69]

Detection and isolation

A number of both natural and synthetic compounds are now known which possess vitamin A activity for man and animals. Plants can synthesize the C_{40} carotenoids and in the animal body some of these can be broken down into the C_{20} molecules which possess vitamin A activity, and hence are termed *provitamins*. The vitamins A themselves are not found in plants.

Two substances of very similar structure have been isolated from animal sources and were originally designated vitamin A_1 and vitamin A_2. Vitamin A_1 was first isolated in the 1920's from fish liver oils. The isolation and purification was conveniently followed by the measurement of the ultraviolet spectra of the concentrates. The ultraviolet spectrum of vitamin A_1 is shown in Figure 12.1 and that of some cod liver oil concentrates in Figure 12.2. Although the structure of the vitamin was

$$=C-C= \qquad -CH_2-C=$$
$$\quad\ \ \ |\qquad\qquad\qquad\qquad\quad |$$
$$\quad\ \ CH_3 \qquad\qquad\qquad\quad CH_3$$

(19)   (20)

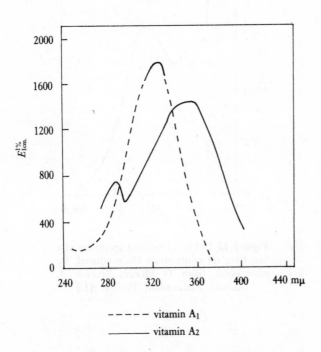

Figure 12.1. The ultraviolet spectra of vitamins A_1 and A_2. [Reproduced, by permission, from *The Vitamins: Chemistry, Physiology and Pathology* (Ed. by W. H. Sebrill and R. S. Harris), Academic Press, New York, 1954, Vol. 1, p. 51.]

established in 1931, it was not until 1942 that a pure crystalline specimen was obtained[6]. Vitamin A_2 was first isolated[87], in the form of the aldehyde, from fresh-water fish liver oils. The ultraviolet spectrum is shown in Figure 12.1.

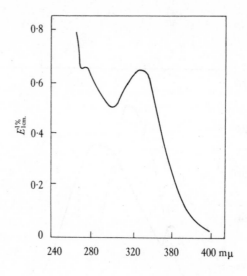

Figure 12.2. The ultraviolet spectrum of a fish liver oil concentrate. [Reproduced, by permission, from T. Moore, *Vitamin A*, Elsevier, Amsterdam, 1957, p. 44.]

Sources

The vitamins A occur only in animals, and mainly in the liver, lungs and kidney. They exist both as the free alcohols and as esters of fatty acids such as palmitic acid. Fish liver oils are rich in vitamin A; the oils from fresh-water fish contain vitamin A_2 as well as vitamin A_1, whereas those from sea-water fish contain only vitamin A_1.

Deficiency disease

Vitamin A activity is associated[76] with reproduction, with the formation of new cells and with normal vision. Deficiency of the vitamins A leads to general dryness of the skin and hair, and to conjunctivitis of the eye. The repiratory passages and the alimentary canal become keratinized. Normal growth is retarded and resistance to infection is lowered. Night blindness is also associated with the early symptoms of vitamin A deficiency.

Daily requirement

The normal adult requires about 3250 international units per day of vitamin A (1 gram of pure vitamin A_1 contains 4,500,000 international units).

Nomenclature[38]

Vitamin A_1 is now termed 'retinol'; the derived aldehyde, formally 'retinene$_1$', is 'retinal' and vitamin A acid is 'retinoic acid'. Vitamin A_2 is now officially '3-dehydroretinol' and retinene$_2$ is '3-dehydroretinal'.

VITAMIN A_1 (RETINOL)

Structure[49,51]

The molecular formula of retinol is $C_{20}H_{30}O$ and upon catalytic hydrogenation it absorbs five molecules of hydrogen per molecule of vitamin to yield perhydroretinol, $C_{20}H_{40}O$. Hence, retinol contains five double bonds. The oxygen atom of retinol was shown to be present as a primary alcoholic hydroxyl group since oxidation yields an acid containing the same number of carbon atoms. Since the molecular formula of a C_{20} acyclic saturated alcohol is $C_{20}H_{42}O$, perhydrovitamin A, and hence retinol itself, must contain one ring. Ozonolysis of retinol yields one mole of geronic acid (13) per mole of the vitamin, so that a β-ionone residue is present in the molecule. Three equivalents of acetic acid are obtained on Kuhn–Roth oxidation, and when retinol is treated with alcoholic hydrogen chloride followed by dehydrogenation with selenium[27], 1,6-dimethylnaphthalene is obtained. The carbon skeleton of the vitamin was established by the synthesis[51] of perhydroretinol (26). β-Ionone (7) underwent a Reformatsky reaction to yield the unsaturated ester 21 directly. The substance was hydrogenated to remove the double bonds and then reduced to the alcohol 22 by sodium amalgam. A malonic ester synthesis with 22 yielded the acid 23 which was converted into the methyl ketone 24. A second Reformatsky reaction gave 25 and this was reduced to 26. This product was shown to be identical with the material obtained by catalytic hydrogenation of retinol.

Animal feeding experiments indicated a close similarity between β-carotene (4) and retinol, and retinol was thus allotted structure 27. The numbering system adopted in 1947 by the International Union of Pure and Applied Chemistry is shown in 27.

Synthesis

The structure 27 for retinol has been confirmed by several syntheses, some of which have been used for the commercial production of the pure vitamin. Several reviews of this subject have appeared[7,13,28,29,37,39,43,45,48,52,64].

The first claim to a synthesis of retinol was that made by Kuhn and

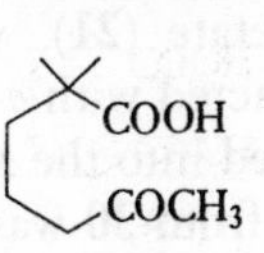
COOH
COCH3

(13)

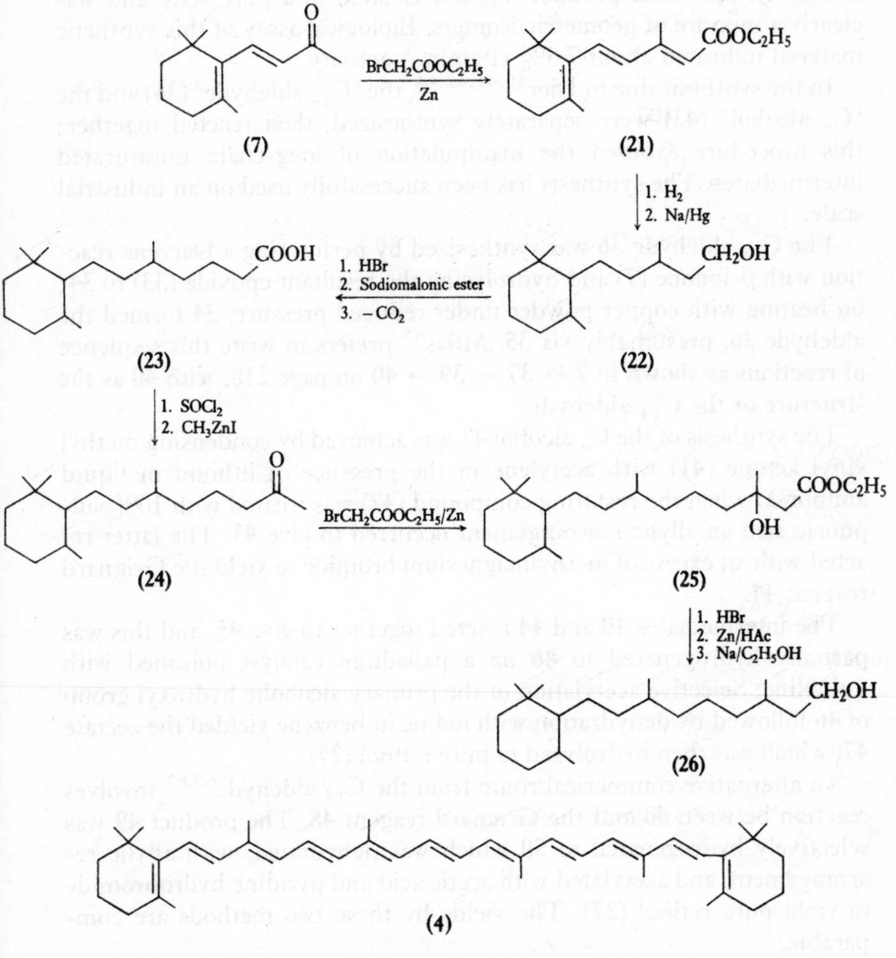
O
BrCH2COOC2H5
Zn
COOC2H5
(7)
(21)
1. H2
2. Na/Hg
COOH
1. HBr
2. Sodiomalonic ester
3. −CO2
CH2OH
(23)
(22)
1. SOCl2
2. CH3ZnI
O
COOC2H5
BrCH2COOC2H5/Zn
OH
(24)
(25)
1. HBr
2. Zn/HAc
3. Na/C2H5OH
CH2OH

(26)

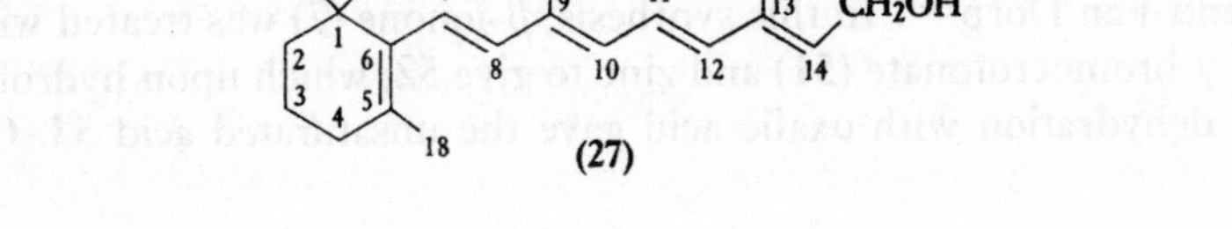

(4)

16 17
19
20
15
7
11
1
9
13
CH2OH
2
6
3
5
8
10
12
14
4
18

(27)

Morris[55]. β-Ionylidineethyl acetate (21), which had previously been synthesized by Karrer[50], was reacted with o-toluidinemagnesium bromide to yield 28; this was converted into the anil 30 via the iminochloride (29). The aldehyde 31 obtained from 30 was condensed with β-methylcrotonaldehyde to give the unsaturated aldehyde 32, which was reduced to retinol. The final product was not isolated in a pure state and was clearly a mixture of geometric isomers. Biological assay of this synthetic material indicated about 7·5% vitamin A activity.

In the synthesis due to Isler[40,41,42,44], the 'C$_{14}$ aldehyde' (36) and the 'C$_6$ alcohol' (43) were separately synthesized, then reacted together; this procedure avoided the manipulation of long-chain unsaturated intermediates. The synthesis has been successfully used on an industrial scale.

The C$_{14}$ aldehyde 36 was synthesized by performing a Darzens reaction with β-ionone (7) and hydrolysing the resultant epoxide (33) to 34; on heating with copper powder under reduced pressure, 34 formed the aldehyde 36, presumably via 35. Milas[65] prefers to write this sequence of reactions as shown in 7 → 37 → 39 → 40 on page 218, with 40 as the structure of the C$_{14}$ aldehyde.

The synthesis of the C$_6$ alcohol 43 was achieved by condensing methyl vinyl ketone (41) with acetylene in the presence of lithium in liquid ammonia; when the resulting compound (42) was treated with 10% sulphuric acid an allylic rearrangement occurred to give 43. The latter reacted with an excess of methylmagnesium bromide to yield the Grignard reagent 44.

The intermediates 40 and 44 reacted together to give 45, and this was partially hydrogenated to 46 on a palladium catalyst poisoned with quinoline. Selective acetylation of the primary alcoholic hydroxyl group of 46 followed by dehydration with iodine in benzene yielded the acetate 47, which was then hydrolysed to pure retinol (27).

An alternative commerical route from the C$_{14}$ aldehyde[63,67] involves reaction between 40 and the Grignard reagent 48. The product 49 was selectively hydrogenated to 50 which was dehydrated, with allylic rearrangement, and acetylated with acetic acid and pyridine hydrobromide to yield pure retinol (27). The yields by these two methods are comparable.

Another synthesis using β-ionone as starting material was patented by Arens and Van Dorp[2,3]. In this synthesis, β-ionone (7) was treated with methyl γ-bromocrotonate (51) and zinc to give 52, which upon hydrolysis and dehydration with oxalic acid gave the unsaturated acid 53. On

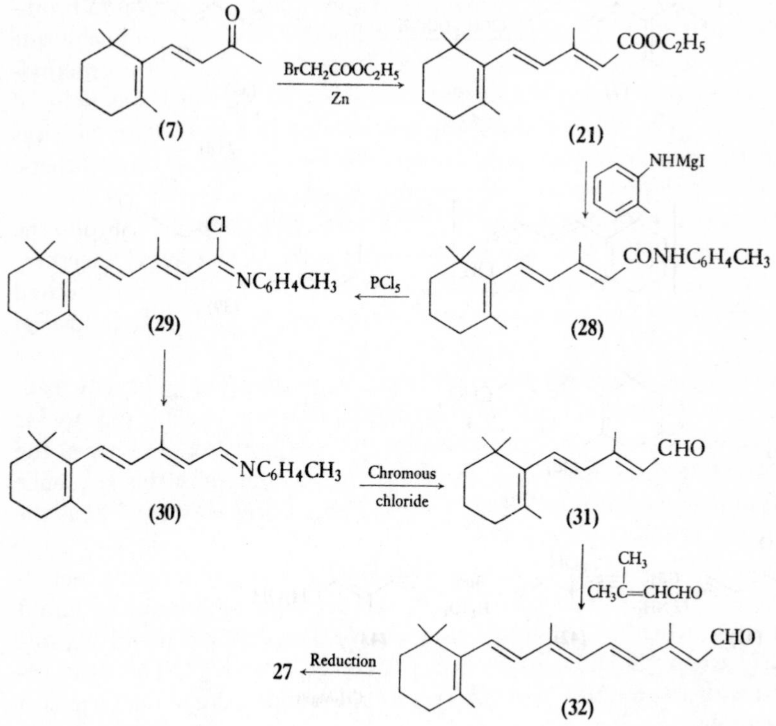

$$\text{(7)} \xrightarrow[\text{Zn}]{\text{BrCH}_2\text{COOC}_2\text{H}_5} \text{(21)} \quad \text{COOC}_2\text{H}_5$$

(7) → (21)

(21) → (28) via NHMgI reagent

$$\text{(28)} \xrightarrow{\text{PCl}_5} \text{(29)}$$

(29) CONHC$_6$H$_4$CH$_3$

(29) NC$_6$H$_4$CH$_3$, Cl

(29) → (30)

$$\text{(30)} \xrightarrow[\text{chloride}]{\text{Chromous}} \text{(31)}$$

(30) NC$_6$H$_4$CH$_3$

(31) CHO

$$\text{(31)} \xrightarrow{\text{CH}_3\text{C}=\text{CHCHO (CH}_3)} \text{(32)}$$

(32) CHO

$$27 \xleftarrow{\text{Reduction}} \text{(32)}$$

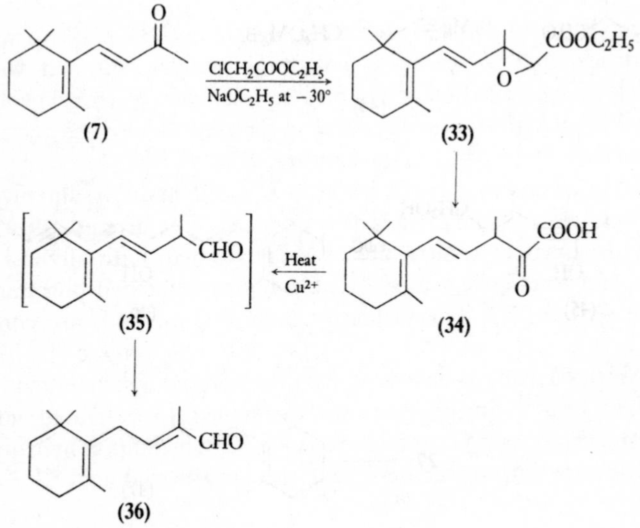

$$\text{(7)} \xrightarrow[\text{NaOC}_2\text{H}_5 \text{ at } -30°]{\text{ClCH}_2\text{COOC}_2\text{H}_5} \text{(33)}$$

(33) COOC$_2$H$_5$, O

(33) → (34)

(34) COOH, O

$$\text{(34)} \xrightarrow[\text{Cu}^{2+}]{\text{Heat}} \text{(35)}$$

(35) CHO

(35) → (36)

(36) CHO

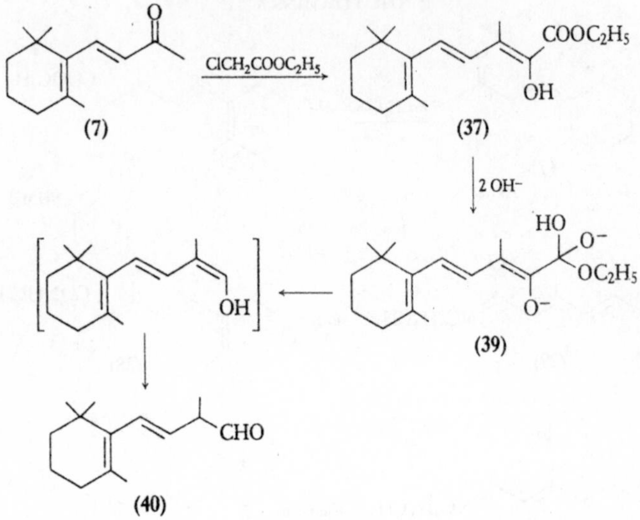

O
$ClCH_2COOC_2H_5$
$COOC_2H_5$
OH
(7)
(37)
2 OH^-
HO
O^-
OC_2H_5
O^-
OH
(39)
CHO
(40)

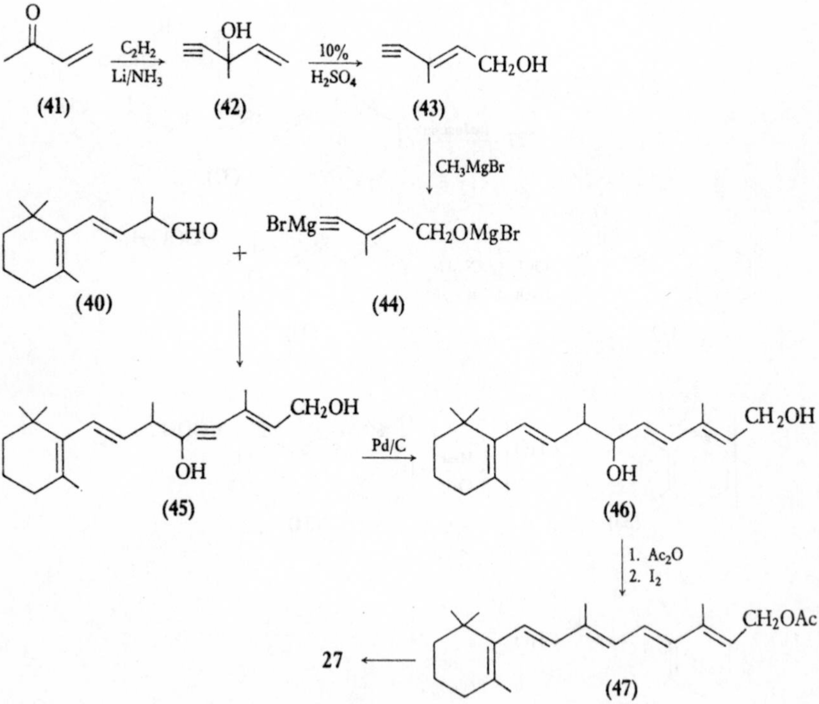

O
C_2H_2
Li/NH_3
OH
10%
H_2SO_4
CH_2OH
(41)
(42)
(43)
CH_3MgBr
CHO
BrMg
CH_2OMgBr
+
(40)
(44)
CH_2OH
OH
Pd/C
CH_2OH
OH
(45)
(46)
1. Ac_2O
2. I_2
CH_2OAc
27
(47)

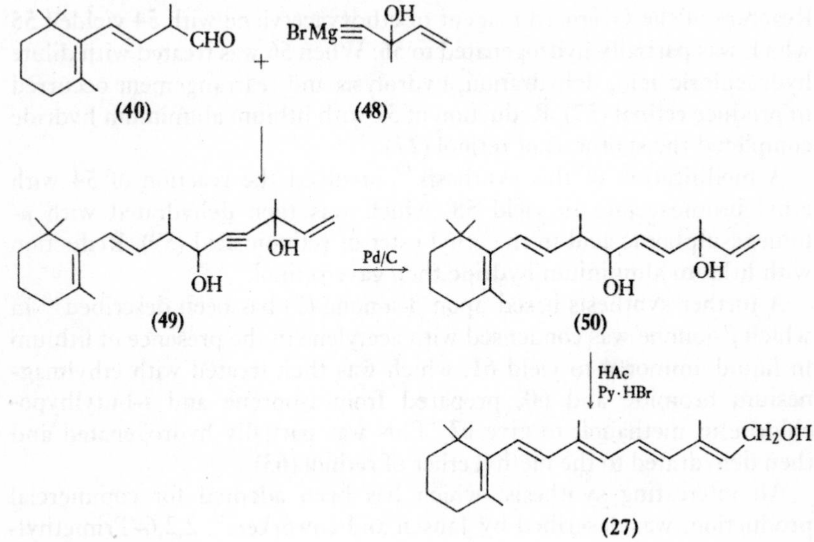
CHO
BrMg
OH
+
(40)
(48)
OH
OH
Pd/C
OH
OH
(49)
(50)
HAc
Py·HBr
CH₂OH
(27)

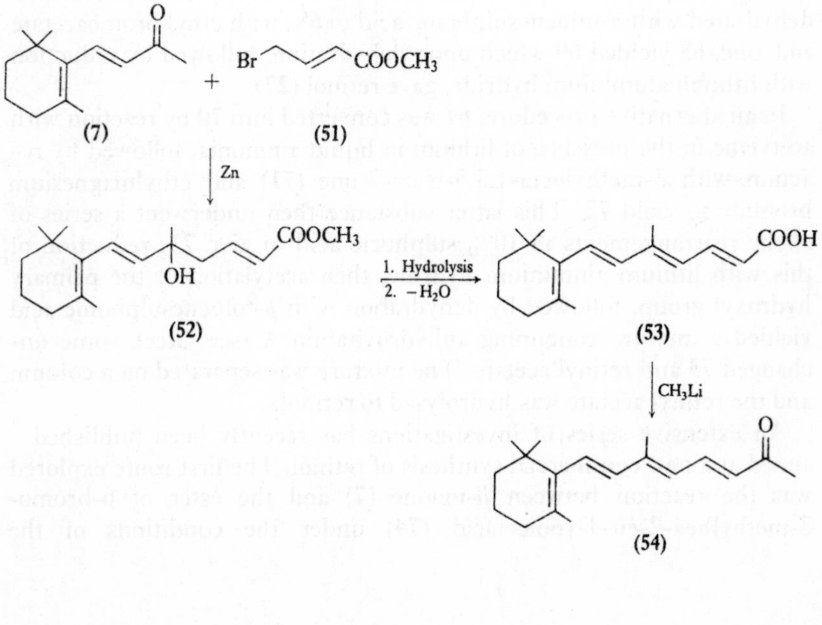
O
Br
COOCH₃
+
(7)
(51)
Zn
COOCH₃
OH
1. Hydrolysis
2. −H₂O
COOH
(52)
(53)
CH₃Li
O
(54)

treatment with methyllithium, **53** was converted into the ketone **54**. Reaction of the Grignard reagent of ethoxyacetylene with **54** yielded **55** which was partially hydrogenated to **56**. When **56** was treated with dilute hydrochloric acid, dehydration, hydrolysis and rearrangement occurred to produce retinal (**57**). Reduction of **57** with lithium aluminium hydride completed the synthesis of retinol (**27**).

A modification of this synthesis[90] involved the reaction of **54** with ethyl bromoacetate to yield **58**, which was then dehydrated with *p*-toluenesulphonic acid to the ethyl ester of retinoic acid (**59**). Reduction with lithium aluminium hydride then gave retinol.

A further synthesis based upon β-ionone (**7**) has been described[72] in which β-ionone was condensed with acetylene in the presence of lithium in liquid ammonia to yield **61**, which was then treated with ethylmagnesium bromide and **60**, prepared from isoprene and *t*-butylhypochlorite in methanol, to give **62**. This was partially hydrogenated and then dehydrated to the methyl ether of retinol (**63**).

An interesting synthesis, which has been adapted for commercial production, was described by Jansen and coworkers[5]. 2,2,6-Trimethylcyclohexanone (**64**), prepared by treatment of 2-methylcyclohexanone with methyl iodide and sodamide, was condensed with 3-methylocta-3,5-dien-1-yn-7-ol (**65**) to produce the C_{18} diol **66**. This was partially reduced with lithium aluminium hydride, then oxidized to **67** with specially prepared manganese dioxide. This hydroxy ketone was then dehydrated with *p*-toluenesulphonic acid to **68**; with ethyl bromoacetate and zinc, **68** yielded **69** which upon dehydration, followed by reduction with lithium aluminium hydride, gave retinol (**27**).

In an alternative procedure, **64** was converted into **70** by reaction with acetylene in the presence of lithium in liquid ammonia, followed by reaction with 3-methylocta-1,3,5-trien-7-one (**71**) and ethylmagnesium bromide to yield **72**. This latter substance then underwent a series of allylic rearrangements in 10% sulphuric acid to give **73**; reduction of this with lithium aluminium hydride, then acetylation of the primary hydroxyl group, followed by dehydration with *p*-toluenesulphonic acid yielded a mixture containing anhydrovitamin A (see later), some unchanged **73** and retinyl acetate. The mixture was separated on a column and the retinyl acetate was hydrolysed to retinol.

An extensive series of investigations has recently been published[77] aimed at a new commercial synthesis of retinol. The first route explored was the reaction between β-ionone (**7**) and the ester of 6-bromo-3-methylhex-2-en-4-ynoic acid (**74**) under the conditions of the

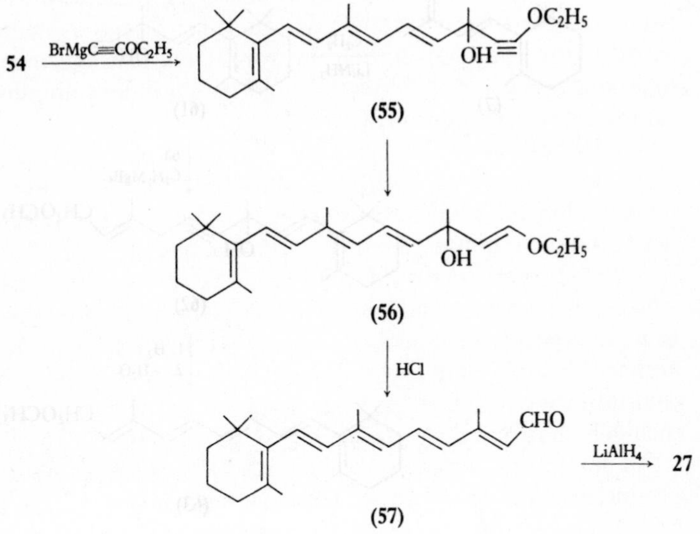

54
BrMgC≡COC2H5
OC2H5
OH
(55)
OH
OC2H5
(56)
HCl
CHO
LiAlH4
27
(57)

O
(54)
BrCH2COOC2H5
Zn+
COOC2H5
OH
(58)
– H2O
COOC2H5
LiAlH4
27
(59)

Cl
OCH3
(60)

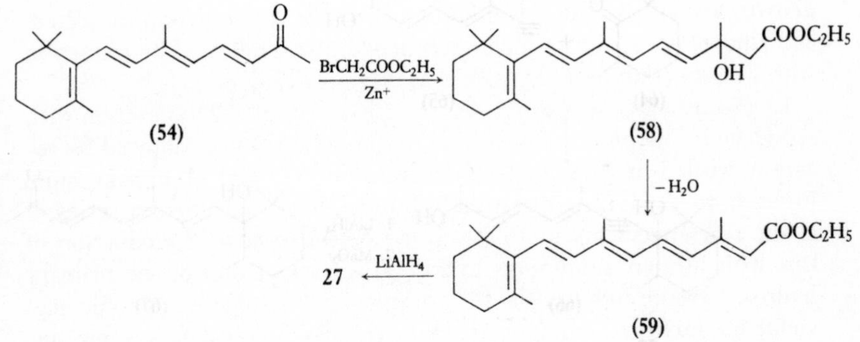

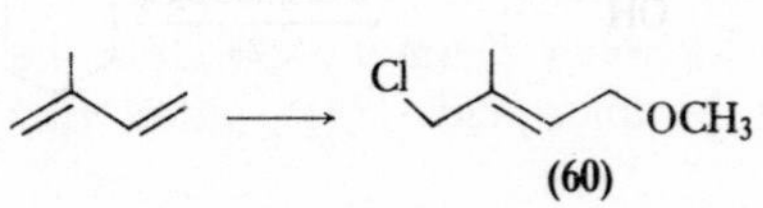

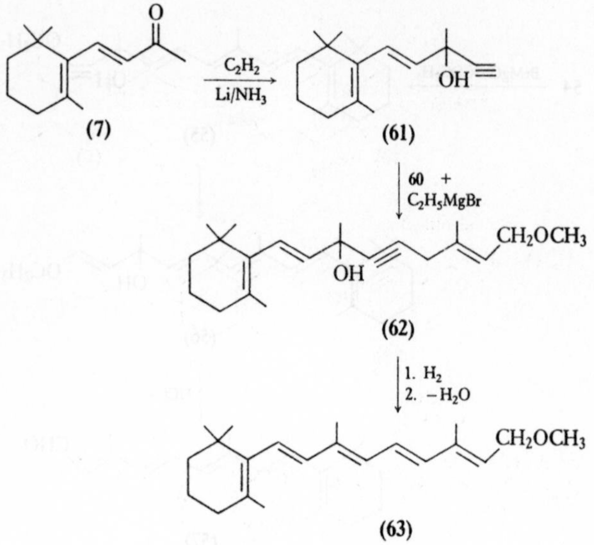
O
C_2H_2
Li/NH_3
OH
(7)
(61)
60 +
C_2H_5MgBr
CH_2OCH_3
OH
(62)
1. H_2
2. $-H_2O$
CH_2OCH_3
(63)

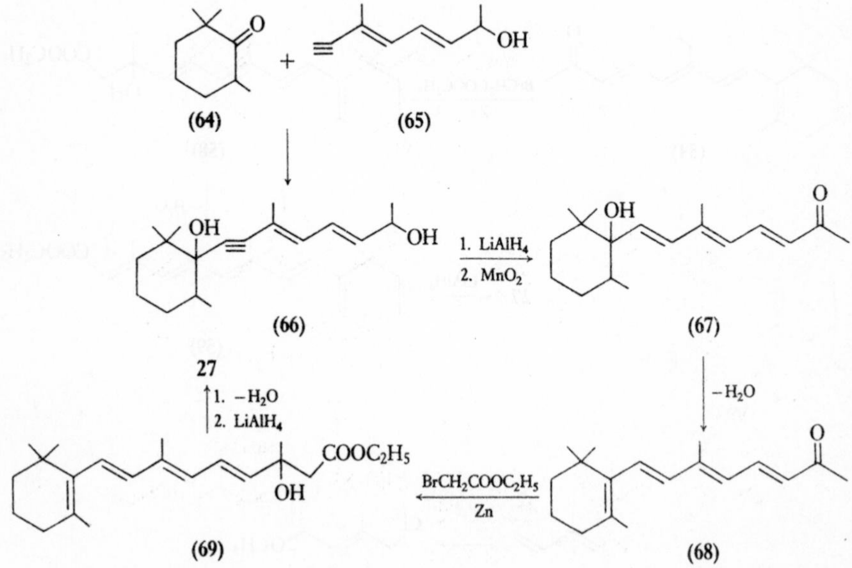
O
OH
+
(64)
(65)
OH
OH
1. $LiAlH_4$
2. MnO_2
OH
O
(66)
(67)
27
1. $-H_2O$
2. $LiAlH_4$
$-H_2O$
$COOC_2H_5$
OH
$BrCH_2COOC_2H_5$
Zn
O
(69)
(68)

The reaction scheme showing compounds (64), (70), (71), (72), (73), (27) with reagents C₂H₂/Li/NH₃; 71 + C₂H₅MgBr; 10% H₂SO₄; and LiAlH₄, Ac₂O, −H₂O, Hydrolysis.

$$ (64) \xrightarrow[\text{Li/NH}_3]{\text{C}_2\text{H}_2} (70) $$

$$ (70) \xrightarrow[\text{C}_2\text{H}_5\text{MgBr}]{\underset{+}{71}} (72) $$

$$ (72) \xrightarrow{10\% \text{H}_2\text{SO}_4} (73) $$

$$ (73) \xrightarrow[\substack{1.\ \text{LiAlH}_4 \\ 2.\ \text{Ac}_2\text{O} \\ 3.\ -\text{H}_2\text{O} \\ 4.\ \text{Hydrolysis}}]{} 27 $$

The second reaction scheme showing compounds (7) + (74) → (75) → (76) → (77) → 27 with reagents Zn; −H₂O; H₂/Pd; LiAlH₄.

$$ (7) + (74) \xrightarrow{\text{Zn}} (75) $$

$$ (75) \xrightarrow{-\text{H}_2\text{O}} (76) $$

$$ (76) \xrightarrow{\text{H}_2/\text{Pd}} (77) $$

$$ (77) \xrightarrow{\text{LiAlH}_4} 27 $$

8*

Reformatsky reaction. The product (75) was dehydrated with p-toluene-sulphonic acid in benzene to yield 76 which was partially reduced by hydrogen in the presence of a lead-poisoned catalyst[56] to give the ethyl ester of retinoic acid (77). Reduction of this with lithium aluminium hydride completed the synthesis of retinol (27).

The bromo ester 74 was synthesized using 78, readily available through a Reppe-type reaction, as starting material. By heating 78 with acetic acid, the monoacetate 79 was obtained; upon oxidation with chromium trioxide in acetone, 79 yielded 4-oxopent-2-yn-1-yl acetate (80). A Reformatsky reaction between 80 and ethyl bromoacetate gave 6-acetoxy-3-hydroxy-3-methylhex-4-ynoic acid ester (81) which on dehydration and hydrolysis gave 6-hydroxy-3-methylhex-2-en-4-ynoic acid (82). Treatment of the last compound with phosphorus tribromide gave the required compound 74.

Although the reactions from 7 and 74 proceeded satisfactorily on an industrial scale, no satisfactory technical synthesis of 74 could be developed. Attention was then turned[77] to the application of the Wittig reaction[89,91,100]. This consisted, in its original form, in the conversion of triphenylphosphine, via the phosphonium bromide 83, into the ylide 84 with a strong base which yielded a terminal olefin (85) on reaction with a ketone. With alkyl halides other than methyl, a mixture of geometrical isomers is usually formed and the ratio will depend upon the base used, the temperature of the reaction, and the direction of coupling (that is whether $R^1Ph_3P^+ + R^2CHO$ or $R^1CHO + R^2P^+Ph_3$ is used).

The bromo compound 86 was converted[77] into the phosphonium salt 87 and thence, with phenyllithium in tetrahydrofuran, to the ylide 88. The latter reacted with β-ionone (7) at room temperature to yield 89, which, on partial reduction, gave deoxyretinol (90) as a mixture of geometrical isomers. The all-*trans* isomer crystallized out on standing, and this was oxidized with selenium dioxide to retinol (27).

A closer study of the Wittig reaction showed that the phenyllithium could be replaced by other proton acceptors such as alkali alkoxides which are easier to handle on a large scale. Retinoic acid ester (93) was easily obtained from β-ionylidine acetaldehyde (91) and the ylide 92. The latter was prepared from triphenylphosphine and γ-bromocrotonic ester (51).

A systematic study was then made of various routes to retinol, and these are summarized in Figure 12.3. The best *overall* yields (i.e. total mixture of geometrical isomers) was found for the $C_{13} + C_7$ scheme. Here, the ylide 94 was formed, without isolation, by adding a proton

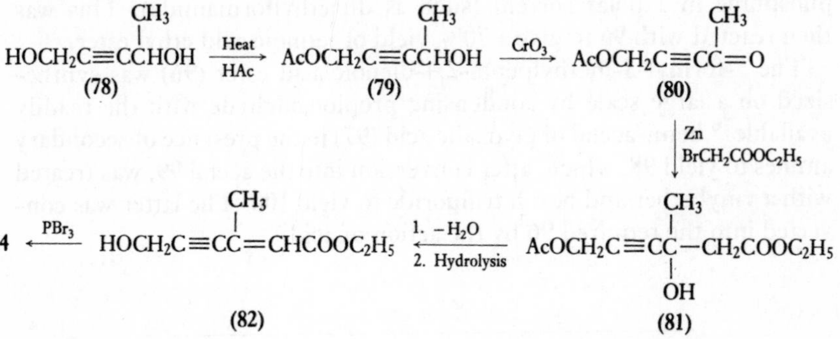

$$\underset{(78)}{HOCH_2C\equiv CCHOH} \xrightarrow[HAc]{Heat} \underset{(79)}{AcOCH_2C\equiv CCHOH} \xrightarrow{CrO_3} \underset{(80)}{AcOCH_2C\equiv CC=O}$$

with CH_3 above C in (78), (79), (80).

$$\Big\downarrow \begin{array}{c} Zn \\ BrCH_2COOC_2H_5 \end{array}$$

$$74 \xleftarrow{PBr_3} \underset{(82)}{HOCH_2C\equiv CC=CHCOOC_2H_5} \xleftarrow[\substack{2.\ Hydrolysis}]{1.\ -H_2O} \underset{(81)}{AcOCH_2C\equiv CC-CH_2COOC_2H_5}$$

with CH_3 groups and OH on (81).

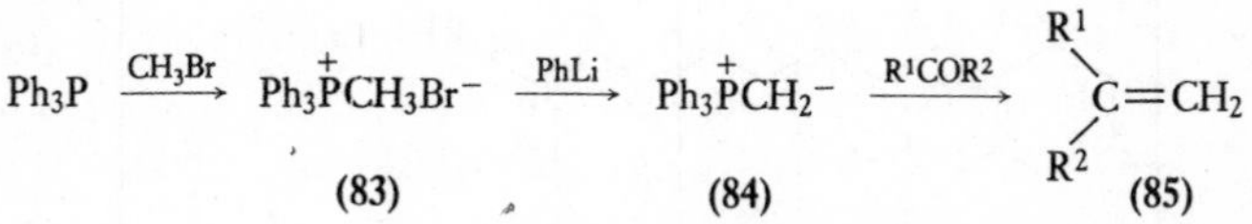

$$Ph_3P \xrightarrow{CH_3Br} \underset{(83)}{Ph_3\overset{+}{P}CH_3Br^-} \xrightarrow{PhLi} \underset{(84)}{Ph_3\overset{+}{P}CH_2^-} \xrightarrow{R^1COR^2} \underset{(85)}{\overset{R^1}{\underset{R^2}{>}}C=CH_2}$$

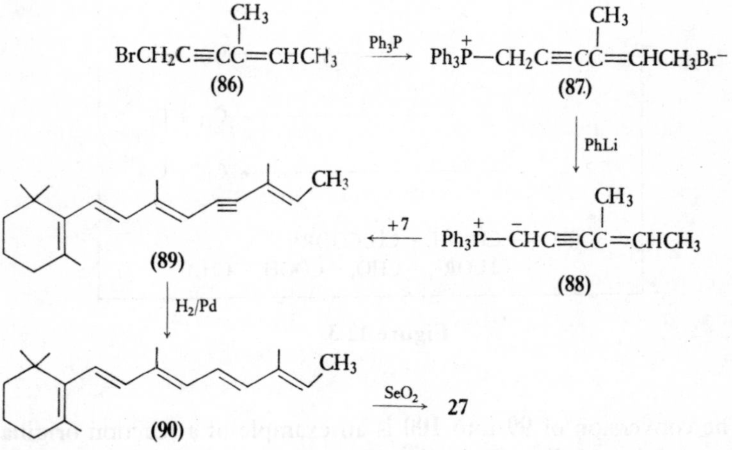

$$\underset{(86)}{BrCH_2C\equiv CC=CHCH_3} \xrightarrow{Ph_3P} \underset{(87)}{Ph_3\overset{+}{P}-CH_2C\equiv CC=CHCH_3Br^-}$$

with CH_3 groups.

$$\Big\downarrow PhLi$$

(89)

$$\xleftarrow{+7} \underset{(88)}{Ph_3\overset{+}{P}-\overset{-}{C}HC\equiv CC=CHCH_3}$$

with CH_3.

$$\Big\downarrow H_2/Pd$$

(90)

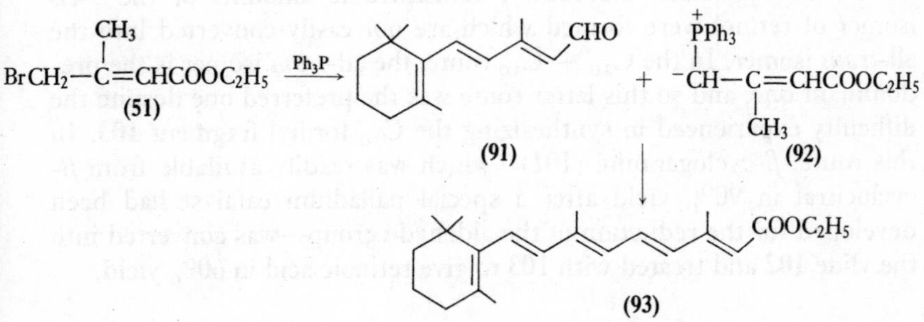

$$\xrightarrow{SeO_2} 27$$

$$\underset{(51)}{BrCH_2-C=CHCOOC_2H_5} \xrightarrow{Ph_3P}$$

with CH_3.

(91)

$$+ \underset{(92)}{^-CH-C=CHCOOC_2H_5}$$

with $\overset{+}{P}Ph_3$ and CH_3.

(93)

donor (such as halogen acid) to β-ionol (**95**) in the presence of triphenyl-phosphine in a polar solvent (such as dimethylformamide). This was then reacted with **96** to give a 70% yield of retinoic acid ethyl ester.

The 5-formyl-3-methylpenta-2,4-dienoic acid ester (**96**) was synthe-sized on a large scale by condensing propionaldehyde with the readily available[78] hemi-acetal of glyoxalic acid (**97**) in the presence of secondary amines to yield **98**, which, after conversion into the acetal **99**, was treated with a vinyl ether and boron trifluoride to yield **100**. The latter was con-verted into the required **96** by the action of acid.

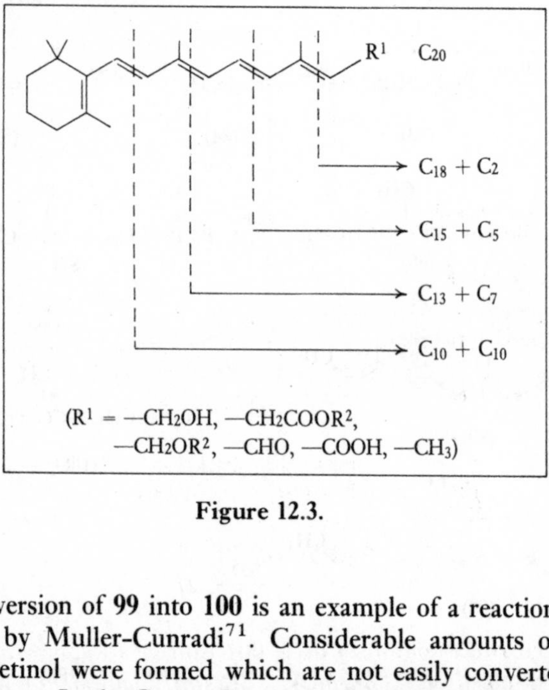

Figure 12.3.

The conversion of **99** into **100** is an example of a reaction originally discovered by Muller-Cunradi[71]. Considerable amounts of the 9-*cis* isomer of retinol were formed which are not easily converted into the all-*trans* isomer. In the $C_{10} + C_{10}$ route, the all-*trans* isomer is the pre-dominant one, and so this latter route was the preferred one despite the difficulty experienced in synthesizing the C_{10} formyl fragment **103**. In this route, β-cyclogeraniol (**101**)—which was readily available from β-cyclocitral in 90% yield after a special palladium catalyst had been developed for the reduction of the aldehyde group—was converted into the ylide **102** and treated with **103** to give retinoic acid in 60% yield.

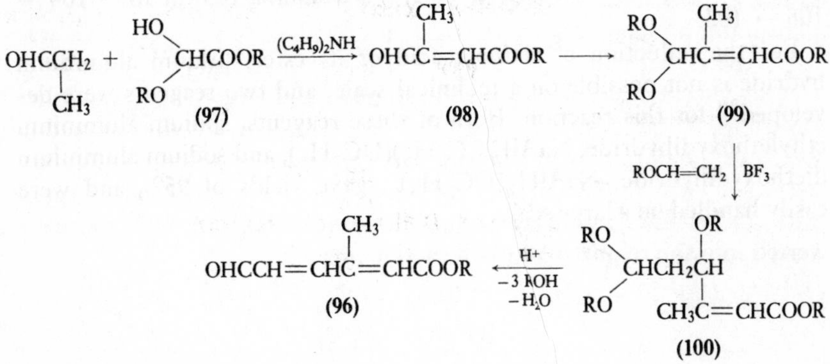

$$\underset{\underset{CH_3}{|}}{OHCCH_2} + \underset{\underset{RO}{|}}{\overset{HO}{\underset{|}{CHCOOR}}} \xrightarrow{(C_4H_9)_2NH} \underset{(98)}{OHC\overset{\overset{CH_3}{|}}{C}=CHCOOR} \longrightarrow \underset{(99)}{\overset{RO}{\underset{RO}{|}}\overset{\overset{CH_3}{|}}{CHC}=CHCOOR}$$

(97)　　　　　(98)　　　　　(99)

$$\Big\downarrow \overset{ROCH=CH_2}{\quad} BF_3$$

$$\underset{(96)}{OHCCH=CH\overset{\overset{CH_3}{|}}{C}=CHCOOR} \overset{H^+}{\underset{\substack{-3\ ROH \\ -H_2O}}{\longleftarrow}} \underset{(100)}{\overset{RO}{\underset{RO}{|}}CHCH_2\overset{\overset{OR}{|}}{CH} \atop CH_3\overset{\overset{|}{C}}{}=CHCOOR}$$

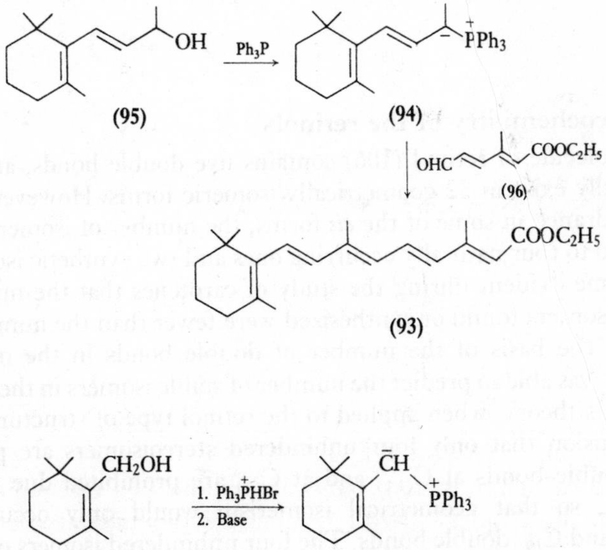

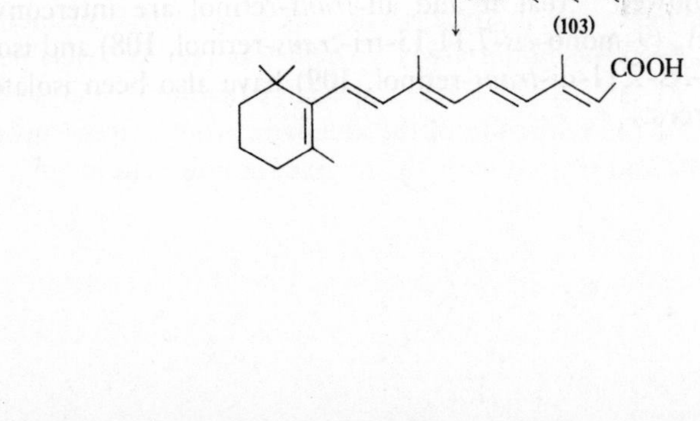

(96)　　　　　(100)

(95)　　　　　(94)

(96)

(93)

(101)　　　　　(102)

(103)

The formyl compound **103** was prepared from **96** by methods similar to those used to convert **97** into **96** and are summarized in **96** → **104** → **105** → **103**.

For the reduction of retinoic acid or its ester, lithium aluminium hydride is not possible on a technical scale, and two reagents were developed[88] for this reaction. Both of these reagents, sodium aluminium ethylethoxydihydride, $NaAlH_2(C_2H_5)(OC_2H_5)$, and sodium aluminium diethoxydihydride, $NaAlH_2(OC_2H_5)_2$, gave yields of 95% and were easily handled on a large scale.

The stereochemistry of the retinols

The molecule of retinol (**106**) contains five double bonds, and could theoretically exist in 32 geometrically isomeric forms. However, due to steric hindrance in some of the *cis* forms, the number of isomers known is confined to four naturally occurring ones and two synthetic isomers.

It became evident during the study of carotenes that the number of *cis–trans* isomers found or synthesized were fewer than the number predicted on the basis of the number of double bonds in the molecule. Pauling[74] was able to predict the number of stable isomers in the polyene series. This theory, when applied to the retinol type of structure, led to the conclusion that only four unhindered stereoisomers are possible; the *cis* double bonds at $C_{(11)}$ and at $C_{(7)}$ are prohibited due to steric hindrance, so that geometrical isomerism would only occur about the $C_{(13)}$ and $C_{(9)}$ double bonds. The four unhindered isomers of retinol are[33]: firstly, all-*trans*-retinol (**27**) and the neovitamin A_a (13-*cis*-7,9,11-tri-*trans*-retinol, **107**) which was first isolated by Robeson and Baxter[81] who also showed[82] that it and all-*trans*-retinol are interconvertible; isovitamin A_a (9-mono-*cis*-7,11,13-tri-*trans*-retinol, **108**) and isovitamin A_b (9,13-di-*cis*-7,11-di-*trans*-retinol, **109**) have also been isolated from natural sources.

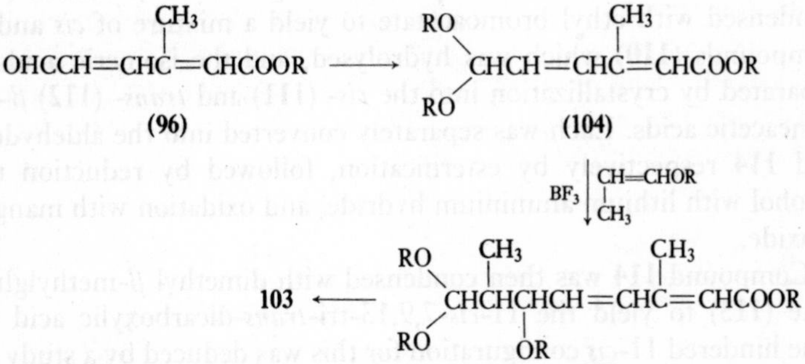

$$OHCHCH=CHC=CHCOOR \overset{CH_3}{\underset{}{}} \longrightarrow \overset{RO}{\underset{RO}{}} CHCH=CHC=CHCOOR \overset{CH_3}{\underset{}{}}$$

(96)   (104)

$$BF_3 \downarrow \overset{CH=CHOR}{\underset{CH_3}{}}$$

$$103 \longleftarrow \overset{RO}{\underset{RO}{}} CHCHCHCH=CHC=CHCOOR \overset{CH_3}{\underset{OR}{}} \overset{CH_3}{}$$

(105)

$$\overset{7\quad 8\quad 9\;\; 10\quad 11\quad 12\quad 13\; 14\quad 15}{CH=CH-C=CH-CH=CH-C=CH-CH_2OH} \overset{CH_3 \qquad CH_3}{}$$

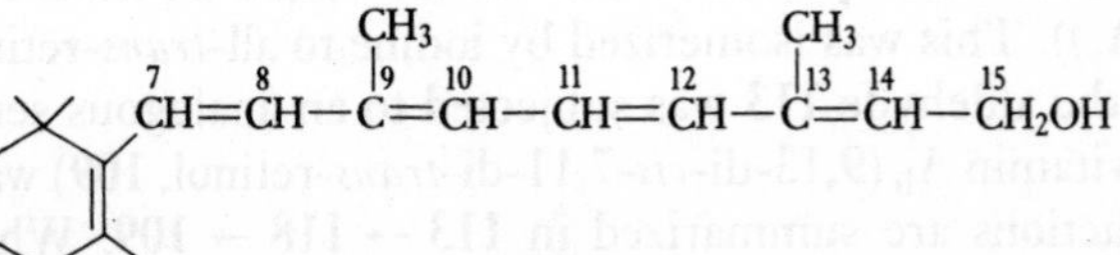

(106)

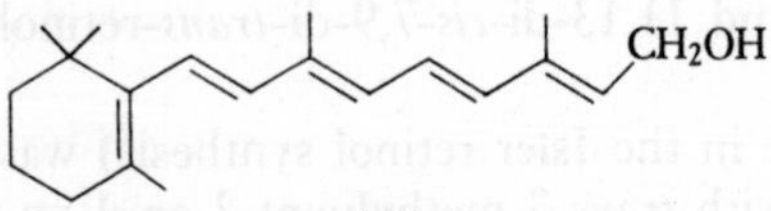

(27)

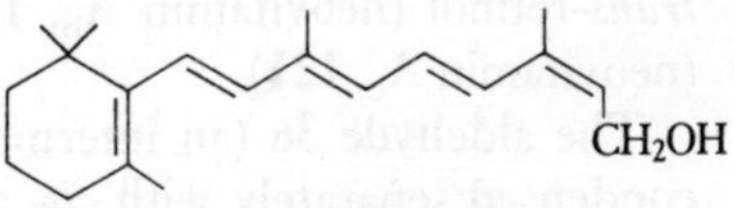

(107)

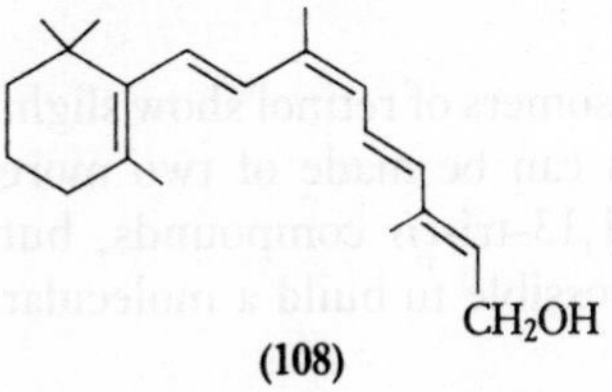

(108)

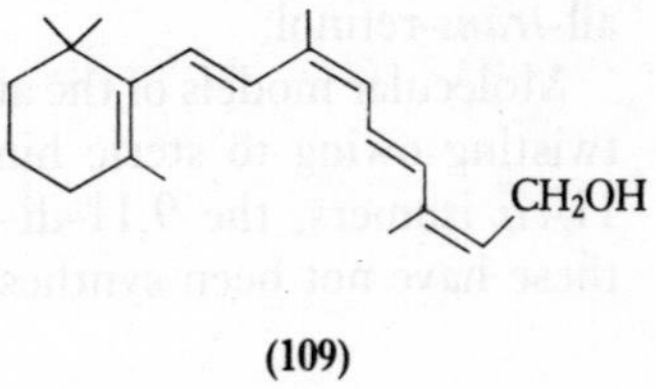

(109)

The synthesis and stereochemistry allotment for the 'unhindered' isomers was achieved[9,10,83] in the following manner. β-Ionone (7) was condensed with ethyl bromoacetate to yield a mixture of cis and trans compounds (110) which was hydrolysed, and the isomeric acids were separated by crystallization into the cis- (111) and trans- (112) β-ionyl-idineacetic acids. Each was separately converted into the aldehydes 113 and 114 respectively by esterification, followed by reduction to the alcohol with lithium aluminium hydride, and oxidation with manganese dioxide.

Compound 114 was then condensed with dimethyl β-methylglutaconate (115) to yield the 11-cis-7,9,13-tri-trans-dicarboxylic acid (116). The hindered 11-cis configuration for this was deduced by a study of the synthesis of γ-alklyidene-β-methylglutaconic acids and a comparison of their ultraviolet spectra with the spectrum of 116. The removal of one molecule of carbon dioxide from 116 produced neoretinoic acid$_a$ (13-cis-7,9,11-tri-trans-retinoic acid, 117) the ester of which was reduced with lithium aluminium hydride to 107 (13-cis-7,9,11-tri-trans-retinol (neo-vitamin A$_a$)). This was isomerized by iodine to all-trans-retinol.

When the aldehyde 113 was subjected to an analogous series of reactions, isovitamin A$_b$ (9,13-di-cis-7,11-di-trans-retinol, 109) was obtained. These reactions are summarized in 113 → 118 → 109. When 109 was isomerized with iodine, the product was isovitamin A$_a$ (9-mono-cis-7,11,13-tri-trans-retinol, 108).

The Pauling theory, as applied in the vitamin A type of compounds, was found to require modification when two $C_{(11)}$ cis isomers of retinol[34,73] were synthesized. These compounds are 11-cis-7,9,13-tri-trans-retinol (neovitamin A$_b$, 120) and 11,13-di-cis-7,9-di-trans-retinol (neovitamin A$_c$, 121).

The aldehyde 36 (an intermediate in the Isler retinol synthesis) was condensed separately with cis- and with trans-3-methylpent-2-en-4-yn-1-ol (122) under the conditions used in the Isler synthesis. The structures of the cis and trans isomers of 122 was proved by Oroshink[73] and later confirmed by a study of their nuclear magnetic resonance spectra. Neovitamin A$_b$ (120) was obtained[73] by use of trans-122 and neovitamin A$_c$ (121) from cis-122. Isomerization occurred with iodine in each case to all-trans-retinol.

Molecular models of the above two 11-cis isomers of retinol show slight twisting owing to steric hindrance; models can be made of two more 11-cis isomers, the 9,11-di-cis and the 9,11,13-tri-cis compounds, but these have not been synthesized. It is not possible to build a molecular

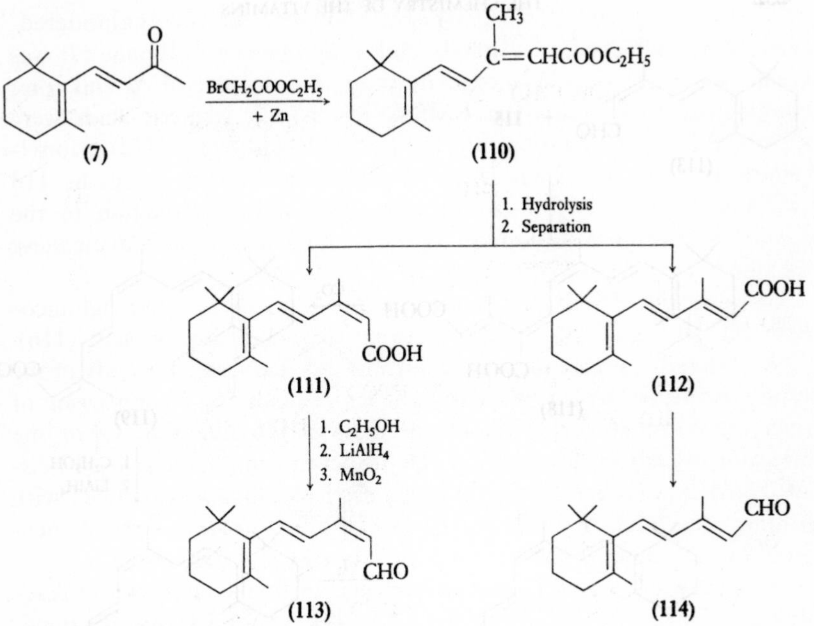
O
$BrCH_2COOC_2H_5$
+ Zn
(7)
CH_3
$C{=}CHCOOC_2H_5$
(110)
1. Hydrolysis
2. Separation
COOH
(111)
COOH
(112)
1. C_2H_5OH
2. $LiAlH_4$
3. MnO_2
CHO
(113)
CHO
(114)

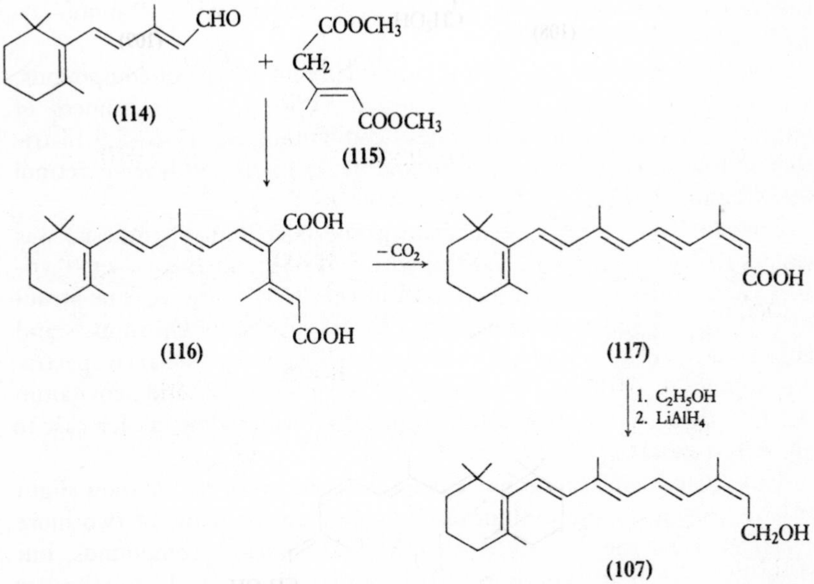
CHO
(114)
+
$COOCH_3$
CH_2
$COOCH_3$
(115)
COOH
COOH
(116)
$-CO_2$
COOH
(117)
1. C_2H_5OH
2. $LiAlH_4$
CH_2OH
(107)

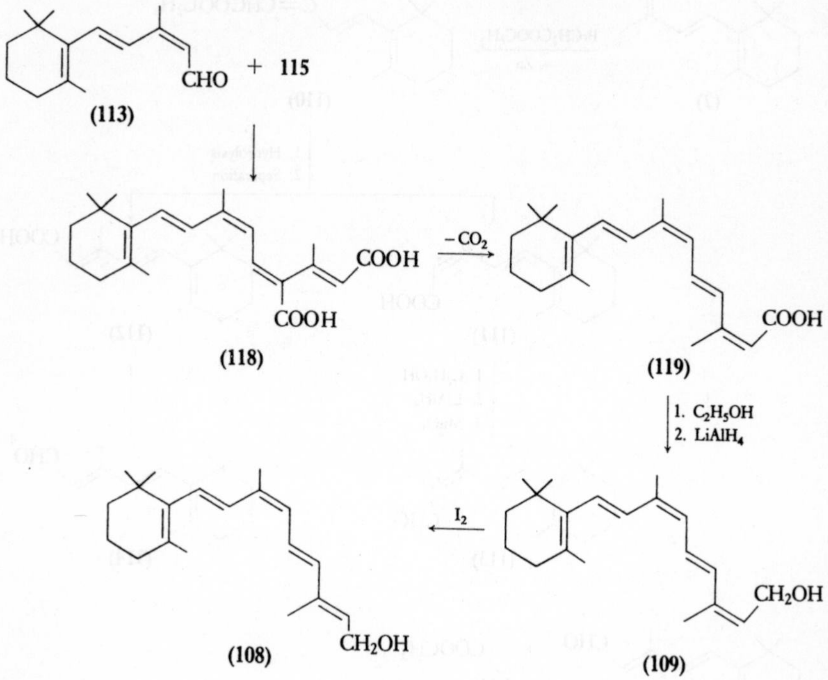
CHO
+ 115
(113)
COOH
COOH
(118)
$-CO_2$
COOH
(119)
1. C_2H_5OH
2. $LiAlH_4$
I_2
CH_2OH
(108)
CH_2OH
(109)

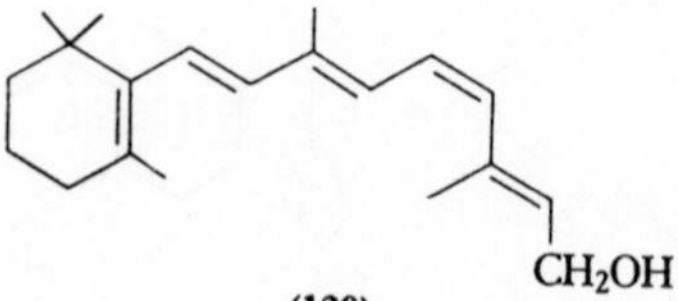
CH_2OH

(120)

(121)

(35)   (36)

(122)

model of a 7-*cis*-retinol, due to severe interference between the $C_{(9)}$ methyl group and the methyl groups of the cyclohexane ring, although unsuccessful attempts have been made[96] to synthesize such a compound.

In the preparation of the C_{15} aldehyde required by Kuhn and Morris in the first synthesis of retinol, β-ionone (7) is condensed with ethyl bromoacetate in a Reformatsky reaction to yield 123. It is now known that the dehydration product of 123 is the retro acid 124, which can be isomerized to a mixture of the *cis* and *trans* C_{15} acids (125 and 126 respectively). These can be separated and converted into the corresponding aldehydes 127a and 127b. Matsui has shown[59] that these C_{15} aldehydes condense readily with ethyl senecioate (128) in liquid ammonia in the presence of alkali metal amides. When potassamide is used, a *trans* configuration at $C_{(13)}$ results, whereas with lithium or sodium amides a $C_{(13)}$ *cis* geometry is produced. Thus, all the known unhindered geometrical isomers of retinol are easily available.

In the standard vitamin A assay with rats, neovitamin A_a acetate showed 75% of the activity of all-*trans*-retinol, whereas isovitamin A_a, isovitamin A_b and neovitamin A_b possessed 25% of the activity of all-*trans*-retinol.

Synthetic analogues of retinol[66]

A large number of compounds have been synthesized and tested for vitamin A activity, and from these results some generalizations concerning the structure–activity relationship emerge. Thus, an active compound must possess a β-ionone ring, at least eleven carbon atoms in the side-chain containing four conjugated double bonds in the all-*trans* configuration and which are also conjugated with the ring double bond.

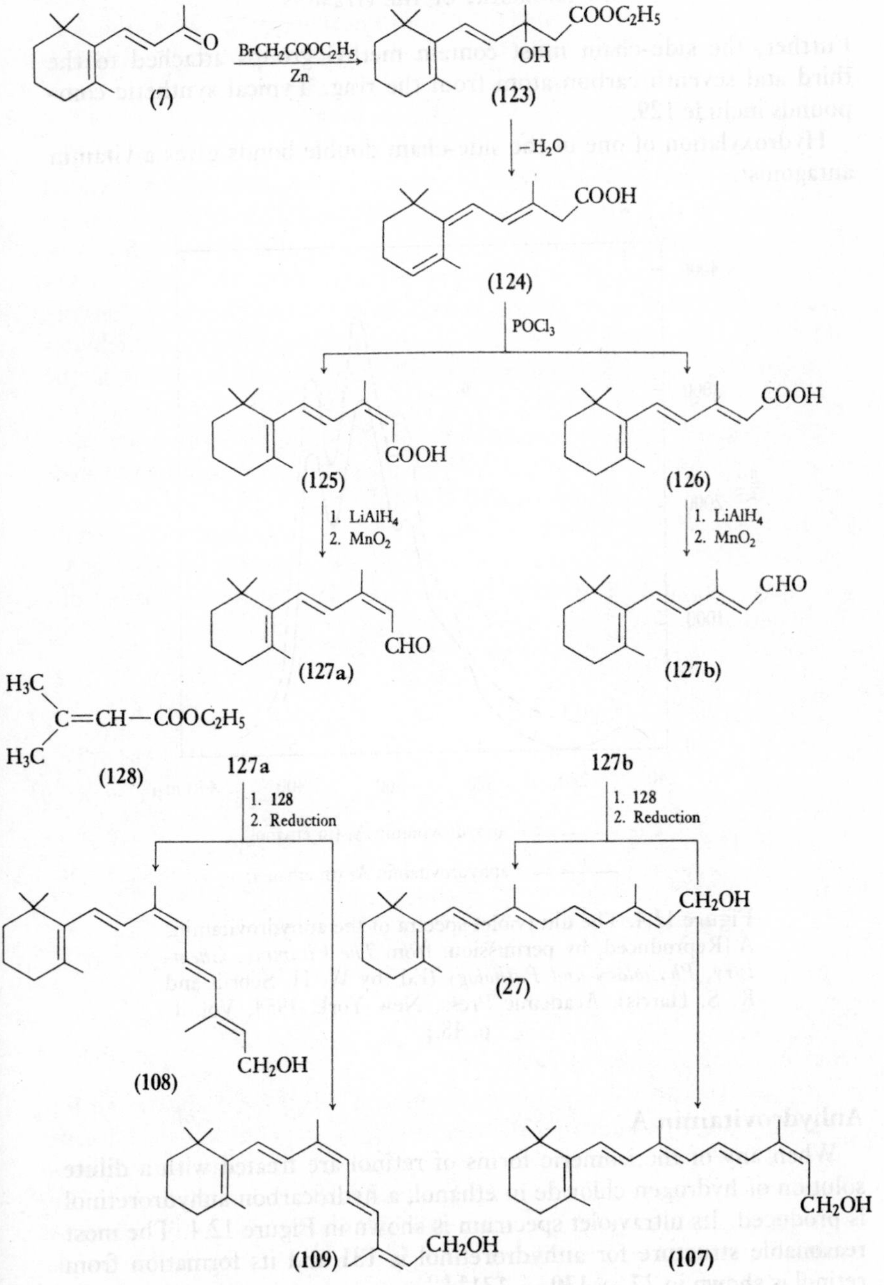

O
BrCH2COOC2H5
Zn
COOC2H5
OH
(7)
(123)
−H2O
COOH
(124)
POCl3
COOH
COOH
(125)
(126)
1. LiAlH4
2. MnO2
1. LiAlH4
2. MnO2
CHO
CHO
(127a)
(127b)
H3C
C=CH—COOC2H5
H3C
(128)
127a
127b
1. 128
2. Reduction
1. 128
2. Reduction
CH2OH
(27)
CH2OH
(108)
CH2OH
(109)
CH2OH
(107)

Further, the side-chain must contain methyl groups attached to the third and seventh carbon atom from the ring. Typical synthetic compounds include **129**.

Hydroxylation of one of the side-chain double bonds gives a vitamin antagonist.

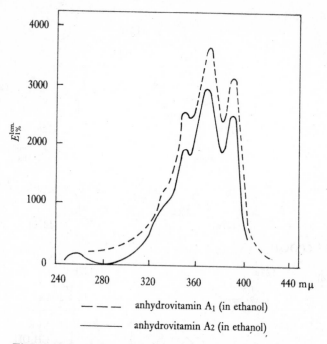

$E_{1\%}^{\text{1cm.}}$

240   280   320   360   400   440 mμ

– – – – anhydrovitamin A₁ (in ethanol)

———— anhydrovitamin A₂ (in ethanol)

Figure 12.4. The ultraviolet spectra of the anhydrovitamins A. [Reproduced, by permission, from *The Vitamins: Chemistry, Physiology and Pathology* (Ed. by W. H. Sebrill and R. S. Harris), Academic Press, New York, 1954, Vol. 1, p. 48.]

Anhydrovitamin A

When any of the isomeric forms of retinol are treated with a dilute solution of hydrogen chloride in ethanol, a hydrocarbon anhydroretinol is produced. Its ultraviolet spectrum is shown in Figure 12.4. The most reasonable structure for anhydroretinol is **131** and its formation from retinol is shown in **27 → 130 → 131**[4,60].

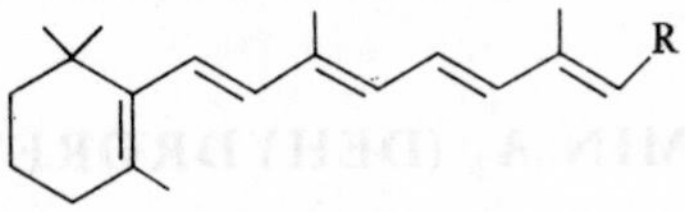

$$\left(129, \quad R=CH_3, \quad \text{[structure with CHO]}, \quad \text{[structure with CHO]}, \quad \text{[structure with O]}\right)$$

$$\text{[bicyclic structure]} \quad CH=CH-\overset{\overset{\displaystyle CH_3}{|}}{C}=CH-CH=CH-\overset{\overset{\displaystyle CH_3}{|}}{C}=CH-CH_2OH$$

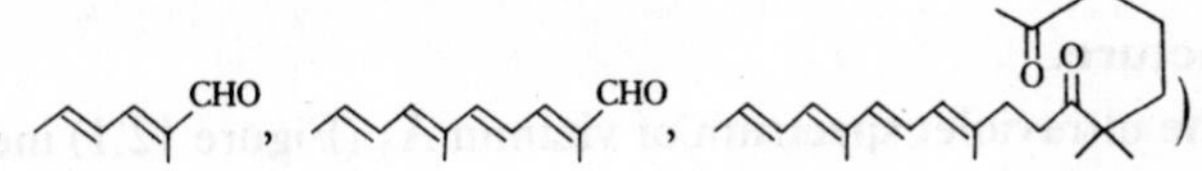

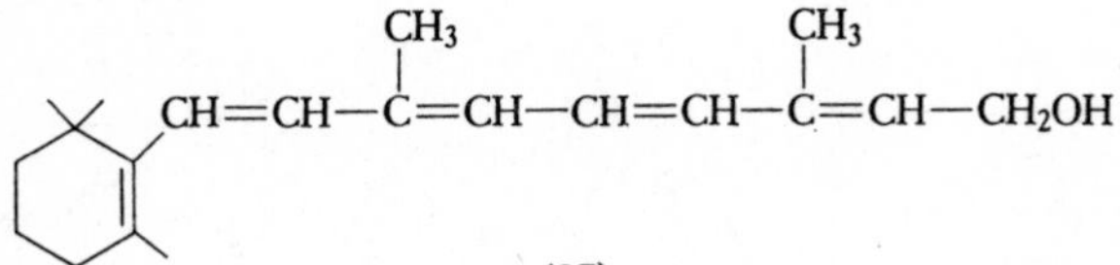

(27)

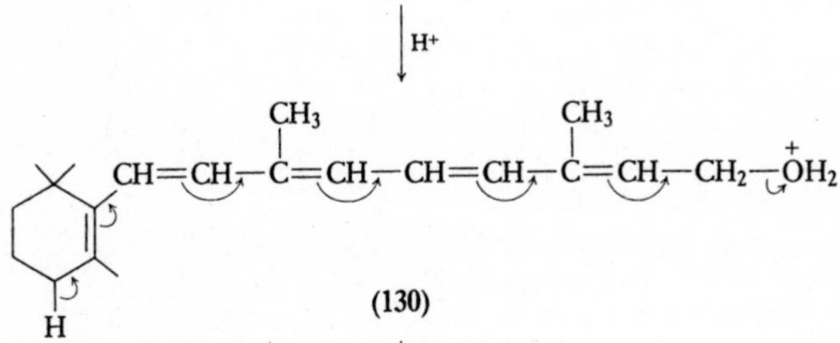

$$\downarrow H^+$$

$$\text{[bicyclic structure with H]} \quad CH=CH-\overset{\overset{\displaystyle CH_3}{|}}{C}=CH-CH=CH-\overset{\overset{\displaystyle CH_3}{|}}{C}=CH-CH_2-\overset{+}{O}H_2$$

(130)

$$\downarrow$$

$$\text{[bicyclic structure]} \quad CH-CH=\overset{\overset{\displaystyle CH_3}{|}}{C}-CH=CH-CH=\overset{\overset{\displaystyle CH_3}{|}}{C}-CH=CH_2$$

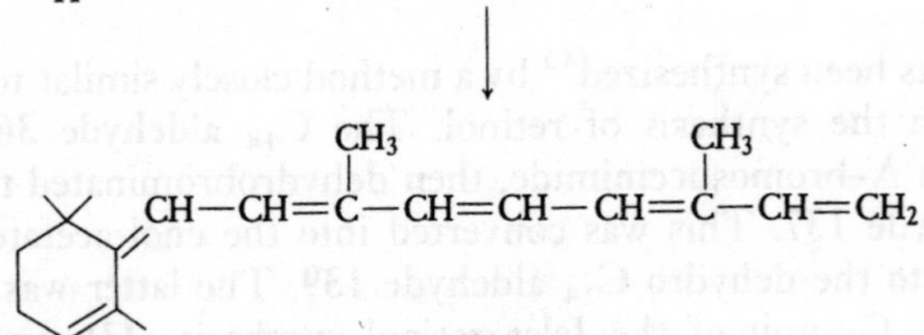

(131)

VITAMIN A₂ (DEHYDRORETINOL)

Structure

The ultraviolet spectrum of vitamin A_2 (Figure 12.1) indicated that it possesses one more conjugated double bond than retinol, and structure 132 was first proposed[18]. This was later modified[15,16] to 133 when dehydroretinol was synthesized[15,16] from the methyl ester of retinoic acid (134) by bromination with N-bromosuccinimide to 135 followed by elimination of hydrogen bromide with 4-phenylmorpholine and reduction of the resulting 136 with lithium aluminium hydride.

Synthesis

Vitamin A_2 has been synthesized[45] by a method closely similar to that used by Isler in the synthesis of retinol. The C_{14} aldehyde 36 was brominated with N-bromosuccinimide, then dehydrobrominated to the retro C_{14} aldehyde 137. This was converted into the enol acetate 138 and hydrolysed to the dehydro C_{14} aldehyde 139. The latter was condensed with the C_6 unit of the Isler retinol synthesis (43), and the product (140) was partially hydrogenated, acetylated, dehydrated and hydrolysed to dehydroretinol (133).

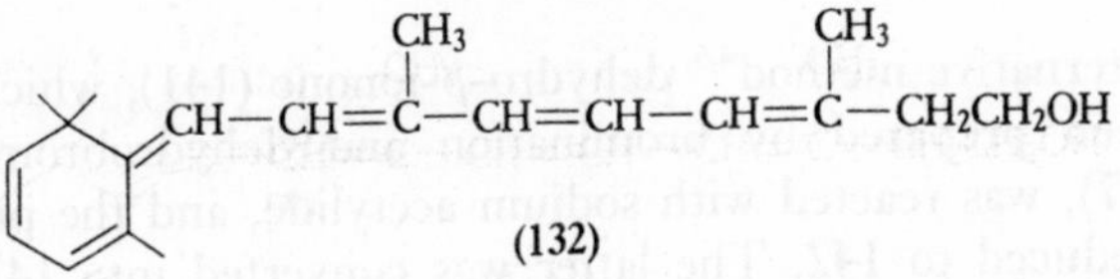

$$CH_3 \quad\quad CH_3$$

(132)

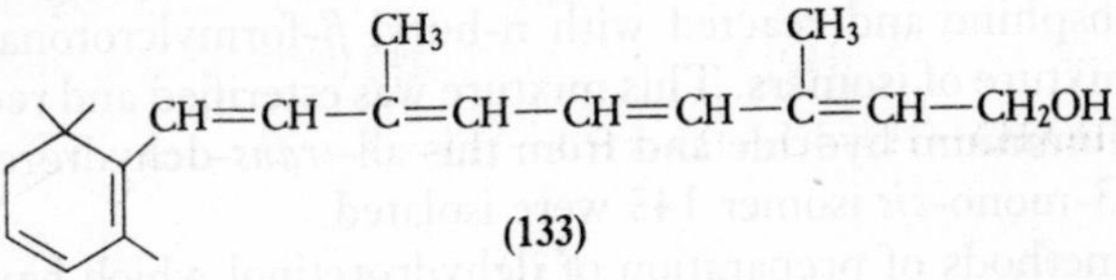

$$CH_3 \quad\quad CH_3$$

(133)

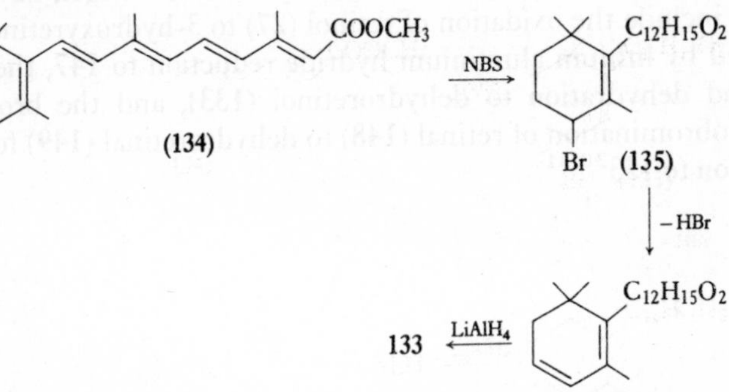

COOCH₃

(134)

$C_{12}H_{15}O_2$

Br (135)

NBS

– HBr

$C_{12}H_{15}O_2$

133 ← LiAlH₄ ←

(136)

CHO

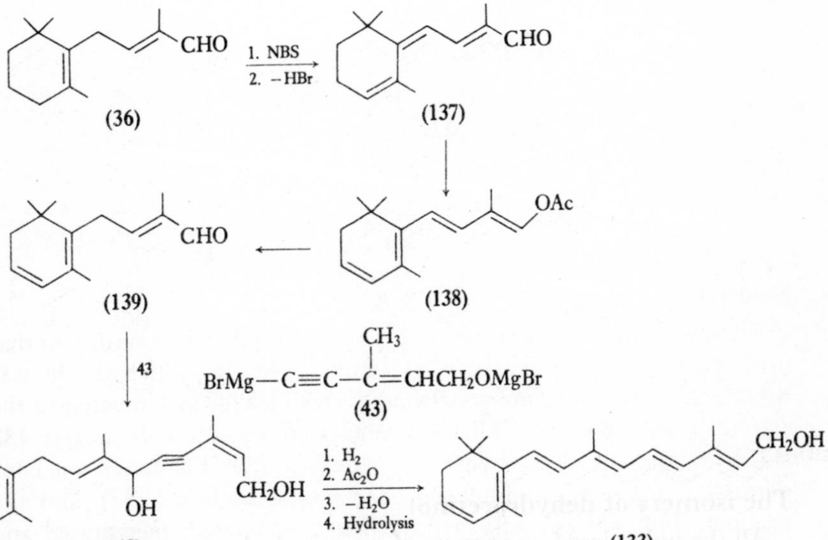

(36)

1. NBS
2. – HBr

CHO

(137)

OAc

(138)

CHO

(139)

43

CH₃

BrMg—C≡C—C=CHCH₂OMgBr

(43)

OH   CH₂OH

(140)

1. H₂
2. Ac₂O
3. – H₂O
4. Hydrolysis

CH₂OH

(133)

In an alternative method[45] dehydro-β-ionone (141), which had previously been prepared by bromination and dehydrobromination of β-ionone (7), was reacted with sodium acetylide, and the product was partially reduced to 142. The latter was converted into 143 with triphenylphosphine and reacted with n-butyl β-formylcrotonate to yield 144 as a mixture of isomers. This mixture was esterified and reduced with lithium aluminium hydride and from this all-*trans*-dehydroretinol (133) and the 13-mono-*cis* isomer 145 were isolated.

Other methods of preparation of dehydroretinol which have been reported include the oxidation of retinol (27) to 3-hydroxyretinenal (146), followed by lithium aluminium hydride reduction to 147, then acetylation and dehydration to dehydroretinol (133), and the bromination–dehydrobromination of retinal (148) to dehydroretinal (149) followed by reduction to 133[30,31].

The isomers of dehydroretinol

All the unhindered *cis* isomers of vitamin A_2 have now been synthesized[45] by the method used by Matsui for the isomers of vitamin A_1

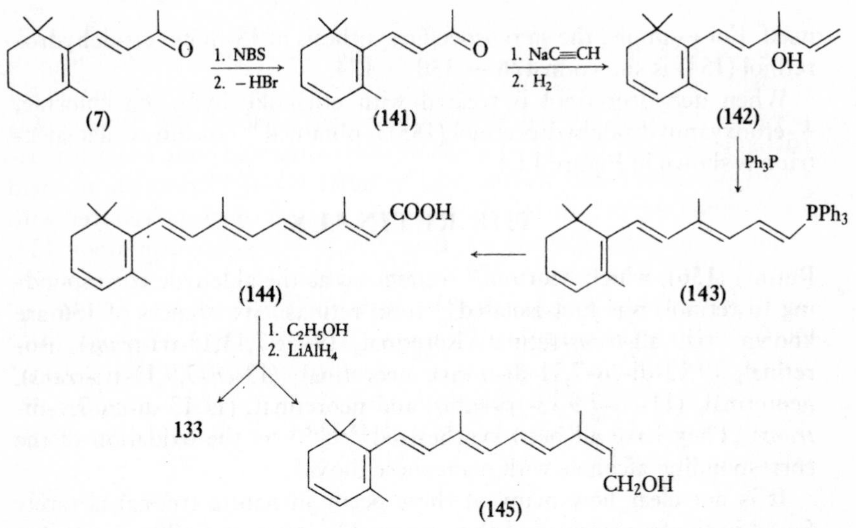
O
1. NBS
2. −HBr
O
1. NaC≡CH
2. H₂
OH
(7)
(141)
(142)
Ph₃P
COOH
PPh₃
(144)
(143)
1. C₂H₅OH
2. LiAlH₄
133
CH₂OH
(145)

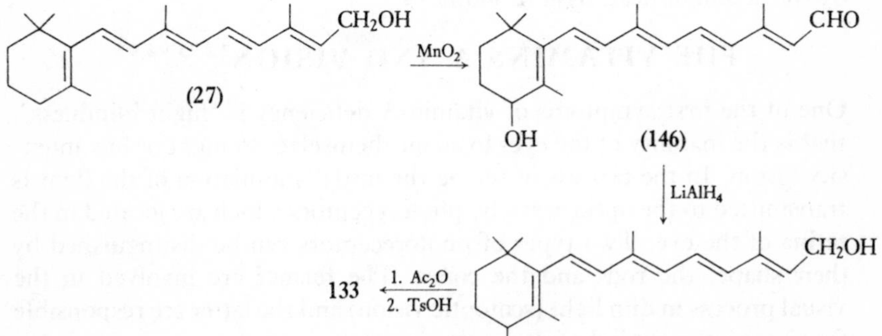
CH₂OH
MnO₂
CHO
(27)
OH
(146)
LiAlH₄
CH₂OH
133
1. Ac₂O
2. TsOH
OH
(147)

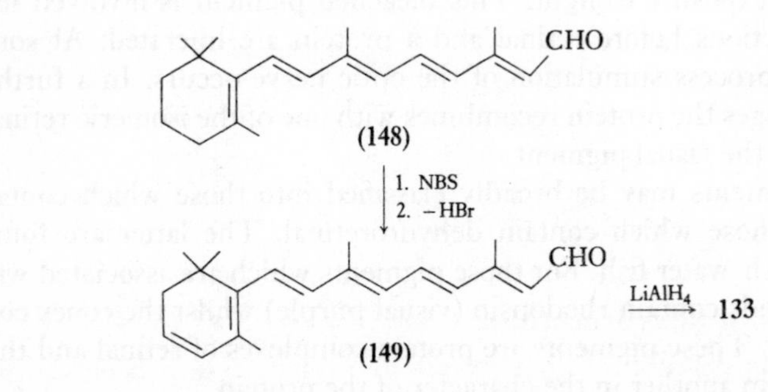
CHO
(148)
1. NBS
2. −HBr
CHO
LiAlH₄
133
(149)

itself. For example, the stereospecific synthesis of 13-mono-*cis*-dehydro-
retinol (154) is shown in 126 → 150 → 154.

When dehydroretinol is treated with ethanolic hydrogen chloride,
4′-ethoxyanhydrodehydroretinol (155) is obtained[30]. Its ultraviolet spectrum is shown in Figure 12.4.

THE RETINALS

Retinal (156), which Morton[70] recognized as the aldehyde corresponding to retinol, was first isolated[93] from retinas. Six isomers of 156 are
known, viz. all-*trans*-retinal, isoretinal$_a$ (9-*cis*-7,11,13-tri-*trans*), iso-
retinal$_b$ (9,13-di-*cis*-7,11-di-*trans*), neoretinal$_a$ (13-*cis*-7,9,11-tri-*trans*),
neoretinal$_b$ (11-*cis*-7,9,13-tri-*trans*) and neoretinal$_c$ (11,13-di-*cis*-7,9-di-
trans). They have all been synthesized[34,73,84] by the oxidation of the
corresponding alcohols with manganese dioxide.

It is not clear how many of these occur in nature (retinal is rarely
found in the free state), and they are readily interconvertible in solution
by the action of heat, light or iodine.

THE VITAMINS A AND VISION[32,75,94,95]

One of the first symptoms of vitamin A deficiency is 'night blindness',
that is the inability of the eyes to adapt themselves to night or low inten-
sity vision. In the process of seeing the initial stimulation of the light is
transmitted to the optic nerve by photoreceptors which are located in the
retina of the eye. Two types of photoreceptors can be distinguished by
their shape, the rods and the cones. The former are involved in the
visual process in dim light (scotoptic vision) and the latter are responsible
for vision in bright light (photoptic vision).

The rods and cones each contain a light-sensitive pigment which is
bleached on exposure to light. This bleached pigment is involved in a
series of reactions before retinal and a protein are liberated. At some
stage in the process stimulation of the optic nerve occurs. In a further
series of changes the protein recombines with one of the isomeric retinals
to regenerate the visual pigment.

Visual pigments may be broadly classified into those which contain
retinal and those which contain dehydroretinal. The latter are found
mostly in fresh-water fish. For those pigments which are associated with
retinal, the rods contain rhodopsin (visual purple) whilst the cones contain iodopsin. These pigments are protein complexes of retinal and they
differ one from another in the character of the protein.

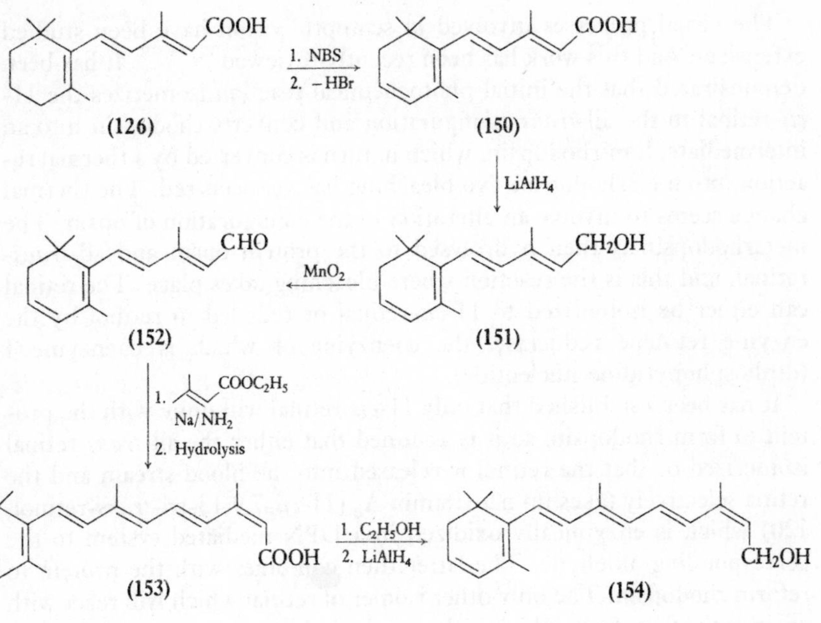

(126) → (150)

1. NBS
2. − HBr

(150) → (151)

LiAlH₄

(152) ← (151)

MnO₂

(153)

1. [structure] COOC₂H₅
   Na/NH₂
2. Hydrolysis

(154)

1. C₂H₅OH
2. LiAlH₄

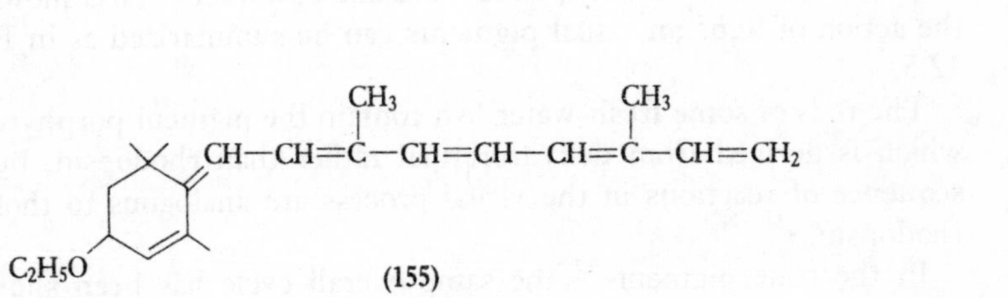

$$CH-CH=C-CH=CH-CH=C-CH=CH_2$$

(155)

$$CH=CH-C=CH-CH=CH-C=CH-CHO$$

(156)

The visual processes involved in scotoptic vision have been studied extensively and this work has been recently reviewed[32,75,98]. It has been demonstrated that the initial photochemical reaction isomerizes the 11-cis-retinal to the all-trans configuration and converts rhodopsin into an intermediate, lumirhodopsin, which in turn is converted by a thermal reaction into metarhodopsin. No bleaching has yet occurred. The thermal change seems to involve an alteration in the configuration of opsin. The metarhodopsin is then hydrolysed to the protein opsin and all-trans-retinal, and this is the reaction where bleaching takes place. The retinal can either be isomerized to 11-cis-retinal or reduced to retinol by the enzyme retinene reductase, the coenzyme of which is coenzyme I (diphosphopyridine nucleotide).

It has been established that only 11-cis-retinal will unite with the protein to form rhodopsin, so it is assumed that either the all-trans-retinal isomerized or that the retinol is released into the blood stream and the retina selectively takes up neovitamin A_b (11-cis-7,9,13-tri-trans-retinol, 120) which is enzymically oxidized in a DPN mediated system to the corresponding aldehyde. The latter then combines with the protein to reform rhodopsin. The only other isomer of retinal which will react with opsin is the 9-cis form which yields isorhodopsin, a pigment which is not of natural occurrence.

Further work, especially by Hubbard and coworkers[35], has shown that the action of light on visual pigments can be summarized as in Figure 12.5.

The rods of some fresh-water fish contain the pigment porphyropsin, which is derived from dehydroretinal rather than rhodopsin, but the sequence of reactions in the visual process are analogous to those for rhodopsin.

In the cone pigments[97] the same overall cycle has been shown to occur.

PROVITAMINS A

The normal requirements of vitamin A can be supplied by certain carotenes which are converted into retinol in the intestine. Of the eighty or so carotenoids listed by Karrer[53], only eleven may serve as provitamins A; these include α-, β- and γ-carotene.

There is considerable evidence to support the view that β-carotene (158) is metabolized to vitamin A in the animal body and then stored in the liver[20]. Two main routes have been considered[19,22,23] for this conversion: (a) central cleavage in β-carotene of the $C_{(15)}$—$C_{(15')}$ double bond leading to two molecules of vitamin A per molecule of β-carotene; and (b) terminal oxidation, where the β-carotene molecule is progressively degraded to yield ultimately one molecule of vitamin A. Experimentally, it is difficult to establish the route that is followed since the amount of vitamin A formed from the administration of a dose of β-carotene is very small. The central fission of β-carotene[36] in vivo has been claimed[8,54] to take place in the presence of α-tocopherol. In attempts to establish chemical analogues for this postulated symmetrical fission of

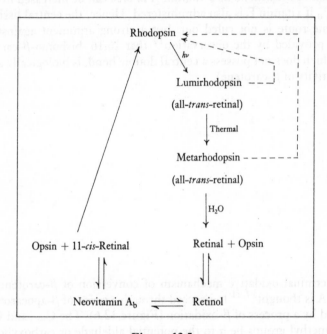

Figure 12.5.

β-carotene, the effects of various oxidizing agents have been studied. Chromium trioxide attacks the double bonds of the β-ionone rings of β-carotene, whereas alkaline potassium permanganate attacks the ends of the long carbon chain between the ionone residues, leading to long–chain aldehydes (the β-apocarotenals). Oxidation of β-carotene with hydrogen peroxide in the presence of osmium tetroxide gave good yields of retinal and a whole series of β-apocarotenals[21]. It was concluded that the reagent preferentially attacks the penultimate bond in the conjugated system of β-carotene.

In biological assays retinol exhibits an activity of 3.32×10^6 international units per gram, whereas β-carotene contains 1.667×10^6 international units per gram[92]. (One international unit $= 0.6 \times 10^{-6}$ g of pure β-carotene dissolved in coconut oil, with the addition of hydroquinone.) Also, α- and γ-carotenes possess one-half of the β-carotene activity. These results favour the terminal cleavage and stepwise degradation of β-carotene. However, Moore has found[68] that the efficiency of conversion of β-carotene into vitamin A *in vivo* can be increased to more than 50% if vitamin E is also administered. Hence, the central fission of β-carotene route is not ruled out, but a strong argument against this route is provided by the observation[12] that 16,16'-bishomo-β-carotene (157), which does not possess a central double bond, is biologically active (20% activity of β-carotene).

The terminal oxidative mechanism of conversion of β-carotene into vitamin A is thought[17,21] to proceed through a series of β-apocarotenals produced by a process of β-oxidation (Figure 12.6). The $C_{(9')}$ and $C_{(13')}$ branch-methyl groups lie α to the potential aldehyde or carboxylic acid group and will thus be degraded away, but when the central double bond is reached, β-oxidation is blocked by the $C_{(13)}$ methyl group which is β to the central carbon atom of β-carotene. Support for this overall route is provided by the fact that β-apo-8'-carotenal (159) is biologically active and β-apo-12'-carotenal (160) is more active than β-carotene in growth tests. Further, β-apo-10'-carotenal and β-apo-12'-carotenal have been isolated from horse intestines. However, when experimental animals are given large doses of β-carotene, no compounds intermediate in size between β-carotene and vitamin A could be detected; this may be because the intermediates are strongly bound to proteins. Several of these intermediate β-apocarotenals have been synthesized[22,85,86]

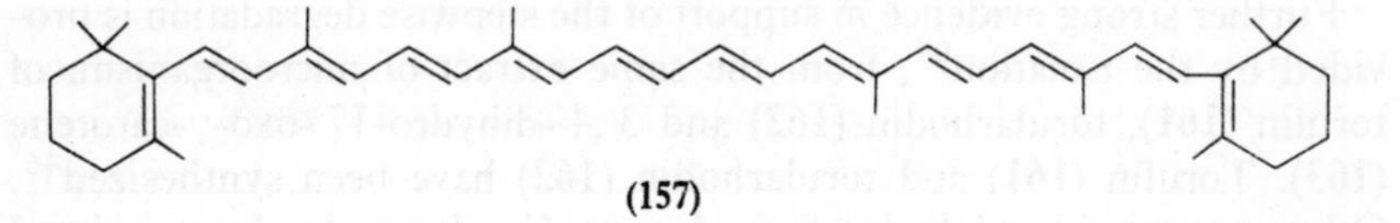

(157)

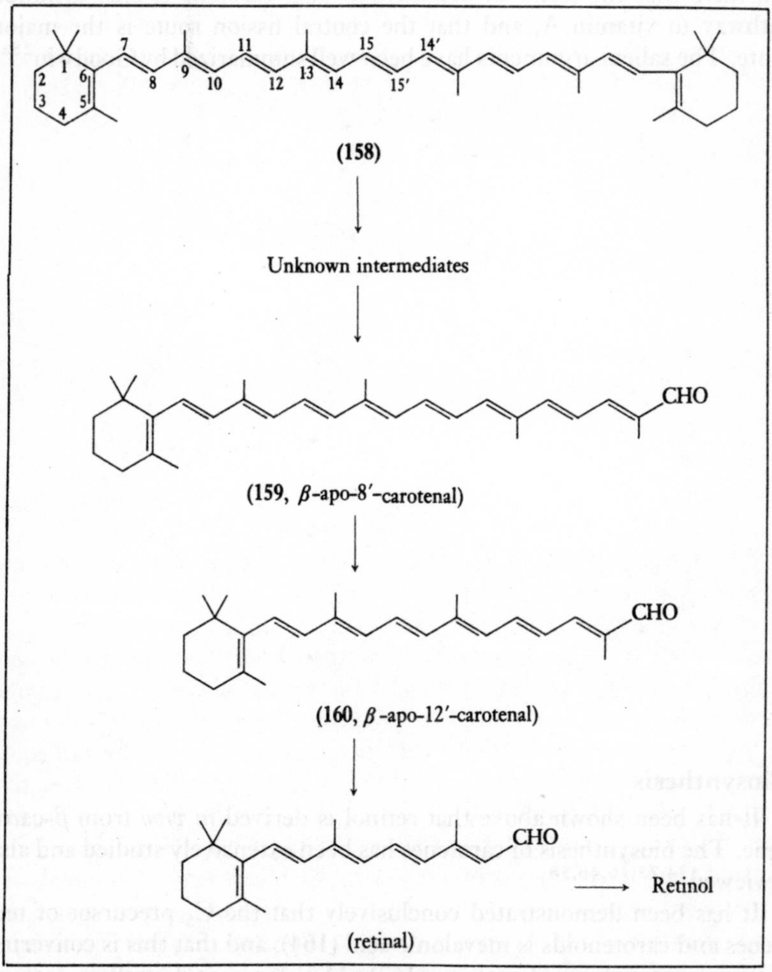

(158)

↓

Unknown intermediates

↓

(159, β-apo-8′-carotenal)

↓

(160, β-apo-12′-carotenal)

↓

(retinal)

→ Retinol

Figure 12.6.

9

Further strong evidence in support of the stepwise degradation is provided by the isolation[99], from the same extract of microorganism, of torulin (161), torularhodin (162) and 3′,4′-dihydro-17′-oxo-γ-carotene (163). Torulin (161) and torularhodin (162) have been synthesized[46]. Other carotenoid aldehydes from C_{27} to C_{40} have also been isolated from microorganisms[99].

Glover[22], after a careful consideration of the available evidence, now considers that the terminal degradation of β-carotene is only a minor pathway to vitamin A, and that the central fission route is the major route. The salient arguments have been well summarized by Goodwin[25a].

Biosynthesis

It has been shown above that retinol is derived *in vivo* from β-carotene. The biosynthesis of carotenes has been extensively studied and also reviewed[24,25,26,46,58].

It has been demonstrated conclusively that the C_5 precursor of terpenes and carotenoids is mevalonic acid (164), and that this is converted into isopentenylpyrophosphate (167). Mevalonic acid itself is formed from acetylcoenzyme A as indicated in 168 → 171 → 164.

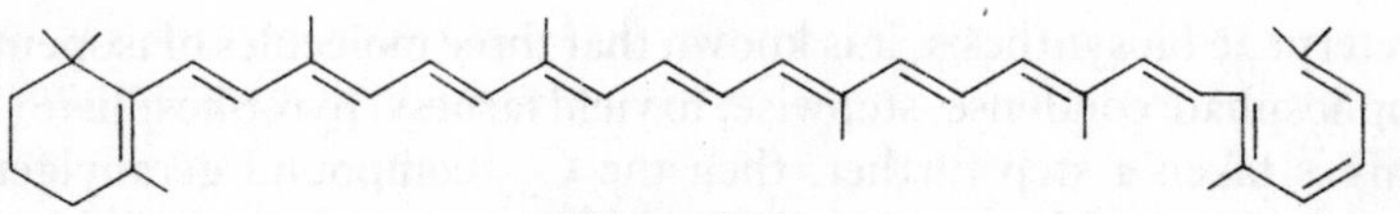

(161, torulin)

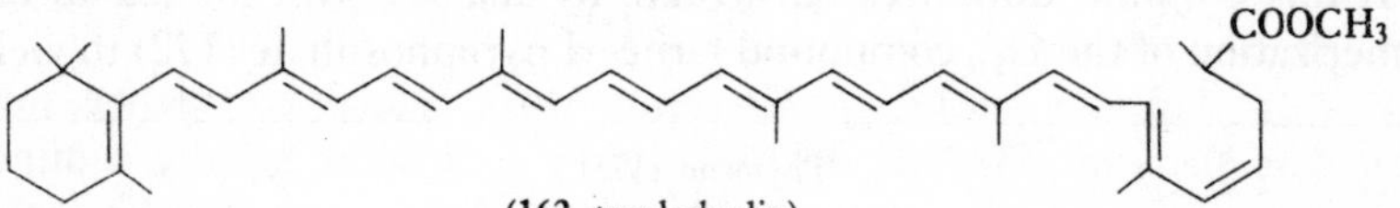

(162, torularhodin)

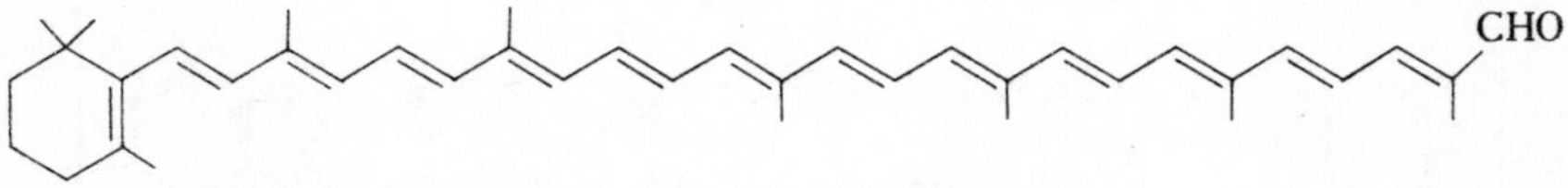

(163, 3′,4′-dihydro-17′-oxo-γ-carotene)

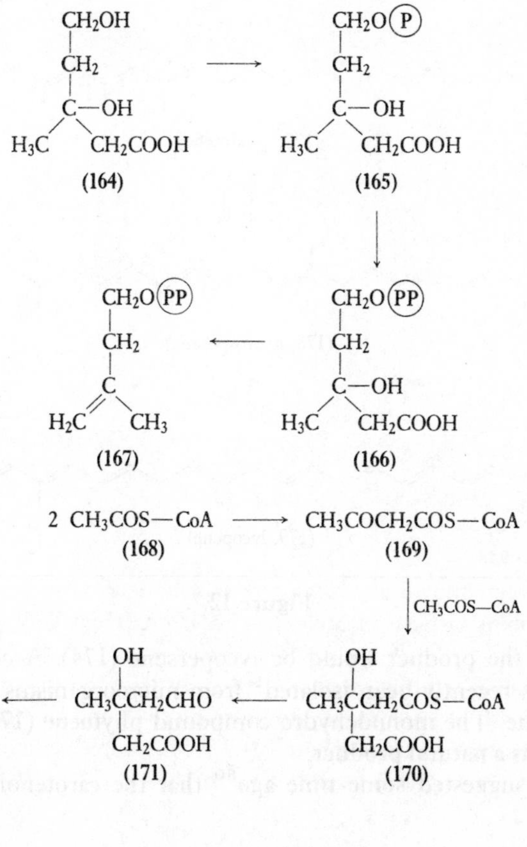

$$
\begin{array}{ccc}
\text{CH}_2\text{OH} & & \text{CH}_2\text{O}\,\text{(P)} \\
| & & | \\
\text{CH}_2 & & \text{CH}_2 \\
| & \longrightarrow & | \\
\text{C—OH} & & \text{C—OH} \\
\text{H}_3\text{C}\quad\text{CH}_2\text{COOH} & & \text{H}_3\text{C}\quad\text{CH}_2\text{COOH} \\
(164) & & (165)
\end{array}
$$

$$
\begin{array}{ccc}
\text{CH}_2\text{O}\,\text{(PP)} & & \text{CH}_2\text{O}\,\text{(PP)} \\
| & & | \\
\text{CH}_2 & & \text{CH}_2 \\
| & \longleftarrow & | \\
\text{C} & & \text{C—OH} \\
\text{H}_2\text{C}\quad\text{CH}_3 & & \text{H}_3\text{C}\quad\text{CH}_2\text{COOH} \\
(167) & & (166)
\end{array}
$$

$$
2\ \text{CH}_3\text{COS—CoA} \longrightarrow \text{CH}_3\text{COCH}_2\text{COS—CoA}
$$
$$
(168) \qquad\qquad\qquad (169)
$$

$$\downarrow \text{CH}_3\text{COS—CoA}$$

$$
\begin{array}{ccccc}
 & & \text{OH} & & \text{OH} \\
 & & | & & | \\
164 \longleftarrow & \text{CH}_3\text{CCH}_2\text{CHO} & \longleftarrow & \text{CH}_3\text{CCH}_2\text{COS—CoA} \\
 & & | & & | \\
 & & \text{CH}_2\text{COOH} & & \text{CH}_2\text{COOH} \\
 & & (171) & & (170)
\end{array}
$$

In terpene biosynthesis, it is known that three molecules of isopentenyl pyrophosphate condense, stepwise, to yield farnesyl pyrophosphate (172). If this is taken a step further, then the C_{20} compound geranylgeranyl pyrophosphate (173) would be formed.

If this C_{20} unit dimerizes tail-to-tail, by analogy with the tail-to-tail dimerization of the C_{15} compound farnesyl pyrophosphate (172) to yield

Phytoene (175)

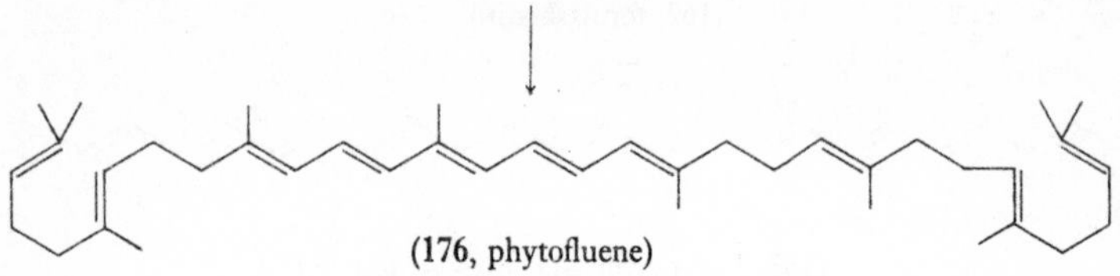

(176, phytofluene)

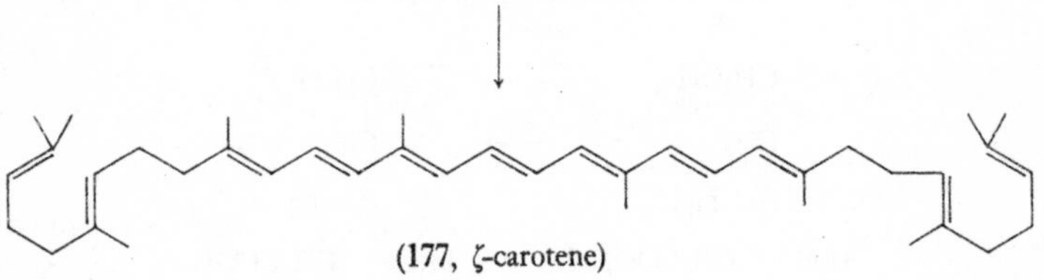

(177, ζ-carotene)

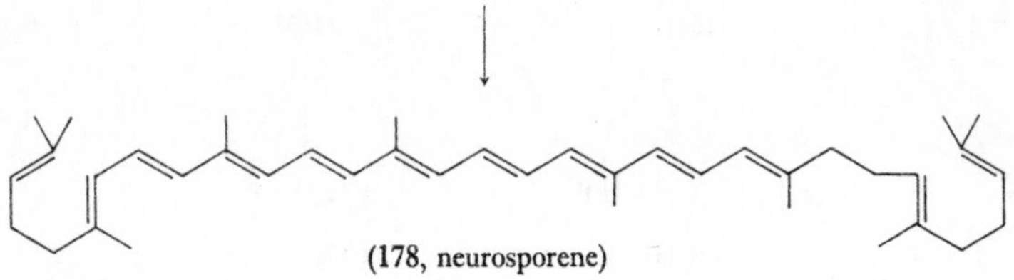

(178, neurosporene)

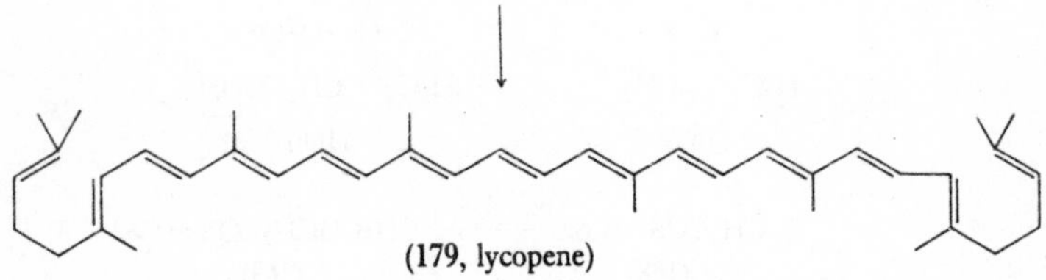

(179, lycopene)

Figure 12.7.

squalene, the product would be lycopersene (174). A colourless carotenoid has recently been isolated[1] from microorganisms which may be
lycopersene. The monodehydro compound phytoene (175) is, however,
known[79] as a natural product.

It was suggested some time ago[80] that the carotenoids are derived

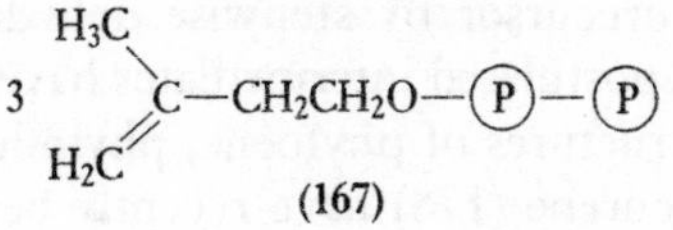

$$3 \quad \underset{H_2C}{\overset{H_3C}{>}}C-CH_2CH_2O-\text{(P)}-\text{(P)}$$

(167)

↓

$$\underset{H_3C}{\overset{H_3C}{>}}C=CHCH_2CH_2-\overset{CH_3}{\underset{|}{C}}=CH-CH_2CH_2-\overset{CH_3}{\underset{|}{C}}=CHCH_2O-\text{(P)}-\text{(P)}$$

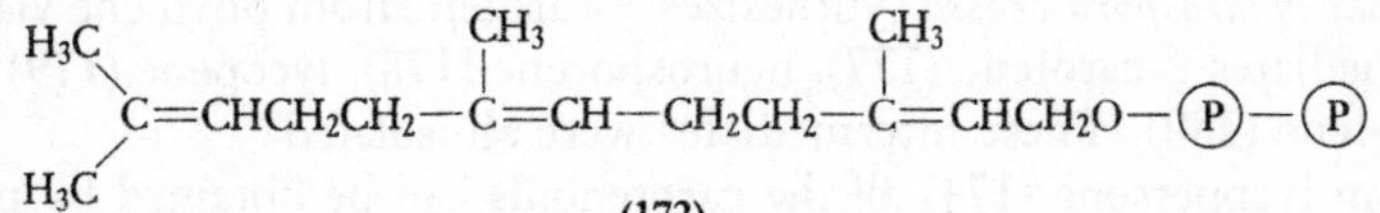

(172)

↓

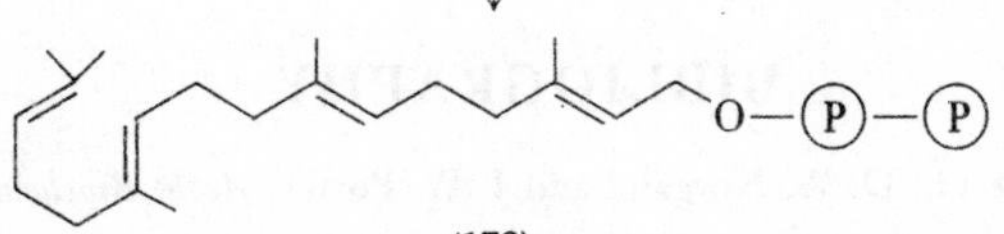

(173)

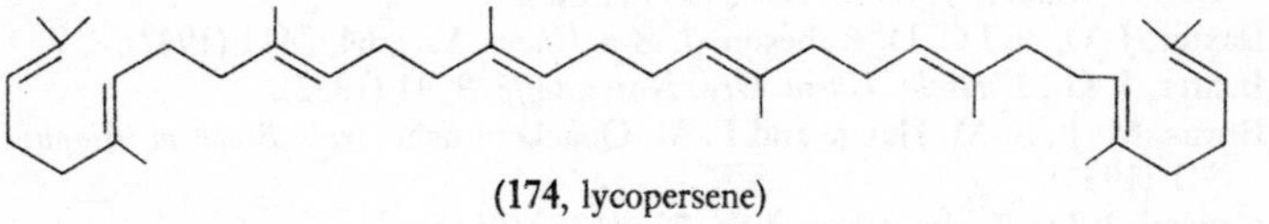

(174, lycopersene)

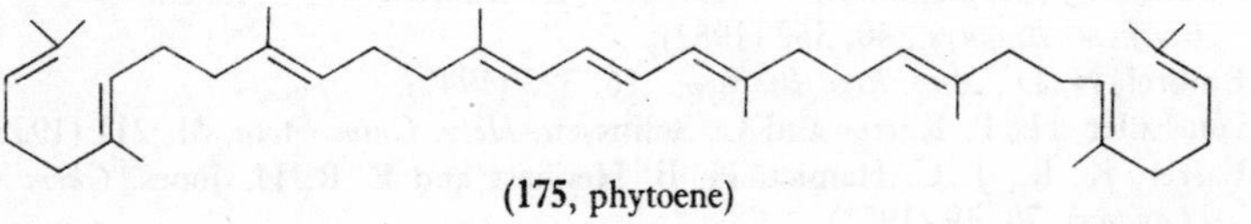

(175, phytoene)

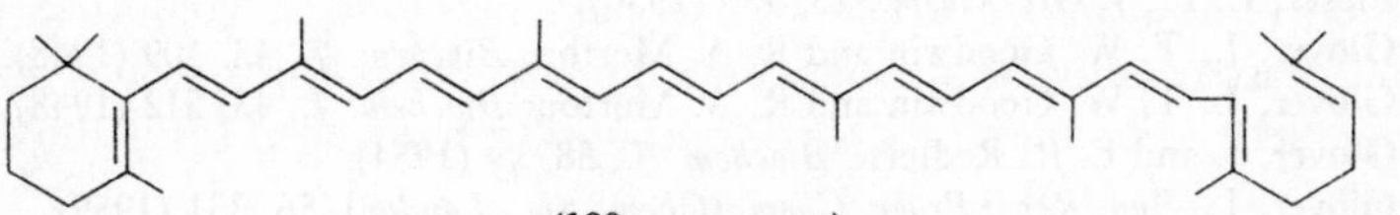

(180, γ-carotene)

from some colourless precursor by stepwise dehydrogenation (Figure 12.7) and several of the postulated intermediates have been isolated from natural sources. The structures of phytoene, phytofluene (176), ζ-carotene (177), and neurosporene (178) have recently been confirmed[11] by n.m.r. spectroscopy and synthesis.

Further support for this stepwise dehydrogenation is provided by the fact that *Neurospora crassa* synthesizes γ-carotene from phytoene via the intermediates ζ-carotene (177), neurosporene (178), lycopene (179) and γ-carotene (180). These intermediates were all isolated[47].

From lycopersene (174) all the carotenoids can be obtained by plausible processes involving dehydrogenation, cyclization, aromatization, introduction of oxygen functions, rearrangement and isomerization[25].

BIBLIOGRAPHY

1. Anderson, D. G., D. W. Norgand and J. W. Porter, *Arch. Biochem. Biophys.*, **88**, 68 (1960).
2. Arens, J. F. and D. A. Van Dorp, *Nature*, **157**, 190 (1946); **160**, 189 (1947).
3. Arens, J. F. and D. A. Van Dorp, *Rec. Trav. Chim.*, **65**, 338 (1946).
4. Arens, J. F. and D. A. Van Dorp, *Rec. Trav. Chim.*, **67**, 973 (1948).
5. Attenburrow, J., A. B. F. Cameron, J. H. Chapman, R. M. Evans, A. B. A. Jansen and T. Walker, *J. Chem. Soc.*, 1094 (1952).
6. Baxter, J. G. and C. D. Robeson, *J. Am. Chem. Soc.*, **64**, 2411 (1942).
7. Baxter, J. G., *Fortschr. Chem. Org. Naturstoffe*, **9**, 41 (1952).
8. Burns, M. J., S. M. Hauge and F. M. Quackenbush, *Arch. Biochem. Biophys.*, **30**, 341 (1951).
9. Cawley, J. D., *J. Am. Chem. Soc.*, **77**, 4125 (1955).
10. Cawley, J. D. and D. R. Nelan, *J. Am. Chem. Soc.*, **77**, 4130 (1955).
11. Davis, J. B., L. M. Jackman, P. T. Siddons and B. C. L. Weedon, *Proc. Chem. Soc.*, 261 (1961).
12. Deuel, H. J., H. H. Inhoffen, J. Ganguly, L. Wallcave and L. Zeichmeister, *Arch. Biochem. Biophys.*, **40**, 352 (1952).
13. Embrei, N. D., *Ann. Rev. Biochem.*, **16**, 323 (1947).
14. von Euler, H., P. Karrer and U. Solmssen, *Helv. Chim. Acta*, **21**, 211 (1938).
15. Farrer, K. R., J. C. Hamlet, H. B. Henbest and E. R. H. Jones, *Chem. Ind. (London)*, **70**, 49 (1951).
16. Farrer, K. R., J. C. Hamlet, H. B. Henbest and E. R. H. Jones, *J. Chem. Soc.*, 2657 (1952).
17. Fazakerley, S. and J. Glover, *Biochem. J.*, **65**, 38P (1957).
18. Fieser, L. F., *J. Org. Chem.*, **15**, 930 (1950).
19. Glover, J., T. W. Goodwin and R. A. Morton, *Biochem. J.*, **43**, 109 (1948).
20. Glover, J., T. W. Goodwin and R. A. Morton, *Biochem. J.*, **43**, 512 (1948).
21. Glover, J. and E. R. Redfern, *Biochem. J.*, **58**, xv (1954).
22. Glover, J., *Ann. Rept. Progr. Chem. (Chem. Soc. London)*, **56**, 331 (1959).
23. Glover, J., *Vitamins Hormones*, **18**, 371 (1960).

24. Goodwin, T. W., *Recent Advances in Biochemistry*, Churchill, London, 1960, p. 262.
25. Goodwin, T. W., *Ann. Rev. Plant Physiol.*, 12, 219 (1961).
25a. Goodwin, T. W., *The Biosynthesis of Vitamins and Related Compounds*, Academic Press, London, 1963, Chap. 14.
26. Grob, E. C., *Biosynthesis of Terpenes and Sterols*, Churchill, London, 1959.
27. Heilbron, I. M., R. A. Morton and E. T. Webster, *Biochem. J.*, 26, 1194 (1932).
28. Heilbron, I. M., *J. Chem. Soc.*, 386 (1948).
29. Heilbron, I. M. and B. C. L. Weedon, *Bull. Soc. Chim. France*, 83 (1958).
30. Henbest, H. B., E. R. H. Jones, T. C. Owen and V. Thaller, *J. Chem. Soc.*, 2763 (1955).
31. Henbest, H. B., E. R. H. Jones and T. C. Owen, *J. Chem. Soc.*, 4909 (1957).
32. Hubbard, R. and G. Wald, *J. Gen. Physiol.*, 36, 269 (1952).
33. Hubbard, R. and G. Wald, *Science*, 115, 60 (1952).
34. Hubbard, R., *J. Am. Chem. Soc.*, 78, 4662 (1956).
35. Hubbard, R. and A. Kropf, *Nature*, 183, 448 (1959).
36. Hunter, R. F., *Nature*, 158, 257 (1946).
37. Hunter, R. F., *Research (London)*, 3, 453 (1950).
38. I.U.P.A.C. Commission on the Nomenclature of Biological Chemistry, *J. Am. Chem. Soc.*, 82, 5575 (1960).
39. Inhoffen, H. H. and F. Bohlmann, *Fortschr. Chem. Forsch.*, 1, 175 (1949).
40. Isler, O., M. Koefler, W. Huber and A. Roncoe, *Experientia*, 2, 31 (1946).
41. Isler, O., W. Huber, A. Roncoe and M. Koefler, *Helv. Chim. Acta*, 30, 1911 (1947).
42. Isler, O., A. Roncoe, W. Guex, N. C. Hindley, W. Huber, K. Dialer and M. Koefler, *Helv. Chim. Acta*, 32, 489 (1949).
43. Isler, O., *Chimia (Aarau)*, 4, 103 (1950).
44. Isler, O., *Chem. Eng. News*, 29, 3962 (1951).
45. Isler, O., R. Rüegg, U. Schwieter and J. Würsch, *Vitamins Hormones*, 18, 295 (1960).
46. Isler, O., R. Rüegg and P. Schudel, *Recent Progress in the Chemistry of Natural and Synthetic Colouring Matters and Related Fields* (Ed. by T. S. Gore, B. S. Joshi, S. V. Sunthaukar and B. D. Tilak), Academic Press, New York, 1962, p. 39.
47. Jensen, S. L., G. Cohen-Bazine, T. O. M. Nakayamo and R. Y. Stanier, *Biochem. Biophys. Acta*, 29, 477 (1958).
48. Johnson, A. W., *Sci. Progr. (London)*, 36, 496 (1948).
49. Karrer, P., R. Morf and K. Schöpp, *Helv. Chim. Acta*, 14, 1036, 1431 (1931).
50. Karrer, P., H. Salomon, R. Morf and O. Walker, *Helv. Chim. Acta*, 15, 878 (1932).
51. Karrer, P. and R. Morf, *Helv. Chim. Acta*, 16, 557, 625 (1933).
52. Karrer, P., *Österr. Chemiker-Ztg.*, 49, 215 (1948).
53. Karrer, P. and E. Jucker, *Carotenoids*, Elsevier, 1950, p. 43.
54. Koehn, C. J., *Arch. Biochem. Biophys.*, 17, 337 (1948).
55. Kuhn, R. and C. J. O. R. Morris, *Ber.*, 70, 853 (1937).
56. Lindler, H., *Helv. Chim. Acta*, 35, 446 (1952).
57. Mackinney, G., *J. Am. Chem. Soc.*, 56, 488 (1934).
58. Mackinney, G., *Metabolic Pathways* (Ed. by D. M. Greenberg), Academic Press, New York, Vol. I, 1960, p. 481.
59. Matsui, M., S. Okano, K. Yamashita, M. Miyano, S. Kitamura, A. Kobayashi, T. Sato and R. Mikami, *J. Vitaminol. (Kyōto)*, 4, 178 (1958).

60. Meunier, P., *Compt. Rend.*, **227**, 206 (1948).
61. Milas, N. A. and S. Sussman, *J. Am. Chem. Soc.*, **58**, 1302 (1936).
62. Milas, N. A. and S. Sussman, *J. Am. Chem. Soc.*, **59**, 2545 (1937).
63. Milas, N. A., *Science*, **103**, 581 (1946).
64. Milas, N. A., *Vitamins Hormones*, **5**, 1 (1947).
65. Milas, N. A. in *The Vitamins: Chemistry, Physiology and Pathology* (Ed. by W. H. Sebrell and R. S. Harris), Academic Press, New York, Vol. I, 1954, p. 38.
66. Milas, N. A. in *The Vitamins: Chemistry, Physiology and Pathology* (Ed. by W. H. Sebrell and R. S. Harris), Academic Press, New York, Vol. I, 1954, p. 55.
67. Milas, N. A., *U.S. Pat.*, 2,369,156 (1945).
68. Moore, T., *Biochem. J.*, **34**, 1321 (1940).
69. Moore, T., *Vitamin A*, Elsevier, Amsterdam, 1957.
70. Morton, R. A., *Nature*, **153**, 69 (1944).
71. Muller-Cunradi, M. and K. Pieroh, *U.S. Pat.*, 2,165,962 (1939).
72. Oroshnik, W., *J. Am. Chem. Soc.*, **67**, 1627 (1945).
73. Oroshnik, W., *J. Am. Chem. Soc.*, **78**, 2651 (1956).
74. Pauling, L., *Fortschr. Chem. Org. Naturstoffe*, **3**, 203 (1939).
75. Pitt, G. A. J. and R. A. Morton, Biochemical Society Symposium No. 19, *Steric Aspects of the Chemistry and Biochemistry of Natural Products* (Ed. by J. K. Grant and W. Klyne), Cambridge University Press, 1960, p. 67.
76. Pitt, G. A. J. and R. A. Morton, *Ann. Rev. Biochem.*, **31**, 491 (1962).
77. Pommer, H., *Angew. Chem.*, **72**, 811 (1960).
78. Pommer, H. and W. Arund, *Ger. Pat.*, 1,008,729 (1957).
79. Porter, J. W. and F. P. Zscheile, *Arch. Biochem. Biophys.*, **10**, 547 (1946).
80. Porter, J. W. and R. F. Lincoln, *Arch. Biochem. Biophys.*, **27**, 390 (1950).
81. Robeson, C. D. and J. G. Baxter, *Nature*, **155**, 300 (1945).
82. Robeson, C. D. and J. G. Baxter, *J. Am. Chem. Soc.*, **69**, 136 (1947).
83. Robeson, C. D., J. D. Cawley, L. Weister, M. H. Stern, C. C. Edinger and A. J. Chechak, *J. Am. Chem. Soc.*, **77**, 4111 (1955).
84. Robeson, C. D., W. P. Blum, J. M. Dieterle, J. D. Cawley and J. G. Baxter, *J. Am. Chem. Soc.*, **77**, 4120 (1955).
85. Ruegg, R., H. Lindler, M. Montavon, G. Sancy, S. F. Schaeren, U. Schweiter and O. Isler, *Helv. Chim. Acta*, **42**, 847 (1959).
86. Ruegg, R., M. Montavon, G. Byser, G. Sancy, U. Schweiter and O. Isler, *Helv. Chim. Acta*, **42**, 854 (1959).
87. Salah, M. K. and R. A. Morton, *Biochem. J.*, **43**, Proc. vi (1948).
88. Sarnecki, W., M. Schwarzmann, H. Pommer, G. Hamprecht and G. Hummel, *Belg. Pat.*, 583,531.
89. Schollkopf, U., *Angew. Chem.*, **71**, 260 (1959).
90. Schwarzkopf, O., H. J. Cahnmann, A. D. Lewis, J. Swidinsky and H. M. Wuest, *Helv. Chim. Acta*, **32**, 443 (1949).
91. Trippett, S., in *Advances in Organic Chemistry, Methods and Results* (Ed. by R. A. Raphael, E. C. Taylor and H. Wynberg), Interscience, 1960, Vol. I, p. 83.
92. Underhill, S. W. F. and K. H. Coward, *Biochem. J.*, **33**, 589 (1939).
93. Wald, G., *J. Gen. Physiol.*, **19**, 351 (1935).
94. Wald, G., *Vitamins Hormones*, **1**, 195 (1943).
95. Wald, G., *Harvey Lectures*, **41**, 117 (1945–46).

96. Wald, G., P. K. Brown, R. Hubbard and W. Oroshnik, *Proc. Nat. Acad. Sci. Wash.*, **41**, 438 (1955).
97. Wald, G., P. K. Brown and P. H. Smith, *J. Gen. Physiol.*, **38**, 623 (1955).
98. Wald, G., *Vitamins Hormones*, **18**, 417 (1960).
99. Winterstein, A., *Ber.*, **93**, 2951 (1960).
100. Wittig, G. and U. Schollkopf, *Ber.*, **87**, 1318 (1954).
101. Zechmeister, L., *Chem. Rev.*, **34**, 267 (1944).
102. Zechmeister, L., *Vitamins Hormones*, **7**, 57 (1949).

CHAPTER **13**

The Vitamins E (Tocopherols)

INTRODUCTION – Nomenclature – Detection and isolation – Sources –
Deficiency disease – Daily requirement – Properties – α-TOCOPHEROL –
Structure – THE OTHER TOCOPHEROLS – ε-Tocopherol – ζ-Tocopherol
– η-Tocopherol – δ-Tocopherol – Biosynthesis – Biological function of
tocopherols – Analogues of tocopherols – BIBLIOGRAPHY

INTRODUCTION

THE TERM 'vitamin E' refers to the group of naturally occurring compounds of closely related structure summarized in Table 13.1. The
chemistry and biochemistry of this group has been reviewed[21,34,40].

All the tocols have been synthesized, and, with the exception of tocol
itself and of 5-methyltocol, they have been found in nature.

Nomenclature

Karrer suggested[27] that tocol (**1**) should be regarded as the parent
compound, so that α-tocopherol becomes 5,7,8-trimethyltocol, β-tocopherol is 5,8-dimethyltocol, etc.

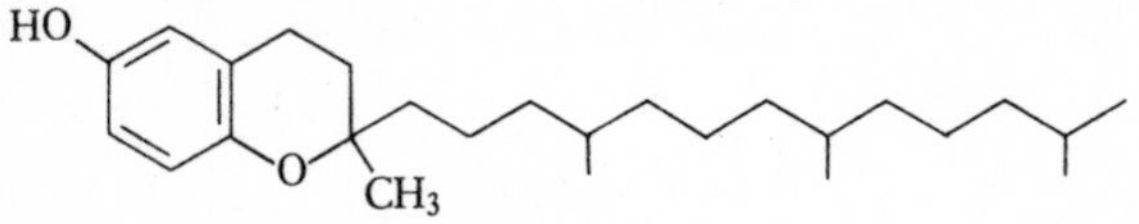

(1)

Detection and isolation

Feeding experiments with rats suggested[11,12] the existence of an anti-
sterility factor, and wheat-germ oil was found to be a good source of this
substance. By 1936 two pure compounds, α- and β-tocopherol, had been
isolated from this source[13]. Subsequently, γ-tocopherol was extracted
from cotton-seed oil[8], δ-tocopherol from soya-bean oil[43], ε-tocopherol
from wheat-germ oil[3,4,43], ζ-tocopherol from bran or palm oil[16] and
η-tocopherol from rice oil[17]. It was later discovered[20] that the ζ-tocopherol from palm oil was different from that obtained from rice oil.

256

Table 13.1. The tocopherols [21, 34].

Structure	Name	Main source	Ref.
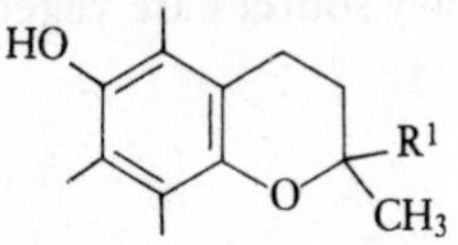	α-tocopherol	Wheat germ	14, 15
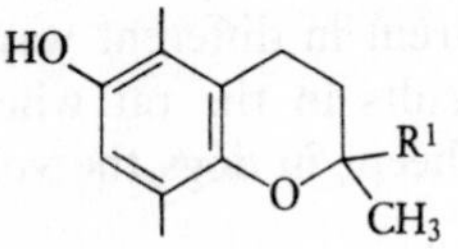	β-tocopherol	Wheat germ	1, 9
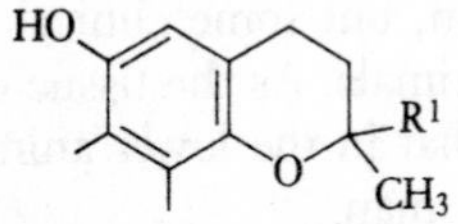	γ-tocopherol	Maize	10
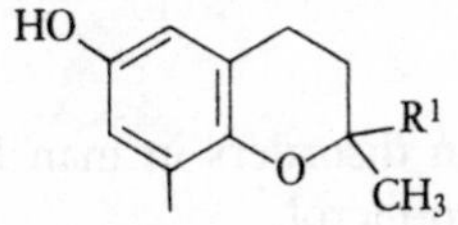	δ-tocopherol	Soya bean	43
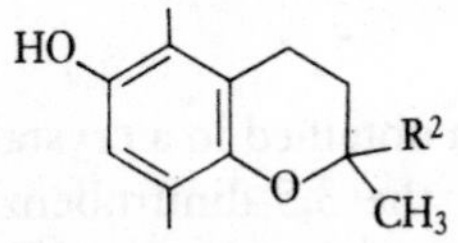	ε-tocopherol	Wheat bran	20
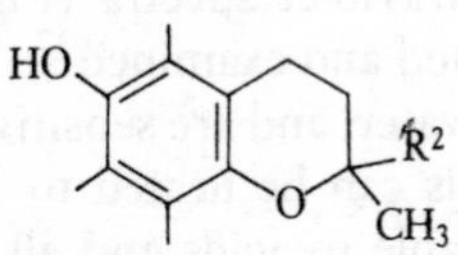	ζ_1-tocopherol	Palm oil	16, 17
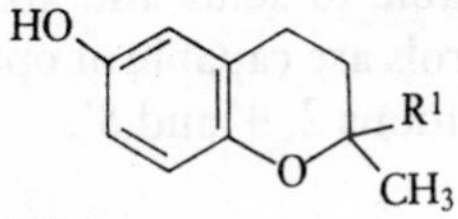	ζ_2-tocopherol	Rice	20
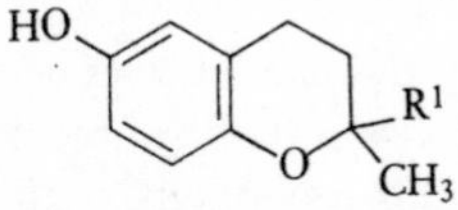	η-tocopherol	Rice	16, 17, 19, 35

$R^1 =$

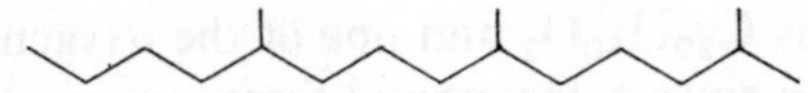

$R^2 =$

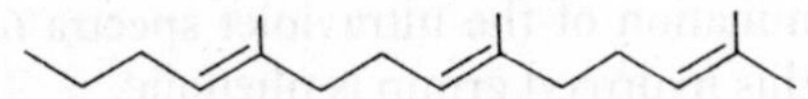

Sources

The vitamins E are widespread in the plant kingdom, but animals contain only very small amounts. The best dietary sources are vegetable oils, eggs and butter.

Deficiency disease

In almost all animals, deficiency of the vitamins E results in muscular degeneration, but the deficiency becomes apparent in different ways in various species of animals. Thus, sterility results in the rat whereas myocardial degeneration occurs in cattle and sheep; in dogs the voluntary muscles degenerate.

There is no known deficiency disease in man, but some clinical disorders are similar to deficiency symptoms in animals. As the tissue concentration of vitamins E in man is similar to that in the lower animals, it is concluded that the vitamin is necessary for man.

Daily requirement

The daily requirement is not known; certain disorders in man have been treated with doses of 200–600 mg of α-tocopherol.

Properties

The tocopherols are oils which have not been obtained in a crystalline state, although crystalline derivatives such as the 3,5-dinitrobenzoate ester are known. They have characteristic ultraviolet spectra (Figure 13.1); the infrared spectra have also been reported and examined[37]. The tocopherols are soluble in fats but insoluble in water, and are sensitive to oxidation. In the absence of air the tocopherols can be heated to 200° without change, and they are also relatively stable to acids and alkalis. They are effective antioxidants. All the tocopherols are capable of optical isomerism due to the asymmetric centres at positions 2, 4′ and 8′.

α-TOCOPHEROL

Structure

The molecular formula is $C_{29}H_{50}O_2$ and one of the oxygen atoms is present as a hydroxyl group since α-tocopherol forms esters and ethers. It was shown[22] by an examination of the ultraviolet spectra of α-tocopherol and its acetate that this hydroxyl group is phenolic.

Hydrogenation of α-tocopherol absorbed four moles of hydrogen and it was deduced[2] that a cyclic ether function is present in the original vitamin.

Pyrolysis of α-tocopherol yielded[14,15] the known durohydroquinone (2).

Oxidation of α-tocopherol with chromic acid under mild conditions yields[14] dimethylmaleic anhydride and a compound A, $C_{21}H_{40}O_2$,

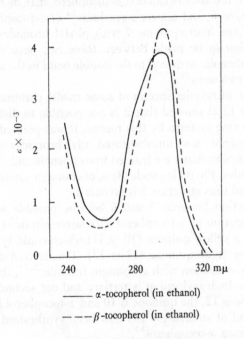

—————— α-tocopherol (in ethanol)

— — — β-tocopherol (in ethanol)

Figure 13.1. The ultraviolet spectra of α- and β-tocopherols. [Reproduced, by permission, from H. R. Rosenberg, *The Chemistry and Physiology of the Vitamins*, Interscience, New York, 1945, p. 439.]

which was shown to be a lactone. The corresponding hydroxy acid was readily reconverted into A, indicating a γ- or δ-lactone structure, the former being preferred. The methyl ester of the hydroxy acid is very difficult to esterify and is stable to oxidation, demonstrating that the hydroxyl group is tertiary.

When α-tocopherol is oxidized with chromic acid under more vigorous conditions[14], diacetyl, acetone and an acid B, $C_{16}H_{32}O_2$, are produced. Kuhn–Roth oxidation of the latter indicated the presence of three C-methyl groups, and structure 3 was proposed for B on the basis of the isoprene rule. It was considered that the acid B is a further degradation product of the lactone A, so that structure 4 represents the latter compound.

On the basis of the above evidence, α-tocopherol may be the chroman 5 or the coumarane 6, and Karrer's synthesis[24] of α-tocopherol by the condensation of the hydroquinone 7 with phytyl bromide (8) did not allow a distinction to be made between these two possibilities, since addition of the phenolic hydroxyl to the double bond in the intermediate 9 could occur in two ways[25].

A study of the ultraviolet spectra of some model chromans and coumaranes (Figure 13.2) showed that it is not possible to distinguish between these two ring systems by this means. It was pointed out[39] later that, whereas phenols and unsubstituted allyl bromides condense to yield coumaranes, chromans are formed from phenols and γ,γ-disubstituted allyl bromides. Phytyl bromide (8) is, of course, a γ,γ-disubstituted allyl bromide, and thus structure 5 is favoured.

A firm distinction between 5 and 6 became possible when it was found[26] that oxidation of α-tocopherol with silver nitrate or with ferric chloride yielded a yellow quinone (10 or 11) which could be reduced to the corresponding hydroquinone (12 or 13). The derived di-p-bromobenzoate resisted oxidation with chromium trioxide[22,23], thus showing that the aliphatic hydroxyl group is tertiary and not secondary. Hence the hydroquinone is 12, the quinone is 10 and α-tocopherol itself is 5.

The compound of structure 6 has now been synthesized and shown to be different from α-tocopherol[42].

The hydroquinone (7) required for the synthesis of α-tocopherol has been prepared from pseudocumene (14) as shown in $14 \rightarrow 16 \rightarrow 7$.

Phytol is not easily prepared, but another synthesis of α-tocopherol has been described[41] which uses the more accessible citral (17) as starting material; this synthesis is summarized in $17 \rightarrow 22 \rightarrow 5$.

There are two asymmetric centres in phytol (at $C_{(7)}$ and $C_{(11)}$) and these have been shown[5,6] to be 7R and 11R (23). It is assumed that the centres at $C_{(4)}'$ and $C_{(8)}'$ of the natural $(+)$-α-tocopherol are the same as these; nothing is known about the stereochemistry at $C_{(2)}$ in the tocopherols. Experiments with animals indicate that whereas the stereochemistry at $C_{(4)}'$ and $C_{(8)}'$ have no effect on the biological activity that at $C_{(2)}$ has.

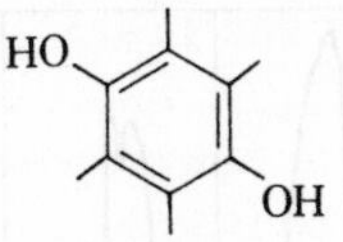

(2)

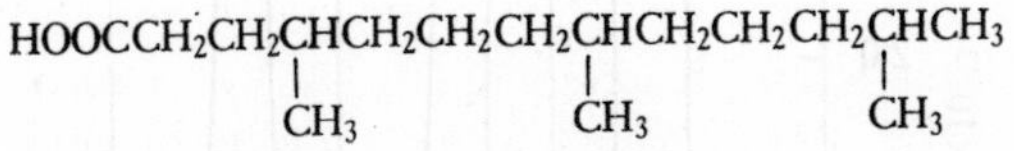

$$HOOCCH_2CH_2CHCH_2CH_2CH_2CHCH_2CH_2CH_2CHCH_3$$

         CH_3 CH_3 CH_3

(3)

$$CH_2CH_2CH_2CHCH_2CH_2CH_2CHCH_2CH_2CH_2CHCH_3$$

  CH_3 CH_3 CH_3 CH_3

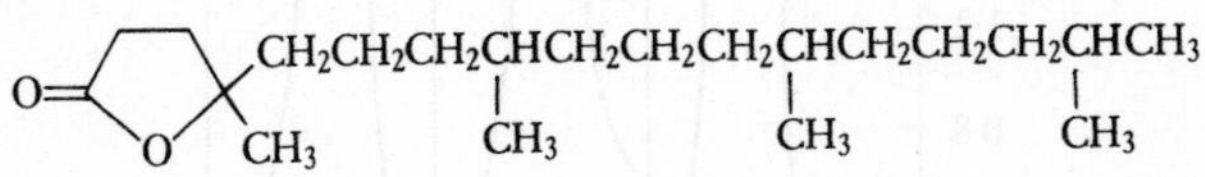

(4)

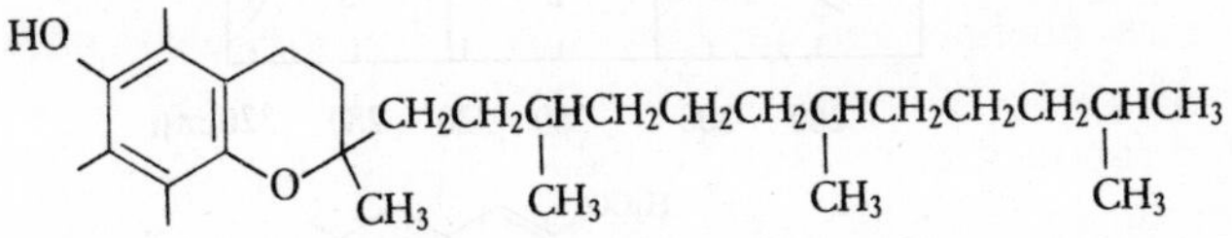

$$CH_2CH_2CHCH_2CH_2CH_2CHCH_2CH_2CH_2CHCH_3$$

  CH_3 CH_3 CH_3 CH_3

(5)

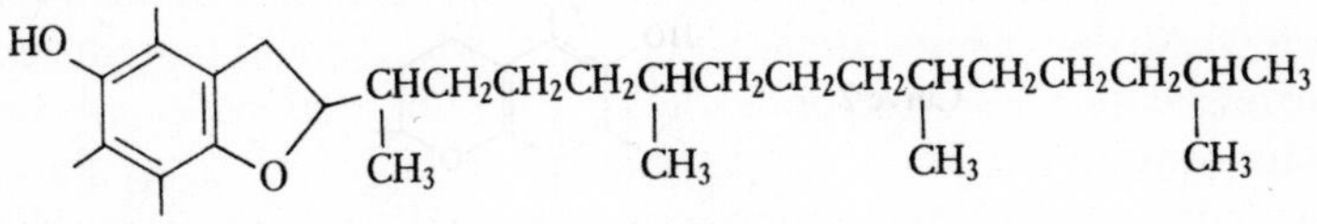

$$CHCH_2CH_2CH_2CHCH_2CH_2CH_2CHCH_2CH_2CH_2CHCH_3$$

  CH_3 CH_3 CH_3 CH_3

(6)

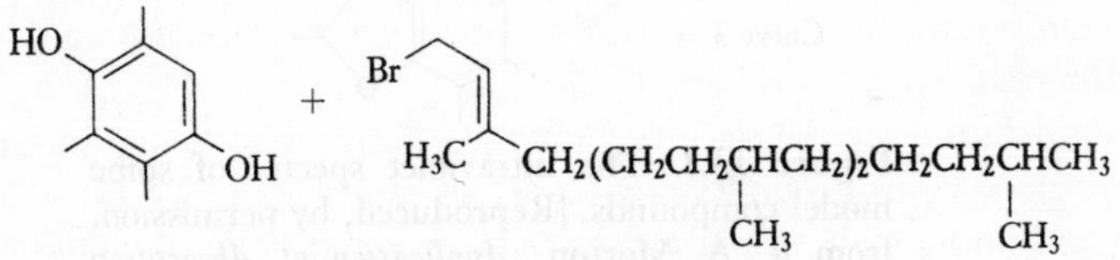

(7)   +

$$H_3C \quad CH_2(CH_2CH_2CHCH_2)_2CH_2CH_2CHCH_3$$

             CH_3 CH_3

(8)

$$\downarrow Zn$$

$$-CH_2(CH_2CH_2CHCH_2)_2CH_2CH_2CHCH_3$$

    CH_3 CH_3 CH_3

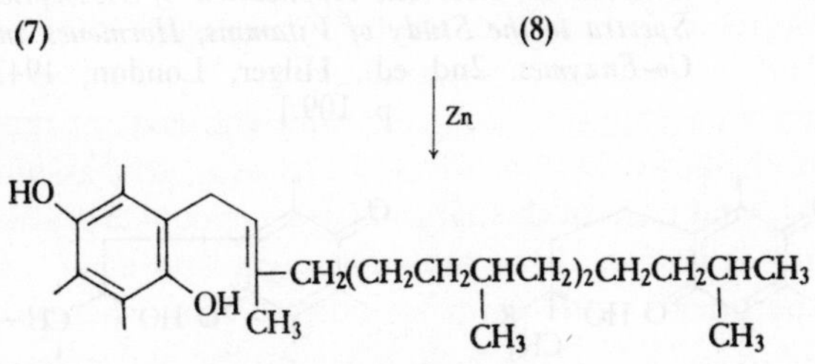

(9)

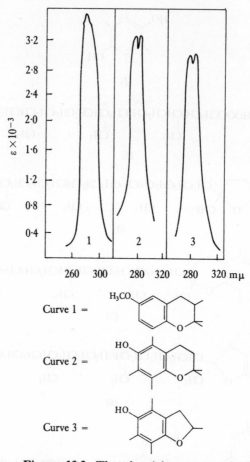

Curve 1 =

Curve 2 =

Curve 3 =

Figure 13.2. The ultraviolet spectra of some model compounds. [Reproduced, by permission, from R. A. Morton, *Application of Absorption Spectra to the Study of Vitamins, Hormones and Co-Enzymes*, 2nd ed., Hilger, London, 1942, p. 109.]

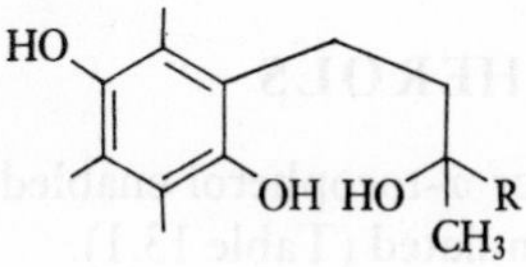

(12)

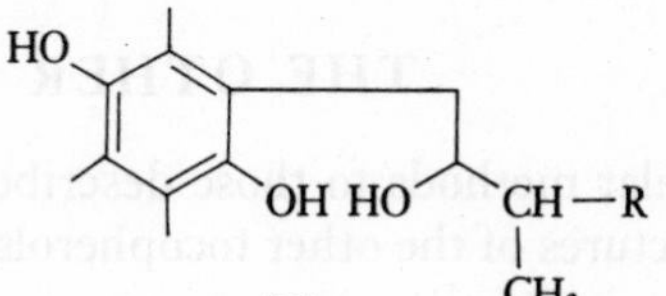

(13)

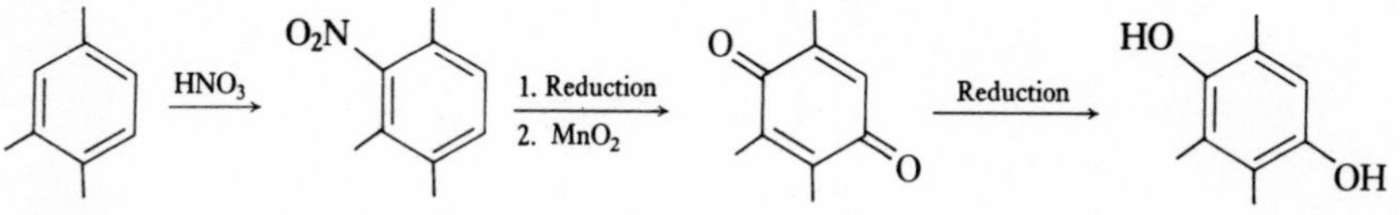

(14) → (15) → (16) → (7)

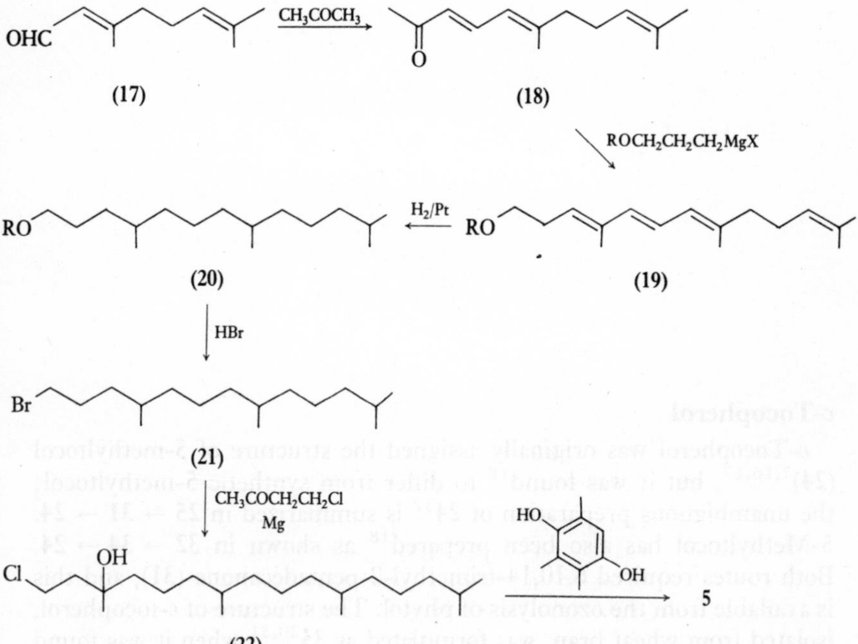

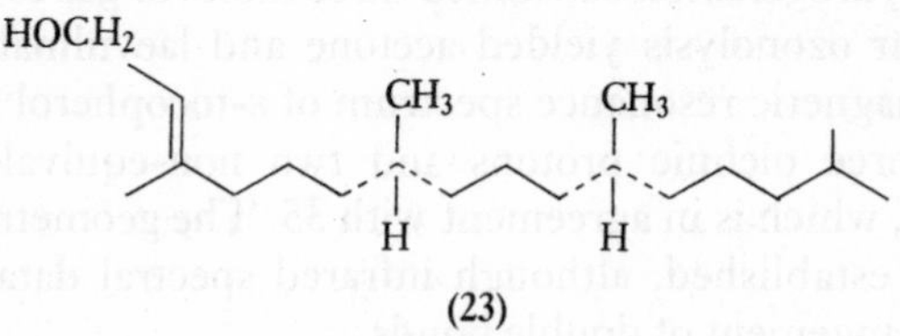

(17) → (18)

(19) → (20)

(21)

(22) → 5

(23)

THE OTHER TOCOPHEROLS

Similar methods to those described above for α-tocopherol enabled the structures of the other tocopherols to be formulated (Table 13.1).

ε-Tocopherol

ε-Tocopherol was originally assigned the structure of 5-methyltocol (24)[7,16,17], but it was found[18] to differ from synthetic 5-methyltocol; the unambiguous preparation of 24[32] is summarized in 25 → 31 → 24. 5-Methyltocol has also been prepared[18] as shown in 32 → 34 → 24. Both routes required 6,10,14-trimethyl-2-pentadecanone (31), and this is available from the ozonolysis of phytol. The structure of ε-tocopherol, isolated from wheat bran, was formulated as 35[20,31] when it was found that catalytic hydrogenation consumed three moles of gas to yield β-tocopherol and that ozonolysis yielded acetone and laevulinaldehyde (36). The nuclear magnetic resonance spectrum of ε-tocopherol indicated the presence of three olefinic protons and two non-equivalent aromatic methyl groups, which is in agreement with 35. The geometry of the side-chain was not established, although infrared spectral data suggested[20] an all-*trans* arrangement of double bonds.

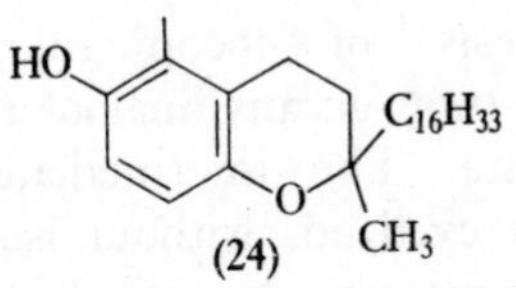

(24)

(25) → (26) → (27)

N-Bromosuccinimide

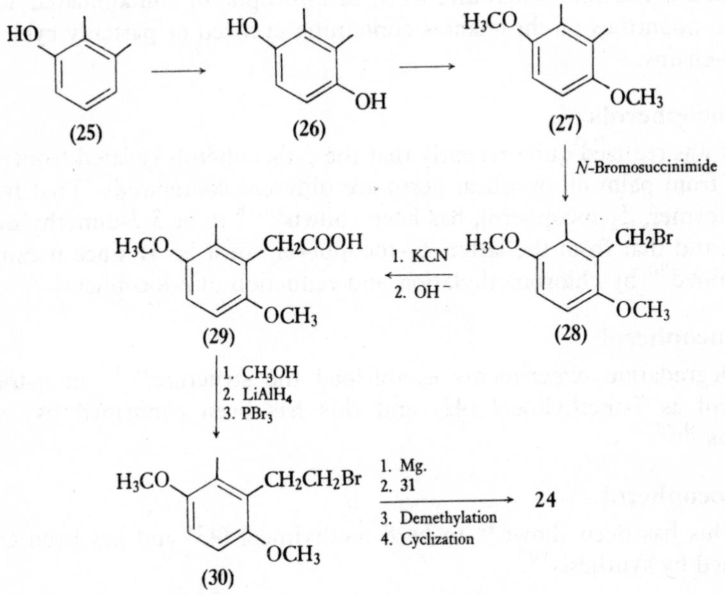

(29) $\xleftarrow[\text{2. OH}^-]{\text{1. KCN}}$ (28)

1. CH_3OH
2. $LiAlH_4$
3. PBr_3

(30) $\xrightarrow[\substack{\text{3. Demethylation} \\ \text{4. Cyclization}}]{\substack{\text{1. Mg.} \\ \text{2. 31}}}$ 24

(32) $\xrightarrow[\substack{\text{2. Mg} \\ \text{3. } CH_2\!-\!CH_2}]{\text{1. } (CH_3)_2SO_4}$ (33)

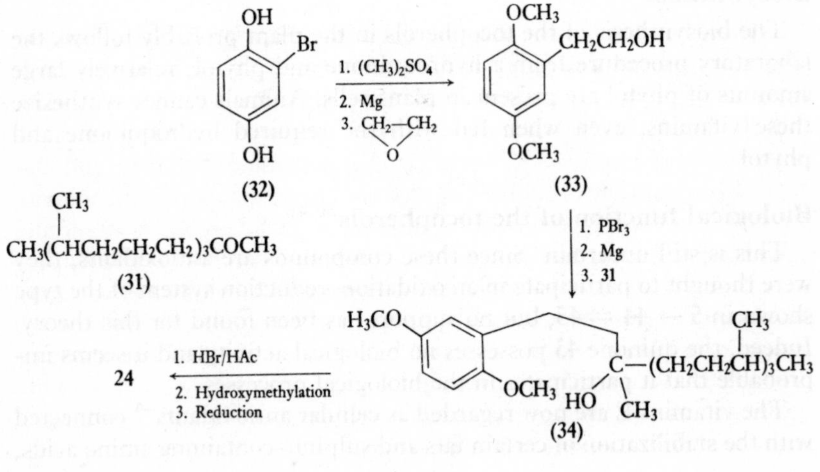

CH_3
$CH_3(CHCH_2CH_2CH_2)_3COCH_3$
(31)

1. PBr_3
2. Mg
3. 31

24 $\xleftarrow[\substack{\text{2. Hydroxymethylation} \\ \text{3. Reduction}}]{\text{1. HBr/HAc}}$ (34)

In an attempted synthesis[31] of ε-tocopherol, 2,5-dimethylquinol (37) was condensed with all-*trans*-geranyllinalool (38) in the presence of boron trifluoride etherate. The intermediate 3-geranylgeranyl-2,5-dimethylquinol (39) was cyclized, without isolation, with anhydrous hydrogen fluoride. Chromatography of the product over alumina yielded a fraction containing 41% of ε-tocopherol contaminated with small quantities of chromanols containing cyclized or partially cyclized side-chains.

ζ-Tocopherols

It was realized quite recently that the ζ-tocopherols isolated from rice and from palm oil or wheat germ are different compounds. That from the former, ζ_2-tocopherol, has been shown[16,18] to be 5,7-dimethyltocol (40) and that from the latter, ζ_1-tocopherol, must be 41 since it can be obtained[20] by chloromethylation and reduction of ε-tocopherol.

η-Tocopherol

Degradation experiments established the structure[16,17] of η-tocopherol as 7-methyltocol (42) and this has been confirmed by synthesis[19,35].

δ-Tocopherol

This has been shown[43] to be 8-methyltocol (43) and has been confirmed by synthesis[19].

Biosynthesis

The biosynthesis of the tocopherols in the plant probably follows the laboratory procedure from a hydroquinone and phytol; relatively large amounts of phytol are present in plant cells. Animals cannot synthesize these vitamins, even when fed with the required hydroquinone and phytol.

Biological function of the tocopherols[36,46]

This is still uncertain. Since these compounds are antioxidants, they were thought to participate in an oxidation–reduction system of the type shown in $5 \rightarrow 44 \rightleftharpoons 45$, but no support has been found for this theory. Indeed, the quinone 45 possesses no biological activity and it seems improbable that it participates in the biological processes.

The vitamins E are now regarded as cellular antioxidants[44] connected with the stabilization of certain fats and sulphur-containing amino acids,

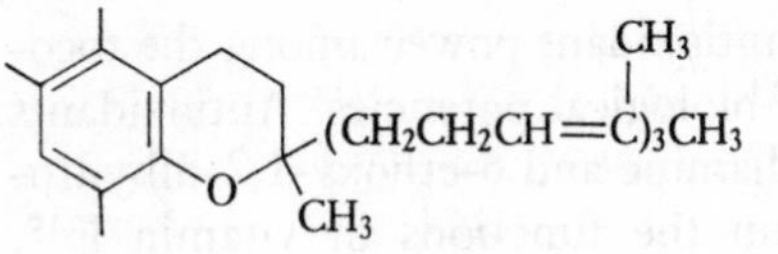

(35)

OHCCH₂CH₂COCH₃

(36)

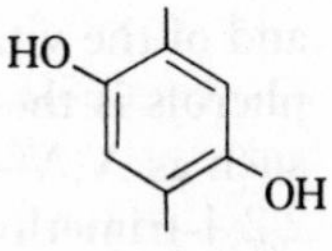

(37)

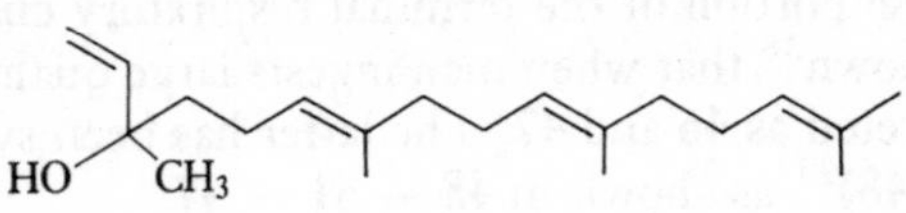

(38)

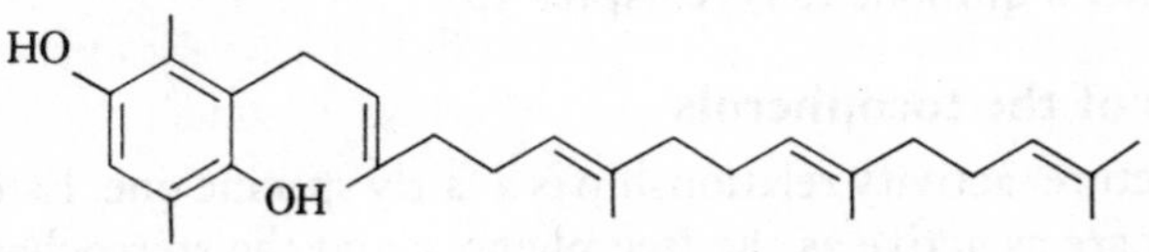

(39)

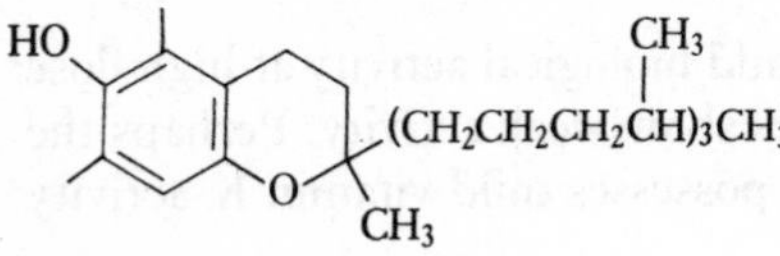

(40)

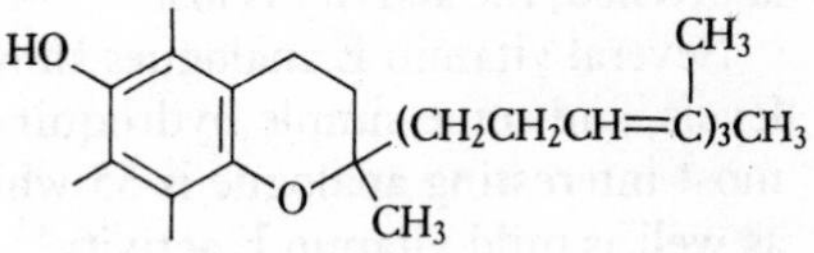

(41)

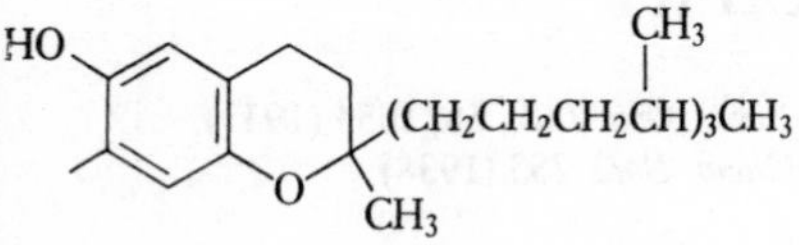

(42)

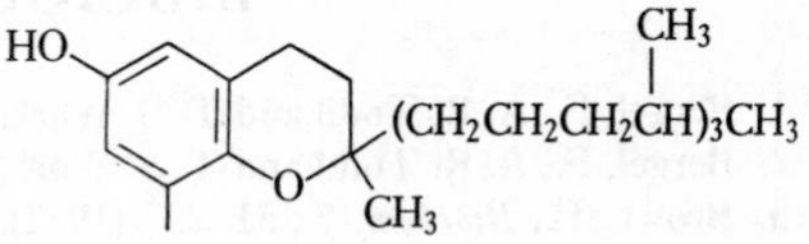

(43)

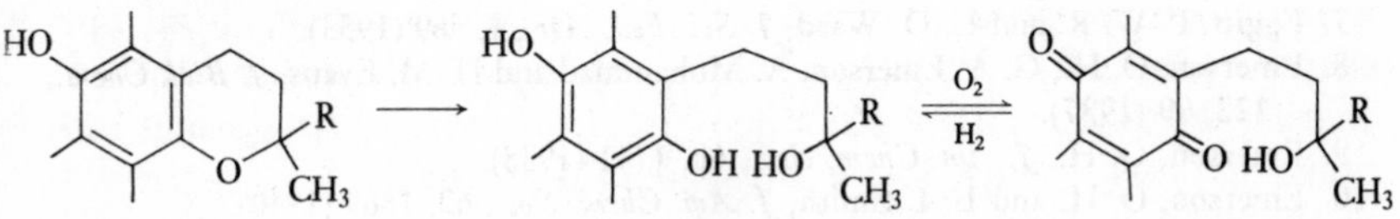

(5) (44) (45)

and of the vitamins A. The order of antioxidant power among the tocopherols is the reverse of the order of biological potencies. Antioxidants such as N,N'-diphenyl-β-phenylenediamine and 6-ethoxy-1,2-dihydro-2,2,4-trimethylquinoline will maintain the functions of vitamin E[36]. Other functions include[46] participation in nucleic acid metabolism, and also it appears that the tocopherols may be a component of the cytochrome reductase portion of the terminal respiratory chain.

It has been shown[38] that when man ingests large quantities of α-tocopherol, it is excreted as **46** and **47**. The latter has been synthesized from laevulinic acid (**48**)[21] as shown in **48** → **51** → **47**.

When α-tocopherol is fed to vitamin E-deficient animals, it is converted[33] into **52**, which is structurally very similar to ubiquinone[50] (**53**) and to Keofler's quinone (**54**) (Chapter 15).

Analogues of the tocopherols

The structure–activity relationship is a fairly specific one. Esters of the tocopherols are as active as the free phenols, and the stereochemistry of the phytyl side-chain is not important to the activity. Minor changes in the side-chain have little effect upon the activity, but if the side-chain is shortened, the activity is lost[26,28,29,30]

Several vitamin E analogues show mild biological activity at high dose levels, and some simple hydroquinones show weak activity. Perhaps the most interesting analogue is **55** which possesses mild vitamin K activity as well as mild vitamin E activity[45].

BIBLIOGRAPHY

1. Bergel, F., A. R. Todd and T. S. Work, *J. Soc. Chem. Ind.*, **56**, 1054 (1937).
2. Bergel, F., A. R. Todd and T. S. Work, *J. Chem. Soc.*, 253 (1938).
3. Brown, F., *Biochem. J.*, **51**, 237 (1952).
4. Brown, F., *Biochem. J.*, **52**, 523 (1952).
5. Burrell, J. W. K., L. M. Jackman and B. C. L. Weedon, *Proc. Chem. Soc.*, 263 (1959).
6. Crabbe, P., C. Djerassi, E. J. Eisenbrawn and S. Liu, *Proc. Chem. Soc.*, 264 (1959).
7. Eggitt, P. W. R. and L. D. Ward, *J. Sci. Fed. Agr.*, **4**, 569 (1953).
8. Emerson, O. H., G. A. Emerson, A. Mohammad and H. M. Evans, *J. Biol. Chem.*, **122**, 99 (1937).
9. Emerson, O. H., *J. Am. Chem. Soc.*, **60**, 1741 (1938).
10. Emerson, O. H. and L. I. Smith, *J. Am. Chem. Soc.*, **62**, 1869 (1940).
11. Evans, H. M. and K. S. Bishop, *Science*, **50**, 650 (1922).
12. Evans, H. M. and K. S. Bishop, *J. Metabolic Res.*, **1**, 335 (1922).

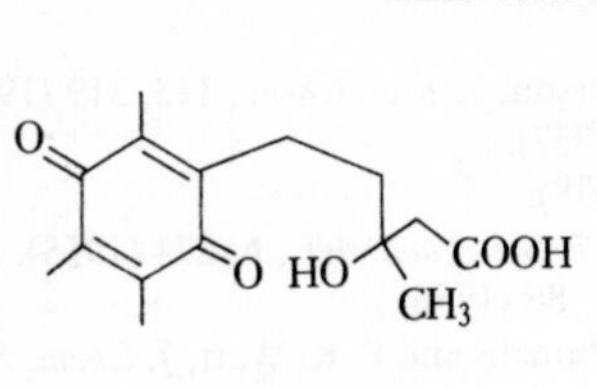

(46)

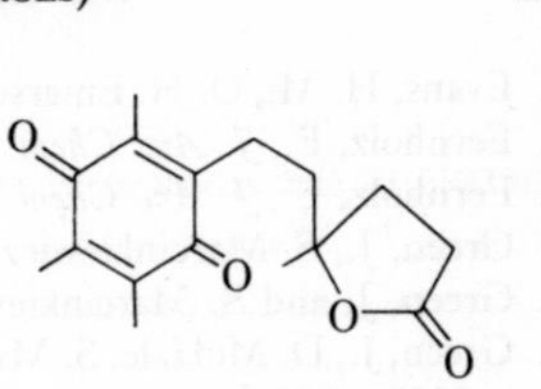

(47)

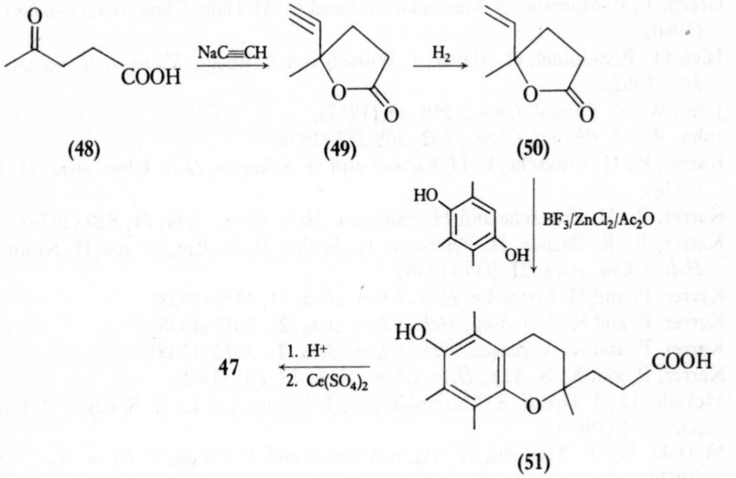

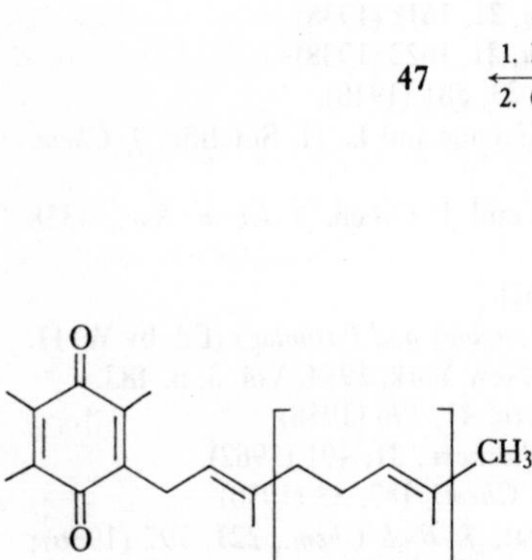

NaC≡CH

H₂

(48)

(49)

(50)

BF₃/ZnCl₂/Ac₂O

47 ←— 1. H⁺
2. Ce(SO₄)₂

(51)

(52)

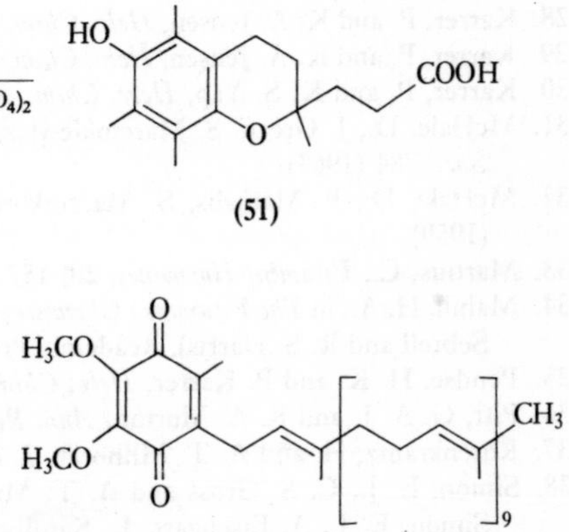

(53)

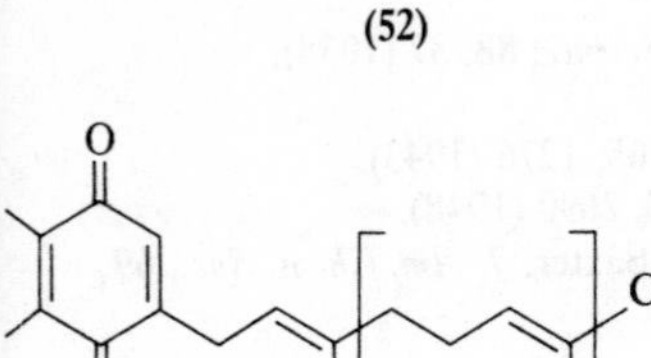

(54)

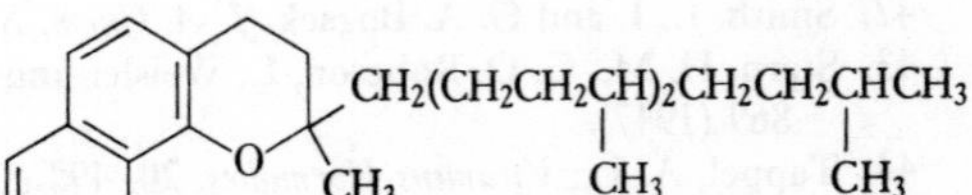

(55)

13. Evans, H. M., O. H. Emerson and G. A. Emerson, *J. Biol. Chem.*, 113, 319 (1936).
14. Fernholz, E., *J. Am. Chem. Soc.*, 59, 1154 (1937).
15. Fernholz, E., *J. Am. Chem. Soc.*, 60, 700 (1938).
16. Green, J., S. Marcinkiewicz and P. R. Watt, *J. Sci. Food Agr.*, 6, 274 (1955).
17. Green, J. and S. Marcinkiewicz, *Nature*, 177, 86 (1956).
18. Green, J., D. McHale, S. Marcinkiewicz, P. Mamalis and P. R. Watt, *J. Chem. Soc.*, 3362 (1959).
19. Green, J., D. McHale, P. Mamalis and S. Marcinkiewicz, *J. Chem. Soc.*, 3374 (1959).
20. Green, J., P. Mamalis, S. Marcinkiewicz and D. McHale, *Chem. Ind. (London)*, 73 (1960).
21. Isler, O., P. Schudel, H. Mayer, J. Würsch and R. Rüegg, *Vitamins Hormones*, 20, 389 (1962).
22. John, W., *Z. Physiol. Chem.*, 250, 11 (1937).
23. John, W., *Z. Physiol. Chem.*, 252, 208,222 (1938).
24. Karrer, P., H. Fritzsche, B. H. Ringier and H. Salomon, *Helv. Chim. Acta*, 21, 520 (1938).
25. Karrer, P., H. Fritzsche and H. Salomon, *Helv. Chim. Acta*, 21, 820 (1938).
26. Karrer, P., R. Escher, H. Fritzsche, H. Keller, B. H. Ringier and H. Salomon, *Helv. Chim. Acta*, 21, 939 (1938).
27. Karrer, P. and H. Fritzsche, *Helv. Chim. Acta*, 21, 1234 (1938).
28. Karrer, P. and K. A. Jensen, *Helv. Chim. Acta*, 21, 1612 (1938).
29. Karrer, P. and K. A. Jensen, *Helv. Chim. Acta*, 21, 1622 (1938).
30. Karrer, P. and K. S. Yap, *Helv. Chim. Acta*, 23, 581 (1940).
31. McHale, D., J. Green, S. Marcinkiewicz, J. Feeney and L. H. Sutcliffe, *J. Chem. Soc.*, 784 (1963).
32. McHale, D., P. Mamalis, S. Marcinkiewicz and J. Green, *J. Chem. Soc.*, 3358 (1959).
33. Martius, C., *Vitamins Hormones*, 20, 457 (1962).
34. Mahill, H. A., in *The Vitamins: Chemistry, Physiology and Pathology* (Ed. by W. H. Sebrell and R. S. Harris), Academic Press, New York, 1954, Vol. 3, p. 483.
35. Pendse, H. K. and P. Karrer, *Helv. Chim. Acta*, 41, 396 (1958).
36. Pitt, G. A. J. and R. A. Morton, *Ann. Rev. Biochem.*, 31, 491 (1962).
37. Rosenkrantz, H. and A. T. Milhorat, *J. Biol. Chem.*, 187, 83 (1950).
38. Simon, E. J., C. S. Gross and A. T. Milhorat, *J. Biol. Chem.*, 221, 797 (1956); Simon, E. J., A. Eisengart, L. Sundheim and A. T. Milhorat, *J. Biol. Chem.*, 221, 807 (1956).
39. Smith, L. I., H. E. Ungnade and W. W. Prichard, *Science*, 88, 37 (1938).
40. Smith, L. I., *Chem. Rev.*, 27, 287 (1940).
41. Smith, L. I. and J. A. Sprung, *J. Am. Chem. Soc.*, 65, 1276 (1943).
42. Smith, L. I. and G. A. Bogack, *J. A. Chem. Soc.*, 70, 2690 (1948).
43. Stern, H. M., C. D. Robeson, L. Weisler and J. G. Baxter, *J. Am. Chem. Soc.*, 69, 869 (1947).
44. Tappel, A. L., *Vitamins Hormones*, 20, 493 (1962).
45. Tishler, M., L. F. Fieser and N. L. Wendler, *J. Am. Chem. Soc.*, 62, 1982 (1940).
46. Vasington, F. D., S. M. Reichard and A. Nason, *Vitamins Hormones*, 18, 43 (1960).

CHAPTER 14

The Vitamins D

INTRODUCTION – Daily requirement – VITAMINS D – Deficiency disease – Structure of ergosterol – The other provitamins – The structure of ergocalciferol – Nomenclature of ergocaciferol and other vitamins D – The other vitamins D – The irradiation products of ergosterol – The irradiation sequence from ergosterol to ergocaciferol – Synthesis in the vitamin D group – Synthesis of cholesterol – The biosynthesis of steroids – BIBLIOGRAPHY

INTRODUCTION

SEVERAL substances possessing vitamin D activity have now been recognized, together with their corresponding provitamins, and all are derivatives of the steroids.

The steroids are a widely occurring group of substances which contain the tetracyclic nucleus 1; included in this group are sterols, bile acids, sex hormones, adrenocortical hormones, cardiac glycosides, sapogenins, toad poisons, the D vitamins and provitamins and some alkaloids. Almost all of these groups of compounds (with the notable exception of the D vitamins) yield, amongst other products, 1,2–cyclopentenophenanthrene (2, R = H) or 3′–methyl-1,2–cyclopentenophenanthrene (2, R = CH_3) when dehydrogenated with selenium. A full account of the chemistry of steroids is given in the recent books by Fieser[26] and Shoppee[63]. In the vast majority of steroids R^1 and R^2 in 1 are methyl groups, although some compounds are known in which these are replaced by —CHO or —CH_2OH group. A few steroids are known in which ring A or rings A and B are aromatic; in these cases, of course, R^1 is absent. R^3 may be absent, or may consist of two, four, five, eight, nine or ten carbon atoms in a saturated or unsaturated branched chain. In certain compounds R^3 forms part of a heterocyclic ring. In the saturated nucleus 1 there are six dissimilar asymmetric centres ($C_{(5)}$, $C_{(8)}$, $C_{(9)}$, $C_{(10)}$, $C_{(13)}$ and $C_{(14)}$). If the group R^3 is present there is another asymmetric centre at $C_{(17)}$. The sterols possess a hydroxyl group at $C_{(3)}$ which gives yet another asymmetric centre. The steroids may also differ one from another by the number and position of unsaturation and by the number and position of hydroxyl, carbonyl and carboxylic acid groupings.

Rings A and B in 1 are *cis*-fused in some steroids and *trans*-fused in others. Rings B and C are invariably *trans*-fused, and the C and D rings are most commonly *trans*-fused (C/D *cis* fusion occurs in the toad poisons and cardiac glycosides). Thus, cholestane is 3 and coprostane is 4; taking into account the non-planarity of cyclohexane rings, these compounds are better represented as 5 and 6 respectively[6,7,49].

The angular methyl groups $(1, R^1 = R^2 = CH_3)$ have been shown to bear a *cis* relationship to each other, and by convention these are shown to project above the general plane of the ring system. The side-chain $(1, R^3)$ at $C_{(17)}$ also projects above the plane. A $C_{(3)}$ hydroxyl group may project above or below the plane. It is now known that the conventional way of writing steroid structures is correct in absolute configurational terms.

The rules of nomenclature of steroids are summarized in reference 46. The numbering system is shown in 7; the nucleus is fairly flat and may be considered to be planar for the purpose of nomenclature. Groups which are attached to the nucleus and lying above the plane of the ring system are termed β, and bonds joining them to the nucleus are shown in graphic formulae as full-line bonds. Groups joined to the nucleus which project below the plane are termed α and are represented by dotted-line bonds. Groups whose configurations are unknown are termed ξ (xi) and are represented by wavy-line bonds. The parent compounds of the

(1)

(2)

(3)

(4)

(5)

(6)

(7)

steroids are 5α-oestrane (8), 5β-oestrane (9), 5α/5β-androstane (10, R = H), 5α/5β-pregnane (10, R = C₂H₅), 5α/5β-cholane (10, R = CHCH₃CH₂CH₂CH₃) and 5α/5β-cholestane (10, R = CHCH₃CH₂-CH₂CH₂CH(CH₃)₂). Thus 10, R = CHCH₃CH₂CH₂CH₂CH(CH₃)₂, with the 5α configuration, called 5α-cholestane, replaces the old name cholestane, and 5β-cholestane replaces coprostane. The stereochemistry of the other ring junctions is assumed to be the same as in 8, 9 and 10, but if there is a difference this is indicated in the name. Thus, 11 would be 5α,14β,17α-pregnane. For substituents, the nature is indicated by the usual prefix or suffix and the position is indicated by the number of the carbon atom to which it is attached. Unsaturation is always indicated by a suffix, and for substituents proper only one kind in each compound is indicated by a suffix, the remainder appearing in the name as prefixes. The substituent to be indicated by a suffix is chosen from the list: carboxylic acid (or derivative), carbonyl, alcohol, amine, ether. A halogen substituent is always indicated by a prefix. Thus, 12 is 5α-cholest-8(14)-en-3β-ol.

The shortening of a side-chain or loss of a methyl group is indicated by the prefix 'nor-' with the number of the atom which is lost. The same prefix is used to indicate a ring contraction, together with a capital letter to show which ring is affected. Similarly, ring expansion is indicated by the prefix 'homo-' and preceded by a capital letter to show the ring affected. Ring fission with the addition of two hydrogen atoms to the terminal groups is indicated by the prefix 'seco-' and removal of a whole ring is represented by the prefix 'des-' with a capital letter to indicate the ring affected. The prefix 'epi-' means an inversion of configuration at a particular centre, 'lumi-' means an isomer formed by the action of light and 'anhydro-' indicates the loss of hydrogen and hydroxyl from adjacent carbon atoms with the formation of a double bond.

The history of structural studies on cholesterol is summarized by Turner and Harris[68] and accounts of the structural determination are given in references 26 and 63. Nowadays, with a large body of knowledge available on many steroids of all types, the most common methods of structural elucidation include infrared, ultraviolet and nuclear magnetic resonance spectroscopy, optical rotatory dispersion[22], selenium dehydrogenation, oxidation, reduction and interrelationship with compounds of known structure by partial synthesis.

When pure cholesterol is heated under reflux in an inert solvent in the presence of 'floridin' (a catalytically active bauxite from Florida) a substance termed 'ketone 250' is produced which has about one tenth of

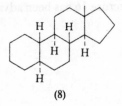

(8)   (9)

(10)

(11)

(12)

the vitamin activity of vitamin D_3. The structure **16** has been advanced[27] for this substance (p. 279).

Daily requirement

The human daily requirement for the vitamins D varies with age, but it is estimated that a daily dose of 0·025 mg ergocalciferol will prevent rickets in an otherwise healthy child.

VITAMINS D

Deficiency disease

Rickets is a disease of higher animals due to faulty bone formation which results in soft uncalcified bone which is easily deformed when subject to stress. This disease was associated with a dietary deficiency more than one hundred years ago, and cod-liver oils were in use to prevent and to cure rickets in the eighteen seventies. The antiricketic activity was found[83] in the unsaponifiable fraction of these oils. Hess observed[36,37] that antiricketic activity was produced when certain foods were irradiated, and it was soon realized[37,61,66] that the activity was due to the activation of steroid provitamins contained in the foods. The active principle was called[56] vitamin D, but it was realized almost immediately to be a mixture of substances. The primary action of the vitamins D^{58} is to increase absorption of calcium from the intestine.

The provitamins are widely distributed in both the plant and animal kingdoms, whereas the D vitamins themselves occur only in animals. These provitamins are 3β-hydroxy-$\Delta^{5,7}$-steroids (**13**), which are inactive, but which upon irradiation are converted into compounds of the type **14** where ring B has opened. The D vitamins and provitamins differ from each other in the nature of the group R.

The vitamins D are summarized in Table 14.1[42]. There is no vitamin D_1 since it was shown[4,74] that the substance originally called vitamin D_1

(13) → (14)

Table 14.1. The provitamins and vitamins D.

Provitamin (13)	R	Vitamin (14)
Ergosterol		D$_2$ Ergocalciferol
7-Dehydrocholesterol		D$_3$ Cholocalciferol
22,23-Dihydroergosterol		D$_4$
7-Dehydrositosterol		D$_5$
7-Dehydrostigmasterol		D$_6$
7-Dehydrocampesterol		D$_7$

is a molecular compound of vitamin D_2 and lumisterol$_2$ (15). The pro-vitamins have very similar ultraviolet spectra (the spectrum of ergosterol, provitamin D_2, is shown in Figure 14.1), and is characteristic of the diene system in ring B (13).

The ultraviolet spectra of steroids has been reviewed[24]. Conjugated homoannular dienes usually absorb at 260–285 mµ with ε_{max} about 5,000–15,000, whereas heteroannular dienes (for example $\Delta^{3,5}$-cholesta-diene) show a maximum at about 220–250 mµ with ε_{max} 14,000–28,000. By applying the empirical Woodward rules[80] it is possible to extract structurally useful information from the ultraviolet spectrum of a con-jugated diene. The rules are summarized as follows:

Parent diene (heteroannular)	214 mµ
Parent diene (homoannular)	253
Double bond extending conjugation	+30
Alkyl substituent or ring residue	+5
Exocyclic location of a double bond	+5

Thus, for $\Delta^{3,5}$-cholestadiene (17):

Parent diene	214 mµ
Substituents ($C_{(2)}$, $C_{(10)}$, $C_{(7)}$)	3 × 5
One exocyclic double bond	5
λ_{max} (calc.)	234 mµ
λ_{max} (observed)	234 mµ

For ergosterol (18):

Parent diene	253 mµ
Substituents ($C_{(4)}$, $C_{(10)}$, $C_{(9)}$, $C_{(14)}$)	4 × 5
2 × exocyclic bonds ($\Delta^{5,6}$ exocyclic to ring A and $\Delta^{7,8}$ exocyclic to ring C)	2 × 5
λ_{max} (calc.)	283 mµ
λ_{max} (observed)	283 mµ

These rules and their application are also discussed by de Mayo[57].

7-Dehydrostigmasterol (Table 14.1) differs from ergosterol in having an ethyl group in place of a methyl group at $C_{(24)}$. Sitosterol is a mixture of stereoisomers at $C_{(24)}$ and differs from cholesterol in having this $C_{(24)}$ ethyl group. Campesterol differs from 22,23-dihydroergosterol in the configuration of the $C_{(28)}$ methyl group.

The $C_{(3)}$ epimers of vitamins D_2 and D_3 have also been prepared but these have only about one twentieth of the activity of the 'natural' isomers. The 3-oxo, 3-thio, 3-chloro and 3-bromo derivatives of vitamins

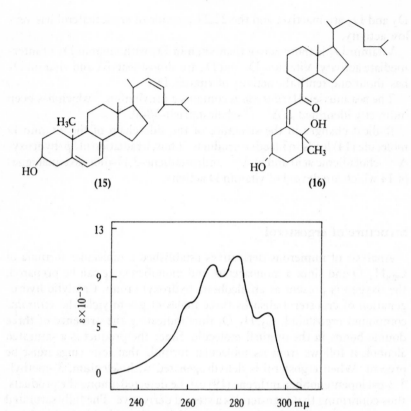

Figure 14.1. The ultraviolet spectrum of ergosterol (in ethanol). [Reproduced, by permission,
from A. E. Gillam and E. S. Stern, *Absorption
Spectroscopy in Organic Chemistry*, 2nd ed.,
Arnold, London, 1957, p. 205.]

10

D_2 and D_3 are inactive, and the 22,23-epoxide of ergocalciferol has very low activity.

Vitamin D_3 is more active than vitamin D_2 with vitamin D_4 of inter-mediate activity. Vitamins D_5 and D_6 are almost inactive and vitamin D_7 has about one-tenth the activity of vitamin D_2.

The sea mussel *Mytilus edulis* contains a provitamin[10] which has been indirectly identified as $\Delta^{5,7,20}$-cholestatrien-3β-ol.

Radical changes in the structure of the side-chain of the vitamin D molecule (14) leads to inactive products. Thus, irradiation of 3β-hydroxy-$\Delta^{5,7}$-choladienic acid and of $\Delta^{5,7}$-androstadiene-3,17-diol gave analogues of 14 which are devoid of vitamin D activity.

Structure of ergosterol

Analysis of numerous derivatives established a molecular formula of $C_{28}H_{44}O$ and since a monoacetate and monobenzoate can be prepared, the oxygen is present as an alcoholic hydroxyl group. Catalytic hydro-genation of ergosterol absorbs three moles of gas to yield the *saturated* compound ergostanol, $C_{28}H_{50}O$, thus indicating the presence of three double bonds in the original molecule. Since the product is a saturated alcohol, it follows from its molecular formula that four rings must be present. When ergosterol is dehydrogenated with selenium, 3'-methyl-1,2-cyclopentenophenanthrene (19) can be detected among the products, thus confirming that ergosterol is a steroid derivative. The fully saturated compound, ergostanol, when converted into its chloride and reduced with sodium in amyl alcohol, yields the parent hydrocarbon ergostane. Chromic acid oxidation of ergostane gives a monocarboxylic acid (20) identical with norallocholanic acid; the latter has been obtained from cholesterol (21) as shown in 21 → 22 → 20. This demonstrates that ergo-stane has the same configuration as cholestane. When ergostanol acetate is oxidized with chromic acid the same compound 23 is obtained as that resulting from chromic acid oxidation of dihydrocholesteryl acetate (24). Hence, the alcoholic hydroxyl group of ergostanol is at $C_{(3)}$ and thus the nucleus and the first five carbon atoms of the $C_{(17)}$ side-chain of ergo-sterol have the same skeletal structure as the nucleus and first five carbon atoms of the side-chain of cholesterol. When cholestanol is oxidized with chromic acid under more severe conditions, the C_8 ketone 25 is pro-duced, whereas similar treatment of ergostanol yields the C_9 ketone 26. Hence the structure of ergostanol must be 27 and all that remains is the

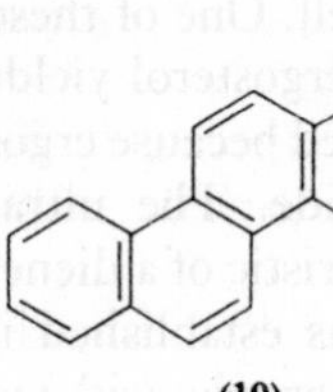

CH₃

(19)

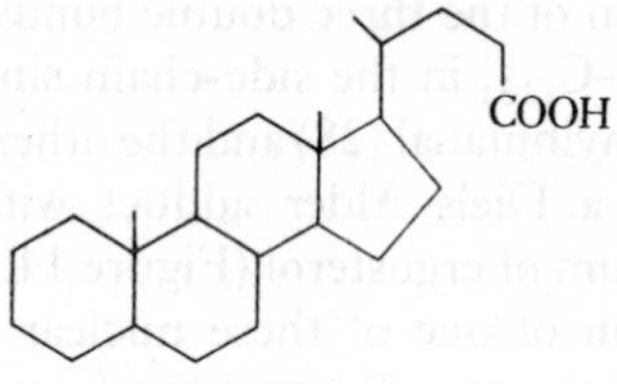

COOH

(20)

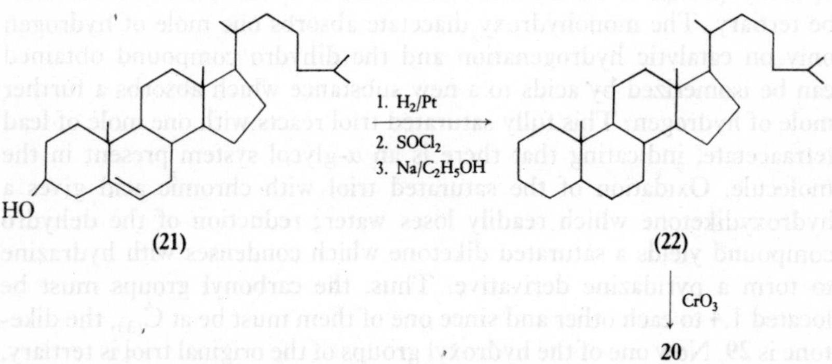

1. H₂/Pt
2. SOCl₂
3. Na/C₂H₅OH

HO

(21)

(22)

CrO₃

20

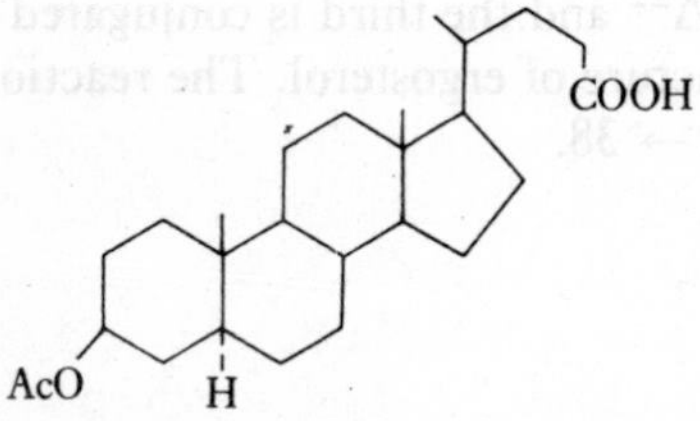

COOH

AcO   H

(23)

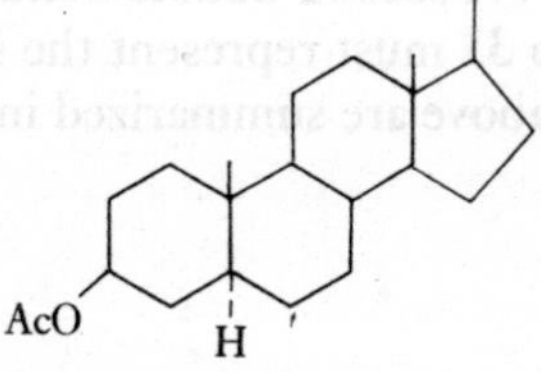

AcO   H

(24)

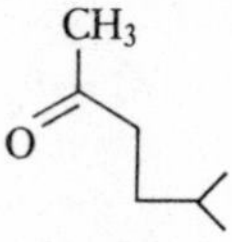

CH₃

O

(25)

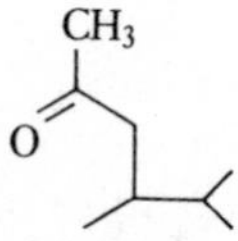

CH₃

O

(26)

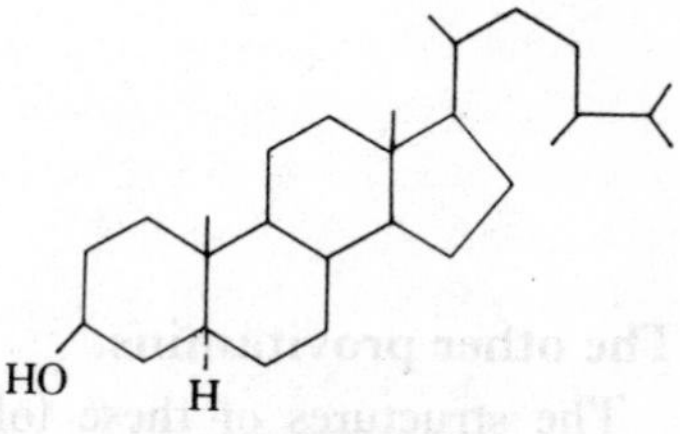

HO   H

(27)

location of the three double bonds in ergosterol itself. One of these is at $C_{(22)}$—$C_{(23)}$ in the side-chain since ozonolysis of ergosterol yields 2,3-dimethylbutanal (28) and the other two are conjugated because ergosterol forms a Diels–Alder adduct with maleic anhydride. The ultraviolet spectrum of ergosterol (Figure 14.1) is also characteristic of a diene. The position of one of these nuclear double bonds was established in the following way. Treatment of ergosterol with perbenzoic acid yields a doubly unsaturated triol monobenzoate, and since only two of the hydroxyl groups of the derived triol can be acetylated, one of these must be tertiary. The monohydroxy diacetate absorbs one mole of hydrogen only on catalytic hydrogenation and the dihydro compound obtained can be isomerized by acids to a new substance which absorbs a further mole of hydrogen. This fully saturated triol reacts with one mole of lead tetraacetate, indicating that there is an α-glycol system present in the molecule. Oxidation of the saturated triol with chromic acid gives a hydroxydiketone which readily loses water; reduction of the dehydro compound yields a saturated diketone which condenses with hydrazine to form a pyridazine derivative. Thus, the carbonyl groups must be located 1,4 to each other and since one of them must be at $C_{(3)}$, the diketone is 29. Now one of the hydroxyl groups of the original triol is tertiary, and there must also be an α-glycol system present, so the saturated triol must be 30. From this it follows that one of the double bonds of ergosterol is Δ^5. A second double bond is Δ^{22} and the third is conjugated to the first, so 31 must represent the structure of ergosterol. The reactions described above are summarized in 32 → 38.

The other provitamins

The structures of these follow mainly from their partial synthesis from steroids of known structure. Several different such partial syntheses

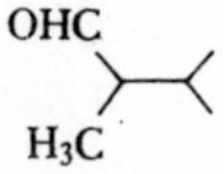

OHC

H₃C

(28)

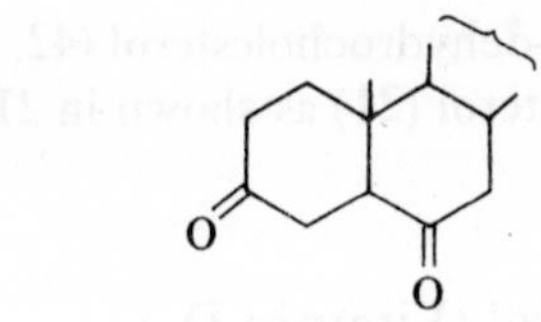

(29)

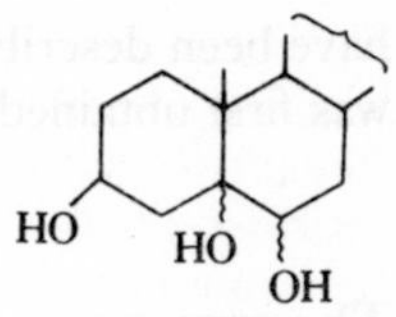

HO HO OH

(30)

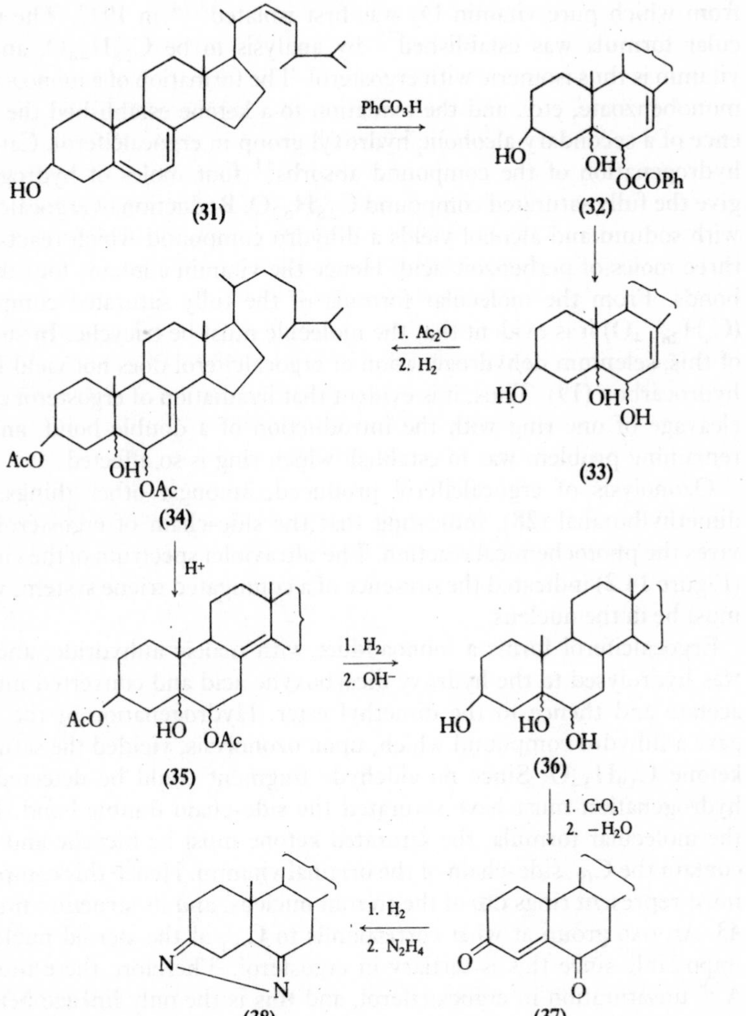

HO

(31)

PhCO₃H

HO OH OCOPh

(32)

1. Ac₂O
2. H₂

HO OH OH

(33)

AcO OH OAc

(34)

H⁺

AcO HO OAc

(35)

1. H₂
2. OH⁻

HO HO OH

(36)

1. CrO₃
2. −H₂O

N N

(38)

1. H₂
2. N₂H₄

O O

(37)

have been described[26]. Thus, 7–dehydrocholesterol (**42**, provitamin D$_3$) was first obtained[78] from cholesterol (**21**) as shown in **21** → **39** → **42**.

The structure of ergocalciferol (Vitamin D$_2$)

The irradiation of ergosterol (**31**) with ultraviolet light gives a mixture from which pure vitamin D$_2$ was first isolated[5,74] in 1932. The molecular formula was established[77] by analysis to be C$_{28}$H$_{44}$O, and the vitamin is thus isomeric with ergosterol. The formation of a monoacetate, monobenzoate, etc., and the oxidation to a ketone established the presence of a secondary alcoholic hydroxyl group in ergocalciferol. Catalytic hydrogenation of the compound absorbs[51] four moles of hydrogen to give the fully saturated compound C$_{28}$H$_{52}$O. Reduction of ergocalciferol with sodium and alcohol yields a dihydro compound which reacts with three moles of perbenzoic acid. Hence the vitamin contains four double bonds. From the molecular formula of the fully saturated compound (C$_n$H$_{2n-4}$O) it is evident that the molecule must be tricyclic. In support of this, selenium dehydrogenation of ergocalciferol does not yield Diels' hydrocarbon (**19**). Thus, it is evident that irradiation of ergosterol causes cleavage of one ring with the introduction of a double bond, and the remaining problem was to establish which ring is so affected.

Ozonolysis of ergocalciferol produced, amongst other things, 2,3-dimethylbutanal (**28**), indicating that the side-chain of ergosterol survives the photochemical reaction. The ultraviolet spectrum of the vitamin (Figure 14.2) indicated the presence of a conjugated triene system, which must be in the nucleus.

Ergocalciferol forms a monoadduct with maleic anhydride, and this was hydrolysed to the hydroxy dicarboxylic acid and converted into the acetate and thence to the dimethyl ester. Hydrogenation of the latter gave a dihydro compound which, upon ozonolysis, yielded the saturated ketone C$_{19}$H$_{34}$O. Since no aldehyde fragment could be detected, the hydrogenation must have saturated the side-chain double bond. From the molecular formula, the saturated ketone must be bicyclic and must contain the C$_{(9)}$ side-chain of the original vitamin. Hence this compound must represent rings c/d of the steroid nucleus, and its structure must be **43**. An oxo group at what corresponds to C$_{(9)}$ of the steroid nucleus is impossible since this is tertiary in ergosterol. Therefore there must be $\Delta^{7,8}$ unsaturation in ergocalciferol, and this is the only linkage between rings c and d and the remainder of the molecule. Ring b of ergosterol

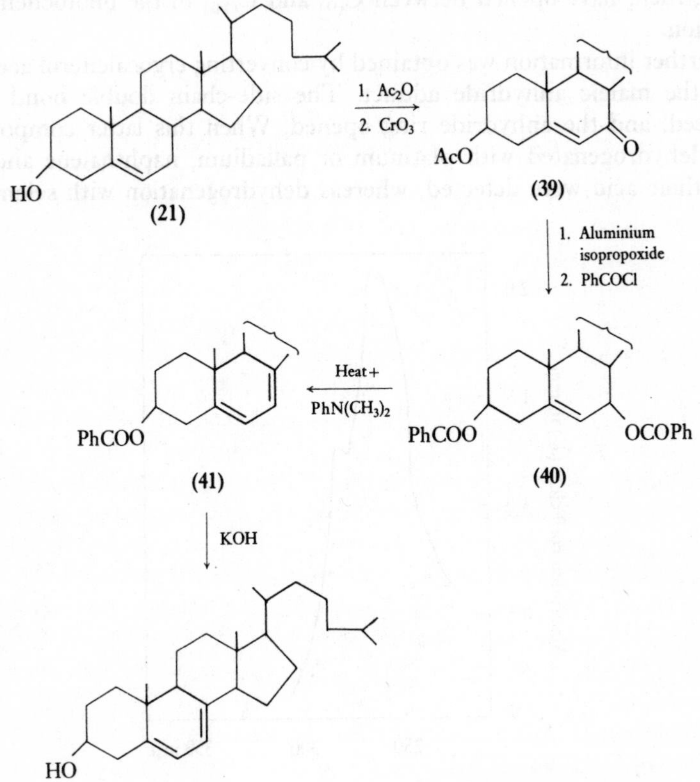

(21) → 1. Ac₂O 2. CrO₃ → (39)

(39) → 1. Aluminium isopropoxide 2. PhCOCl → (40)

(40) → Heat + PhN(CH₃)₂ → (41)

(41) → KOH → (42)

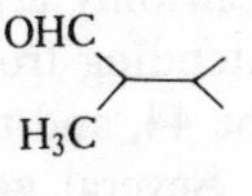

(28)

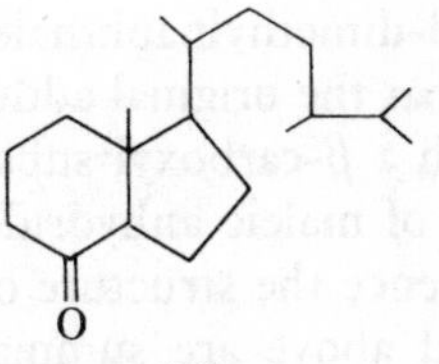

(43)

must, then, have opened between $C_{(9)}$ and $C_{(10)}$ in the photochemical reaction.

Further information was obtained by converting ergocalciferol acetate into the maleic anhydride adduct. The side-chain double bond was reduced, and the anhydride ring opened. When this latter compound was dehydrogenated with platinum or palladium, naphthalene and β-naphthoic acid were detected, whereas dehydrogenation with selenium

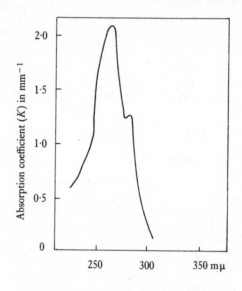

Figure 14.2. The ultraviolet spectrum of ergocalciferol (in hexane). [Reproduced, by permission, from H. R. Rosenberg, *The Chemistry and Physiology of the Vitamins*, Interscience, New York, 1945, p. 390.]

gave 2,3-dimethylnaphthalene. The formation of β-naphthoic acid means that the original adduct must possess a hydronaphthalene structure with a β-carboxyl substituent. This system can only arise by the addition of maleic anhydride to a diene system extending from $C_{(6)}$ to $C_{(19)}$. Hence the structure of ergocalciferol must be **44**, and the results discussed above are summarized in Figure 14.3. Several geometrical isomers of **44** are possible but the molecule was originally written in the

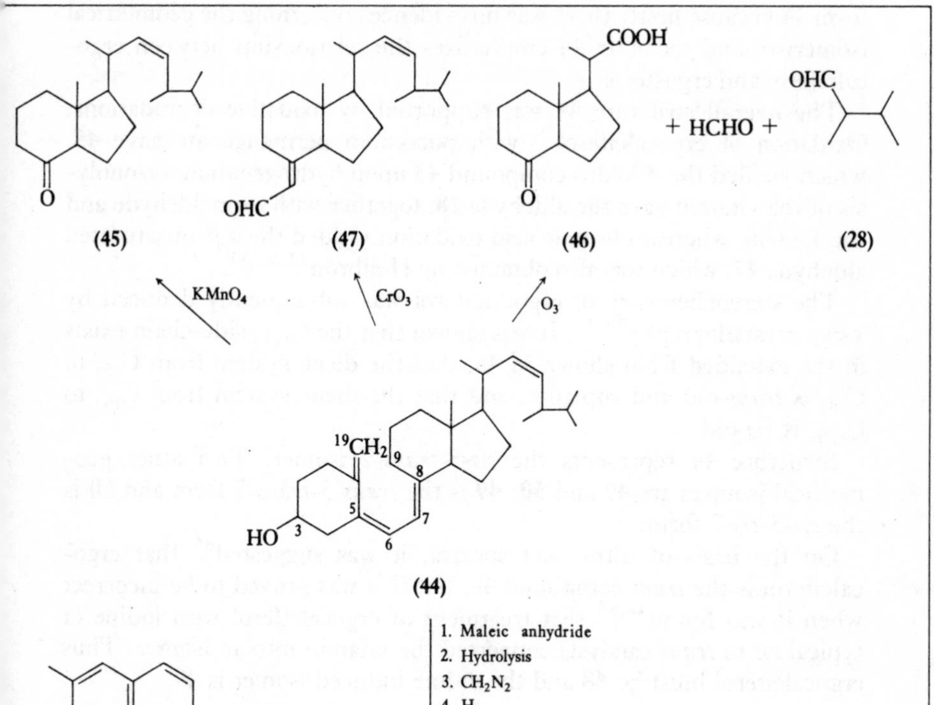
COOH
OHC
+ HCHO +
OHC
(45)
(47)
(46)
(28)
KMnO4
CrO3
O3
19CH2
HO
(44)
1. Maleic anhydride
2. Hydrolysis
3. CH2N2
4. H2
Se
COOCH3
AcO
COOCH3
CH
Naphthalene
+
β-naphthoic
acid
Pd
O3
O
(43)

Figure 14.3.

form **44** because firstly there was no evidence concerning the geometrical isomerism and secondly **44** emphasizes the relationship between ergocalciferol and ergosterol.

The overall structure **44** was supported by oxidative degradations. Oxidation of ergocalciferol[79] with potassium permanganate gave **45**, which yielded the dihydro compound **43** upon hydrogenation. Ozonolysis of the vitamin gave the aldehyde **28**, together with formaldehyde and the acid **46**, whereas chromic acid oxidation yielded the α,β-unsaturated aldehyde **47**, which was also obtained by Heilbron[33,34,35].

The stereochemistry of ergocalciferol was subsequently deduced by x-ray crystallography[38,39]. It was shown that the $C_{(17)}$ side-chain exists in the extended from shown in **48**, that the diene system from $C_{(5)}$ to $C_{(8)}$ is *trans*-oid and coplanar, and that the diene system from $C_{(6)}$ to $C_{(19)}$ is *cis*-oid.

Structure **44** represents the *cis*-5-*trans*-7 isomer. Two other geometrical isomers are **49** and **50**; **49** is the *trans*-5-*trans*-7 form and **50** is the *cis*-5-*cis*-7 form.

On the basis of ultraviolet spectra, it was suggested[65] that ergocalciferol is the *trans* compound **49**, but this was proved to be incorrect when it was found[44,50] that treatment of ergocalciferol with iodine (a typical *cis* to *trans* catalyst) converted the vitamin into an isomer. Thus ergocalciferol must be **48** and the iodine induced isomer is **49**.

Nomenclature of ergocalciferol and other vitamins D

For systematic nomenclature, the steroid name and numbering is retained. Cleavage of ring B is indicated by the prefix '9,10-seco-'. The stereochemistry of the hydroxyl group is referred to the $C_{(10)}$ and $C_{(13)}$ methyl groups of the provitamin; a β-configuration indicates a *cis* relationship. The hydrogen atom at $C_{(6)}$ may be on the same or on the opposite side to the $C_{(4)}$—$C_{(5)}$ bond of ring A and is designated as *cis* or *trans* respectively. The 9,10-seco-10(19),5,7-trienes exist in a preferred form about the $C_{(6)}$—$C_{(7)}$ single bond and this is designated by the letter '*s*' preceding the term *cis* or *trans*. Thus, ergocalciferol (**48**) is fully described as   3β-hydroxy-9,10-seco-6(*cis*)-6,7-*s*-*trans*-ergosta-10(19),5,7,22-tetraene.

The other vitamins D

The general structure for a D vitamin is **51** where R can vary, and the structures of vitamins D_3, D_4, D_5, D_6 and D_7 follow by analogy with ergocalciferol (**48**) and from the known structures of the provitamins.

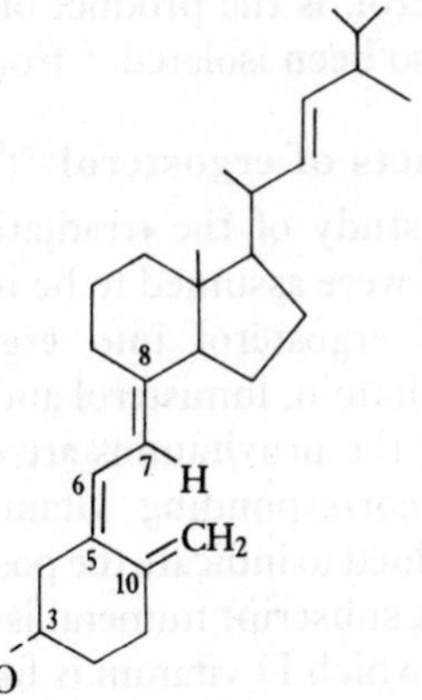

(48)

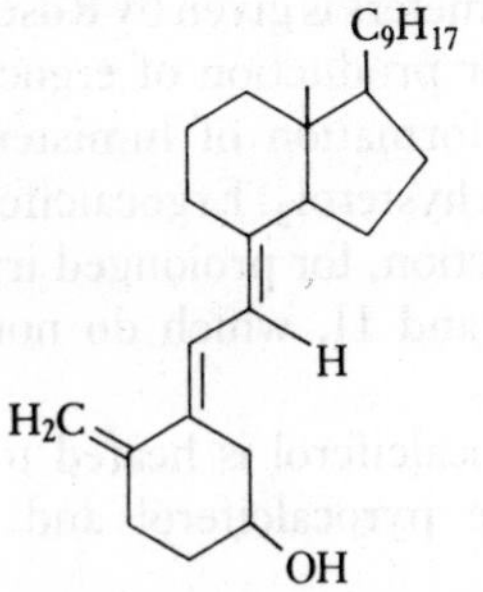

C_9H_{17}

(49)

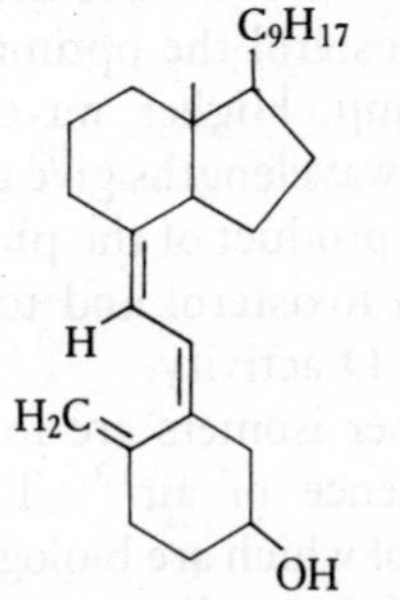

C_9H_{17}

(50)

R

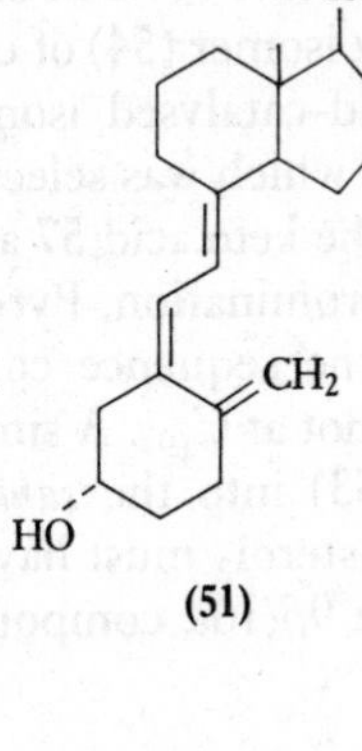

(51)

Vitamin D_3, cholocalciferol, is the product of irradiation of 7-dehydro-cholesterol, and it has also been isolated[12] from tuna-liver oils.

The irradiation products of ergosterol[26,63]

Windaus, during his study of the irradiation of ergosterol, isolated several substances which were assumed to be intermediates in the photo-chemical conversion of ergosterol into ergocalciferol. These inter-mediates are named previtamin, lumisterol and tachysterol. There is evi-dence to show that all of the provitamins are converted through similar intermediates into the corresponding vitamin D structure, and the steroid numbering is retained to indicate the positions of functional groups when describing them. A subscript numeral is added to the name of each intermediate to indicate which D vitamin is formed ultimately.

The formation of the various intermediates is a function of the wave-length of the activating radiation, the duration of the irradiation and of the solvent. A full discussion of these parameters is given by Rosenberg[59]. For ergosterol the optimum radiation, for production of ergocalciferol, is 280 mμ. Higher wavelengths favour formation of lumisterol$_2$, and shorter wavelengths give good yields of tachysterol$_2$. Ergocalciferol is not the end product of the photochemical reaction, for prolonged irradiation leads to toxisterol and to suprasterols I and II, which do not possess vitamin D activity.

Further isomers are formed when ergocalciferol is heated to 190° in the absence of air[13]. The products are pyrocalciferol and isopyro-calciferol which are biologically inactive.

The first irradiation intermediate of ergosterol to be isolated[5,75] was called lumisterol$_2$. Now, isopyrocalciferol was known to differ from ergosterol only at $C_{(9)}$ since both compounds gave the same $\Delta^{9,11}$-de-hydro compound. Since ergosterol has been shown to be 52, isopyro-calciferol must be the $9\beta,10\beta$ isomer 53. The structure of lumisterol$_2$ has been shown[15] to be the $9\beta,10\alpha$ isomer (54) of ergosterol. Oppenauer oxi-dation of lumisterol$_2$ and acid-catalysed isomerization of the product gave the conjugated ketone 55 which was selectively hydrogenated to 56. Ozonolysis of the latter gave the keto acid 57 after the side-chain double bond had been protected by bromination. Pyrolysis of this acid gave the tricyclic ketone 58. During the sequence configurational changes are possible at $C_{(8)}$ and $C_{(10)}$ but not at $C_{(9)}$. A similar sequence of reactions converted isopyrocalciferol (53) into the *same* ketone (58). Thus, the ketone 58 and, therefore, lumisterol$_2$ must have the 9β-configuration. It follows that lumisterol$_2$ is the $9\beta,10\alpha$ compound 54 and pyrocalciferol

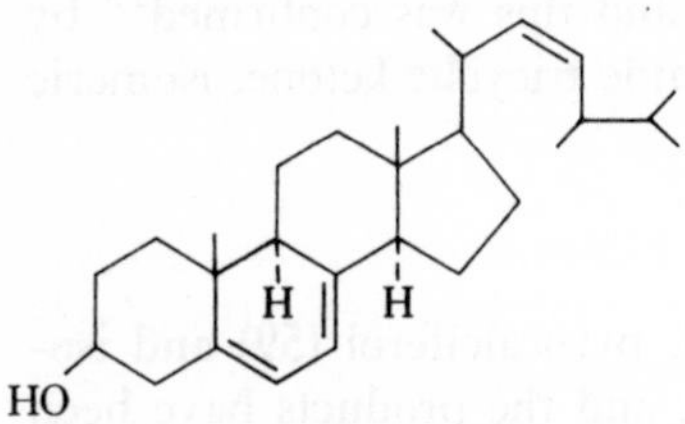

(52)

(53)

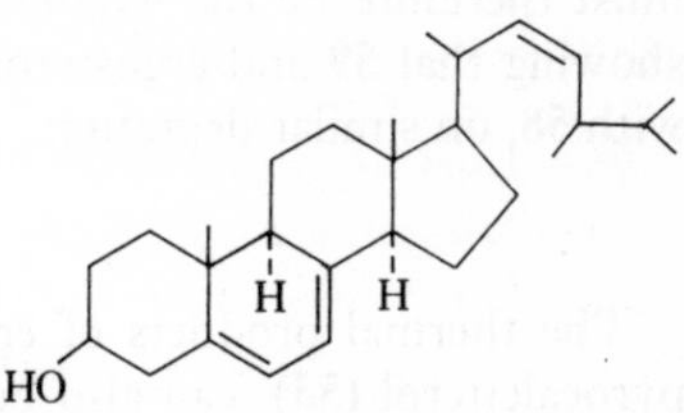

1. Oppenauer
2. H⁺

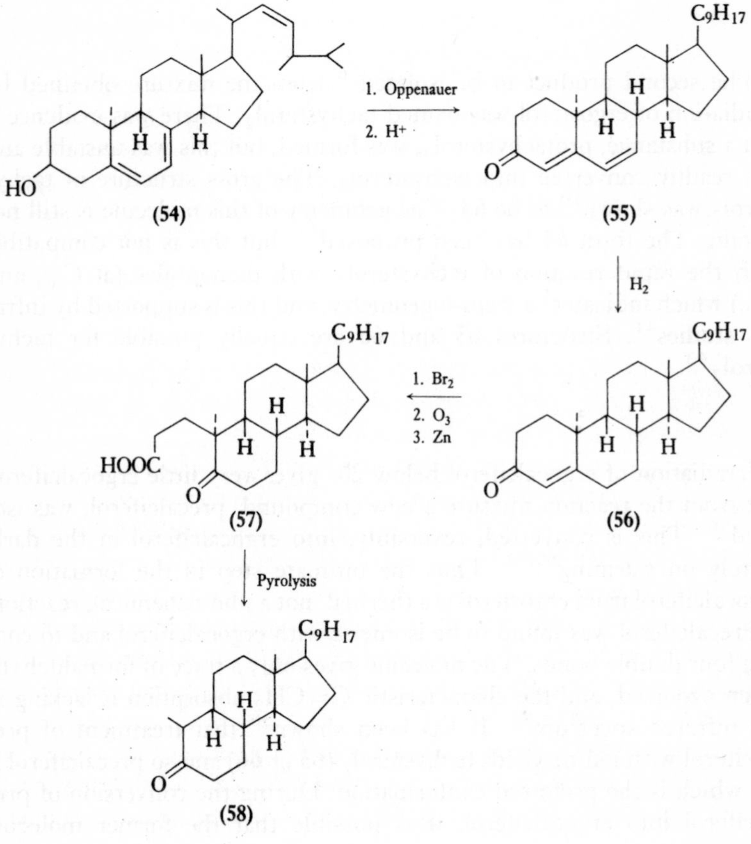

(54)

(55)

H₂

1. Br₂
2. O₃
3. Zn

(57)

(56)

Pyrolysis

(58)

must therefore be the $9\alpha,10\alpha$ isomer **59**, and this was confirmed[15] by showing that **59** and ergosterol gave the same tricyclic ketone, isomeric with **58**, on similar degration.

The thermal products of ergocalciferol, pyrocalciferol (**59**) and iso-pyrocalciferol (**53**), can also be irradiated, and the products have been identified as valency tautomers of the parent compounds[18]. Thus, photoisopyrocalciferol is **60**; it can be oxidized to the ketone **61** which is isomerized by alkali to **62**. The structure **60**, which contains a cyclo-butene double bond, is supported by infrared and nuclear magnetic resonance data. Photopyrocalciferol differs from photoisopyrocalciferol (**60**) in the stereochemistry at $C_{(9)}$ and $C_{(10)}$.

The second product to be isolated[76] from the mixture obtained by irradiation of ergosterol was named tachysterol$_2$. There was evidence[73] that a substance, protachysterol$_2$, was formed, but this was unstable and was readily converted into tachysterol$_2$. The gross structure of tachy-sterol$_2$ was shown[10] to be **63**. The geometry of this molecule is still not certain. The form **64** has been proposed[11], but this is not compatible with the rapid reaction of tachysterol$_2$ with dienophiles (at $C_{(6)}$ and $C_{(9)}$) which indicates[1] a *trans*-6 geometry, and this is supported by infra-red studies[41]. Structures **65** and **66** are equally possible for tachy-sterol$_2$[43].

Irradiation of ergocalciferol below 20° gives very little ergocalciferol, but from the reaction mixture a new compound, precalciferol, was iso-lated[70]. This is converted, reversibly, into ergocalciferol in the dark, merely on warming[69,72]. Thus the ultimate step in the formation of ergocalciferol from ergosterol is a thermal, not a photochemical, reaction.

Precalciferol was found to be isomeric with ergocalciferol and to con-tain four double bonds. The molecule gives only a trace of formaldehyde when ozonized, and the characteristic $C{=}CH_2$ absorption is lacking in the infrared spectrum[71]. It has been shown[50] that treatment of pre-calciferol with iodine yields tachysterol$_2$ (**65** or **66**) and so precalciferol is **67**, which is the preferred conformation. During the conversion of pre-calciferol into ergocalciferol, it is possible that the former molecule

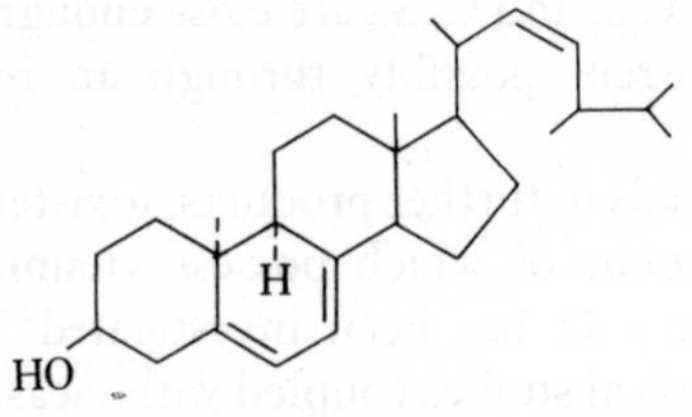

(59)

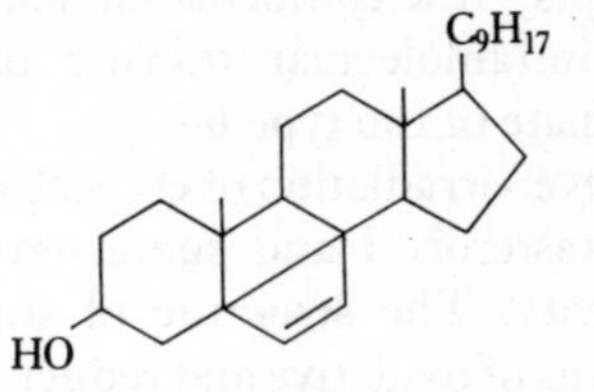

(60)

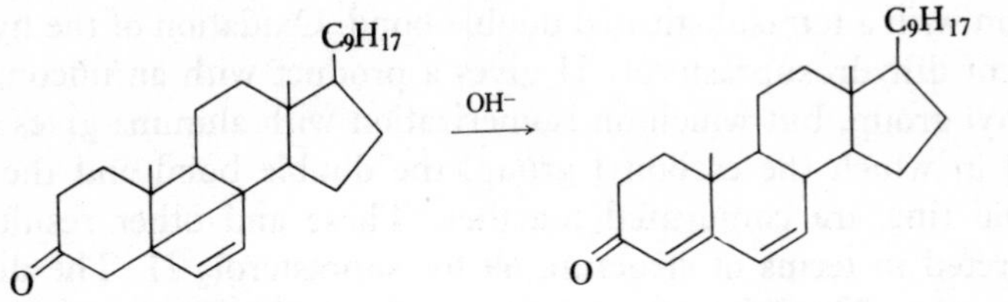

(61)

(62)

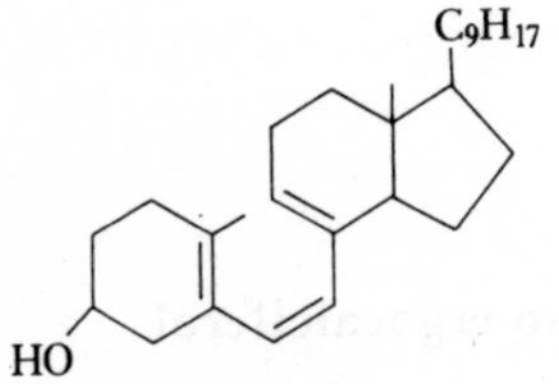

(63)

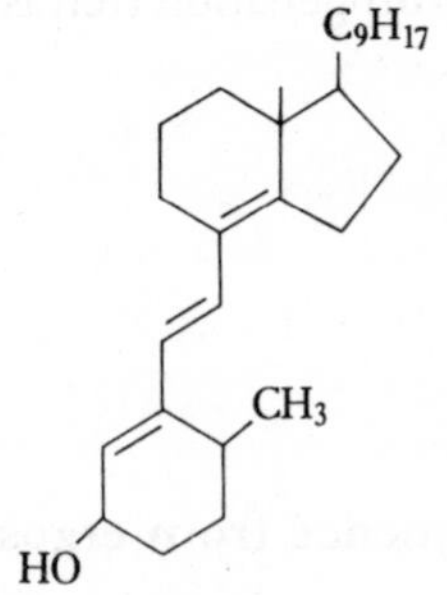

(64)

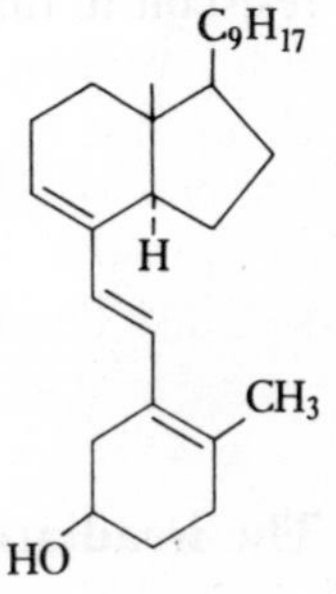

(65)

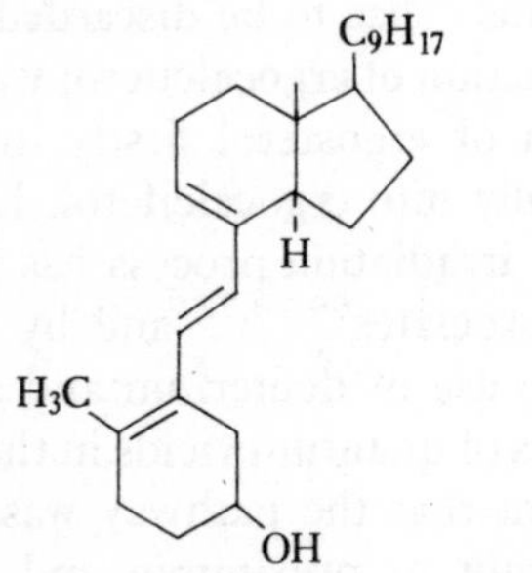

(66)

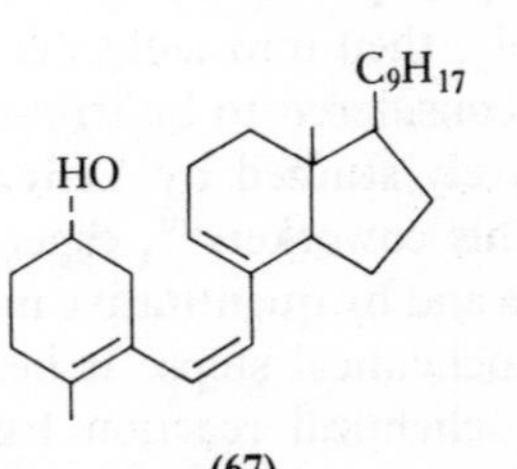

(67)

adopts[55] the conformation **63**, where $C_{(9)}$ and $C_{(10)}$ are close enough for an intramolecular transfer of hydrogen, possibly through an intermediate of the type **68**.

Over-irradiation of ergocalciferol leads to further products, toxisterol$_2$, suprasterol$_2$ I and suprasterol$_2$ II, none of which possess vitamin D activity. The structure of suprasterol$_2$ II has been investigated[19] by means of oxidative and reductive chemical studies coupled with measurements of ultraviolet, infrared and nuclear magnetic resonance spectra. The dihydro derivative was shown to possess a cyclopropane ring in conjugation with a tetrasubstituted double bond. Oxidation of the hydroxyl group of dihydrosuprasterol$_2$ II gives a product with an unconjugated carbonyl group, but which on isomerization with alumina gives a compound in which the carbonyl group, the double bond and the cyclopropane ring are conjugated together. These and other results were interpreted in terms of structure **69** for suprasterol$_2$ II. The dihydroketone is thus **70** and its isomerization product is **71**. Further reduction of **70** results in hydrogenolysis of the cyclopropane ring to **72**, and this is resistant to further hydrogenation (tetrasubstituted double bond).

The irradiation sequence from ergosterol to ergocalciferol

With the isolation and characterization of precalciferol and with the realization that it is converted thermally into ergocalciferol, the classical scheme of intermediates due to Windaus[76] has to be discarded. In this early scheme it was assumed that production of ergocalciferol was a stepwise process involving the conversion of ergosterol firstly into lumisterol$_2$, then into tachysterol$_2$ and finally into ergocalciferol. Each step was considered to be irreversible. The irradiation process has been extensively studied by Velluz and his associates[69,70,71] and by Havinga and his coworkers[30], especially by the use of deuterium and radioisotopes and by quantitative measurements of quantum yields in the various photochemical steps. It became evident that the pathway was a direct photochemical reaction from provitamin to previtamin and that the lumisterol and tachysterol are produced in side-reactions. There is still

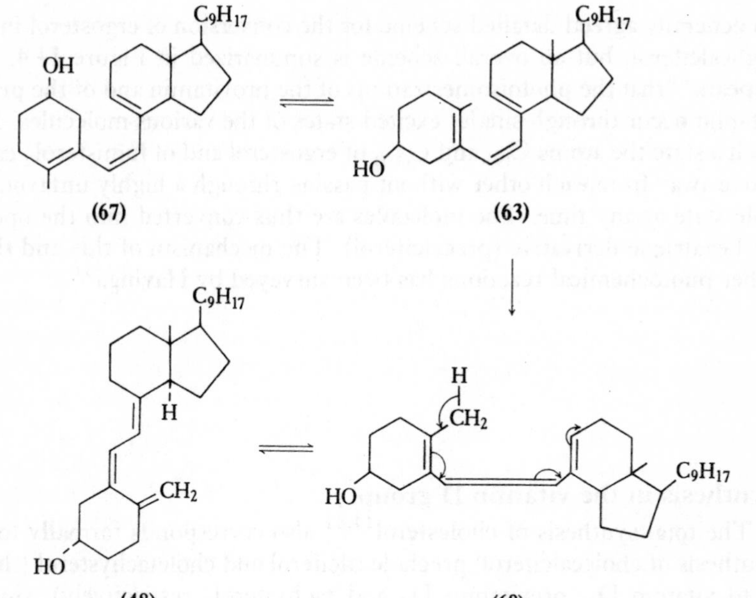

(67) ⇌ (63)

(48) ⇌ (68)

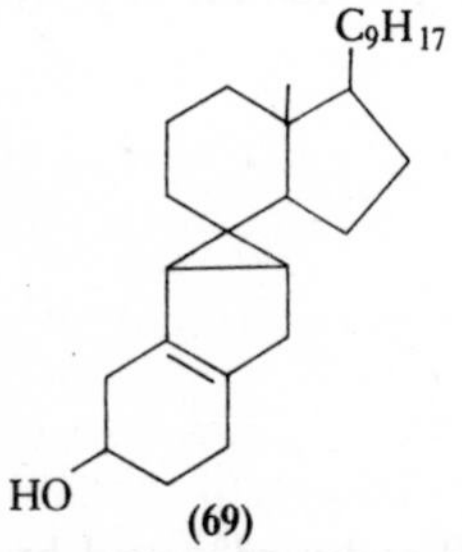

(69) 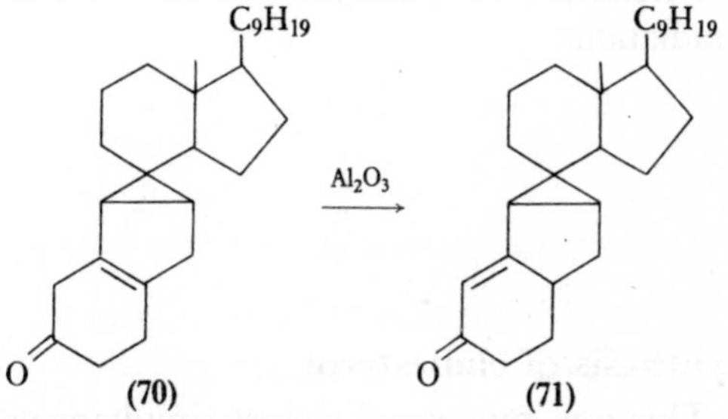   (70) $\xrightarrow{Al_2O_3}$ (71)

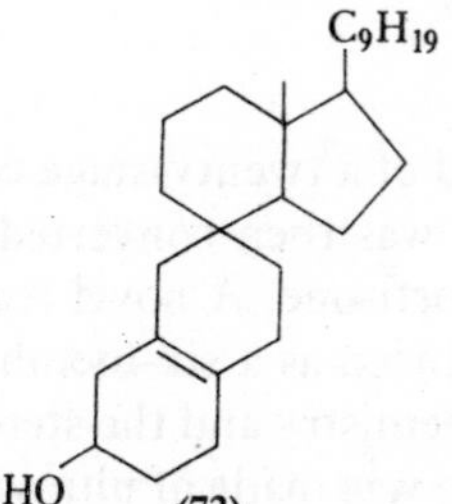

(72)

no generally agreed detailed scheme for the conversion of ergosterol into ergocalciferol, but an overall scheme is summarized in Figure 14.4. It appears[30] that the photoisomerizations of the provitamin and of the pre-vitamin occur through singlet excited states of the various molecules. In such a state the atoms $C_{(9)}$ and $C_{(10)}$ of ergosterol and of lumisterol$_2$ can move away from each other without passing through a highly unfavour-able state at any time. The molecules are thus converted into the open *cis*-hexatriene derivative (precalciferol). The mechanism of this and the other photochemical reactions has been surveyed by Havinga[31].

Synthesis in the vitamin D group

The total synthesis of cholesterol[14,81] also corresponds formally to a synthesis of cholecalciferol, precholecalciferol and choletachysterol (that is to vitamin D$_3$, previtamin D$_3$ and tachysterol$_3$ respectively), since cholesterol had previously been converted (see above under 'the other provitamins') to 7-dehydrocholesterol and thence to vitamin D$_3$ by irradiation.

Synthesis of cholesterol

This was announced almost simultaneously by Woodward[81] and by Robinson[14].

The Woodward synthesis

Essentially this consisted of a twenty-stage conversion of the *p*-benzo-quinone 73 into 74 which was then converted into cholesterol, proges-terone, testosterone and cortisone. A novel feature of the synthesis was that ring D was first introduced as a six-membered ring and later modi-fied. This simplified the chemistry and the stereochemistry. Throughout the synthesis, extensive use was made of ultraviolet and infrared spectro-scopy in elucidating the course of reactions.

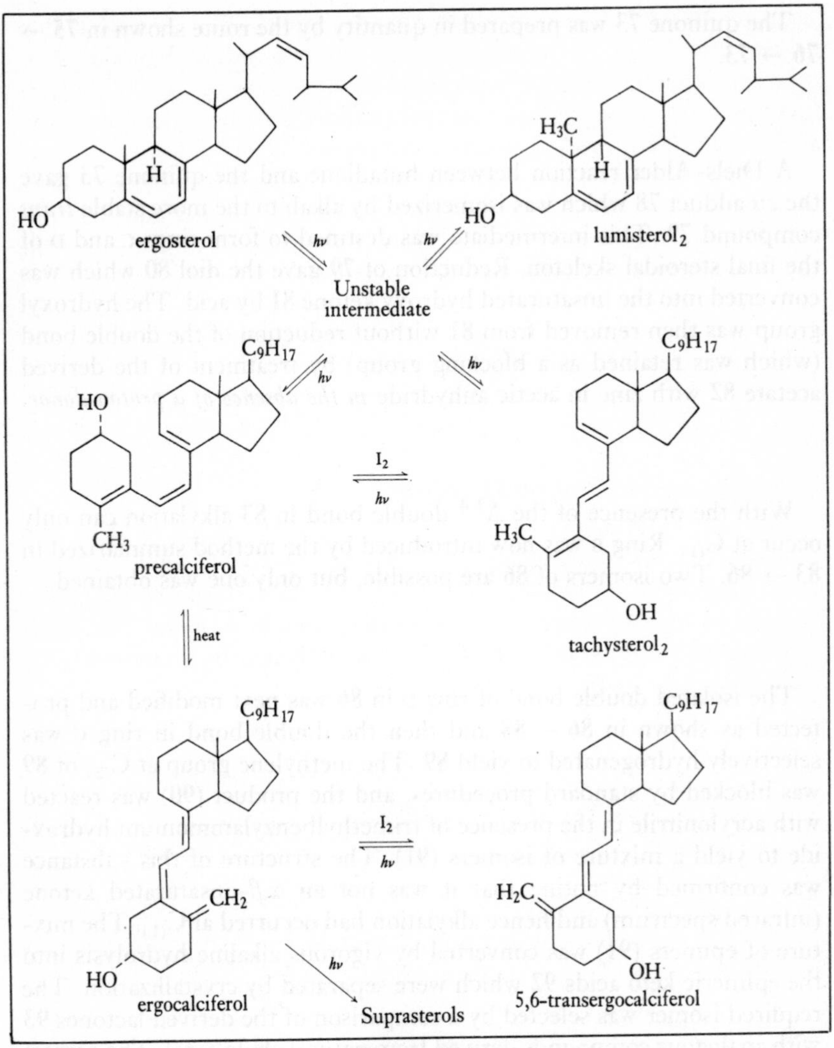

Figure 14.4.

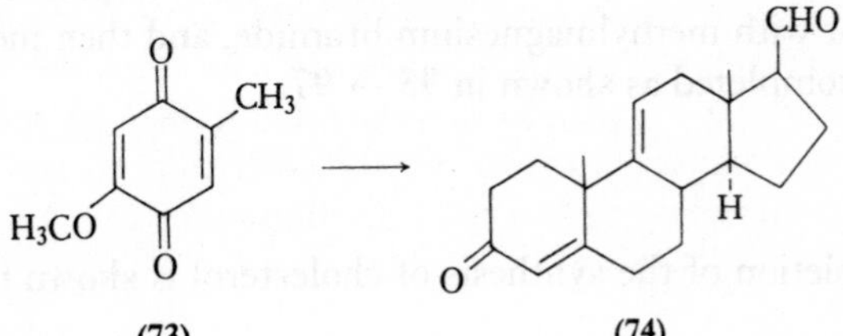

Structure labels within the figure:

ergosterol

lumisterol₂ (H₃C)

Unstable intermediate

C₉H₁₇

precalciferol (CH₃)

tachysterol₂ (H₃C, OH)

ergocalciferol (CH₂)

Suprasterols

5,6-transergocalciferol (H₂C, OH)

I₂ / hν

heat

hν

(73)   (74)

The quinone 73 was prepared in quantity by the route shown in 75 → 76 → 73.

A Diels–Alder reaction between butadiene and the quinone 73 gave the *cis* adduct 78 which was isomerized by alkali to the more stable *trans* compound 79. This intermediate was destined to form rings C and D of the final steroidal skeleton. Reduction of 79 gave the diol 80 which was converted into the unsaturated hydroxy ketone 81 by acid. The hydroxyl group was then removed from 81 without reduction of the double bond (which was retained as a blocking group) by treatment of the derived acetate 82 with zinc in acetic anhydride *in the absence of a proton donor*.

With the presence of the $\Delta^{3,4}$ double bond in 83 alkylation can only occur at $C_{(1)}$. Ring B was now introduced by the method summarized in 83 → 86. Two isomers of 86 are possible, but only one was obtained.

The isolated double bond of ring D in 86 was next modified and protected as shown in 86 → 88 and then the double bond in ring C was selectively hydrogenated to yield 89. The methylene group at $C_{(3)}$ of 89 was blocked by standard procedures, and the product (90) was reacted with acrylonitrile in the presence of trimethylbenzylammonium hydroxide to yield a mixture of isomers (91). The structure of this substance was confirmed by noting that it was not an α,β-unsaturated ketone (infrared spectrum) and hence alkylation had occurred at $C_{(1)}$. The mixture of epimers (91) was converted by vigorous alkaline hydrolysis into the epimeric keto acids 92 which were separated by crystallization. The required isomer was selected by a comparison of the derived lactones 93 with analogous compounds derived from natural cholesterol. The correct isomer of 93 was then converted into the ketone 95 (presumably via 94) by treatment with methylmagnesium bromide, and then modification of ring D was completed as shown in 95 → 97.

The completion of the synthesis of cholesterol is shown in 97 → 105.

(75) → HNO$_3$ → (76) → Sn/HCl → (77) → FeCl$_3$ → 73

(73) + (diene) → (78)

(78) → Alkali → (79) → LiAlH$_4$ → (80) → H$^+$ → (81)

(82) → (ZnO compound) → (83)

(83) → HCOOC$_2$H$_5$ → (84) → C$_2$H$_5$COCH=CH$_2$ / KOC(CH$_3$)$_3$ → (85) → KOH → (86)

(86) → OsO$_4$ → (87) → Acetone → (88)

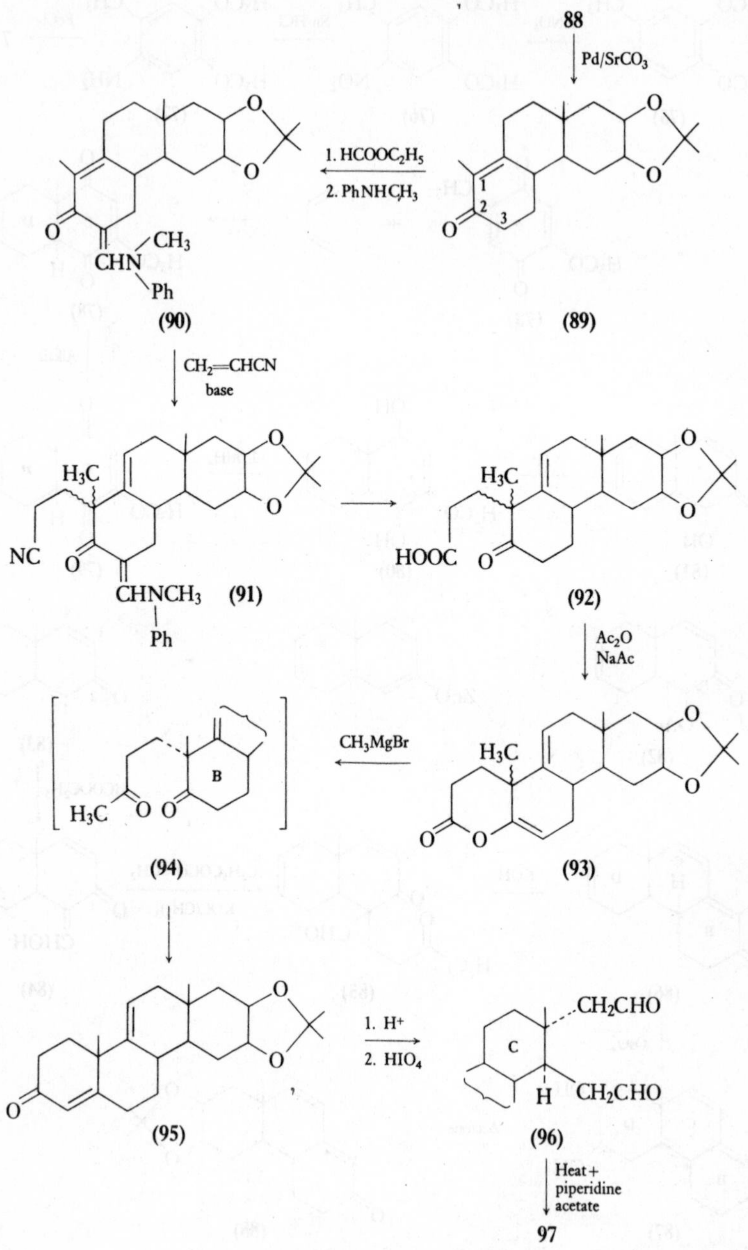
88
Pd/SrCO$_3$
1. HCOOC$_2$H$_5$
2. PhNHCH$_3$
CH$_3$
CHN
Ph
(90)
1
2
3
(89)
CH$_2$=CHCN
base
H$_3$C
NC
CHNCH$_3$
Ph
(91)
H$_3$C
HOOC
(92)
Ac$_2$O
NaAc
CH$_3$MgBr
B
H$_3$C
(94)
H$_3$C
(93)
1. H$^+$
2. HIO$_4$
CH$_2$CHO
C
H
CH$_2$CHO
(95)
(96)
Heat+
piperidine
acetate
97

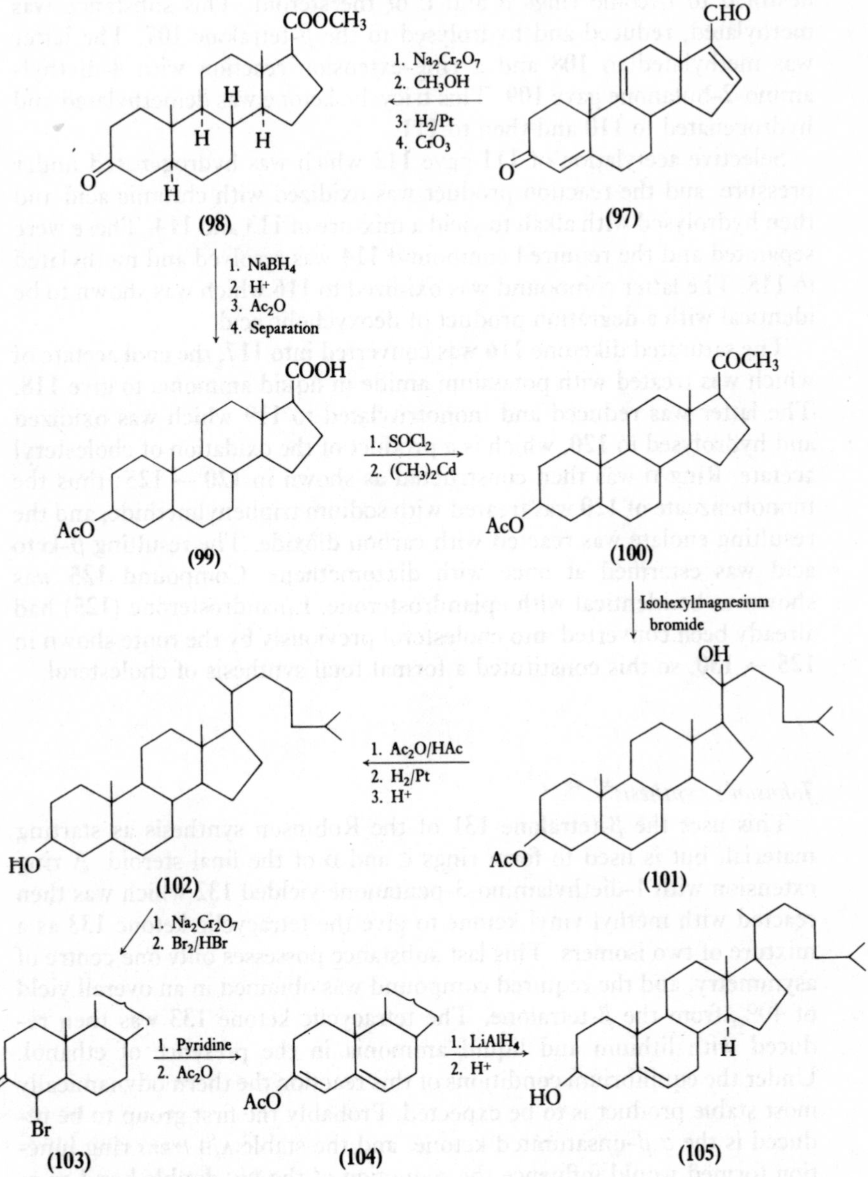

The starting material was 1,2-dihidroxy anthulene (106) whose re...

(structures and reaction scheme omitted — chemical diagrams)

Compound **(98)** with reagents:
1. Na$_2$Cr$_2$O$_7$
2. CH$_3$OH
3. H$_2$/Pt
4. CrO$_3$

Compound **(97)**

Compound **(98)** with reagents:
1. NaBH$_4$
2. H$^+$
3. Ac$_2$O
4. Separation

Compound **(99)** with reagents:
1. SOCl$_2$
2. (CH$_3$)$_2$Cd

Compound **(100)**

Isohexylmagnesium bromide

Compound **(102)** with reagents:
1. Ac$_2$O/HAc
2. H$_2$/Pt
3. H$^+$

Compound **(101)**

Compound **(102)** with reagents:
1. Na$_2$Cr$_2$O$_7$
2. Br$_2$/HBr

Compound **(103)** with reagents:
1. Pyridine
2. Ac$_2$O

Compound **(104)** with reagents:
1. LiAlH$_4$
2. H$^+$

Compound **(105)**

Robinson's synthesis[14]

The starting material was 1,6-dihydroxynaphthalene (106) which was destined to become rings B and C of the steroid. This substance was methylated, reduced and hydrolysed to the β-tetralone 107. The latter was methylated to 108 and a ring-extension reaction with 4-diethyl-amino-2-butanone gave 109. This tricyclic ketone was demethylated and hydrogenated to 110 and then to 111.

Selective acetylation of 111 gave 112 which was hydrogenated under pressure, and the reaction product was oxidized with chromic acid and then hydrolysed with alkali to yield a mixture of 113 and 114. These were separated and the required compound 114 was resolved and methylated to 115. The latter compound was oxidized to 116 which was shown to be identical with a degration product of deoxycholic acid.

The saturated diketone 116 was converted into 117, the enol acetate of which was treated with potassium amide in liquid ammonia to give 118. The latter was reduced and monotritylated to 119 which was oxidized and hydrolysed to 120, which is a product of the oxidation of cholesteryl acetate. Ring D was then constructed as shown in 120 → 125; thus the monobenzoate of 120 was treated with sodium triphenylmethide, and the resulting enolate was reacted with carbon dioxide. The resulting β-keto acid was esterified at once with diazomethane. Compound 125 was shown to be identical with epiandrosterone. Epiandrosterone (125) had already been converted into cholesterol previously by the route shown in 125 → 130, so this constituted a formal total synthesis of cholesterol.

Johnson's synthesis[47,48]

This uses the β-tetralone 131 of the Robinson synthesis as starting material, but is used to form rings C and D of the final steroid. A ring extension with 1-diethylamino-3-pentanone yielded 132 which was then reacted with methyl vinyl ketone to give the tetracyclic ketone 133 as a mixture of two isomers. This last substance possesses only one centre of asymmetry, and the required compound was obtained in an overall yield of 40% from the β-tetralone. The tetracyclic ketone 133 was then reduced with lithium and liquid ammonia in the presence of ethanol. Under the equilibrium conditions of this reaction the thermodynamically most stable product is to be expected. Probably the first group to be reduced is the α,β-unsaturated ketone, and the stable A/B *trans* ring junction formed would influence the reduction of the B/C double bond so as

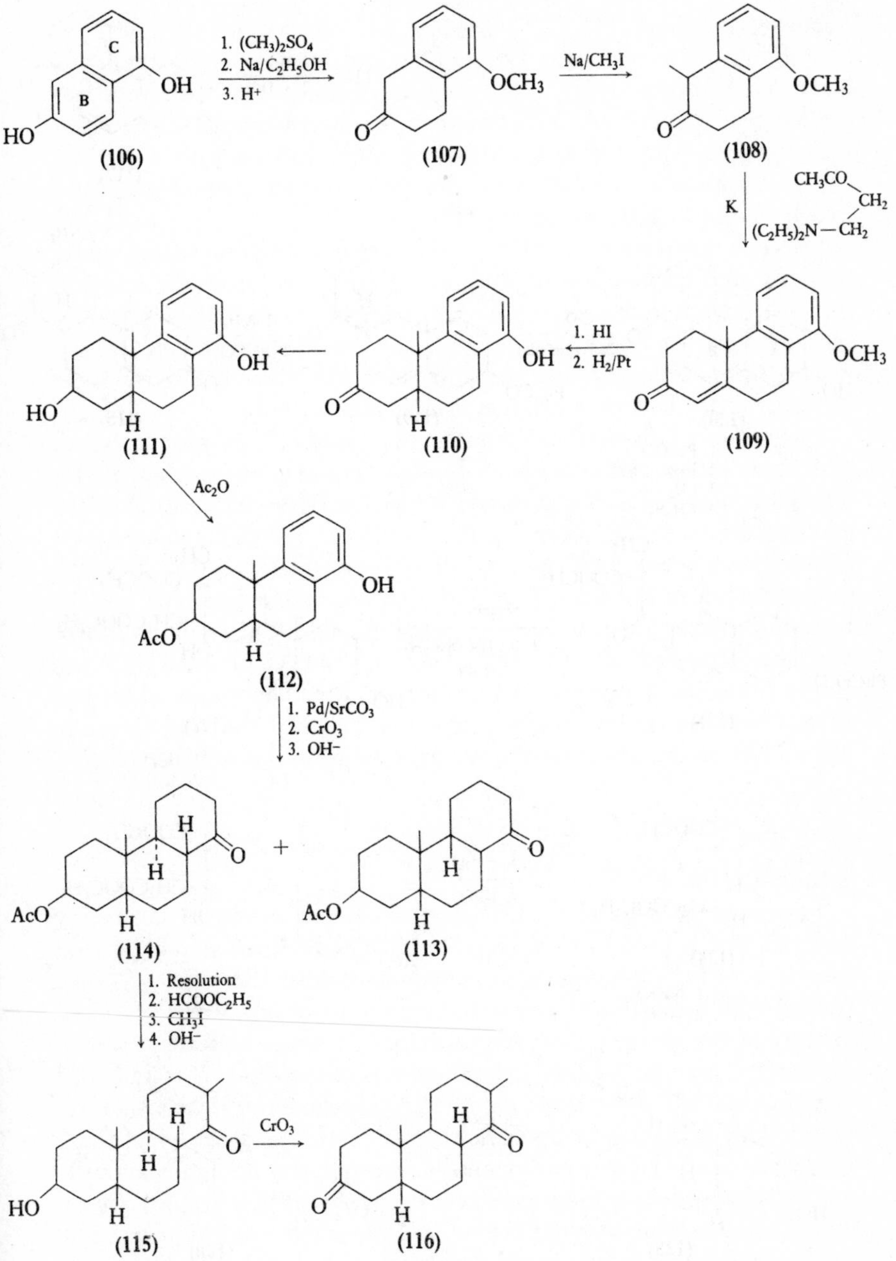
C
B
OH
HO
(106)
1. (CH3)2SO4
2. Na/C2H5OH
3. H+
OCH3
O
(107)
Na/CH3I
OCH3
O
(108)
K
CH3CO
CH2
(C2H5)2N—CH2
OCH3
O
(109)
1. HI
2. H2/Pt
OH
O
H
(110)
OH
HO
H
(111)
Ac2O
OH
AcO
H
(112)
1. Pd/SrCO3
2. CrO3
3. OH−
H
O
H
AcO
H
(114)
+
O
H
AcO
H
(113)
1. Resolution
2. HCOOC2H5
3. CH3I
4. OH−
H
O
H
HO
H
(115)
CrO3
H
O
O
H
(116)

$116 \xrightarrow[\text{2. } -\text{HBr}]{\text{1. Br}_2}$ (117)

(117) → 1. Ac$_2$O 2. KNH$_2$ → (118)

(118) → 1. LiAlH$_4$ 2. Ph$_3$CCl → (119)

(119) → 1. CrO$_3$ 2. Hydrolysis → (120)

(120) → 1. PhCOCl 2. Base 3. CO$_2$ 4. CH$_2$N$_2$ → (121)

(121) → 1. Separation 2. BrCH$_2$COOC$_2$H$_5$ + Zn → (122)

(122) → 1. H$_2$/Pt 2. Ac$_2$O → (123)

(123) → 1. $-$H$_2$O 2. H$_2$/Pt → (124)

(124) → 1. NaOCH$_3$ 2. $-$CO$_2$ → (125)

(125) → 1. CrO$_3$ 2. Br$_2$ 3. $-$HBr → (126)

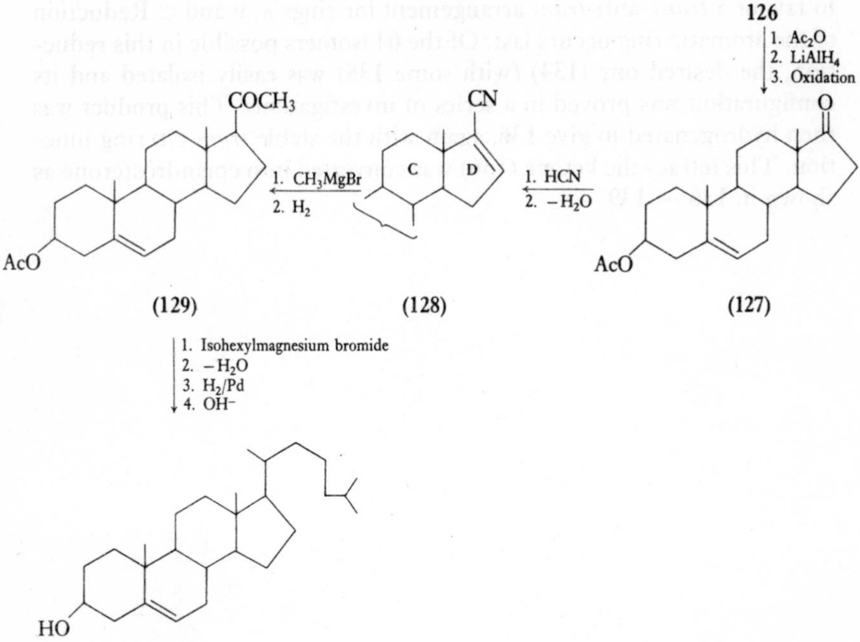
126
1. Ac_2O
2. $LiAlH_4$
3. Oxidation
1. HCN
2. $-H_2O$
1. CH_3MgBr
2. H_2
1. Isohexylmagnesium bromide
2. $-H_2O$
3. H_2/Pd
4. OH^-
$COCH_3$
CN
C
D
AcO
HO
(129)
(128)
(127)

(130)

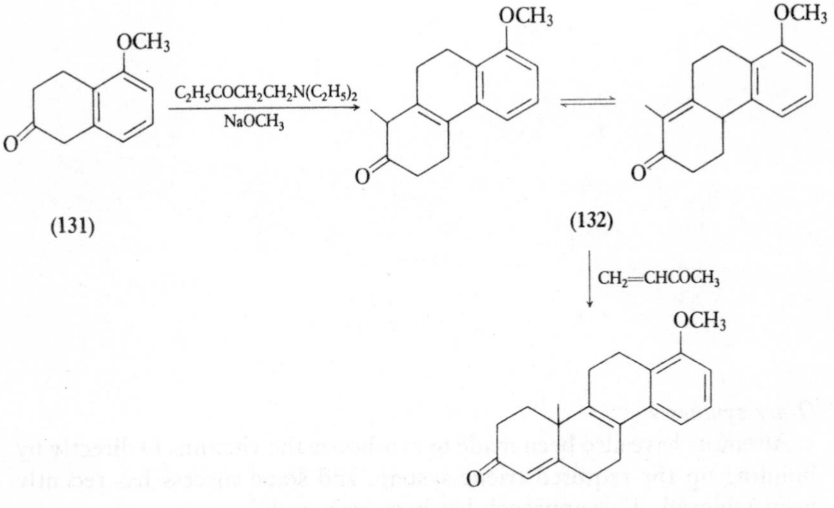
OCH_3
$C_2H_5COCH_2CH_2N(C_2H_5)_2$
$NaOCH_3$
$CH_2{=}CHCOCH_3$
(131)
(132)

(133)

to favour a *trans*–anti-*trans* arrangement for rings A, B and C. Reduction of the aromatic ring occurs last. Of the 64 isomers possible in this reduction, the desired one (134) (with some 135) was easily isolated and its configuration was proved in a series of investigations. This product was then hydrogenated to give 136, again with the stable *trans* C/D ring junction. This tetracyclic ketone (136) was converted into epiandrosterone as shown in 136 → 139.

Other syntheses

Attempts have also been made to synthesize the vitamins D directly by building up the required triene system, and some success has recently been achieved. This approach has been reviewed[55].

The main difficulty is that all three double bonds of the vitamin are

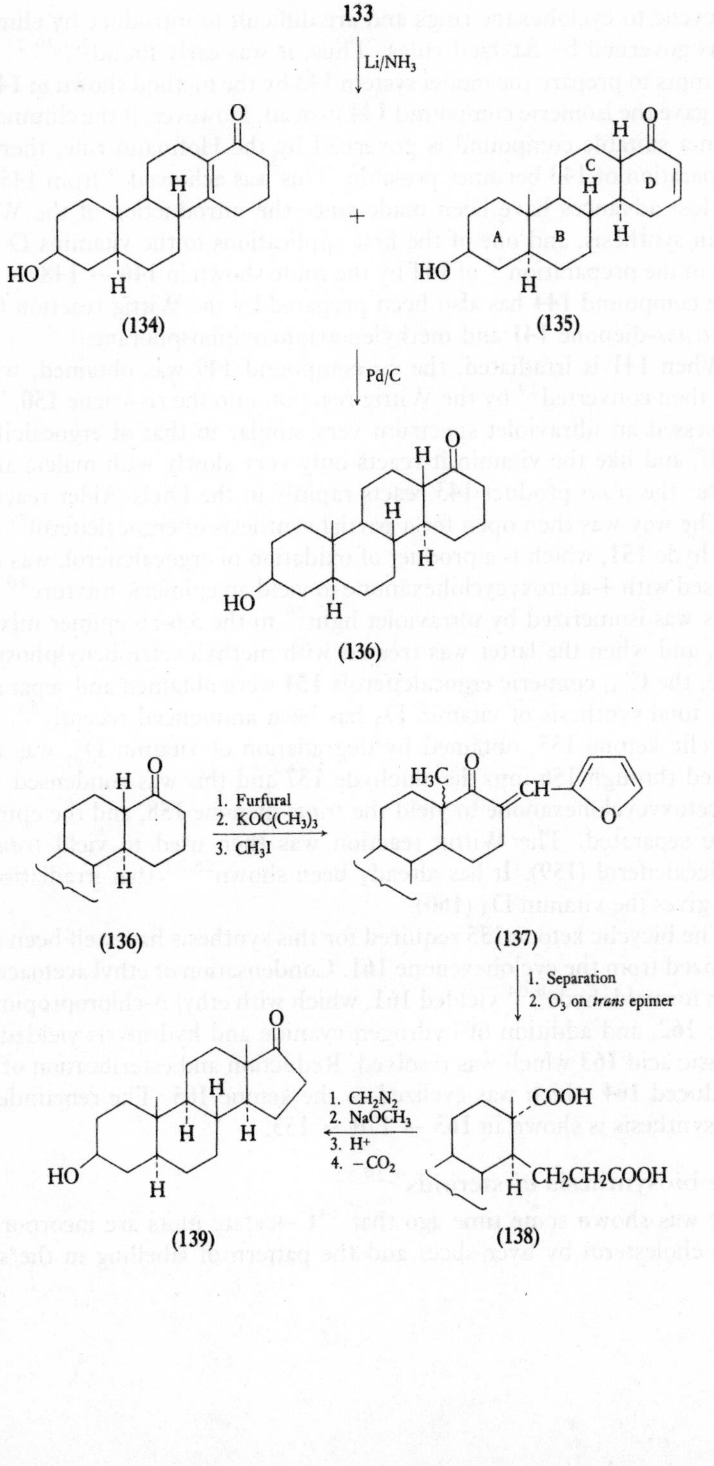

133

↓ Li/NH₃

(134)   +   (135)

↓ Pd/C

(136)

(136) → 1. Furfural 2. KOC(CH₃)₃ 3. CH₃I → (137)

↓ 1. Separation 2. O₃ on *trans* epimer

(139)   ← 1. CH₂N₂ 2. NaOCH₃ 3. H⁺ 4. − CO₂ ← (138)

exocyclic to cyclohexane rings and are difficult to introduce by eliminations governed by Saytzeff rules. Thus, it was early found[2,3,20,21] that
attempts to prepare the model system 143 by the method shown in 140 →
143 gave the isomeric compound 144 instead. However, if the elimination
from a suitable compound is governed by the Hofmann rule, then the
preparation of 143 becomes possible. This was achieved[54] from 145.

Most advances have been made since the introduction of the Wittig
olefin synthesis, and one of the first applications to the vitamins D field
was in the preparation[29] of 144 by the route shown in 146 → 148 → 144.
The compound 144 has also been prepared by the Wittig reaction from
the *trans*-dienone 141 and methylenetriphenylphosphorane.

When 141 is irradiated, the *cis* compound 149 was obtained, which
was then converted[29] by the Wittig reaction into the *cis*-triene 150. This
possessed an ultraviolet spectrum very similar to that of ergocalciferol
itself, and like the vitamin it reacts only very slowly with maleic anhydride; the *trans* product 143 reacts rapidly in the Diels–Alder reaction.

The way was then open for a partial synthesis of ergocalciferol[29]; the
aldehyde 151, which is a product of oxidation of ergocalciferol, was condensed with 4-acetoxycyclohexanone to yield an epimeric mixture[40] 152.
This was isomerized by ultraviolet light[29] to the 5,6-*cis* epimer mixture
153, and when the latter was treated with methylenetriphenylphosphorane, the $C_{(3)}$ epimeric ergocalciferols 154 were obtained and separated.

A total synthesis of vitamin D_3 has been announced recently[45]. The
bicyclic ketone 155, obtained by degradation of vitamin D_3, was converted through 156 into the aldehyde 157 and this was condensed with
4-acetoxycyclohexanone to yield the *trans*-dienone 158, and the epimers
were separated. The Wittig reaction was then used to yield *trans*-5-
cholecalciferol (159). It has already been shown[28,32] that irradiation of
159 gives the vitamin D_3 (160).

The bicyclic ketone 155 required for this synthesis has itself been synthesized from the cyclohexenone 161. Condensation of ethyl acetoacetate
with formaldehyde[8,64] yielded 161, which with ethyl β-chloropropionate
gave 162, and addition of hydrogen cyanide and hydrolysis yielded the
dibasic acid 163 which was resolved. Reduction and esterification of 163
produced 164 which was cyclized to the ketone 165. The remainder of
the synthesis is shown in 165 → 170 → 155.

The biosynthesis of steroids[9,28,32]

It was shown some time ago that ^{14}C-acetate units are incorporated
into cholesterol by liver slices and the pattern of labelling in the side-

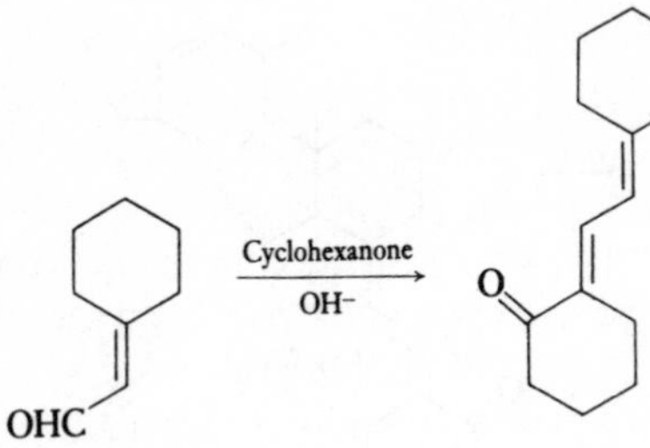

(140)   (141) 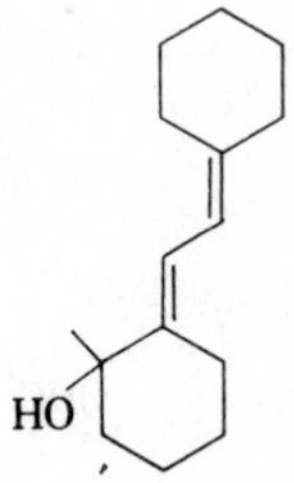   (142)

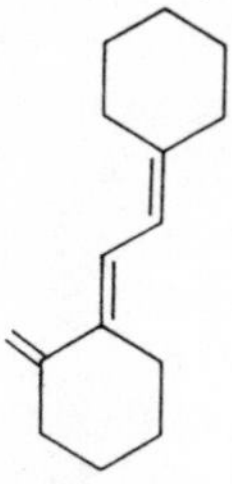

(143) 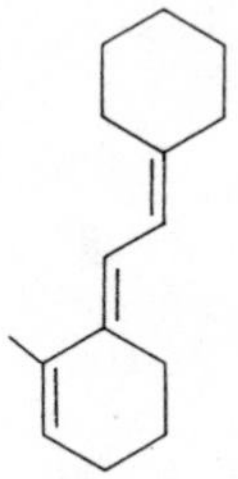   (144) 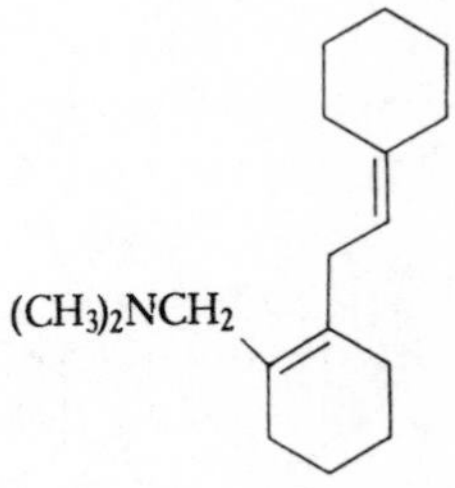   (145)

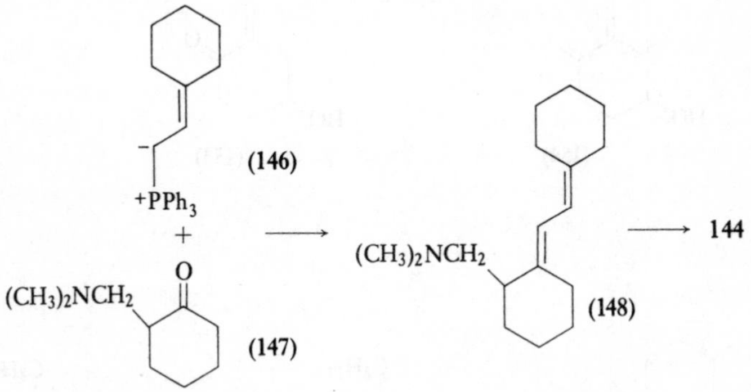

(146)

(147)

(148)   144

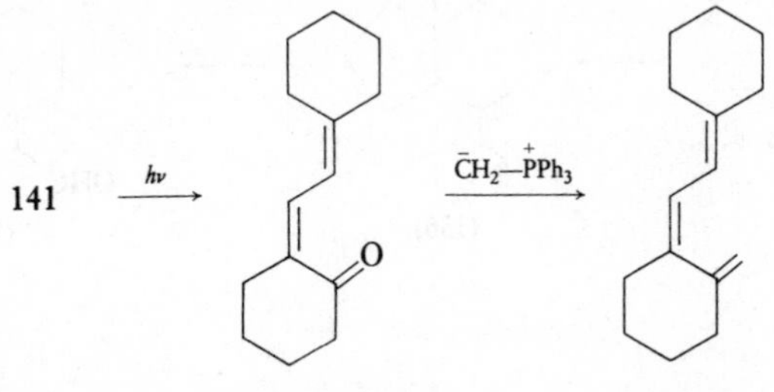

141   $\xrightarrow{h\nu}$ (149) $\xrightarrow{\bar{C}H_2-\overset{+}{P}Ph_3}$ (150)

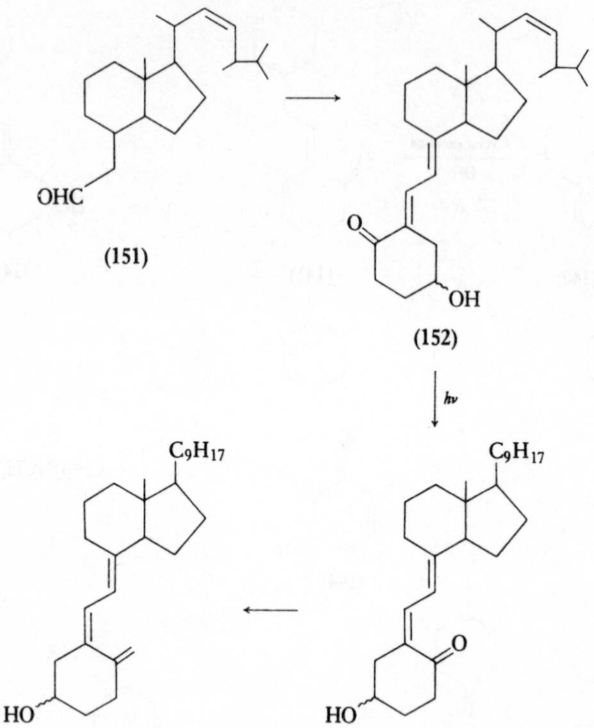

(151)

(152)

$h\nu$

C$_9$H$_{17}$

C$_9$H$_{17}$

HO

(154)

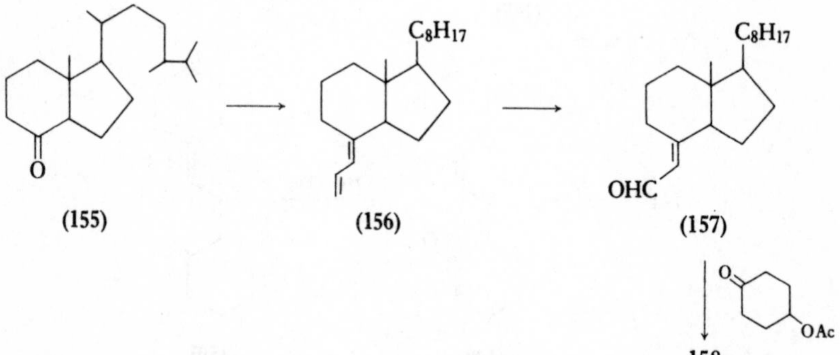

HO

(153)

C$_8$H$_{17}$

C$_8$H$_{17}$

(155)

(156)

OHC

(157)

158

OAc

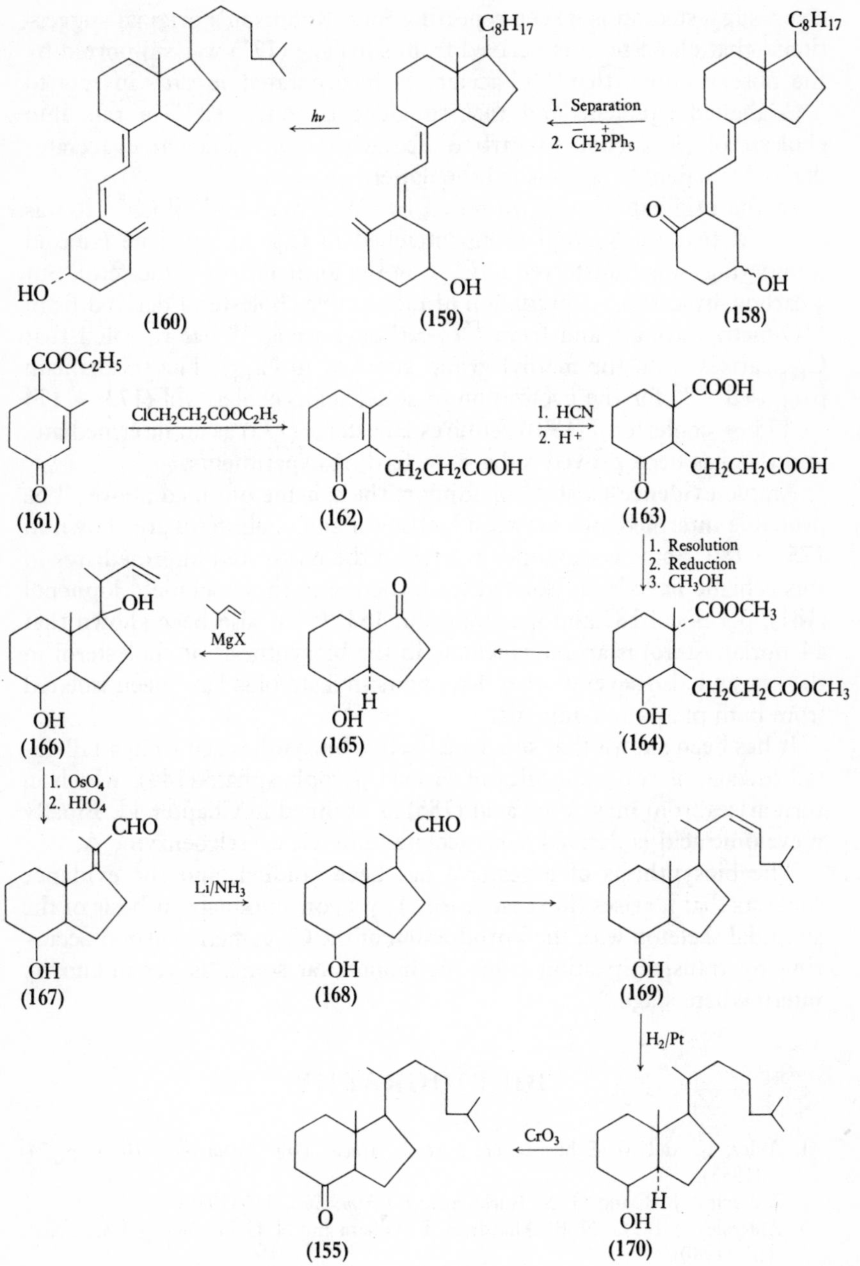

C8H17
C8H17
hν
1. Separation
2. CH2PPh3
HO
OH
OH
O
(160)
(159)
(158)
COOC2H5
ClCH2CH2COOC2H5
CH2CH2COOH
1. HCN
2. H+
COOH
CH2CH2COOH
O
O
O
(161)
(162)
(163)
1. Resolution
2. Reduction
3. CH3OH
OH
MgX
O
COOCH3
CH2CH2COOCH3
H
OH
OH
OH
(166)
(165)
(164)
1. OsO4
2. HIO4
CHO
Li/NH3
CHO
OH
OH
OH
(167)
(168)
(169)
H2/Pt
CrO3
H
O
OH
(155)
(170)

chain suggested an isoprene repeating unit. Robinson's original suggestion[25] that cholesterol is derived from squalene (171) was supported by the observation[52] that ^{14}C-acetate is incorporated *in vivo* in rats to ^{14}C-labelled squalene and that squalene is converted[53] in rats into cholesterol. A carbon-by-carbon degradation of radioactive acetate-derived squalene[17] established the pattern shown in 172.

In the original scheme proposed by Woodward and Bloch[82] it was assumed that the methyl group attached to $C_{(8)}$ of squalene (steroid numbering) was transferred to $C_{(13)}$ in the formation of cholesterol, but a carbon-by-carbon degradation of radioactive cholesterol derived from ^{14}C-methyl acetate and from ^{14}C-carboxyl acetate[16] has revealed that $C_{(18)}$ arises from the methyl group attached to $C_{(14)}$. The mechanism proposed[62,67] for the cyclization of squalene to cholesterol (173 → 174 → 175 → cholesterol (180)) requires lanosterol (175) as an intermediate, and this has been proved to be so in feeding experiments.

Ample evidence exists[28] to support the scheme outlined above. The probable intermediates between lanosterol and cholesterol are shown in 175 → 180. Some compounds related to the postulated intermediates in this scheme have been isolated from cacti, and they include[23] lophenol (181), perniocol 182 and macdougallin 183. It has also been shown that 14-norlanosterol is an intermediate in the biosynthesis of cholesterol in the rat, and also several other 4-monomethyl steroids have been isolated from both plants and animals.

It has been shown that squalene itself is biosynthesized from a tail-to-tail linkage of two molecules of farnsyl pyrophosphate (184), which in turn arises from mevalonic acid (185) as outlined in Chapter 12. Finally mevalonic acid is derived from acetate units via acetylcoenzyme A.

The biosynthesis of ergosterol has been studied, and the evidence suggests that it arises (in yeast at least) by a conventional synthesis of the steroidal skeleton with the introduction of the $C_{(28)}$ methyl group occurring by transmethylation from methionone at some, as yet unknown, intermediate stage.

BIBLIOGRAPHY

1. Alder, K. and M. Schumacher, *Fortschr. Chem. Org. Naturstoffe*, **10**, 1 (p. 74) (1953).
2. Aldersley, J. B. and G. N. Burkhardt, *J. Chem. Soc.*, 545 (1938).
3. Aldersley, J. B., G. N. Buckhardt, A. E. Gillam and N. C. Hindley, *J. Chem. Soc.*, 10 (1940).

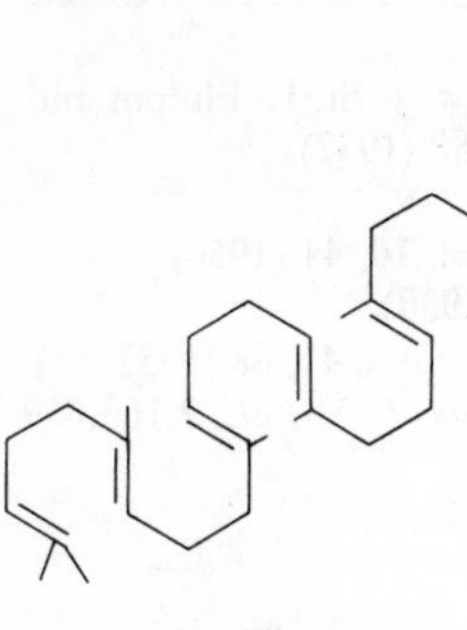

(171)

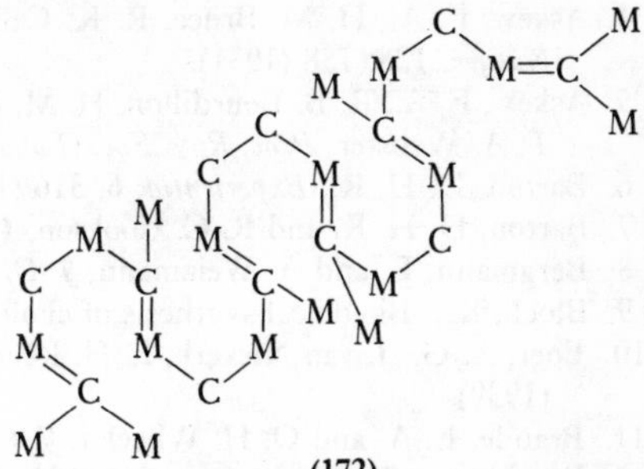

(172)

M = carbon from methyl of acetic acid
C = carbon from COOH of acetic acid

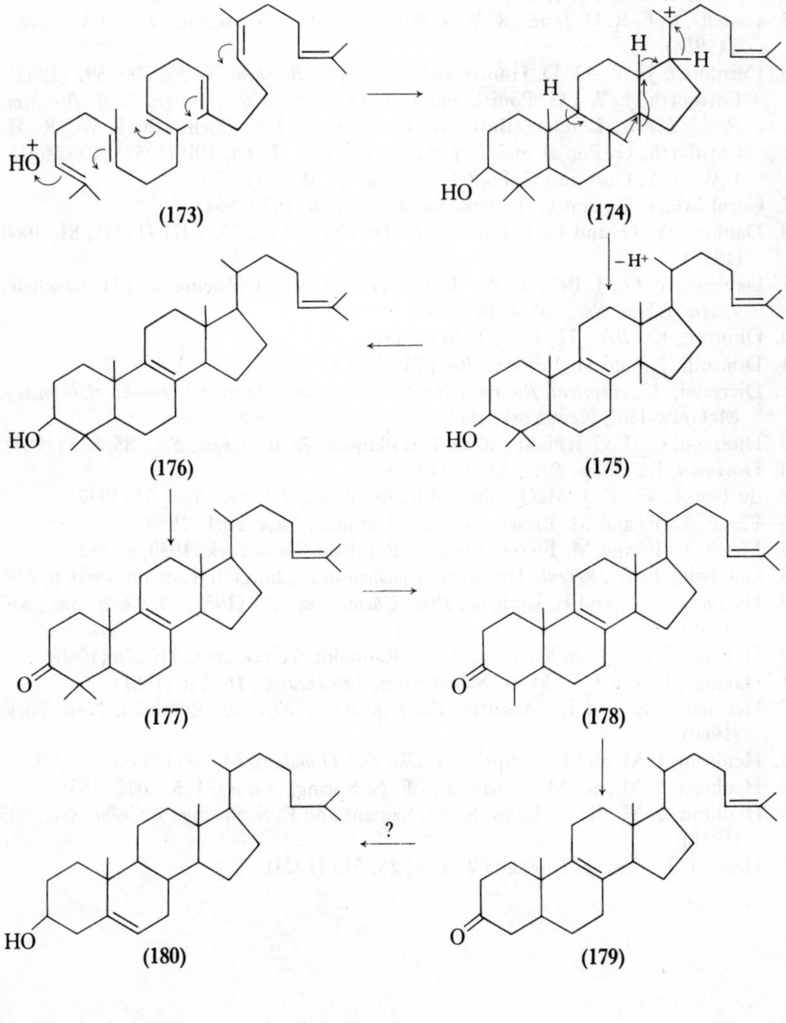

(173)

(174)

(175)

(176)

(177)

(178)

(179)

(180)

4. Askew, F. A., H. M. Bruce, R. K. Callow, J. St. L. Philpot and T. A. Webster, *Nature*, **128**, 758 (1931).
5. Askew, F. A., R. B. Bourdillon, H. M. Bruce, R. K. Callow, J. St. L. Philpot and T. A. Webster, *Proc. Roy. Soc. (London)*, Ser. B, **109**, 488 (1932).
6. Barton, D. H. R., *Experientia*, **6**, 316 (1950).
7. Barton, D. H. R. and R. C. Cookson, *Quart. Rev. (London)*, **10**, 44 (1956).
8. Bergmann, E. and A. Weizmann, *J. Org. Chem.*, **4**, 267 (1939).
9. Bloch, K., 'Biological synthesis of cholesterol', *Harvey Lectures*, **47**, 68 (1952–53).
10. Boer, A. G., J. van Niekerk, E. H. Reerink and A. van Wijk, *U.S. Pat.*, 2,163,659 (1939).
11. Braude, E. A. and O. H. Wheeler, *J. Chem. Soc.*, 320 (1955).
12. Brockmann, H., *Z. Physiol.*, **241**, 104 (1936).
13. Busse, P., *Z. Physiol. Chem.*, **214**, 211 (1933).
14. Cardwell, H. M. E., J. W. Cornforth, S. R. Duff, H. Holtermann and R. Robinson, *J. Chem. Soc.*, 361 (1953).
15. Castells, J., E. R. H. Jones, R. W. J. Williams and G. D. Meakins, *Proc. Chem. Soc.*, 7 (1958).
16. Cornforth, J. W., G. D. Hunter and G. Popjak, *Biochem. J.*, **54**, 590, 597 (1953); Cornforth, J. W., G. Popjak and I. Y. Gore, *Proc. 2nd Intern. Conf. Biochem. Probl. Lipids*, London, Butterworths, 1956, p. 216; Cornforth, J. W., R. H. Cornforth, G. Popjak and I. Y. Gore, *Biochem. J.*, **66**, 10P (1957); Cornforth, J. W., I. Y. Gore and G. Popjak, *Biochem. J.*, **65**, 94 (1957).
17. Cornforth, J. W. and G. Popjak, *Biochem. J.*, **58**, 403 (1954).
18. Dauben, W. G. and G. J. Fonken, *J. Am. Chem. Soc.*, **79**, 2971 (1957); **81**, 4060 (1959).
19. Dauben, W. G., I. Bell, T. W. Hulton, G. F. Laws, A. Rheiner and H. Urschele, *J. Am. Chem. Soc.*, **80**, 4116 (1958).
20. Dimroth, K., *Ber.*, **71**, 1333, 1346 (1938).
21. Dimroth, K. and H. Jonsson, *Ber.*, **71**, 2658 (1938).
22. Djerrassi, C., *Optical Rotatory Dispersion, Applications to Organic Chemistry*, McGraw-Hill, New York, 1960.
23. Djerrassi, C., J. C. Knight and D. I. Wilkinson, *J. Am. Chem. Soc.*, **85**, 835 (1963).
24. Dorfman, L., *Chem. Rev.*, **53**, 47 (1953).
25. du Feu, E. C., F. J. McQuillin and R. Robinson, *J. Chem. Soc.*, 53 (1937).
26. Fieser, L. F. and M. Fieser, *Steroids*, Reinhold, New York, 1959.
27. Fieser, L. F. and M. Fieser, *Steroids*, Reinhold, New York, 1959, p. 163.
28. Goodwin, T. W., *Recent Advances in Biochemistry*, Churchill, London, 1960, p. 229.
29. Harrison, I. T. and B. Lythgoe, *Proc. Chem. Soc.*, 261 (1957); *J. Chem. Soc.*, 837 (1958).
30. Havinga, E., R. J. de Koch and M. P. Rappoldt, *Tetrahedron*, **11**, 276 (1960).
31. Havinga, E. and J. L. M. A. Schlatmann, *Tetrahedron*, **16**, 146 (1961).
32. Heftmann, E. and E. Mosettig, *Biochemistry of Steroids*, Reinhold, New York, (1960).
33. Heilbron, I. M. and F. S. Spring, *Chem. Ind. (London)*, **54**, 795 (1935).
34. Heilbron, I. M., K. M. Samant and F. S. Spring, *Nature*, **135**, 1072 (1935).
35. Heilbron, I. M., R. N. Jones, K. M. Samant and F. S. Spring, *J. Chem. Soc.*, 905 (1936).
36. Hess, A. F., *Am. J. Diseases Children*, **28**, 517 (1924).

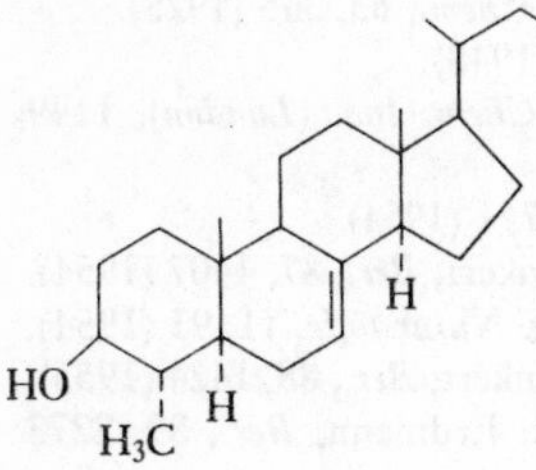

HO

H₃C H

(181)

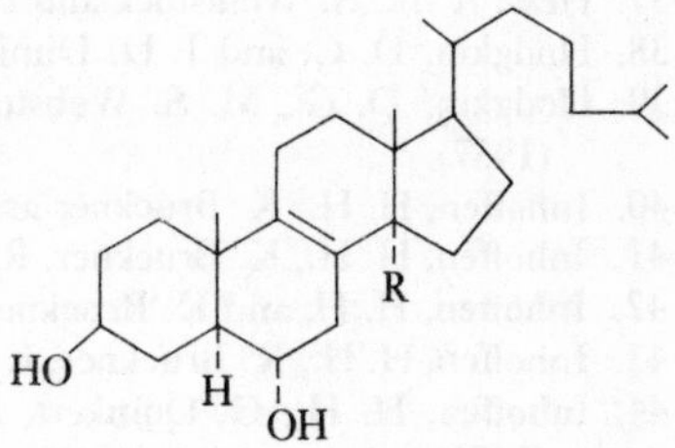

HO

H OH

(182, R = H; 183, R = CH₃)

H₃C
  C=CHCH₂CH₂C=CHCH₂CH₂C=CHCH₂—O—P—O—P—OH
H₃C

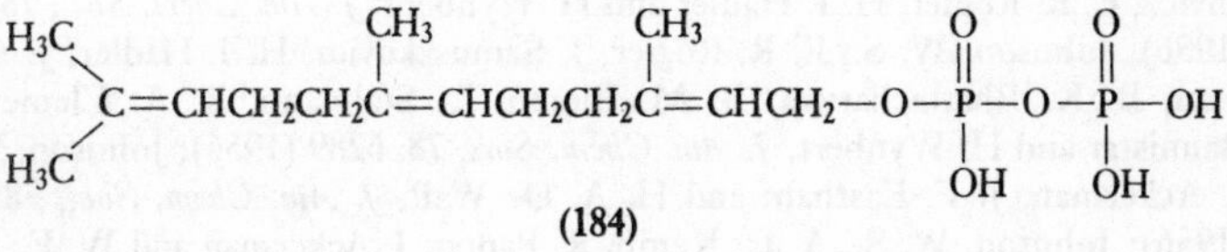

(184)

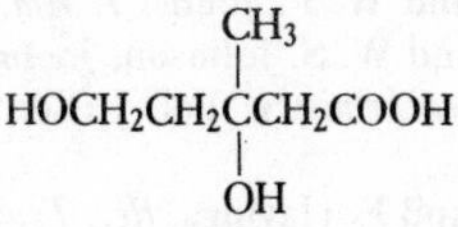

CH₃

HOCH₂CH₂CCH₂COOH
         OH

(185)

11*

37. Hess, A. F., A. Weinstock and F. D. Helman, *J. Biol. Chem.*, **63**, 305 (1925).
38. Hodgkin, D. C. and J. D. Dimitz, *Nature*, **162**, 608 (1948).
39. Hodgkin, D. C., M. S. Webster and J. D. Dimitz, *Chem. Ind. (London)*, 1149 (1957).
40. Inhoffen, H. H., K. Bruckner and R. Grundel, *Ber.*, **87**, 1 (1954).
41. Inhoffen, H. H., K. Bruckner, R. Grundel and G. Quinkert, *Ber.*, **87**, 1407 (1954).
42. Inhoffen, H. H. and K. Bruckner, *Fortschr. Chem. Org. Naturstoffe*, **11**, 93 (1954).
43. Inhoffen, H. H., K. Bruckner, K. Irmscher and G. Quinkert, *Ber.*, **88**, 1424 (1955).
44. Inhoffen, H. H., G. Quinkert, H. J. Hess and H. M. Erdmann, *Ber.*, **89**, 2273 (1956).
45. Inhoffen, H. H., *Angew. Chem.*, **70**, 576 (1958).
46. International Union of Pure and Applied Chemistry, *Nomenclature of Organic Chemistry*, Butterworths, London, 1958, p. 73.
47. Johnson, W. S., *J. Am. Chem. Soc.*, **78**, 6278 (1956); Johnson, W. S., J. Szmusz-kovicz, E. R. Rogier, H. I. Hadler and H. Wynberg, *J. Am. Chem. Soc.*, **78**, 6285 (1956); Johnson, W. S., E. R. Rogier, J. Szmuszkovicz, H. I. Hadler, J. Acker-man, B. K. Bhattacharyya, B. M. Bloom, L. Stalmann, R. A. Clement, B. Bannister and H. Wynbert, *J. Am. Chem. Soc.*, **78**, 6289 (1956); Johnson, W. S., J. Ackerman, J. F. Eastham and H. A. De Walt, *J. Am. Chem. Soc.*, **78**, 6302 (1956); Johnson, W. S., A. D. Kemp, R. Pappo, J. Ackerman and W. F. Johns, *J. Am. Chem. Soc.*, **78**, 6312 (1956); Johnson, W. S., E. R. Rogier and J. Acker-man, *J. Am. Chem. Soc.*, **78**, 6322 (1956); Johnson, W. S., B. Bannister and R. Pappo, *J. Am. Chem. Soc.*, **78**, 6331 (1956).
48. Johnson, W. S., R. Pappo and W. F. Johns, *J. Am. Chem. Soc.*, **78**, 6339 (1956); Pappo, R., B. M. Bloom and W. S. Johnson, *J. Am. Chem. Soc.*, **78**, 6347 (1956).
49. Klyne, W., *Progress in Stereochemistry*, Vol. I (Ed. by W. Klyne), Butterworths, London, 1954, p. 36.
50. Koevoet, A. L., A. Verloop and E. Havinga, *Rec. Trav. Chim.*, **74**, 788, 1125 (1955).
51. Kuhn, R. and E. F. Möller, *Angew. Chem.*, **47**, 145 (1934).
52. Langdon, R. G. and K. Bloch, *J. Biol. Chem.*, **200**, 129 (1953).
53. Langdon, R. G. and K. Bloch, *J. Biol. Chem.*, **200**, 135 (1953).
54. Lythgoe, B., S. Trippett and J. C. Watkins, *J. Chem. Soc.*, 4060 (1956).
55. Lythgoe, B., *Proc. Chem. Soc.*, 141 (1959).
56. McCollum, E. V., N. Simmonds, J. E. Becker and P. G. Shipley, *J. Biol. Chem.*, **65**, 97 (1925).
57. De Mayo, P., *Mono- and Sesquiterpenoids*, Interscience, New York, 1959.
58. Pitt, G. A. J. and R. A. Morton, *Ann. Rev. Biochem.*, **31**, 491 (1962).
59. Rosenberg, H. R., *Chemistry and Physiology of the Vitamins*, Interscience, New York, 1945, p. 368.
60. Rosenberg, H. R., *Chemistry and Physiology of the Vitamins*, Interscience, New York, 1945, p. 377.
61. Rosenheim, O. and T. A. Webster, *Lancet*, 1025 (1925).
62. Ruzicka, L., *Experientia*, **9**, 357 (1953).
63. Shoppee, C. W., *Chemistry of the Steroids*, 2nd ed., Butterworths, London, 1964.
64. Smith, L. I. and G. F. Rouault, *J. Am. Chem. Soc.*, **65**, 631 (1943).
65. Sondheimer, F. and O. H. Wheeler, *Chem. Ind. (London)*, 714 (1955).
66. Steenbock, H., *Science*, **60**, 224 (1924).
67. Tchen, T. T. and K. Bloch, *J. Biol. Chem.*, **226**, 921 (1957).

68. Turner, E. E. and M. M. Harris, *Organic Chemistry*, Longmans Green, London, 1952, p. 566.
69. Velluz, L., G. Amiard and A. Petit, *Bull. Soc. Chim. France*, 501 (1949).
70. Velluz, L. and G. Amiard, *Compt. Rend.*, **228**, 692 (1949).
71. Velluz, L. and G. Amiard, *Bull. Soc. Chim. France*, 205 (1955).
72. Verloop, A., A. L. Koevoet and E. Havinga, *Rec. Trav. Chim.*, **76**, 689 (1957).
73. Windaus, A. and E. Anhagen, *Z. Physiol. Chem.*, **196**, 108 (1931).
74. Windaus, A., O. Linsert, A. Lüttringhaus and G. Weidlich, *Ann.*, **492**, 226 (1932).
75. Windaus, A., K. Dithmar and E. Fernholz, *Ann.*, **493**, 259 (1932).
76. Windaus, A., F. von Werder and A. Lüttringhaus, *Ann.*, **499**, 188 (1932).
77. Windaus, A., F. von Werder and B. Gschaider, *Ber.*, **65**, 1106 (1932).
78. Windaus, A., H. Lettre and F. Schenck, *Ann.*, **520**, 98 (1935).
79. Windaus, A. and W. Grundmann, *Ann.*, **524**, 295 (1936).
80. Woodward, R. B., *J. Am. Chem. Soc.*, **64**, 72 (1942).
81. Woodward, R. B., F. Sondheimer, D. Taub, K. Heusler and W. M. McLamore, *J. Am. Chem. Soc.*, **74**, 4223 (1952).
82. Woodward, R. B. and K. Bloch, *J. Am. Chem. Soc.*, **75**, 2023 (1953).
83. Zucker, T. F., A. M. Pappenheimer and M. Barnett, *Proc. Soc. Exp. Biol. Med.*, **19**, 167 (1922).

CHAPTER 15

The Vitamins K

INTRODUCTION – Detection and isolation – Sources – Deficiency disease – Daily requirement – Properties – VITAMIN K_1 – Structure – Synthesis – VITAMIN K_2 – Structure – Synthesis – Compounds related to the K vitamins – Vitamin K analogues and antagonists – Biosynthesis of vitamins K – Biological function of vitamins K – BIBLIOGRAPHY

INTRODUCTION

THE TERM 'vitamins K' originally referred to the two compounds vitamins K_1 and K_2 which were isolated in the original studies in 1939, and structures were soon assigned to them. However, it was not until 1958, during an extensive synthetic study, that Isler was able to correct the structure assigned to vitamin K_2. At the same time Isler and his associates prepared several synthetic analogues of these vitamins, some of which have now been isolated from natural sources.

Detection and isolation

During a study of chick nutrition[9,39,40] it was found that good growth and health was maintained on a diet containing fish meal as the source of fat-soluble vitamins, but if the fish meal was first extracted with ether, a high mortality rate, due to haemorrhage, occurred. This effect was shown not to be due to a lack of cholesterol or of the vitamins A, C, D or E[10,11], thus indicating the existence of a new fat-soluble vitamin, and this was designated vitamin K. Alfalfa was also found to contain this factor, and during extraction and concentration, two forms were recognized, termed vitamins K_1 and K_2.

Vitamin K_1 was first obtained in a pure state from alfalfa[12,33], and in the same year vitamin K_2 was isolated[6,7,36,41,42] from putrefied fish meal. Subsequently vitamin K_2 was detected in a number of bacteria.

Sources

Vitamin K_1 occurs in all green, leafy tissues, but the best sources are alfalfa, carrot tops, cabbage and spinach. Vitamin K_2 occurs principally in bacteria.

318

Deficiency disease

The vitamins K are necessary for the maintenance of normal blood coagulation. The blood-clotting enzyme, thrombin, is derived from its precursor, prothrombin, and the latter exists in the blood in an inactive form. It becomes activated for thrombin formation by substances such as 'factor v' and 'factor vii'; vitamin K is concerned with the formation of factor vii and of prothrombin. Haemophilia is not a haemorrhage caused by lack of prothrombin or factor vii, and is not cured by vitamin K.

Daily requirement

The vitamins K are required by man, and by all animals so far studied; they do not seem to be vitamins for most microorganisms.

The average daily requirement for man is not known with certainty, but it has been estimated to be 1 mg.

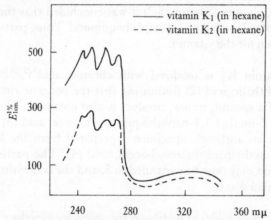

Figure 15.1. The ultraviolet spectra of vitamins K_1 and K_2. [Reproduced, by permission, from R. A. Morton, *Application of Absorption Spectra to the Study of Vitamins, Hormones and Co-Enzymes*, 2nd ed., Hilger, London, 1942, p. 121.]

Properties

Vitamin K_1 is a yellow oil and vitamin K_2 is a yellow crystalline solid. Both are stable to heat, but are sensitive to alkali and to light. They exhibit characteristic and similar absorption spectra (Figure 15.1).

Several reviews of the chemistry and biochemistry of the K vitamins have appeared recently[31,54,56].

VITAMIN K$_1$

Structure

Elemental analysis and a molecular-weight determination established a molecular formula of $C_{31}H_{46}O_2$. Catalytic hydrogenation of the vitamin resulted in the uptake of four moles of hydrogen to yield a colourless octahydro derivative, which on exposure to air was oxidized to a yellow hexahydrovitamin K$_1$. The latter could be hydrogenated, with the absorption of one mole of hydrogen, to yield the same octahydro compound. The yellow colour of the hexahydro compound suggested the presence of a 1,4-quinone structure rather than a 1,2-quinone; the latter are usually red. The presence of a 1,4-naphthoquinone was indicated by the redox potential of the vitamin[32] and by a comparison[15] of the ultraviolet spectrum of the original vitamin with that of 1,4-naphthoquinone. By comparing the spectrum of vitamin K$_1$ with the spectra of substituted 1,4-naphthoquinones (Figure 15.2) it was concluded that the vitamin is a derivative of a 2,3-dialkyl-1,4-naphthoquinone. Thus, part-structure 1 may be written for the vitamin.

When vitamin K$_1$ is oxidized with chromic acid[5,37,41] the major product is phthalic acid (2) (indicating that the benzene ring is unsubstituted) and a second, minor, product is also obtained. The latter was identified as 2-methyl-1,4-naphthoquinone-3-acetic acid (3) by a comparison with an authentic specimen[38] prepared from the known 1,4-diacetoxy-2-methylnaphthalene-3-acetic acid (4). The part-structure 1 for the vitamin may now be expanded to 5, and the octahydro derivative can be formulated as 6.

Since only three moles of hydrogen are necessary to reduce vitamin K$_1$ (5) to the part-structure shown in 6, there must be one double bond in the side-chain attached to $C_{(3)}$[4]. Vitamin K$_1$ can be reductively acetylated[4] to the diacetyldihydro derivative (7) and this, upon oxidation with chromic acid[38], yields 1,4-diacetoxy-2-methylnaphthalene-3-acetic acid (4) and a ketone, $C_{18}H_{36}O$, which was identified as 6,10,14-trimethyl-2-pentadecanone (8) by comparison with an authentic sample previously prepared[20] from phytol (9).

From these results the structure of vitamin K$_1$ is established as 2-methyl-3-phytyl-1,4-naphthoquinone (phylloquinone, 10). The hexa- and octahydro derivatives are thus 11 and 12 respectively.

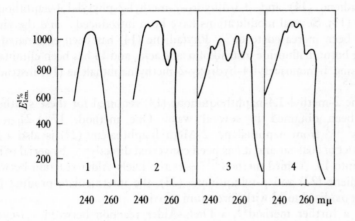

Figure 15.2. The ultraviolet spectra of model compounds.
[Reproduced, by permission, from R. A. Morton, *Application of
Absorption Spectra to the Study of Vitamins, Hormones and Co-
Enzymes*, 2nd ed., Hilger, London, 1942, p. 124.]

Synthesis

Structure 10 for vitamin K_1 has been confirmed by several syntheses. In one, 2-methyl-1,4-naphthoquinone (13) was condensed with phytyl bromide[1] and in a slight modification[5,37] the monosodium salt of 1,4-dihydroxy-2-methylnaphthalene was reacted with phytyl bromide. In Fieser's method, 13 was reacted with phytol (9) itself in the presence of oxalic acid. The latter method was used commercially[16,17] when an overall yield of 25% was obtained. The main by-products were[55] phytadiene (14) and 2,3-dihydro-2-methyl-2-phytyl-1,4-naphthoquinone (15). Several modifications have been introduced[25] and the yields have been increased to 66%. Phytadiene (14) has been eliminated by using boron trifluoride instead of oxalic acid, and 15 has been eliminated by using 1-monoacetyl-4-hydroxy-2-methylnaphthalene (16) instead of 13[26,28].

The 2-methyl-1,4-naphthoquinone (13) required for these syntheses has been obtained in several ways. One method, $17 \rightarrow 21 \rightarrow 13$, starts[52,53] from naphthalene. 2-Methylnaphthalene (21) is also a by-product of coal-tar and it has been converted directly[2,57] by aerial oxidation into 13. A third method[8,19] uses the Diels–Alder reaction between butadiene (22) and p-toluquinone (23), the intermediate product (24) being oxidized to 13 with chromium trioxide.

In a further method[24], a Diels–Alder reaction between 1,3-cyclohexadiene (25) and p-toluquinone (23) yielded the adduct 26, which was isomerized to 27, oxidized to 28 and pyrolysed to 13.

Racemic vitamin K_1 has been synthesized by the condensation of isophytol (29) with menadiol-1-benzoate (30) in the presence of boron trifluoride etherate[35]. Isophytol has been synthesized by a number of methods[31]. In one, citral (31, obtained from lemon grass) was used as a starting material. This was condensed with acetone to yield ψ-ionone (32) which was hydrogenated to 33. The latter was then reacted with sodium acetylide in liquid ammonia, and the triple bond was partially hydrogenated to yield 34. Treatment with phosphorus tribromide followed by an ethyl acetoacetate synthesis converted 34 into tetrahydrofarnesylacetone (35), which was hydrogenated to 36, and this, upon condensation with sodium acetylide followed by partial reduction, gave isophytol (29).

A total synthesis of isophytol (29) from acetone has also been described[31] in which successive isoprene units were built on by the use of sodium acetylide and an ethyl acetoacetate synthesis as above $37 \rightarrow 47 \rightarrow 29$.

(7)

(8)

(9)

(10)

(11)

(12)

(13)

(14)

(15)

(16)

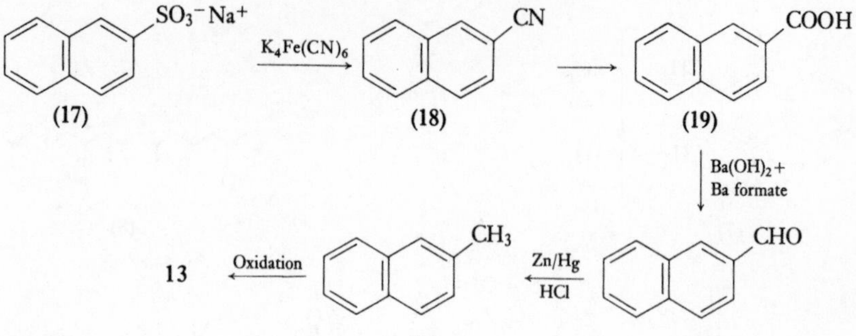

(17) (18) (19) (20) (21)

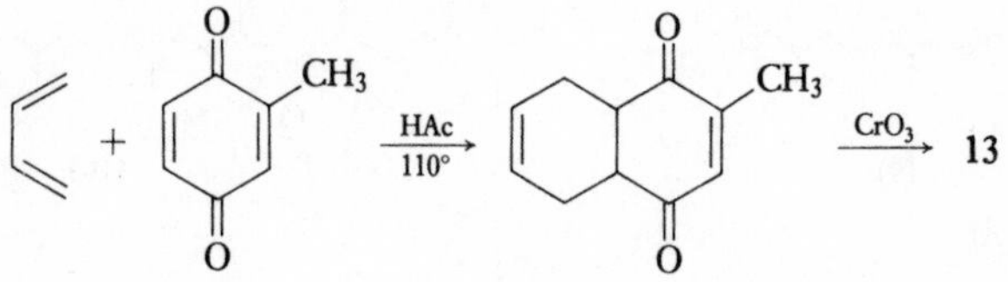

(22) (23) (24)

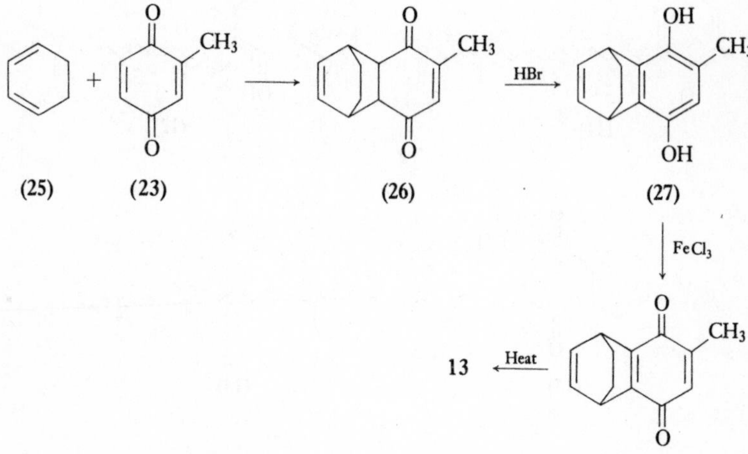

(25) (23) (26) (27)

(28)

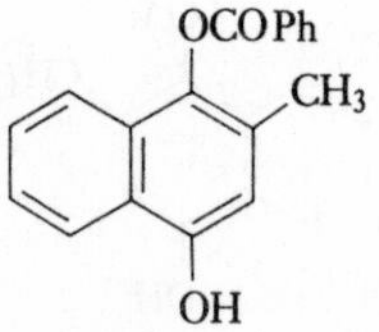

(30)

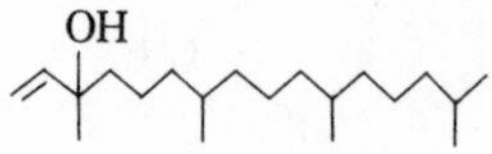

(29)

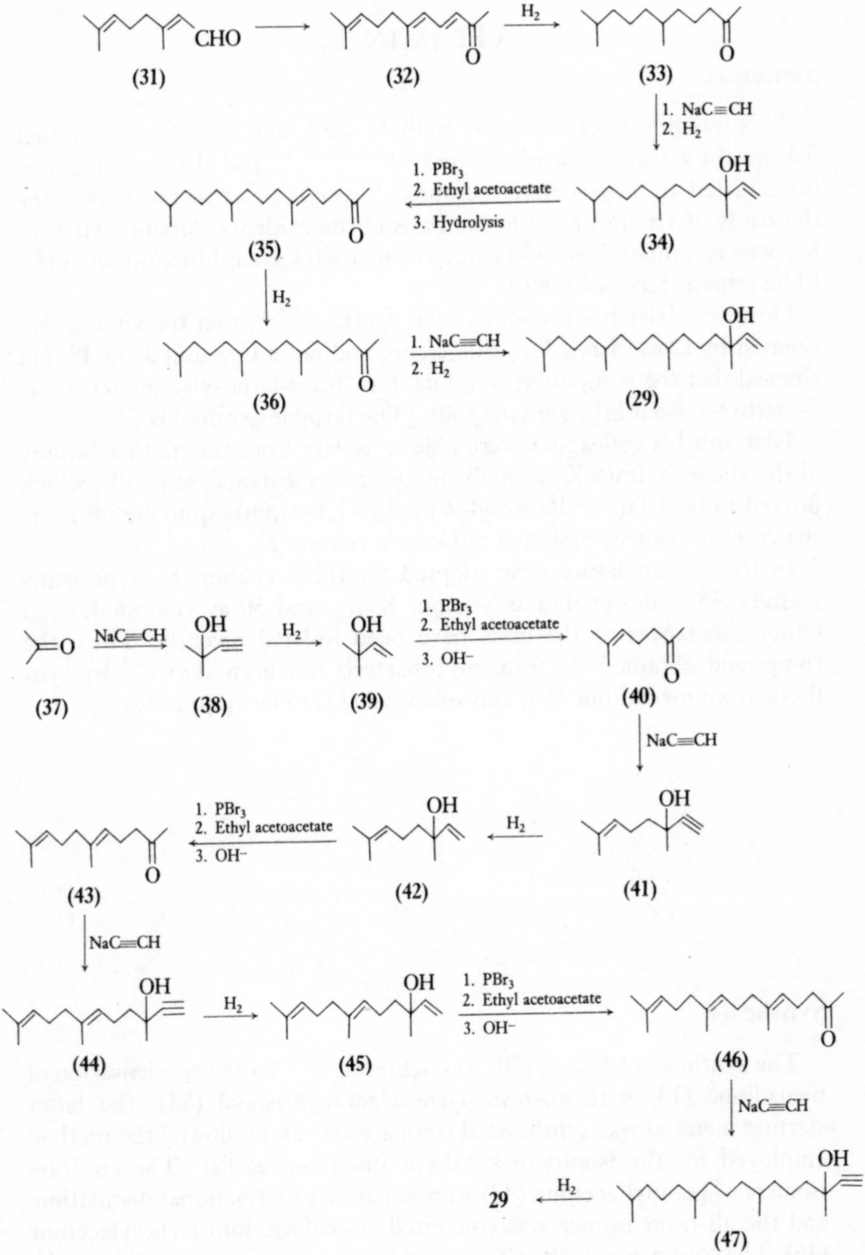

(31) → (32) → H₂ → (33)

1. NaC≡CH
2. H₂

(35) ← 1. PBr₃ / 2. Ethyl acetoacetate / 3. Hydrolysis ← (34)

↓ H₂

(36) → 1. NaC≡CH / 2. H₂ → (29)

(37) → NaC≡CH → (38) → H₂ → (39) → 1. PBr₃ / 2. Ethyl acetoacetate / 3. OH⁻ → (40)

↓ NaC≡CH

(43) ← 1. PBr₃ / 2. Ethyl acetoacetate / 3. OH⁻ ← (42) ← H₂ ← (41)

↓ NaC≡CH

(44) → H₂ → (45) → 1. PBr₃ / 2. Ethyl acetoacetate / 3. OH⁻ → (46)

↓ NaC≡CH

29 ← H₂ ← (47)

VITAMIN K₂

Structure

This was first isolated as a crystalline solid, m.p. 54°, from putrefied fish meal by Doisy and his coworkers[6,7,36,41,42] and the structure was investigated by degradative methods[7,38] very similar to those used for the study of vitamin K_1. On the basis of the evidence obtained vitamin K_2 was formulated as 3-difarnesyl-2-methyl-1,4-naphthoquinone (48). [The terpene farnesol is 49.]

However, Isler has shown by total synthesis[29,30] that the vitamin K_2 isolated by Doisy has a C_{35} side-chain, and not a C_{30} unit as in 48. He showed that the compound is in fact 3-all-*trans*-farnesylgeranylgeranyl-2-methyl-1,4-naphthoquinone (50). [The terpene geraniol is 51.]

Isler and his colleagues were able to isolate from the mother liquors of the above vitamin K_2 a small amount of a substance, m.p. 50°, which proved to be 3-farnesylfarnesyl-2-methyl-1,4-naphthoquinone (48), the structure previously assigned to Doisy's vitamin K_2.

In the nomenclature now adopted for these vitamin K_2-type compounds, 48 is designated as vitamin $K_{2(30)}$ and 50 as vitamin $K_{2(35)}$. Other substances of the class have been isolated recently. Thus, the compound obtained[2,47] from mycobacteria has been shown[48] by synthesis from menadione (13) and solanesol (52) to be vitamin $K_{2(45)}$.

Synthesis

The synthesis of $K_{2(35)}$ (50) was achieved[29,30] by the condensation of menadione (13) with all-*trans*-farnesylgeranyllinalool (53); the latter starting material was synthesized from acetone and followed the method employed for the isophytol synthesis described earlier. The *cis–trans* isomers of geranyl acetone (43) were separated by fractional distillation, and the all-*trans* isomer was converted, as before, into farnesylacetone (46). The separation of the all-*trans* and mono-*cis* forms was achieved by

(48)

(49)

(50)

(51)

(13)

(52)

(53)

chromatography of the derived semicarbazones over alumina. Farnesyl acetone (46) was then converted into 53 as shown in $46 \rightarrow 54 \rightarrow 60 \rightarrow 53$. The C_{23}, C_{28} and C_{33} ketones (56, 58 and 60 respectively) were separated and the all-*trans* form of each was employed in subsequent stages of the synthesis.

The intermediate C_5, C_{10}, C_{15}, C_{20}, C_{25} and C_{30} alcohols in the above synthesis were each condensed with menadione (13) to yield lower isoprenologues of the K_2 vitamins. In addition to these all-*trans* compounds, four mono-*cis* isomers (61, 62, 63 and 64) were also prepared[29,30].

Isler has extended this synthetic work[48] to the preparation of vitamins $K_{2(45)}$ and $K_{2(50)}$.

Compounds related to the K vitamins

The structural analogy between the vitamins K and the vitamins E, especially the tocoquinones (e.g. 65), was pointed out some time ago. More recently, a series of quinones has been isolated from natural

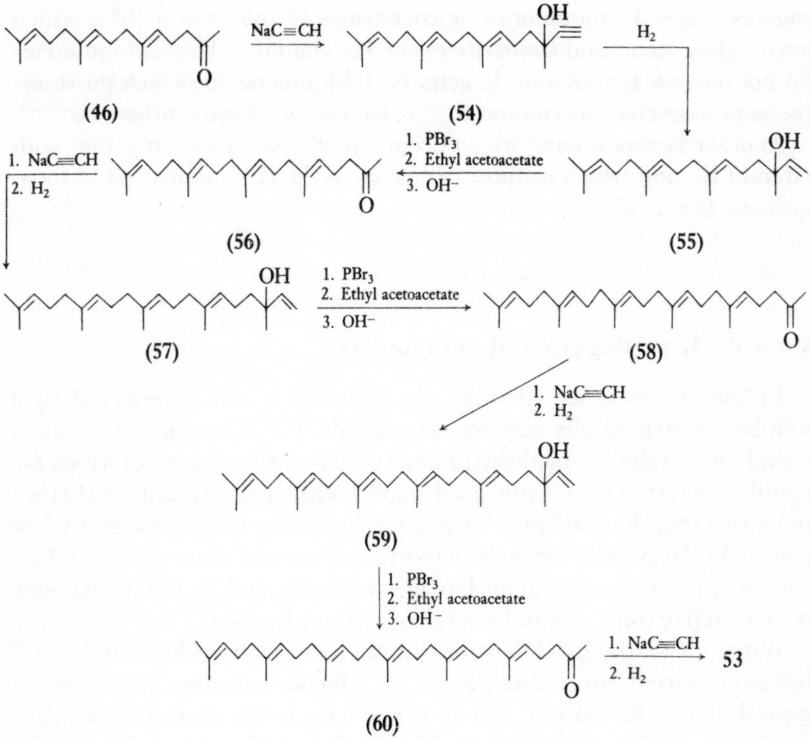
NaC≡CH
OH
O
(46)
(54)
H2
OH
1. PBr3
2. Ethyl acetoacetate
3. OH−
1. NaC≡CH
2. H2
O
(56)
(55)
OH
1. PBr3
2. Ethyl acetoacetate
3. OH−
(57)
O
(58)
1. NaC≡CH
2. H2
OH
(59)
1. PBr3
2. Ethyl acetoacetate
3. OH−
1. NaC≡CH
2. H2
53
O
(60)

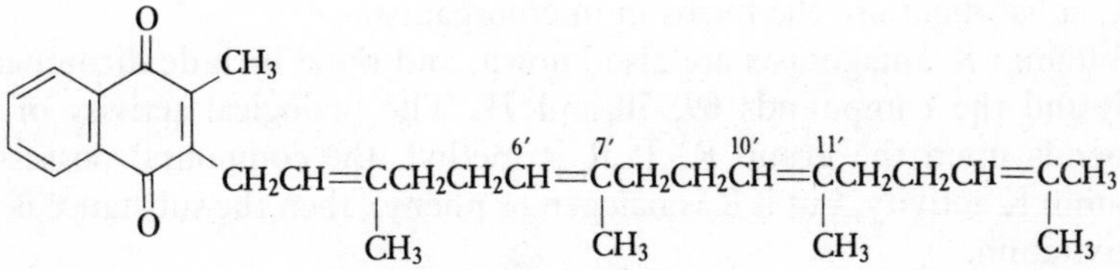
O
CH3
6′
7′
10′
11′
CH2CH=CCH2CH2CH=CCH2CH2CH=CCH2CH2CH=CCH3
O
CH3
CH3
CH3
CH3

(61, 6′,7′-mono-*cis*; 62, 10′,11′-mono-*cis*)

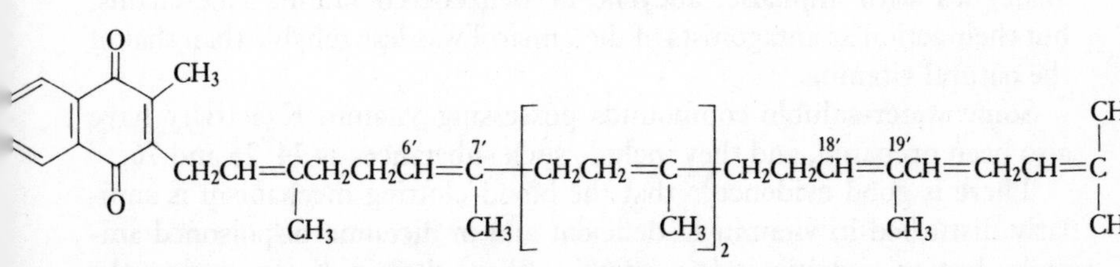
O
CH3
CH3
6′
7′
18′
19′
CH2CH=CCH2CH2CH=C—CH2CH2=C—CH2CH2CH=CCH=CH2CH=C
O
CH3
CH3
CH3
CH3
CH3
2

(63, 6′,7′-mono-*cis*; 64, 18′,19′-mono-*cis*)

sources, termed ubiquinones or coenzymes Q $(66, n = 5-9)^{46}$, which have a close structural similarity to the K_2 vitamins. These ubiquinones do not possess any vitamin K activity. Ubiquinone 30, which possesses the same side-chain as vitamin $K_{2(30)}$, has recently been synthesized[22,23].

Another benzoquinone which occurs in all green leaves together with vitamin K_1 and which is quite analogous to the K vitamins and to toco-quinone (65) is 67[14,34].

Vitamin K analogues and antagonists

In contrast to other vitamins, the vitamins K can be replaced by a number of structurally simpler compounds[18,50]. Vitamin K activity is found only in the 1,4-naphthoquinone system, or in structures which are readily converted *in vivo* into a 1,4-naphthoquinone. Menadione (13) is a potent vitamin K analogue; if the 2-methyl group is replaced by hydrogen or by larger alkyl groups activity is decreased or reversed. A $C_{(3)}$ substituent is not essential for biological activity, and, in fact, menadione is more active (on a weight basis) than vitamin K_1 itself.

When ^{14}C-2-methyl-1,4-naphthoquinone was fed to chicks and rats[44] it was converted into vitamin $K_{2(20)}$[49]. Martius considers this to be the typical *animal* K vitamin, just as vitamin K_1 is the characteristic plant form, and the K_2 vitamins with 30, 35, 40 and 45 carbon atoms in the $C_{(3)}$ substituent are the forms in microorganisms.

Vitamin K antagonists are also known, and these include dicoumarol (68) and the compounds 69, 70 and 71. The biological activity of 72 depends upon the group R. If R is methyl, the compound possesses vitamin K activity, but if R is halogen or phenyl, then the substance is an antivitamin.

Analogues of vitamin K_1 (73) have been synthesized[19,27] as well as analogues with aliphatic, alicyclic or benzene-containing side-chains, but their action as antagonists of dicoumarol was less reliable than that of the natural vitamins.

Some water-soluble compounds possessing vitamin K activity have also been prepared, and they include such substances as 74, 75 and 76.

There is good evidence[31] that the blood-clotting mechanism is similarly disturbed in vitamin K-deficient and in dicoumarol-poisoned animals, but menadione is less effective than vitamin K_1 in curing the dicoumarol-poisoned animals. This is readily explained by the fact that

(65)

(66)

(67)

(68)

(69)

(70)

(71)

(72)

$(73, x = 0-5)$

(74)

(75)

(76)

menadione is converted *in vivo* into vitamin $K_{2(20)}$, and there is sufficient $K_{2(20)}$ in the animal to provide the amount required in vitamin K-deficient animals, but there is not enough to provide the high amount of $K_{2(20)}$ required to counteract dicoumarol poisoning.

Biosynthesis of vitamins K

Nothing is known about the origin of the ring system in either vitamin K_1 or K_2. Martius's observation[44] that menadione is biosynthesized into vitamin $K_{2(20)}$ suggests that the natural vitamins arise by the substitution of the appropriate side-chain on to preformed menadione. In the ubiquinones it has been shown[59] that $2\text{-}^{14}C$-mevalonate, when fed to rats, is incorporated into the side-chain as indicated in 77.

Biological function of the vitamins K

There is evidence that vitamin K_1 is involved in oxidative phosphorylation reactions *in vivo* and the subject has been reviewed[13,31,43,45]. It has been found that oxidation and phosphorylation are inactivated by ultraviolet light, but are restored by the addition of vitamin K_1. Menadione is inactive. It has been suggested[51] that vitamin K_1 is enzymically cyclized to chromanol derivatives of the type 78. This chromanol has been synthesized[58] and found[3] to reduce cytochrome c in cell-free extracts of *Mycobacterium phlei*.

BIBLIOGRAPHY

1. Almquist, H. J. and A. A. Klose, *J. Biol. Chem.*, **132**, 469 (1940).
2. Arnold, R. T. and R. Larson, *J. Org. Chem.*, **5**, 250 (1940).
3. Asano, A., A. F. Brodie, A. F. Wagner, P. E. Wittreich and K. Folkers, *J. Biol. Chem.*, **237**, PC 2411 (1962).
4. Binkley, S. B., D. W. MacCorquodale, L. C. Cheney, S. A. Thayer, R. W. McKee and E. A. Doisy, *J. Am. Chem. Soc.*, **61**, 1612 (1939).
5. Binkley, S. B., L. C. Cheney, W. F. Holcomb, R. W. McKee, S. A. Thayer, D. W. MacCorquodale and E. A. Doisy, *J. Am. Chem. Soc.*, **61**, 2558 (1939).
6. Binkley, S. B., D. W. MacCorquodale, S. A. Thayer and E. A. Doisy, *J. Biol. Chem.*, **130**, 219 (1939).
7. Binkley, S. B., R. W. McKee, S. A. Thayer and E. A. Doisy, *J. Biol. Chem.*, **133**, 721 (1940).
8. Chuang, C. K. and C.-T. Han, *Ber.*, **68**, 876 (1935).
9. Dam, H., *Biochem. Z.*, **220**, 158 (1930); **215**, 475 (1929).
10. Dam, H., *Nature*, **133**, 909 (1934).
11. Dam, H. and F. Schönhegder, *Biochem. J.*, **28**, 1355 (1934).

(77)

(78)

12. Dam, H., A. Geiger, J. Glavind, P. Karrer, W. Karrer, E. E. Rothschild and H. Salomon, *Helv. Chim. Acta*, 22, 310 (1939).
13. Dam, H. and E. Søndergaard, *Wiss. Veroffentl. Deut. Ges. Ernährung*, 4, 67 (1959).
14. Erickson, R. E., C. H. Chunk, N. R. Trenner, B. H. Anson and K. Folkers, *J. Am. Chem. Soc.*, 81, 4999 (1959).
15. Ewing, T. D., J. M. Vanderbelt and O. Kamm, *J. Biol. Chem.*, 131, 345 (1939).
16. Fieser, L. F., *J. Am. Chem. Soc.*, 61, 2559 (1939).
17. Fieser, L. F., *J. Am. Chem. Soc.*, 61, 3467 (1939).
18. Fieser, L. F., M. Tishler and W. L. Sampson, *J. Biol. Chem.*, 137, 659 (1941).
19. Fieser, L. F. and F. C. Chang, *J. Am. Chem. Soc.*, 64, 2043 (1942).
20. Fisher, G. F. and K. Lowenberg, *Ann.*, 464, 69 (1928).
21. Francis, J., J. Madinaveitia, H. M. MacTurc and G. A. Snow, *Nature*, 163, 365 (1949).
22. Gloor, U. and D. Wiss, *Experientia*, 14, 410 (1958).
23. Gloor, U., O. Isler, R. A. Morton, R. Ruegg and O. Wiss, *Helv. Chim. Acta*, 41, 2357 (1958).
24. Grdinic, M. R. and U. K. Jugovic, *Archiv. Khem.*, 23, 73 (1951); *Chem. Abstr.*, 46, 11165g (1952).
25. Hirschmann, R., R. Miller and N. L. Wendler, *J. Am. Chem. Soc.*, 76, 4592 (1954).
26. Isler, O. and K. Doebel, *Angew. Chem.*, 65, 264 (1953).
27. Isler, O., R. Ruegg, A. Studer and R. Jurgens, *Z. Physiol. Chem.*, 295, 290 (1953).
28. Isler, O. and K. Doebel, *Helv. Chim. Acta*, 37, 225 (1954).
29. Isler, O., R. Ruegg, L. H. Chopard-dit-Jean, A. Winterstein and O. Wiss, *Chimia (Aarau)*, 12, 69 (1958).
30. Isler, O., R. Ruegg, L. H. Chopard-dit-Jean, A. Winterstein and O. Wiss, *Helv. Chim. Acta*, 41, 786 (1958).
31. Isler, O. and O. Wiss, *Vitamins Hormones*, 17, 53 (1959).
32. Karrer, P. and A. Geiger, *Helv. Chim. Acta*, 22, 945 (1939).
33. Karrer, P., A. Geiger, R. Legler, A. Ruegger and H. Salomon, *Helv. Chim. Acta*, 22, 1464 (1939).
34. Kofler, M., A. Langemann, R. Ruegg, U. Gloor, U. Schwieter, J. Wursch, O. Wiss and O. Isler, *Helv. Chim. Acta*, 42, 2252 (1959).
35. Lindler, H., *U.S. Pat.*, 2,839,570 (1958).
36. MacCorquodale, D. W., S. B. Binkley, R. W. McKee, S. A. Thayer and E. A. Doisy, *Proc. Soc. Exptl. Biol. Med.*, 40, 482 (1939).
37. MacCorquodale, D. W., S. B. Binkley, S. A. Thayer and E. A. Doisy, *J. Am. Chem. Soc.*, 61, 1928 (1939).
38. MacCorquodale, D. W., L. C. Cheney, S. B. Binkley, W. F. Holcomb, R. W. McKee, S. A. Thayer and E. A. Doisy, *J. Biol. Chem.*, 131, 357 (1939).
39. McFarlane, W. D., W. R. Graham and F. Richardson, *Biochem. J.*, 25, 358 (1931).
40. McFarlane, W. D., W. R. Graham and G. E. Hall, *J. Nutr.*, 4, 331 (1931).
41. McKee, R. W., S. B. Binkley, D. W. MacCorquodale, S. A. Thayer and E. A. Doisy, *J. Am. Chem. Soc.*, 61, 1295 (1939).
42. McKee, R. W., S. B. Binkley, S. A. Thayer, D. W. MacCorquodale and E. A. Doisy, *J. Biol. Chem.*, 131, 327 (1939).
43. Martius, K. C., *Ciba Found. Symp., Regulation Cell Metab., 1958*; *Deut. Med. Wochschr.*, 83, 1701 (1958).
44. Martius, K. C. and H. O. Esser, *Biochem. Z.*, 331, 1 (1958).

45. Martius, K. C., *Angew. Chem.*, **73**, 597 (1961).
46. Morton, R. A., *Vitamins Hormones*, **19**, 1 (1961).
47. Noll, H., *J. Biol. Chem.*, **232**, 919 (1958); Noll, H. and E. Jackin, *J. Biol. Chem.*, **232**, 903 (1958).
48. Noll, H., R. Ruegg, U. Gloor, R. Ryser and O. Isler, *Helv. Chim. Acta*, **43**, 433 (1960).
49. Pitt, G. A. J. and R. A. Morton, *Ann. Rev. Biochem.*, **31**, 491 (1962).
50. Rosenberg, H. R., *Chemistry and Physiology of the Vitamins*, Interscience, New York, 1945, p. 494.
51. Russell, P. J. and A. F. Brodie, *Biochem. Biophys. Acta*, **50**, 76 (1961); Brodie, A. F., *Federation Proc.*, **20**, 995 (1961).
52. Sah, P. P. T., *Rec. Trav. Chim.*, **59**, 461 (1940).
53. Sah, P. P. T., W. Brull and H. Halzen, *Ber.*, **73**, 762 (1940).
54. Sebrell, W. H. and R. S. Harris, *The Vitamins: Chemistry, Physiology and Pathology*, Academic Press, New York, 1954, Vol. II, p. 387.
55. Tishler, M., L. F. Fieser and N. L. Wendler, *J. Am. Chem. Soc.*, **62**, 1982 (1940).
56. Thomson, R. H., *Naturally Occurring Quinones*, Butterworths, London, 1957, p. 141.
57. Vesely, V. and J. Kapp, *Rec. Trav. Chim.*, **44**, 360 (1925).
58. Wagner, A. F., P. E. Wittreich, B. Arison, N. R. Trenner and K. Folkers, *J. Am. Chem. Soc.*, **85**, 1178 (1963).
59. Wiss, O. and U. Gloor, *Vitamins Hormones*, **18**, 485 (1960).

CHAPTER 16

Essential Fatty Acids
(Vitamins F)

INTRODUCTION – LINOLEIC ACID – Structure and synthesis – LINO-
LENIC ACID – Structure and synthesis – ARACHIDONIC ACID – Structure
and synthesis – BIOLOGICAL FUNCTION OF THE ESSENTIAL FATTY
ACIDS – BIBLIOGRAPHY

INTRODUCTION

FATTY ACIDS occur naturally as the acyl fragments of animal and vegetable fats and of lipids. Animal fats, which are usually solids, are esters of
glycerol or of cholesterol (1) in which the fatty acid is usually saturated
and possesses an even number of carbon atoms in an unbranched chain.
Vegetable fats, which are usually oils, are esters of glycerol or β-sito-
sterol (2) in which the fatty acid usually contains an unsaturated unbranched chain of an even number of carbon atoms. Complex lipids are
fatty acid esters of glycerol which also contain phosphate groups (phospholipids) or phosphate and amino groups (phosphoaminolipids). The
α-lecithins (3) and β-lecithins (4) are examples of lipids which differ one
from another in the nature of the fatty acid components (R^1 and R^2).

The inclusions of fatty acids in the class of vitamins has been a very
controversial one, but evidence has been obtained of deficiency diseases.
For example, the rat develops skin lesions and does not grow well when
its diet is deficient in some fatty acids[4]. The fats are valuable in the diet
as sources of energy and it has been shown[6,21] that fats influence the
absorption of the fat-soluble vitamins A, D, E and K.

The term 'essential fatty acids' at present includes linoleic acid (5)
and linolenic acid (6) of vegetable origin and arachidonic acid (7) of
animal origin although it has been suggested[28] that 6,9,12–octadecatrie-
noic acid 8, 10,13–nonodecadienoic acid (9) and 11,14–eicosadienoic acid
(10) should also be considered as 'essential'.

336

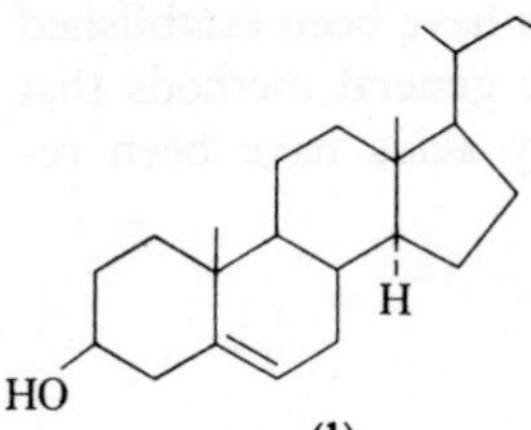

$$CH_2OCOR^1$$
$$|$$
$$CHOCOR^2$$
$$|\quad O$$
$$|\quad \|$$
$$CH_2O-P-O-CH_2CH_2\overset{+}{N}(CH_3)_3$$
$$|$$
$$O^-$$

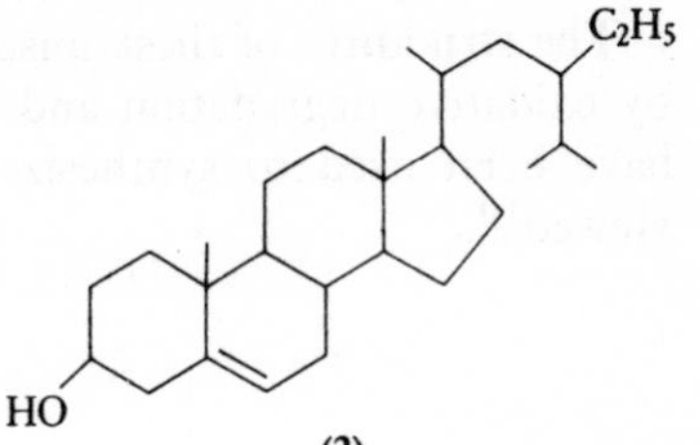

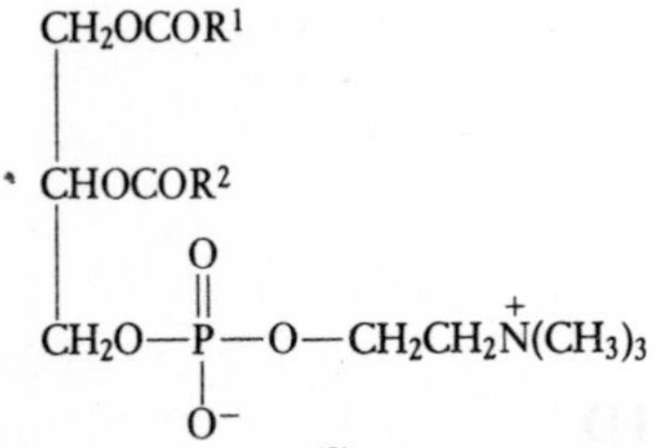

(3)

$$CH_2OCOR^1$$
$$|\quad\quad O$$
$$|\quad\quad \|$$
$$CHO-P-O-CH_2CH_2\overset{+}{N}(CH_3)_3$$
$$|\quad\quad |$$
$$CH_2OCOR^2\quad O^-$$

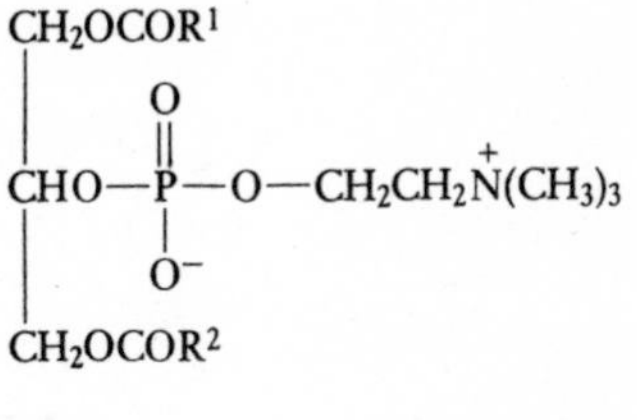

(4)

$$CH_3(CH_2)_4CH{=}CHCH_2CH{=}CH(CH_2)_7COOH$$

(5)

$$CH_3CH_2CH{=}CHCH_2CH{=}CHCH_2CH{=}CH(CH_2)_7COOH$$

(6)

$$CH_3(CH_2)_4CH{=}CHCH_2CH{=}CHCH_2CH{=}CHCH_2CH{=}CH(CH_2)_3COOH$$

(7)

$$CH_3(CH_2)_4CH{=}CHCH_2CH{=}CHCH_2CH{=}CH(CH_2)_4COOH$$

(8)

$$CH_3(CH_2)_4CH{=}CHCH_2CH{=}CH(CH_2)_8COOH$$

(9)

$$CH_3(CH_2)_4CH{=}CHCH_2CH{=}CH(CH_2)_9COOH$$

(10)

The structures of these unsaturated fatty acids have been established by oxidative degradation and by synthesis. The general methods that have been used to synthesize unsaturated fatty acids have been reviewed[10].

LINOLEIC ACID

Structure and synthesis

When linoleic acid is oxidized with cold potassium permanganate[11], hexanoic acid (11), oxalic acid (12) and azelaic acid (13) can be isolated. These three fragments involve the overall loss of one carbon atom from the original compound and suggests that the oxalic acid is a further oxidation product of malonic acid formed initially. Ozonolysis of ethyl linoleate[1] gives hexanoic acid (11), acetaldehyde, carbon dioxide and the monoethyl ester of azelaic acid (13), thus accounting for all the carbon atoms of linoleic acid, whose structure must therefore be 5. Structure 5, possessing two double bonds, represents four geometrical isomeric forms.

The configuration of the 9,10-double bond has been shown to be *cis*[15] by monobromination to 14, followed by hydroxylation with potassium permanganate and debromination and hydrogenation to *trans*-9,10-dihydroxystearic acid (15), which was also obtained by potassium permangante hydroxylation of oleic acid 16. When the dibromide (14) is hydroxylated by peracetic acid[15] then debrominated and hydrogenated, the product is *cis*-9,10-dihydroxystearic acid (17), and this is also the product of peracetic acid hydroxylation of oleic acid (18).

By a study of the Raman and infrared spectra of linoleic acid, it was further concluded[14] that the 11,12-double bond is also *cis*, and so linoleic acid can be represented as in 19. This conclusion has been confirmed by the synthesis of 19[29] summarized in 20 → 27 → 19. The intermediate 25

$$CH_3(CH_2)_4COOH \; + \; HOOCCOOH \; + \; HOOC(CH_2)_7COOH$$
$$(11) \qquad\qquad (12) \qquad\qquad (13)$$

$$CH_3(CH_2)_4\overset{13}{C}H=\overset{12}{C}HCH_2\overset{10}{C}H=\overset{9}{C}H(CH_2)_7HOOH$$
$$(5)$$

$$CH_3(CH_2)_4\overset{Br}{\underset{|}{C}}H-\overset{Br}{\underset{|}{C}}HCH_2CH=CH(CH_2)_7COOH$$
$$(14)$$

1. KMnO₄   1. CH₃CO₃H
2. − Br₂   2. − Br₂
3. H₂   3. H₂

$$CH_3(CH_2)_7-\overset{H}{\underset{OH}{\overset{|}{\underset{|}{C}}}}-\overset{OH}{\underset{H}{\overset{|}{\underset{|}{C}}}}-(CH_2)_7COOH \qquad CH_3(CH_2)_7-\overset{H}{\underset{OH}{\overset{|}{\underset{|}{C}}}}-\overset{H}{\underset{OH}{\overset{|}{\underset{|}{C}}}}-(CH_2)_7COOH$$
$$(15) \qquad\qquad\qquad\qquad\qquad\qquad (17)$$

↑ KMnO₄   ↑ CH₃CO₃H

$$\overset{H}{\underset{CH_3(CH_2)_7}{\diagup}}C=C\overset{H}{\underset{(CH_2)_7COOH}{\diagdown}} \qquad \overset{H}{\underset{CH_3(CH_2)_7}{\diagup}}C=C\overset{(CH_2)_7COOH}{\underset{H}{\diagdown}}$$
$$(16) \qquad\qquad\qquad\qquad\qquad\qquad (18)$$

$$H_3C\diagdown\diagup\diagdown\diagup\diagdown\diagup=\diagup\diagdown=\diagup\diagdown\diagup\diagdown\diagup\diagdown COOH$$
$$(19)$$

$$BrCH_2(CH_2)_4CH_2Br \xrightarrow{2\,NaC\equiv CH} HC\equiv C(CH_2)_6C\equiv CH$$
$$(20) \qquad\qquad\qquad\qquad\qquad (21)$$

↓ CH₃COSH

$$HC\equiv C(CH_2)_6CH_2CH=NOH \xleftarrow{NH_2OH} H\equiv C(CH_2)_6CH=CHSCOCH_3$$
$$(23) \qquad\qquad\qquad\qquad\qquad\qquad (22)$$

↓ (CH₂OH)₂
    H⁺

$$HC\equiv C(CH_2)_6CH_2-\overset{O}{\diagdown}\underset{O}{\diagup} \xrightarrow{C_2H_5MgBr} BrMgC\equiv C(CH_2)_7-\overset{O}{\diagdown}\underset{O}{\diagup}$$
$$(24) \qquad\qquad\qquad\qquad\qquad\qquad (25)$$

required for this synthesis has also been obtained from 9-decynoic acid[3], as shown in **28 → 29 → 25**.

Linoleic acid has also been synthesized[8,20] as shown in **30 → 35 → 27 → 19**. The final product proved to be a mixture which contained 63% linoleic acid. 1-^{14}C-Linoleic acid (**39**) is an important compound for the study of fatty acid metabolism, and it has been prepared from linoleic acid by conversion into the tetrabromide (**36**), followed by treatment of the derived silver salt with bromine (Hunsdiecker reaction[30]) to yield **37** and then with zinc, to give **38**, the Grignard reagent of which is converted into the required **39** by reaction with ^{14}C-carbon dioxide.

LINOLENIC ACID

Structure and synthesis

Linolenic acid is the main unsaturated acid of linseed oil, and it has been isolated[22,24] from this source as the hexabromo derivative. The free acid can be regenerated by treatment with zinc.

$$25 \; + \; CH_3(CH_2)_4C\equiv CCH_2MgBr \longrightarrow CH_3(CH_2)_4C\equiv CCH_2C\equiv C(CH_2)_7\!-\!\underset{O}{\overset{O}{\diamond}}$$

$$(26)$$

$$\downarrow \begin{array}{l} 1.\ H^+ \\ 2.\ Ag_2O \end{array}$$

$$19 \xleftarrow[\text{hydrogenation}]{\text{Partial}} CH_3(CH_2)_4C\equiv CCH_2C\equiv C(CH_2)_7COOH$$

$$(27)$$

$$HC\equiv C(CH_2)_7COOH \xrightarrow[\text{2. LiAlH}_4]{\overset{\overset{\displaystyle CH_3}{|}}{1.\ NHC_6H_5}} HC\equiv C(CH_2)_7CHO \xrightarrow[H^+]{(CH_2OH)_2} 25$$

$$(28) \hspace{6cm} (29)$$

$$Cl(CH_2)_6I \xrightarrow{NaC\equiv CH} HC\equiv C(CH_2)_6Cl \xrightarrow{C_2H_5MgBr} MgBrC\equiv C(CH_2)_6Cl$$

$$(30) \hspace{3cm} (31) \hspace{4cm} (32)$$

$$CH_3(CH_2)_4C\equiv CCH_2OH \xrightarrow{CH_3SO_2Cl} CH_3(CH_2)_4C\equiv CCH_2OSO_2CH_3$$

$$(33) \hspace{5cm} (34)$$

$$\mathbf{19} \hspace{8cm} \downarrow \begin{array}{l} 1.\ 32 \\ 2.\ NaI \end{array}$$

$$\uparrow\ H_2/Pd/CaCO_3$$

$$CH_3(CH_2)_4C\equiv CCH_2C\equiv C(CH_2)_7COOH \xleftarrow[\begin{array}{l}2.\ OH^-\\3.\ -CO_2\end{array}]{\begin{array}{l}1.\ \text{Sodiomalonic}\\ \text{ester}\end{array}} CH_3(CH_2)_4C\equiv CCH_2C\equiv C(CH_2)_6I$$

$$(27) \hspace{7cm} (35)$$

$$CH_3(CH_2)_4\underset{\underset{Br}{|}}{CH}-\underset{\underset{Br}{|}}{CH}CH_2\underset{\underset{Br}{|}}{CH}-\underset{\underset{Br}{|}}{CH}(CH_2)_7COOH$$

$$(36)$$

$$\downarrow \begin{array}{l} 1.\ Ag_2O \\ 2.\ Br_2 \end{array}$$

$$CH_3(CH_2)_4\underset{\underset{Br}{|}}{CH}-\underset{\underset{Br}{|}}{CH}CH_2\underset{\underset{Br}{|}}{CH}-\underset{\underset{Br}{|}}{CH}(CH_2)_7Br$$

$$(37)$$

$$\downarrow Zn$$

$$CH_3(CH_2)_4CH=CHCH_2CH=CH(CH_2)_7Br$$

$$(38)$$

$$\downarrow \begin{array}{l} 1.\ Mg \\ 2.\ CO_2 \end{array}$$

$$CH_3(CH_2)_4CH=CHCH_2CH=CH(CH_2)_7\overset{*}{C}OOH$$

$$(39)$$

The structure **40** for linolenic acid was deduced[7] by oxidative degradations similar to those described above for linoleic acid. The geometry of linolenic acid has been established as the *cis* form **41**.

The structure of linolenic acid has been confirmed by a synthesis[18] starting from the tetrahydropyranyl derivative of propargyl alcohol **43** and the acetylenic Grignard reagent **42**, and is summarized in **42** → **48** → **40**.

ARACHIDONIC ACID

Structure and synthesis

Arachidonic acid is found in animal tissues, and it has been isolated[25] from the lipid phosphalide fraction of beef suprenal glands, and purified via its octabromide.

The structure **49** for arachidonic acid was established[1] by oxidative degradations of the type described above for linoleic acid, and this structure has been confirmed by synthesis[19]. The di-Grignard derivative (**50**)

$$CH_3CH_2CH=CHCH_2CH=CHCH_2CH=CH(CH_2)_7COOH$$
(40)

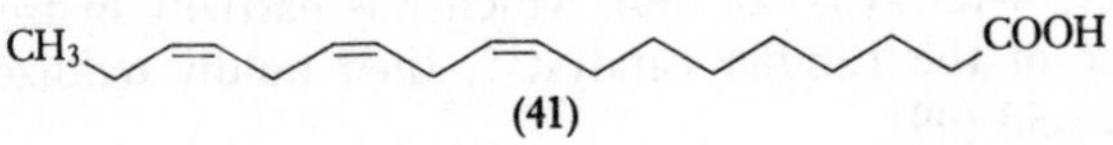

(41)

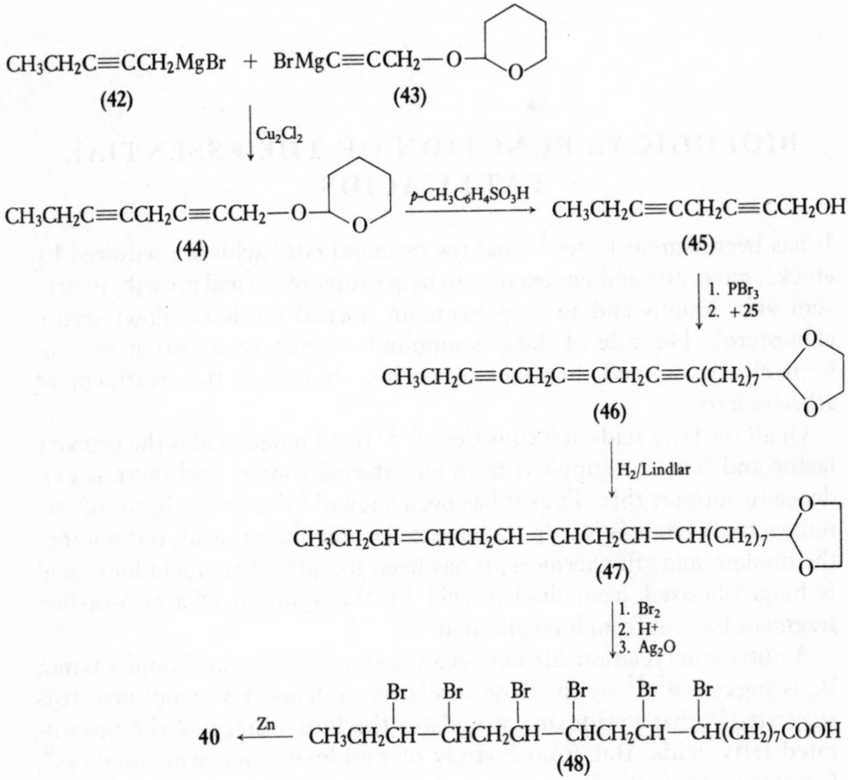

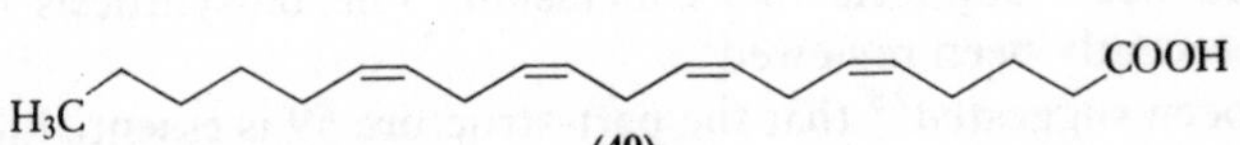

$$CH_3CH_2C\equiv CCH_2MgBr \; + \; BrMgC\equiv CCH_2-O-\text{⬡}$$
(42)   (43)

$\downarrow$ Cu$_2$Cl$_2$

$$CH_3CH_2C\equiv CCH_2C\equiv CCH_2-O-\text{⬡} \quad \xrightarrow{p\text{-}CH_3C_6H_4SO_3H} \quad CH_3CH_2C\equiv CCH_2C\equiv CCH_2OH$$
(44)   (45)

1. PBr$_3$
2. +25

$$CH_3CH_2C\equiv CCH_2C\equiv CCH_2C\equiv C(CH_2)_7-\text{⬠}$$
(46)

$\downarrow$ H$_2$/Lindlar

$$CH_3CH_2CH=CHCH_2CH=CHCH_2CH=CH(CH_2)_7-\text{⬠}$$
(47)

1. Br$_2$
2. H$^+$
3. Ag$_2$O

$$40 \xleftarrow{Zn} \; \overset{Br}{\underset{|}{CH_3CH_2CH}}-\overset{Br}{\underset{|}{CHCH_2CH}}-\overset{Br}{\underset{|}{CHCH_2CH}}-\overset{Br}{\underset{|}{CH(CH_2)_7COOH}}$$
(48)

(49)

12*

of propargyl alcohol was reacted with 1-bromo-2-octyne (51) in the presence of cuprous chloride to give 52, which was converted into the bromide 53 and reacted with 50 as before to yield, ultimately, the triyne 54. The latter was condensed with 5-hexyn-1-ol (55) to yield eicosa-5,8,11,14-tetrayn-1-ol (56), which was partially hydrogenated in the presence of the Lindlar catalyst[13], then mildly oxidized to yield arachidonic acid (49).

In a slight modification, the $C_{(14)}$ bromide 54 was condensed with 5-hexynoic acid (57), and the product (58) was partially hydrogenated to arachidonic acid (49).

BIOLOGICAL FUNCTION OF THE ESSENTIAL FATTY ACIDS

It has been demonstrated[21] that the essential fatty acids are required by chicks, mice, rats and guinea pigs to help promote normal growth, to prevent skin lesions and to help maintain normal levels of blood serum cholesterol. The role of these compounds in human nutrition has not been clearly defined, but they are being studied in the treatment of atherosclerosis.

Of all the fatty acids, it is considered[5,21] that linoleic acid is the primary factor and must be supplied from an external source, and there is evidence to support this. Thus it has been shown[16] that in the lipids of rats radioactive acetate is incorporated into the arachidonic acid, but not into the linoleic acid; furthermore, it has been found[26] that arachidonic acid is biosynthesized from linoleic acid by the addition of a two-carbon fragment but not from linolenic acid.

A nutritional relationship between the essential fatty acids and vitamin B_6 is suggested[2,23] by the close similarity in deficiency symptoms. It is suggested[31] that pyridoxine stimulates the biosynthesis of the unsaturated fatty acids. But from a study of pyridoxine-deficient monkeys[9], Greenberg could find no support for the theory that pyridoxine is involved in the conversion of linoleic acid into arachidonic acid *in vivo*. Other evidence[27] supports this conclusion. The biosynthesis of fatty acids has recently been reviewed[17].

It has been suggested[28] that the part-structure 59 is essential for fatty acid activity.

$XMgC\equiv CCH_2OMgX \quad + \quad CH_3(CH_2)_4C\equiv CCH_2Br$

(50)   (51)

$\downarrow Cu_2Cl_2$

$CH_3(CH_2)_4C\equiv CCH_2C\equiv CCH_2OH \xrightarrow{PBr_3} CH_3(CH_2)_4C\equiv CCH_2C\equiv CCH_2Br$

(52)   (53)

$\downarrow \begin{array}{l}\text{1. 50}\\ \text{2. etc.}\end{array}$

$CH_3(CH_2)_4C\equiv CCH_2C\equiv CCH_2C\equiv CCH_2Br$

(54)

$\downarrow \begin{array}{l}CH\equiv C(CH_2)_4OH\\ (55)\end{array}$

$49 \xrightarrow{\begin{array}{l}\text{1. }H_2/\text{Lindlar}\\ \text{2. Oxidation}\end{array}} CH_3(CH_2)_4C\equiv CCH_2C\equiv CCH_2C\equiv CCH_2C\equiv C(CH_2)_3CH_2OH$

(56)

$54 \quad + \quad CH\equiv C(CH_2)_3COOH$

(57)

$\downarrow Cu_2Cl_2$

$CH_3(CH_2)_4C\equiv CCH_2C\equiv CCH_2C\equiv CCH_2C\equiv C(CH_2)_3COOH$

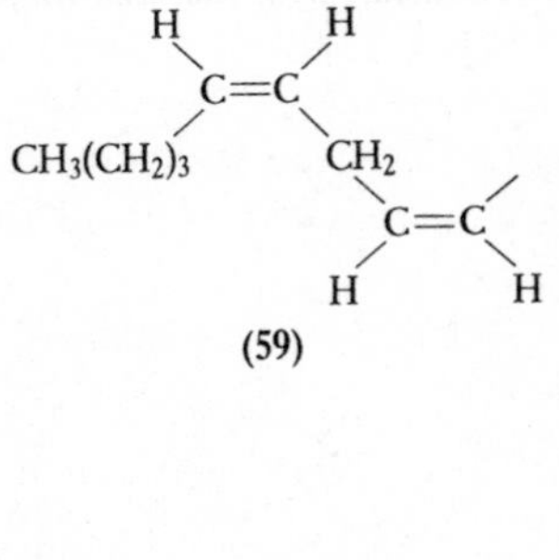

(58)

BIBLIOGRAPHY

1. Arens, C. L. and I. Smedley-MacLean, *Biochem. J.*, 37, 1 (1943).
2. Birch, T. W., *J. Biol. Chem.*, 124, 775 (1938).
3. Black, H. K. and B. C. L. Weedon, *J. Chem. Soc.*, 1785 (1953).
4. Burr, G. O. and M. M. Burr, *J. Biol. Chem.*, 86, 587 (1930); 82, 345 (1929).
5. Burr, G. O., *Federation Proc.*, 1, 224 (1942).
6. Deuel, H. J., *Federation Proc.*, 14, 639 (1955).
7. Erdmann, E., F. Bedford and F. Raspe, *Ber.*, 42, 1334 (1909).
8. Gensler, W. J. and G. R. Thomas, *J. Am. Chem. Soc.*, 72, 4601 (1951).
9. Greenberg, L. D. and H. D. Moon, *Arch. Biochem. Biophys.*, 94, 405 (1961).
10. Gunstone, F. D. in *Progress in Organic Chemistry* (Edited by J. W. Cook), Butterworths, London, 1958, Vol. IV, Chap. 1.
11. Haworth, R. D., *J. Chem. Soc.*, 1456 (1929).
12. Howton, D. R., R. H. Davis and J. C. Nevenzel, *J. Am. Chem. Soc.*, 76, 4970 (1954).
13. Lindler, H., *Helv. Chim. Acta*, 35, 446 (1952).
14. McCutcheon, J. W., M. F. Crawford and H. L. Welch, *Oil Soap (Chicago)*, 18, 9 (1941).
15. McKay, A. F. and A. R. Bader, *J. Org. Chem.*, 13, 75 (1948).
16. Mead, J. F., G. Steinberg and D. R. Howton, *J. Biol. Chem.*, 205, 683 (1953).
17. Mercer, E. I., *Ann. Rept. Progr. Chem. (Chem. Soc., London)*, 58, 353 (1961).
18. Nigam, S. S. and B. C. L. Weedon, *Chem. and Ind. (London)*, 1555 (1955); *J. Chem. Soc.*, 4049 (1956).
19. Osbond, J. M., P. G. Philpott and J. C. Wickens, *J. Chem. Soc.*, 2779 (1961).
20. Raphael, R. A. and F. Sondheimer, *J. Chem. Soc.*, 2100 (1950).
21. Rathman, D. M., *Vegetable Oils in Nutrition*, Corn Products Refining Co., New York, 1957.
22. Rollett, A., *Z. Physiol. Chem.*, 70, 404 (1910).
23. Salmon, W. D., *J. Biol. Chem.*, 123, civ (1938).
24. Shinowara, G. Y. and J. B. Brown, *J. Am. Chem. Soc.*, 60, 2734 (1938).
25. Shinowara, G. Y. and J. B. Brown, *J. Biol. Chem.*, 134, 331 (1940).
26. Steinberg, G., W. H. Slaton, D. R. Howton and J. F. Mead, *J. Biol. Chem.*, 220, 257 (1956).
27. Stokstad, E. L. R., *Ann. Rev. Biochem.*, 31, 451 (1962).
28. Thomassen, H. J., *Nature*, 173, 452 (1954).
29. Walborskey, H. M., R. H. Davis and D. R. Howton, *J. Am. Chem. Soc.*, 73, 2590 (1951).
30. Wilson, C. V., *Org. Reactions*, 9, 332 (1957).
31. Witten, P. W. and R. T. Holman, *Arch. Biochem. Biophys.*, 41, 266 (1952).

CHAPTER 17

Myoinositol (or Mesoinositol)

INTRODUCTION – MYOINOSITOL – Occurrence – Deficiency disease –
Daily requirement – Structure – Synthesis – Biosynthesis – Analogues
of myoinositol – BIBLIOGRAPHY

INTRODUCTION

THERE ARE nine possible stereoisomeric cyclohexitols, and all are now known. Seven of these are optically inactive, so that the name 'mesoinositol' is not a specific one. Configurations and conformations have been assigned to all nine isomers[4,8].

Two systems of nomenclature have been proposed for the cyclohexitols[3,8] and that due to Fletcher will be used here. In this system $C_{(1)}$ is indicated by a small encircled arabic numeral and the direction of counting around the ring is indicated by an arrow. Figure 17.1 summarizes the names, configurations and conformations of the nine isomers; the name myoinositol is reserved[4] for the isomer originally isolated from muscle tissue[18].

MYOINOSITOL

Occurrence

Myoinositol occurs in practically all plant and animal tissues; citrus fruits are a particularly good source.

Deficiency disease

Of the nine isomeric cyclohexitols, only myoinositol is of biological and nutritional interest. It has been known for a long time, and it was one of the first components of 'bios' to be recognized[7,20]. It was not until 1940 that myoinositol was recognized as a growth factor for animals[22,23] when it was found that mice reared on a diet deficient in myoinositol lost weight and hair, and developed fatty livers. Myoinositol was thus regarded as a member of the B group of vitamins, but since the

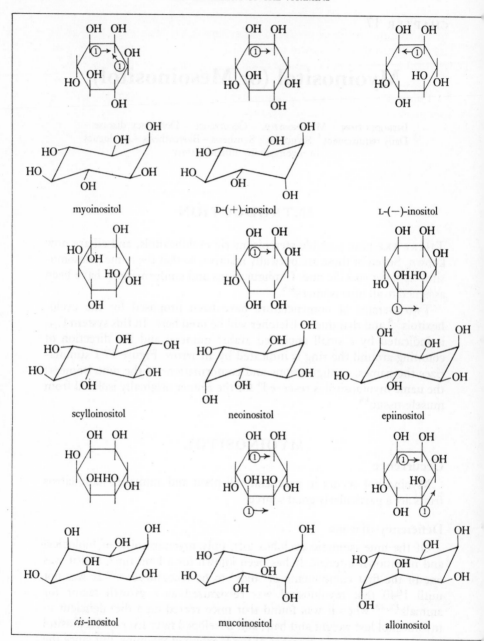

Figure 17.1. The cyclohexitols.

amount required by animals is much greater than the amounts of the other vitamins of the B complex, some doubt has been expressed about its classification as a vitamin at all. Evidence seems to suggest that myoinositol is a structural component of living cells rather than a biological catalyst.

There is no evidence for myoinositol requirement in man, presumably because of its widespread occurrence in foods.

Daily requirement

This is not known for man, but it has been estimated[21] at 1·0 gm per day per 2,500 calories of diet.

Structure

Myoinositol is a sweet-tasting crystalline solid, soluble in water.

It was shown to be a hexahydroxycyclohexane[9,12] by oxidation with nitric acid followed by isomerization, and oxidation in alkaline solution, when hexahydroxybenzene (1), tetrahydroxybenzoquinone (2) and rhodizonic acid (3) were isolated.

By the action of phosphatase on phytin (the mixed calcium magnesium salts of the hexaphosphate of myoinositol), an optically active tetraphosphate[14] and an optically inactive monophosphate[2] were obtained. Hence myoinositol cannot have all its hydroxyl groups on the same side of the ring nor even four adjacent hydroxyl groups on the same side of the ring.

Oxidation of myoinositol with alkaline potassium permanganate yields[15] ($\pm$)-saccharic acid (4), ($\pm$)-talomucic acid (5) and trihydroxyglutaric acid. Thus myoinositol can be either 6 or 7.

The action of *Acetobacter suboxydans* on myoinositol causes dehydrogenation at position 2^{10}, and when the resultant inosose is oxidized[17] with potassium permanganate, ($\pm$)-idosaccharic acid (8) can be isolated, and so the inosose must be 9. Reduction of the latter yields scylloinositol and myoinositol, and hence myoinositol is 6 and scylloinositol is 10.

This structure 6 for myoinositol was also deduced independently by Fischer[6] who converted the compound into its monoisopropylidene derivative (11) and thence to the tetraacetate (12). Removal of the acetone residue yielded 13, which gave tetra-O-acetyl-($\pm$)-idosaccharic acid (14) upon oxidation with lead tetraacetate.

Synthesis

When hexahydroxybenzene is hydrogenated[1,19] over Raney nickel, a mixture of hexahydroxycyclohexanes is produced, from which myoinositol can be isolated by crystallization.

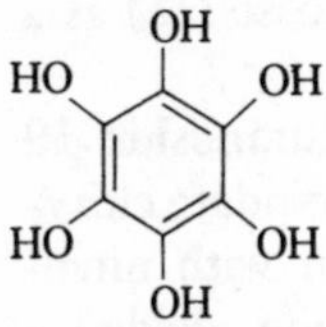

(1) 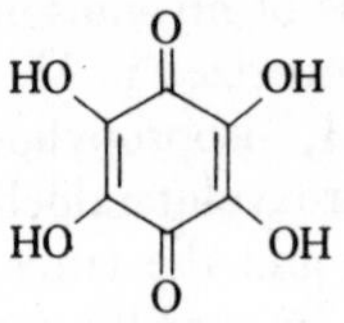   (2) 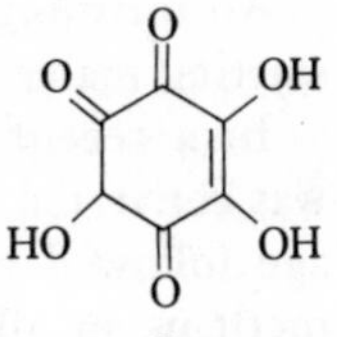   (3)

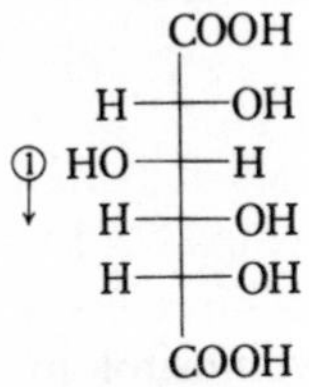

COOH
H—OH
① HO—H
H—OH
H—OH
COOH
(4)

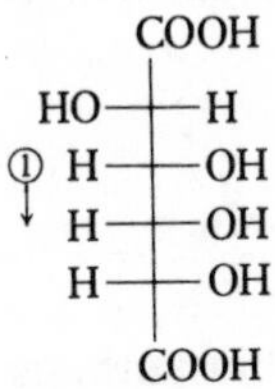

COOH
HO—H
① H—OH
H—OH
H—OH
COOH
(5)

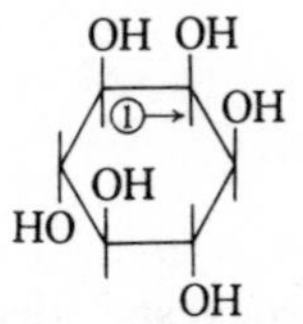

(6) 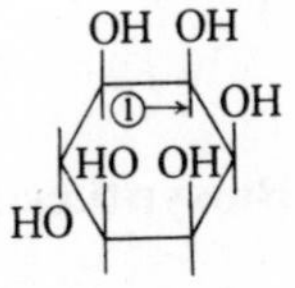   (7)

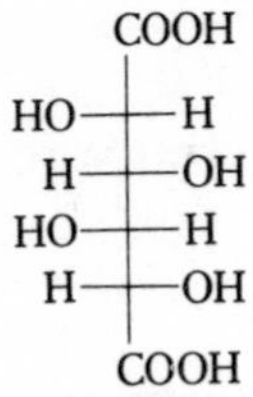

COOH
HO—H
H—OH
HO—H
H—OH
COOH
(8)

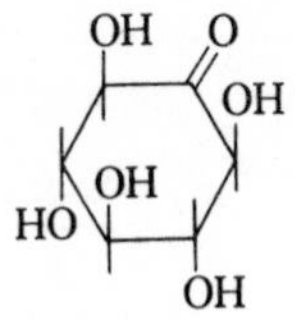

(9) 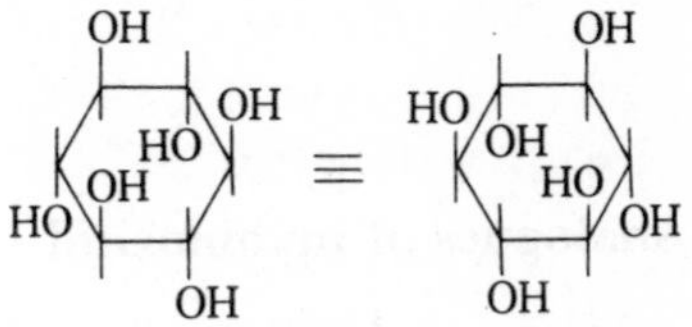   (10)

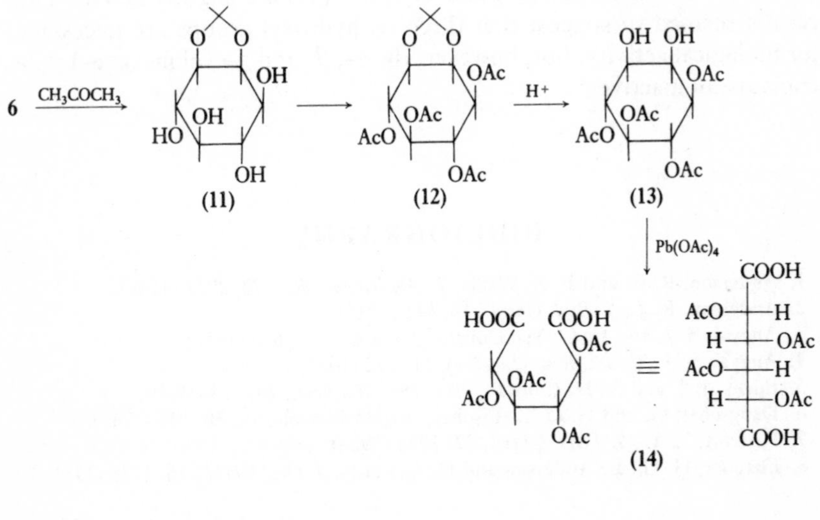

6 $\xrightarrow{CH_3COCH_3}$ (11) → (12) $\xrightarrow{H^+}$ (13)

(13) $\xdownarrow{Pb(OAc)_4}$

COOH
AcO—H
H—OAc
AcO—H
H—OAc
COOH
(14)

An unambiguous synthesis of myoinositol[13] uses D-glucose (15) as a starting material, and is summarized in 15 → 18 → 6.

In a recent synthesis[11], 1,2-isopropylidene-α-D-glucofuranoside 19 was converted to *xylo*-trihydroxyglutaraldehyde (20) by periodate cleavage followed by hydrolysis, and the latter, upon reaction with nitromethane in alkali, followed by acidification and acetylation yielded a mixture of 21 and 22 which were easily separated. Hydrolysis of the former compound gave 17 which was converted to myoinositol as above.

Biosynthesis

Recent evidence suggests[5] that the biosynthesis of myoinositol in animals follows the glucuronic acid pathway (see biosynthesis of vitamin C, Chapter 11). The conversion of labelled inositol to ascorbic acid could not be detected in rats.

Analogues of myoinositol

Myoinositol is the only cyclohexitol to possess biological activity, except possibly for scylloinositol whose activity is very slight. The methyl homologues isomylititol (23) and mylititol (24) are slightly active. The results seemed to suggest that three *cis* hydroxyl groups are necessary for biological activity, but, however, the α-, β- and γ-cyclohexane-1,2,3-triols are all inactive[16].

BIBLIOGRAPHY

1. Anderson, R. C. and E. S. Wallis, *J. Am. Chem. Soc.*, **70**, 2931 (1948).
2. Anderson, R. J., *J. Biol. Chem.*, **18**, 441 (1914).
3. Angyal, S. J. and C. G. MacDonald, *J. Chem. Soc.*, 686 (1952).
4. Angyal, S. J., *Quart. Rev. (London)*, **11**, 212 (1957).
5. Burns, J. J. and A. H. Conway, *Ann. Rev. Biochem.*, **29**, 413 (1960).
6. Dangschat, G. and H. O. L. Fischer, *Naturwissenschaften*, **30**, 146 (1942).
7. Eastcott, E. V., *J. Phys. Chem.*, **32**, 1094 (1928).
8. Fletcher, H. G., L. Anderson and H. A. Lardy, *J. Org. Chem.*, **16**, 1238 (1951).

(15) → (16) (3 steps) → [Ba(OH)₂] → (17) → (18) → 6 (HNO₂)

(19) → (20) → (21) + (22) → (17) ; (23) ; (24)

9. Gelormino, O. and N. E. Artz, *J. Am. Chem. Soc.*, **52**, 2483 (1930).
10. Kluyver, A. J. and A. G. J. Boezaardt, *Rec. trav. Chim.*, **58**, 956 (1939).
11. Lichtenthaler, F. W., *Angew. Chem. (International ed.)*, **1**, 662 (1962).
12. Miquenne, L., *Ann. Chim.*, **12**, 80 (1887).
13. Posternak, S. and T. Posternak, *Helv. Chim. Acta*, **12**, 1165 (1929).
14. Posternak, T., *Helv. Chim. Acta*, **18**, 1283 (1935).
15. Posternak, T., *Helv. Chim. Acta*, **24**, 1056 (1941); **25**, 746 (1942).
16. Posternak, T. and F. Ravenna, *Helv. Chim. Acta*, **30**, 441 (1947).
17. Posternak, T., *Helv. Chim. Acta*, **33**, 1597 (1950).
18. Scherer, D., *Ann.*, **73**, 322 (1850).
19. Wieland, H. and R. S. Wishart, *Ber.*, **47**, 2082 (1914).
20. Wildiers, E., *Cellule Rec. Cytol. Histol.*, **18**, 313 (1901).
21. Williams, R. J., *J. Am. Med. Assoc.*, **119**, 1 (1942).
22. Woolley, D. W., *J. Biol. Chem.*, **136**, 113 (1940).
23. Woolley, D. W., *Science*, **92**, 384 (1940).

Index

Acetaldehyde, active, 24
Acetylcoenzyme A, 188, 312
Adenine triphosphate, 156
Adipic acid, α,α-dimethyl-, 208
  β,β-dimethyl-, 208
Aetiocobalamin, 118
Aetioporphyrins, 107
β-Alanine, preparation, 152
Allocholanic acid, nor-, 280
Alloinositol, 348
Alloxan, 34
Alloxazines, preparation, 31
  properties, 31
  ultraviolet spectra, 31
Amethopterin, 70
Amino acids, decarboxylation, 88
  elimination from, 88
  racemization, 88
  reactions, vitamin B_6 catalysis, 90
  transaminations, 88
1-Amino-2-propanol, 113, 114
Aminopterin, 70
5α/5β-Androstane, 274
Anemia, pernicious, 108, 110
Anhydroleucovorin A, 68
Anhydroretinol, 236 (see also Anhydro-
    vitamin A)
  4′-ethoxy-, 242
  ultraviolet spectrum, 242
Anhydrovitamin A, 220, 236 (see also
    Anhydroretinol)
  ultraviolet spectrum, 236
Animal protein factor, 140
Aniline, 2-amino-3,4-dimethyl-N-D-
    ribityl-, 36
  4,5-dimethyl-2-methylamino-, 34
Antiscorbutic factor, 191
β-Apocarotenals, 245, 246
Aquocobalamin, 110, 113, 128

Arabofuranosidyl bromide, 2,3,5-tri-O-
    acetyl-α-D-, 36
Arachidonic acid, 336
  structure, 342
  synthesis, 342
Ascorbic acid, analogues, 198, 202
  biological function, 204
  biosynthesis, 202
  daily requirement, 192
  deficiency disease, 192
  6-deoxy-, 204
  2,3-di-O-methyl-, 194
  isolation, 191
  occurrence, 191
  oxidase, 204
  structure, 192
  synthesis, 194
  ultraviolet spectrum, 193
  x-ray diffraction studies, 194
Aspartic acid, 154
  deamination, 178
  rearrangement, 142
Avidin, 178
Azelaic acid, 338

Benzimidazoles, alkylation, 107
  5,6-dimethyl-, 114
    -1-β-D-glucopyranosyl-, 116
    -1-ribityl-, 116
    -1-(α-D-ribofuranosyl)-, 116
  oxidation, 107
  properties, 107
  synthesis, 107
  tautomerism, 107
  1,5,6-trimethyl-, 116
  ultraviolet spectra, 114
Biocytin, 178
Biopterin, 52
Bios, 161

Biotin, 161, 166
allo-, 166
analogues, 176
biological function, 176
biosynthesis, 176
complex, 178
daily requirement, 162
deficiency disease, 161
desthio-, 166
  biosynthesis, 176
  synthesis, 172
epi-, 166
epiallo-, 166
  synthesis, 172
isolation, 161
numbering system, 166
oxy-, 176
N-phenyl-, 166
properties, 162
sources, 161
stereochemistry, 166
structure, 162
sulphone, 162, 164
synthesis, 168
  stereospecific, 172
tetradehydro-, 176
Blacktongue, 97
Butanoic acid, 4-(α-tetrahydrofuranyl)-, 182

Campesterol, 278
Carotenes, 228, 244
biosynthesis, 248
α-Carotene, 208, 244, 246
β-Carotene, 208, 210, 214, 244, 246
metabolism, 244
oxidation, 245, 246
γ-Carotene, 208, 244, 246, 252
δ-Carotene, 252
ζ-Carotene, 252
Carotenoids, 208
geometric isomers, 210
structure determination, 208
x-ray crystallography studies, 210
Cholecalciferol—see Vitamin D₃
Cholestane, 272, 274, 280
Cholesterol, 280, 318, 336
structure, 274

Cholesterol—cont.
synthesis, 296
Johnson, 302
Robinson, 302
Woodward, 296
Chromans, ultraviolet spectra, 260
Cinchomeronic acid, 2,6-dimethyl-, 78
Citral, 208, 322
β-cyclo-, 226
Citric acid, 154
Citrovorum factor—see Folinic acid
Cobamic acid, 128
Cobamide, 128
Cobinamide, 128
Cobyric acid, 128
Cobyrinic acid, 128
Cocarboxylase, 22
Codecarboxylase—see Pyridoxal phosphate
Codehydrogenase I—see Coenzyme I
Codehydrogenase II—see Coenzyme II
Coenzyme I, 244 (see also Nicotinamide-adenine dinucleotide)
  structure, 100
  synthesis, 102
Coenzyme II, structure, 102
Coenzyme A, 154, 176, 184, 248
  S-acetyl-, 154 (see also Acetylcoenzyme A)
  biosynthesis, 156
  malonyl-, 176
  methylmalonyl-, rearrangement, 142
  succinyl-, rearrangement, 142
Coenzyme Q, 330
Coenzyme R, 161
Coproporphyrins, 108
Coprostane, 272
Corrin, 107, 124
  biosynthesis, 134
Corrinoid, 128
Corrole, 134
Coumaranes, ultraviolet spectra, 260
Cyanocobalamin, 108
  acid hydrolysis, 113, 114, 118, 120, 122, 126
  alkaline hydrolysis, 120, 122, 126
  analogues, 142
  antagonists, 142

Cyanocobalamin—*cont.*
  biological function, 140
  biosynthesis, 134
  coenzymes, 138
    analogues, 140
    5,6-dimethylbenzimidazole analogue,
      structure, 140
    structure, 140
    synthesis, 140
  daily requirement, 110
  deficiency disease, 110
  discovery, 108
  infrared spectrum, 120
  isolation, 108
  molecular formula, 112
  molecular weight, 112
  nomenclature, 128
  oxidation, 122, 124
  properties, 112
  reaction with
    cyanide ions, 118
    halogens, 124, 126
  sources, 110
  stereochemistry, absolute, 126
  structure, 112
  synthesis, 128
  ultraviolet spectrum, 112
  x-ray crystallographic study, 112, 116,
    118, 122, 124, 126
3-Cyanopyridine, 100
1,2-Cyclopentenophenanthrene, 271
  3'-methyl-, 271, 280
Cyclohexanone, 2,2,6-trimethyl-, 220
Cyclohexitols, nomenclature, 347
Cysteine, in thiamine biosynthesis, 22
  4'-phosphopantothenyl-, 156

Daily requirement, ascorbic acid, 192
  biotin, 162
  cyanocobalamin, 110
  myoinositol, 349
  nicotinic acid, 98
  pantothenic acid, 151
  pteroylglutamic acid, 54
  riboflavin, 32
  thiamine, 6
  tocopherols, 258

Daily requirement—*cont.*
  vitamins A, 213
  vitamins B_6, 76
  vitamins D, 276
  vitamins K, 319
9-Decynoic acid, 340
Deficiency disease, ascorbic acid, 192
  biotin, 161
  cyanocobalamin, 110
  definition, 1
  myoinositol, 347
  nicotinic acid, 97
  pantothenic acid, 150
  pteroylglutamic acid, 54
  riboflavin, 32
  thiamine, 6
  tocopherols, 258
  vitamins A, 213
  vitamin B_6, 75
  vitamins D, 276
  vitamins K, 319
Dehydroascorbic acid, 193, 194, 204
7-Dehydrocholesterol, 284
Dehydro-β-ionone, 240
Dehydroretinal, 213, 240 (*see also* Vitamin
  A_2)
Dehydroretinol, 210, 213, 238
  geometric isomerism, 240
  13-mono-*cis*-, 240
  structure, 238
  synthesis, 238
  trans isomer, 240
  ultraviolet spectrum, 212
7-Dehydrostigmasterol, 278
Dehydrovitamin B_{12}, 122, 126
Deoxypyridoxine, 94
Dibenzyl phosphorochloridate, 118
1,2-Dimethylbenzene, 4,5-dibenzamido-,
  114
Dicoumarol, 330
Dideoxybiladiene, 134
Diels hydrocarbon, 284 (*see also* 1,2-
  Cyclopentenophenanthrene, 3'-
  methyl-)
Dihydrolipoic acid, 188
Dihydroxymaleic acid, 194
9,10-Dihydroxystearic acid, 338
Diphenyl phosphochloridate, 118

Diphosphopyridine nucleotide, 102, 188,
    244 (*see also* Coenzyme I and Nicotin-
    amide–adenine dinucleotide)

11,14-Eicosadienoic acid, 336
Epiinositol, 348
Ergocalciferol, 280, 294
    geometric isomers, 286
    nomenclature, 288
    stereochemistry, 286, 288
        x-ray studies, 288
    structure, 284
    synthesis, 308
    ultraviolet spectrum, 288
Ergostane, 280
Ergostanol, 280
Ergosterol, 278, 296
    biosynthesis, 312
    22,23-dihydro-, 278
    irradiation, products, 294
        sequence, 294
    structure, 280
Ethoxymethylenemalononitrile, 10
Ethyl hydroxymethyleneoxalacetate, 80
Ethyl nicotinate, 98

Factor A, 120
Factor B, 118, 128
    guanosine-3′-phosphate, 138
    guanosine-5′-pyrophosphate, 138
Factor H, 120
Factor U, 54
Factor VIa, 128
Farnesol, 326
Farnesylacetone, 328
Farnesylgeranyllinalool, 326
Farnesylpyrophosphate, 250, 312
Fatty acids, 336
    biosynthesis, 344
    essential, 336
        biological function, 344
    metabolism, 154
Floridin, 274
Folic acid, 52
    5-N-10-N-anhydroformyltetrahydro-,
        68
    as formyl donor, 68

Folic acid—*cont.*
    dihydro-, 66
    10-N-formyltetrahydro-, 68
Folinic acid, structure, 68

L-Galactonic acid, 194
D-Galactose, 194
D-Galacturonic acid, 194
Geraniol, 326
    β-cyclo-, 226
Geronic acid, 208, 214
    iso-, 208
Geranylgeranylpyrophosphate, 250
Geranyllinalool, 266
D-Glucose, 192, 198, 202
D-Glucuronic acid, 202
    pathway, 202
Glutamic acid, γ-glutamyl-γ-glutamyl-,
    62
    rearrangement, 142
Glutaric acid, 208
Glycine, formimino-, 70
Glycolaldehyde, active, 24
Guanosine, 66
L-Gulonic acid, 198, 202
    2-oxo-, 198
    3-oxo-, 202
L-Gulonolactone, 202
    2-oxo-, 202

Haemophilia, 319
Heptanoic acid, (±)-7-carbethoxy-3-
    thioacetoxy-, 184
Hexanone, 2,2,6-trimethylcyclo-, 220
Hexitols, cyclo-, nomenclature, 347
Hexonic acid, (+)-*erythro*-3-oxo-, 204
Hexuronic acid, 191
Hydrazide rule of isorotation, 152
3-Hydroxyanthranilic acid, 100

L-Idonic acid, 192, 198
Inositol, 348
    cis-, 348
Intrinsic factor, 110
Iodopsin, 242
α-Ionone, 208
β-Ionone, 208, 214, 216, 230
    dihydro-, 240

β-Ionylidine acetaldehyde, 224
β-Ionylidineethyl acetate, 216
Isoalloxazines, preparation, 31
  properties, 31
  ultraviolet spectra, 31
Isoascorbic acid, 204
Isogeronic acid, 208

Keofler's quinone, 268
Kiliani synthesis, 198
Krebs cycle, 154, 184
Kynurenine, 100
  N-formyl-, 100

Laevulinic acid, δ-amino-, 134
Lanosterol, 312
Leucovorin, 68
Linoleic acid, 336
  geometric isomers, 338
  structure, 338
  synthesis, 338
Linolenic acid, 336
  geometric isomers, 342
  structure, 340
  synthesis, 342
Lipoic acid, biochemical function, 184
  structure, 182
  synthesis, 182
Liver Lactobacillus casei factor, 54
Lophenol, 312
Lumazine, 6,7-dimethyl-8-ribityl-, 40
Lumichrome, structure, 36
Lumiflavin, structure, 34
  synthesis, 34
Lumirhodopsin, 244
Lumisterol, 290
Lumisterol₂, 278, 290, 294, 296
Lycopene, 208, 252
Lycopersene, 250, 252
Lyxoflavin, 48
L-Lyxose, 194
L-Lyxosone, 194

Macdougallin, 312
Menadione, 322, 326, 328, 330, 332 (see
  also 1,4-Naphthoquinone, 2-methyl-)
3-Mercaptooctanedioic acid, 184

Mesoinositol—see Myoinositol
Metarhodopsin, 244
3-Methyloctane-1,8-dioic acid, 184
Mevalonic acid, 248, 312
Mucoinositol, 348
Myoinositol, 347
  analogues, 352
  biosynthesis, 352
  daily requirement, 349
  deficiency disease, 347
  occurrence, 347
  structure, 349
  synthesis, 350

Napthalene, 1,6-dimethyl-, 214
1,4-Naphthoquinone, 2-methyl-, 322
  2-methyl-3-difarnesyl-, 326
  2-methyl-3-farnesylgeranylgeranyl-,
    326
Neoinositol, 348
Neopyrthiamine, 28
Neurosporene, 252
Nicotinamide, 97 (see also Nicotinic acid)
  commercial source, 100
  ultraviolet spectrum, 98
Nicotinamide–adenine dinucleotide, 102,
  104 (see also Diphosphopyridine
  nucleotide)
Nicotinamide–adenine dinucleotide phosphate, 102, 104 (see also Triphosphopyridine nucleotide)
Nicotinamide coenzyme I, 46
Nicotinamide coenzyme II, 46
Nicotinic acid, 97
  analogues, 104
  biological function, 100
  biosynthesis, 100
  commercial source, 100
  daily requirement, 98
  deficiency disease, 97
  iso-, 98
  isolation, 97
  properties, 98
  sources, 97
  structure, 98
  synthesis, 98
Night blindness, 213, 242
Nitritocobalamin, 113, 128

Nitrones, 130
10,13-Nonodecadienoic acid, 336

6,9,12-Octadecatrienoic acid, 336
n-Octanoic acid, 182
Oestrane, 274
Oleic acid, 338
Oxalacetic acid, 154

Pantoic acid, 151
Pantolactone, 151
Pantotheine-4'-phosphate, 156
Pantothenic acid, analogues, 156
  biological function, 154
  biosynthesis, 154
  daily requirement, 151
  deficiency disease, 150
  detection, 150
  isolation, 150
  ω-methyl-, 150
  occurrence, 150
  properties, 151
  structure, 151
  synthesis, 152
Pantoyltaurine, 156
Pellagra, 97, 100
2-Pentanone, 3-chloro-5-ethoxy-, 14, 16
Pentenylpyrophosphate, iso-, 248
Perniocol, 312
Phosphoaminolipids, 336
Phospholipids, 336
Photoisopyrocalciferol, 292
Photopyrocalciferol, 292
Photosynthesis, 188
Phylloquinone, 320
Phytoene, 250, 252
Phytofluene, 252
Phytol, 260, 264, 320, 322
  iso-, 322
  stereochemistry, 260
Phytyl bromide, 260
Porphobilinogen, 134
Porphin, 107
  derivatives, 108
Porphyrins, 107
  biosynthesis, 134
Precalciferol, 292, 294, 296

Previtamins D, 290, 294
Propanol, 3-hydroxy-2,2-dimethyl-, 152
Propionic acid, 3-hydroxy-2,2-dimethyl-, 151
Protachysterol₂, 292
Provitamins A, 210, 244
Provitamins D, 276, 282, 288, 294
  ultraviolet spectra, 278
Provitamin D₂, 278
Provitamin D₃, 284
Pseudocumene, 260
Pseudoionone, 208, 322
Pseudovitamin B₁₂, 120, 128
Pteridines, 52
  from purines, 52
  properties, 52
  synthesis, 52
Pteridine, pyrimido[5,4-g]-, 40
Pterins, biosynthesis, 40
Pteroyldiglutamylglutamic acid, 54
Pteroylglutamic acid, 52, 110, 204
  4-amino-, 68
  2-amino-3,4-dihydro-4-hydroxy-6-hydroxymethyl-, 66
  2-amino-4-hydroxy-6-carboxylic acid, 66
  analogues, 70
  antagonists, 68, 70
  biological function, 68
  biosynthesis, 66
  daily requirement, 54
  deficiency disease, 54
  detection, 52
  5-N-formyl-, 68
  10-N-formyl-, 54
  isolation, 52
  reduced forms, 66
  sources, 54
  structure, 54
  synthesis, 60
  tetrahydro-, 70, 204
  ultraviolet spectrum, 55
Purines, biosynthesis, 40
Pyridoxal, 75
  enzyme system, 100
  structure, 84
  phosphate, structure, 84
    synthesis, 84

Pyridoxamine, 75
  structure, 84
Pyridoxine, 75, 344
  analogues, 90
  daily requirement, 76
  deficiency disease, 75
  isolation, 75
  occurrence, 75
  properties, 75
  sources, 75
  structure, 76
  synthesis, 80
  ultraviolet spectrum, 77, 78
Pyrimidines, biosynthesis, 20
  numbering, 4
  preparation, 6
  properties, 4
Pyrimidine, 4-amino-5-aminomethyl-2-
    methyl-, 10
  4-amino-5-bromomethyl-2-methyl-, 14
  5-amino-2,6-dihydroxy-4-ribitylam-
    ino-, 40
  4-amino-2,5-dimethyl-, 8
  2,4,5-triamino-6-hydroxy-, 56, 60, 62
Pyrocalciferol, 290, 292
  iso-, 290, 292
Pyruvate, active, 24

Reductone, 62
Retinal, 213, 242
  11-cis-, 244
  3-hydroxy-, 240
Retinal$_a$, iso-, 242
  neo-, 242
Retinal$_b$, iso-, 242
  neo-, 242
Retinal$_c$, neo-, 242
Retinoic acid, 220, 224, 226, 230, 238
Retinol, 208, 210, 213
  analogues, 234
  biological assay, 246
  biosynthesis, 248
  9-cis-, 226
  numbering system, 214
  perhydro-, 213, 214
  stereochemistry, 228
  structure, 213

Retinol—cont.
  synthesis, 214
  ultraviolet spectrum, 210
Retinyl acetate, 220
Rhodopsin, 242, 244
  iso-, 244
Rhizopterin, structure, 62
Ribitylamine, synthesis, 36
Riboflavin, 31
  analogues, 48
  biological function, 44
  biosynthesis, 40
  daily requirement, 32
  deficiency disease, 32
  occurrence, 31
  photolysis, 31
  properties, 31
  structure, 32
  synthesis, 36
  ultraviolet spectrum, 32, 46
Riboflavin–adenine dinucleotide, 40, 44
  structure, 46
  ultraviolet spectrum, 46
Riboflavin mononucleotide, 44
  structure, 46
Rickets, 276

Scurvy, 191, 204
Scylloinositol, 348
  structure, 350
Serine, deamination, 178
Sitosterol, 278, 336
SLR factor, 62
Solanesol, 326
D-Sorbitol, 198
L-Sorbose, 198
Squalene, 250, 312
Steroids, 271
  absolute configuration, 272
  biosynthesis, 154, 308
  nomenclature, 272
  provitamins, 276
  ultraviolet spectra, 278
Streptococcus lactus R factor, 54
Succinic acid, meso-α,β-bisbenzylamino-,
    172
Suprasterol I, 290
Suprasterol$_2$ I, 294

Suprasterol II, 290
Suprasterol₂ II, 294

Tachysterol, 290, 292, 294
L-Tartaric acid, 194
Terpenes, biosynthesis, 154, 250
Thiamine, 8, 184, 188
  analogues, 24
  action of alkali, 16
  biological function, 22
  biosynthesis, 20
  hydroxyethyl-, 24
  occurrence, 6
  redox system, 24
  structure, 8, 14
  synthesis, 14
  ultraviolet spectrum, 7
Thiazoles, biosynthesis, 20
  numbering, 4
  preparation, 4
  properties, 4
Thiazole, 5β-hydroxyethyl-4-methyl-, 12
  4-methyl-5-carboxylic acid, 12
  4-methyl ethiodide, ultraviolet spectrum, 12
Thiazolium salts, as catalysts, 22
Thiochrome, 16
6-Thiotic acid—see Lipoic acid
L-Threonic acid, 194
Threonine, deamination, 178
L-Threose, 202
Tocols, 256
Tocol, 5,7-dimethyl-, 266
  5,8-dimethyl, 256
  5-methyl-, 264
  7-methyl-, 266
  8-methyl-, 266
  5,7,8-trimethyl-, 256
Tocopherols, analogues, 268
  biological function, 266
  biosynthesis, 266
  daily requirement, 258
  deficiency disease, 258
  detection, 256
  isolation, 256
  properties, 258
  sources, 258
  ultraviolet spectrum, 258

α-Tocopherol, 245, 256
  oxidation, 260
  stereochemistry, 260
  structure, 258
  synthesis, 260
β-Tocopherol, 256
γ-Tocopherol, 256
δ-Tocopherol, 256, 266
ε-Tocopherol, 256, 264, 266
ζ₁-Tocopherol, 256, 266
ζ₂-Tocopherol, 256, 266
η-Tocopherol, 256, 266
Tocoquinones, 260, 328
Torularhodin, 248
Torulin, 248
Toxisterol, 290, 294
Triphosphopyridine nucleotide, 102
L-Tryptophan, 100

Ubiquinone, 268, 330 (see also Coenzyme Q)
Uracil, 5-amino-4-D-ribitylamino-, 40
Uronic acid pathway, 202
Uroporphyrin I, 108
Uroporphyrin III, 108, 134
Uroporphyrinogen, 134

Valeric acid, 2-oxo-, 154
  δ-thienyl-2-, 166
Vitamins, classification, 1
  definition, 1
  nomenclature, 2
Vitamins A, 318
  and vision, 242
  daily requirement, 213
  deficiency disease, 213
  detection, 210
  isolation, 210
  nomenclature, 213
  sources, 212
Vitamin A₁—see Retinol
Vitamin A₂—see Dehydroretinol
Vitamin Aₐ, iso-, 234
  neo-, 228, 230
    acetate, 234
Vitamin A_b, iso-, 228, 230, 234
  neo-, 230, 234, 244
Vitamin A_c, neo-, 230

Vitamin B$_C$, 54
  conjugate, 54
Vitamin B$_T$, 3
Vitamin B$_1$—*see* Thiamine
Vitamin B$_2$—*see* Riboflavin
Vitamin B$_3$—*see* Pantothenic acid
Vitamin B$_6$, 75, 88, 344 (*see also* Pyridoxal,
  Pyridoxamine and Pyridoxine)
Vitamin B$_{12}$—*see* Cyanocobalamin
Vitamin B$_{12a}$—*see* Aquocobalamin
Vitamin B$_{12b}$, 128 (*see also* Aquocobala-
  min)
Vitamin C, 318 (*see also* Ascorbic acid)
Vitamins D, 318
  daily requirement, 276
  deficiency disease, 276
  nomenclature, 288
  provitamins, 276
  synthesis, 296, 306
Vitamin D$_1$, 276
Vitamin D$_2$, 278, 280 (*see also* Ergocalci-
  ferol)
  structure, 284
  ultraviolet spectrum, 284
Vitamin D$_3$, 278, 280
  structure, 288
  synthesis, 308
Vitamin D$_4$, 280
  structure, 288
Vitamin D$_5$, 280
  structure, 288
Vitamin D$_6$, 280
  structure, 288
Vitamin D$_7$, 280
  structure, 288
Vitamin E, 246, 256, 318 (*see also*
  Tocopherols)
Vitamin H—*see* Biotin

Vitamins K, 318
  analogues, 328, 330
  biological function, 332
  biosynthesis, 332
  daily requirement, 319
  deficiency disease, 319
  detection, 318
  isolation, 318
  sources, 318
Vitamin K$_1$, 318
  properties, 319
  structure, 320
  synthesis, 322
  ultraviolet spectrum, 319
Vitamin K$_2$, 318
  nomenclature, 326
  properties, 319
  structure, 326
  synthesis, 326
  ultraviolet spectrum, 319
Vitamin M, 54

Weerman degradation, 194
Weerman test, 194
Wittig reaction, 224, 308
Woodward rules, 278

Xylitol, 202
L-Xylose, 198
L-Xylosone, 194, 198
D-Xylulose, 202
  5-phosphate, 202
L-Xylulose, 202

Yeast *Lactobacillus casei* factor, 54
  hydrolysis, 56
  ultraviolet spectrum, 58